THE BEST KNOWN WORKS OF
THOMAS CARLYLE

THE
BEST KNOWN WORKS OF
THOMAS
CARLYLE

Including *Sartor Resartus,*
Heroes and Hero Worship, and
Characteristics

THE BOOK LEAGUE OF AMERICA

New York

1942
BLUE RIBBON BOOKS

CL

PRINTED IN THE UNITED STATES OF AMERICA

CONTENTS

SARTOR RESARTUS
BOOK FIRST

BOOK SECOND

CONTENTS

BOOK THIRD

HEROES AND HERO WORSHIP

LECTURE I.

LECTURE II.

LECTURE III.

LECTURE IV.

LECTURE V.

LECTURE VI.

SARTOR RESARTUS

SARTOR RESARTUS

BOOK FIRST

CHAPTER I.

PRELIMINARY.

CONSIDERING our present advanced state of culture, and how the Torch of Science has now been brandished and borne about, with more or less effect, for five thousand years and upwards; how, in these times especially, not only the Torch still burns, and perhaps more fiercely than ever, but innumerable Rushlights, and Sulphur-matches, kindled thereat, are also glancing in every direction, so that not the smallest cranny or doghole in Nature or Art can remain unilluminated,—it might strike the reflective mind with some surprise that hitherto little or nothing of a fundamental character, whether in the way of Philosophy or History, has been written on the subject of Clothes.

Our Theory of Gravitation is as good as perfect: Lagrange, it is well known, has proved that the Planetary System, on this scheme, will endure forever; Laplace, still more cunningly, even guesses that it could not have been made on any other scheme. Whereby, at least, our nautical Logbooks can be better kept; and water-transport of all kinds has grown more commodious. Of Geology and Geognosy we know enough: what with the labors of our Werners and Huttons, what with the ardent genius of their disciples, it has come about that now, to many a Royal Society, the Creation of a World is little more mysterious than the cooking of a dumpling; concerning which last, indeed, there have been minds to whom the question, *How the apples were got in,* presented difficulties. Why mention our disquisitions on the Social Contract, on the Standard of Taste, on the Migrations of the Herring? Then, have we not a Doctrine of Rent, a Theory of Value; Philosophies of Language, of History, of Pottery, of Apparitions, of Intoxicating Liquors? Man's whole life and environment have been laid open and elucidated; scarcely a fragment or fibre of his Soul, Body, and Possessions, but has been probed, dissected, distilled, desiccated, and scientifically decomposed: our spiritual Faculties, of which it appears there are not a few, have their Stewarts, Cousins, Royer Collards: every cellular, vascular, muscular Tissue glories in its Lawrences, Majendies, Bichâts.

How, then, comes it, may the reflective mind repeat, that the grand Tissue of all Tissues, the only real Tissue, should have been quite overlooked by Science,—the vestural Tissue, namely, of woollen or other cloth; which Man's Soul wears as its utmost wrappage and overall; wherein his whole other Tissues are included and screened, his whole Faculties work, his whole Self lives, moves, and has its being? For if, now and then, some straggling broken-winged thinker has cast an owl's-glance into this obscure region, the

3

most have soared over it altogether heedless; regarding Clothes as a property, not an accident, as quite natural and spontaneous, like the leaves of trees, like the plumage of birds. In all speculations they have tacitly figured man as a *Clothed Animal;* whereas he is by nature a *Naked Animal;* and only in certain circumstances, by purpose and device, masks himself in Clothes. Shakespeare says, we are creatures that look before and after: the more surprising that we do not look round a little, and see what is passing under our very eyes.

But here, as in so many other cases, Germany, learned, indefatigable, deep-thinking Germany comes to our aid. It is, after all, a blessing that, in these revolutionary times, there should be one country where abstract Thought can still take shelter; that while the din and frenzy of Catholic Emancipations, and Rotten Boroughs, and Revolts of Paris, deafen every French and every English ear, the German can stand peaceful on his scientific watch-tower; and, to the raging, struggling multitude here and elsewhere, solemnly, from hour to hour, with preparatory blast of cowhorn, emit his *Höret ihr Herren und lasset's Euch sagen;* in other words, tell the Universe, which so often forgets that fact, what o'clock it really is. Not unfrequently the Germans have been blamed for an unprofitable diligence; as if they struck into devious courses, where nothing was to be had but the toil of a rough journey; as if, forsaking the gold-mines of finance and that political slaughter of fat oxen whereby a man himself grows fat, they were apt to run goose-hunting into regions of bilberries and crowberries, and be swallowed up at last in remote peat-bogs. Of that unwise science, which, as our Humorist expresses it,—

"By geometric scale
Doth take the size of pots of ale;"

Still more, of that altogether misdirected industry, which is seen vigorously thrashing mere straw, there can nothing defensive be said. In so far as the Germans are chargeable with such, let them take the consequence. Nevertheless be it remarked, that even a Russian steppe has tumuli and gold ornaments; also many a scene that looks desert and rock-bound from the distance, will unfold itself, when visited, into rare valleys. Nay, in any case, would Criticism erect not only finger-posts and turnpikes, but spiked gates and impassable barriers, for the mind of man? It is written, "Many shall run to and fro, and knowledge shall be increased." Surely the plain rule is, Let each considerate person have his way, and see what it will lead to. For not this man and that man, but all men make up mankind, and their united tasks the task of mankind. How often have we seen some such adventurous, and perhaps much-censured wanderer light on some out-lying, neglected, yet vitally momentous province; the hidden treasures of which he first discovered, and kept proclaiming till the general eye and effort were directed thither, and the conquest was completed;—thereby, in these his seemingly so aimless rambles, planting new standards, founding new habitable colonies, in the immeasurable circumambient realm of Nothingness and

Night! Wise man was he who counselled that Speculation should have free course, and look fearlessly towards all the thirty-two points of the compass, whithersoever and howsoever it listed.

Perhaps it is proof of the stunted condition in which pure Science, especially pure moral Science, languishes among us English; and how our mercantile greatness, and invaluable Constitution, impressing a political or other immediately practical tendency on all English culture and endeavor, cramps the free flight of Thought,—that this, not Philosophy of Clothes, but recognition even that we have no such Philosophy, stands here for the first time published in our language. What English intellect could have chosen such a topic, or by chance stumbled on it? But for that same unshackled, and even sequestered condition of German Learned, which permits and induces them to fish in all manner of waters, with all manner of nets, it seems probable enough, this abstruse Inquiry might, in spite of the results it leads to, have continued dormant for indefinite periods. The Editor of these sheets, though otherwise boasting himself a man of confirmed speculative habits, and perhaps discursive enough, is free to confess, that never, till these last months, did the above very plain considerations, on our total want of a Philosophy of Clothes, occur to him; and then, by quite foreign suggestion. By the arrival, namely, of a new Book from Professor Teufelsdröckh of Weissnichtwo; treating expressly of this subject, and in a style which, whether understood or not, could not even by the blindest be overlooked. In the present Editor's way of thought, this remarkable Treatise, with its Doctrines, whether as judicially acceded to, or judicially denied, has not remained without effect.

"*Die Kleider, ihr Werden und Wirken* (Clothes, their Origin and Influence): *von Diog. Teufelsdröckh. J. U. D., etc. Stillschweigen und Cog^{nie}. Weissnichtwo,* 1831.

"Here," says the *Weissnichtwo'sche Anzeiger,* "comes a Volume of that extensive, close-printed, close-meditated sort, which, be it spoken with pride, is seen only in Germany, perhaps only in Weissnichtwo. Issuing from the hitherto irreproachable Firm of Stillschweigen and Company, with every external furtherance, it is of such internal quality as to set Neglect at defiance." . . . "A work," concludes the well-nigh enthusiastic Reviewer, "interesting alike to the antiquary, the historian, and the philosophic thinker; a masterpiece of boldness, lynx-eyed acuteness, and rugged independent Germanism and Philanthropy (*derber Kerndeutschheit und Menschenliebè*); which will not, assuredly, pass current without opposition in high places; but must and will exalt the almost new name of Teufelsdröckh to the first ranks of Philosophy, in our German Temple of Honor."

Mindful of old friendship, the distinguished Professor, in this the first blaze of his fame, which however does not dazzle him, sends hither a Presentation-copy of his Book; with compliments and encomiums which modesty forbids the present Editor to rehearse; yet without indicated wish or hope of any kind, except what may be implied in the concluding phrase: *Mochte es* (this remarkable Treatise) *auch im Brittischen Boden gedeihen!*

CHAPTER II.

EDITORIAL DIFFICULTIES.

IF FOR a speculative man, "whose seedfield," in the sublime words of the Poet, "is Time," no conquest is important but that of new ideas, then might the arrival of Professor Teufelsdröckh's Book be marked with chalk in the Editor's calendar. It is indeed an "extensive Volume," of boundless, almost formless contents, a very Sea of Thought; neither calm nor clear, if you will; yet wherein the toughest pearl-diver may dive to his utmost depth, and return not only with sea-wreck but with true orients.

Directly on the first perusal, almost on the first deliberate inspection, it became apparent that here a quite new Branch of Philosophy, leading to as yet undescried ulterior results, was disclosed; farther, what seemed scarcely less interesting, a quite new human Individuality, an almost unexampled personal character, that, namely, of Professor Teufelsdröckh the Discloser. Of both which novelties, as far as might be possible, we resolved to master the significance. But as man is emphatically a proselytizing creature, no sooner was such mastery even fairly attempted, than the new question arose: How might this acquired good be imparted to others, perhaps in equal need thereof: how could the Philosophy of Clothes, and the Author of such Philosophy, be brought home, in any measure, to the business and bosoms of our own English Nation? For if new-got gold is said to burn the pockets till it be cast forth into circulation, much more may new truth.

Here, however, difficulties occurred. The first thought naturally was to publish Article after Article on this remarkable Volume, in such widely-circulating Critical Journals as the Editor might stand connected with, or by money or love procure access to. But, on the other hand, was it not clear that such matter as must here be revealed, and treated of, might endanger the circulation of any Journal extant? If, indeed all party-divisions in the State could have been abolished, Whig, Tory, and Radical, embracing in discrepant union; and all the Journals of the Nation could have been jumbled into one Journal, and the Philosophy of Clothes poured forth in incessant torrents therefrom, the attempt had seemed possible. But, alas, what vehicle of that sort have we, except *Fraser's Magazine?* A vehicle all strewed (figuratively speaking) with the maddest Waterloo-Crackers, exploding distractively and destructively, wheresoever the mystified passenger stands or sits; nay, in any case, understood to be, of late years, a vehicle full to overflowing, and inexorably shut! Besides, to state the Philosophy of Clothes without the Philosopher, the ideas of Teufelsdröckh without something of his personality, was it not to insure both of entire misapprehension? Now for Biography, had it been otherwise admissible, there were no adequate documents, no hope of obtaining such, but rather, owing to circumstances, a special despair. Thus did the Editor see himself, for the while, shut out from all public utterance of these extraordinary Doctrines, and constrained to revolve them, not without disquietude, in the dark depths of his own mind.

So had it lasted for some months; and now the Volume on Clothes, read and again read, was in several points becoming lucid and lucent; the personality of its Author more and more surprising, but, in spite of all that memory and conjecture could do, more and more enigmatic; whereby the old disquietude seemed fast settling into fixed discontent,—when altogether unexpectedly arrives a letter from Herr Hofrath Heuschrecke, our Professor's chief friend and associate in Weissnichtwo, with whom we had not previously corresponded. The Hofrath, after much quite extraneous matter, began dilating largely on the "agitation and attention" which the Philosophy of Clothes was exciting in its own German Republic of Letters; on the deep significance and tendency of his Friend's Volume; and then, at length, with great circumlocution, hinted at the practicability of conveying "some knowledge of it, and of him, to England, and through England to the distant West:" a work on Professor Teufelsdröckh "were undoubtedly welcome to the *Family*, the *National*, or any other of those patriotic *Libraries*, at present the glory of British Literature;" might work revolutions in Thought; and so forth;—in conclusion, intimating not obscurely, that should the present Editor feel disposed to undertake a Biography of Teufelsdröckh, he, Hofrath Heuschrecke, had it in his power to furnish the requisite Documents.

As in some chemical mixture, that has stood long evaporating, but would not crystallize, instantly when the wire or other fixed substance is introduced, crystallization commences, and rapidly proceeds till the whole is finished, so was it with the Editor's mind and this offer of Heuschrecke's. Form rose out of void solution and discontinuity; like united itself with like in definite arrangement: and soon either in actual vision and possession, or in fixed reasonable hope, the image of the whole Enterprise had shaped itself, so to speak, into a solid mass. Cautiously yet courageously through the two pennypost, application to the famed redoubtable OLIVER YORKE was now made: an interview, interviews with that singular man have taken place; with more of assurance on our side, with less of satire (at least of open satire) on his, than we anticipated;—for the rest, with such issue as is now visible. As to those same "patriotic *Libraries*," the Hofrath's counsel could only be viewed with silent amazement; but with his offer of Documents we joyfully and almost instantaneously closed. Thus, too, in the sure expectation of these, we already see our task begun; and this our *Sartor Resartus*, which is properly a "Life and Opinions of Herr Teufelsdröckh," hourly advancing.

Of our fitness for the Enterprise, to which we have such title and vocation, it were perhaps uninteresting to say more. Let the British reader study and enjoy, in simplicity of heart, what is here presented him, and with whatever metaphysical acumen and talent for meditation he is possessed of.

Let him strive to keep a free, open sense; cleared from the mists of prejudice, above all from the paralysis of cant; and directed rather to the Book itself than to the Editor of the Book. Who or what such Editor may be, must remain conjectural, and even insignificant:[1] it is a voice publishing tidings of the Philosophy of Clothes; undoubtedly a Spirit addressing Spirits: whoso hath ears, let him hear.

On one other point the Editor thinks it needful to give warning: namely, that he is animated with a true though perhaps a feeble attachment to the Institutions of our Ancestors; and minded to defend these, according to ability, at all hazards; nay, it was partly with a view to such defence that he engaged in this undertaking. To stem, or if that be impossible, profitably to divert the current of Innovation, such a Volume as Teufelsdröckh's, if cunningly planted down, were no despicable pile, or floodgate, in the logical wear.

For the rest, be it nowise apprehended, that any personal connection of ours with Teufelsdröckh, Heuschrecke, or this Philosophy of Clothes, can pervert our judgment, or sway us to extenuate or exaggerate. Powerless, we venture to promise, are those private Compliments themselves. Grateful they may well be; as generous illusions of friendship; as fair mementos of bygone unions, of those nights and suppers of the gods, when, lapped in the symphonies and harmonies of Philosophic Eloquence, though with baser accompaniments, the present Editor revelled in that feast of reason, never since vouchsafed him in so full measure! But what then? *Amicus Plato, magis amica veritas;* Teufelsdröckh is our friend, Truth is our divinity. In our historical and critical capacity, we hope we are strangers to all the world; have feud or favor with no one,—save indeed the Devil, with whom, as with the Prince of Lies and Darkness, we do at all times wage internecine war. This assurance, at an epoch when puffery and quackery have reached a height unexampled in the annals of mankind, and even English Editors, like Chinese Shopkeepers, must write on their door-lintels *No cheating here,* —we thought it good to premise.

CHAPTER III.

REMINISCENCES.

To THE Author's private circle the appearance of this singular Work on Clothes must have occasioned little less surprise than it has to the rest of the world. For ourselves, at least, few things have been more unexpected. Professor Teufelsdröckh, at the period of our acquaintance with him, seemed to lead a quite still and self-contained life: a man devoted to the higher Philosophies, indeed; yet more likely, if he published at all, to publish a refutation of Hegel and Bardili, both of whom, strangely enough,

[1]With us even he still communicates in some sort of mask, or muffler: and, we have reason to think, under a feigned name!—O. Y.

he included under a common ban; than to descend, as he has here done, into the angry noisy Forum, with an Argument that cannot but exasperate and divide. Not, that we can remember, was the Philosophy of Clothes once touched upon between us. If through the high, silent, meditative Transcendentalism of our Friend we detected any practical tendency whatever, it was at most Political, and towards a certain prospective, and for the present quite speculative, Radicalism; as indeed some correspondence on his part, with Herr Oken of Jena was now and then suspected; though her special contributions to the *Isis* could never be more than surmised at. But, at all events, nothing Moral, still less anything Didactico-Religious, was looked for from him.

Well do we recollect the last words he spoke in our hearing; which indeed, with the Night they were uttered in, are to be forever remembered. Lifting his huge tumbler of *Gukguk*,[1] and for a moment lowering his tobacco-pipe, he stood up in full coffee-house (it was *Zur Grünen Gans*, the largest in Weissnichtwo, where all the Virtuosity, and nearly all the Intellect of the place assembled of an evening); and there, with low, soul-stirring tone, and the look truly of an angel, though whether of a white or of a black one might be dubious, proposed this toast: *Die Sache der Armen in Gottes und Teufels Namen* (The Cause of the Poor, in Heaven's name and ——'s)! One full shout, breaking the leaden silence; then a gurgle of innumerable emptying bumpers, again followed by universal cheering, returned him loud acclaim. It was the finale of the night: resuming their pipes; in the highest enthusiasm amid volumes of tobacco smoke; triumphant, cloud-capt without and within, the assembly broke up, each to his thoughtful pillow. *Bleibt doch ein echter Spass- und Galgen-vogel,* said several; meaning thereby that, one day, he would probably be hanged for his democratic sentiments. *Wo steckt doch der Schalk?* added they, looking round: but Teufelsdröckh had retired by private alleys, and the Compiler of these pages beheld him no more.

In such scenes has it been our lot to live with this Philosopher, such estimate to form of his purposes and powers. And yet, thou brave Teufelsdröckh, who could tell what lurked in thee? Under those thick locks of thine, so long and lank, overlapping roof-wise the gravest face we ever in this world saw, there dwelt a most busy brain. In thy eyes too, deep under their shaggy brows, and looking out so still and dreamy, have we not noticed gleams of an ethereal or else a diabolic fire, and half-fancied that their stillness was but the rest of infinite motion, the *sleep* of a spinning-top? Thy little figure, there as, in loose ill-brushed threadbare habiliments, thou sattest, amid litter and lumber, whole days, to "think and smoke tobacco," held in it a mighty heart. The secrets of man's Life were laid open to thee; thou sawest into the mystery of the Universe farther than another; thou hadst *in petto* thy remarkable Volume on Clothes. Nay, was there not in that clear logically-founded Transcendentalism of thine; still more, in thy

---

[1]Gukguk is unhappily only an academical—beer.

meek, silent, deep-seated Sansculottism, combined with a true princely Courtesy of inward nature, the visible rudiments of such speculation? But great men are too often unknown, or what is worse, misknown. Already, when we dreamed not of it, the warp of thy remarkable Volume lay on the loom; and silently, mysterious shuttles were putting-in the woof!

How the Hofrath Heuschrecke is to furnish biographical data, in this case, may be a curious question; the answer of which, however, is happily not our concern, but his. To us it appeared, after repeated trial, that in Weissnichtwo, from the archives or memories of the best-informed classes, no Biography of Teufelsdröckh was to be gathered; not so much as a false one. He was a stranger there, wafted thither by what is called the course of circumstances; concerning whose parentage, birthplace, prospects, or pursuits, curiosity had indeed made inquiries, but satisfied herself with the most indistinct replies. For himself, he was a man so still and altogether unparticipating, that to question him even afar off on such particulars was a thing of more than usual delicacy: besides, in his sly way, he had ever some quaint turn, not without its satirical edge, wherewith to divert such intrusions, and deter you from the like. Wits spoke of him secretly as if he were a kind of Melchizedek, without father or mother of any kind; sometimes, with reference to his great historic and statistic knowledge, and the vivid way he had of expressing himself like an eye-witness of distant transactions and scenes, they called him the *Ewige Jude,* Everlasting, or as we say, Wandering Jew.

To the most, indeed, he had become not so much a Man as a Thing; which Thing doubtless they were accustomed to see, and with satisfaction; but no more thought of accounting for than for the fabrication of their daily *Allgemeine Zeitung,* or the domestic habits of the Sun. Both were there and welcome; the world enjoyed what good was in them, and thought no more of the matter. The man Teufelsdröckh passed and repassed, in his little circle, as one of those originals and nondescripts, more frequent in German Universities than elsewhere; of whom, though you see them alive, and feel certain enough that they must have a History, no History seems to be discoverable; or only such as. men give of mountain rocks and antediluvian ruins: That they have been created by unknown agencies, are in a state of gradual decay, and for the present reflect light and resist pressure; that is, are visible and tangible objects in this phantasm world, where so much other mystery is.

It was to be remarked that though, by title and diploma, *Professor der Allerley-Wissenschaft,* or as we should say in English, "Professor of Things in General," he had never delivered any Course; perhaps never been incited thereto by any· public furtherance or requisition. To all appearance, the enlightened Government of Weissnichtwo, in founding their New University, imagined they had done enough, if, "in times like ours," as the half-official Program expressed it, "when all things are rapidly or slowly resolving themselves into Chaos, a Professorship of this kind had been established; whereby, as occasion called, the task of bodying somewhat forth again from such Chaos might be, even slightly, facilitated." That actual Lectures should be held, and Public Classes for the "Science of Things in General," they doubtless considered premature; on which ground too they had only established the Professorship, nowise endowed it; so that Teufelsdröckh, "recommended by the highest Names," had been promoted thereby to a Name merely.

Great, among the more enlightened classes, was the admiration of this new Professorship: how an enlightened Government had seen into the Want of the Age (*Zeitbedürfniss*); how at length, instead of Denial and Destruction, we were to have a science of Affirmation and Reconstruction; and Germany and Weissnichtwo were where they should be, in the vanguard of the world. Considerable also was the wonder at the new Professor, dropt opportunely enough into the nascent University; so able to lecture, should occasion call; so ready to hold his peace for indefinite periods, should an enlightened Government consider that occasion did not call. But such admiration and such wonder, being followed by no act to keep them living, could last only nine days; and, long before our visit to that scene, had quite died away. The more cunning heads thought it was all an expiring clutch at popularity, on the part of a Minister, whom domestic embarrassments, court intrigues, old age, and dropsy soon afterwards finally drove from the helm.

As for Teufelsdröckh, except by his nightly appearances at the *Grüne Gans*, Weissnichtwo saw little of him, felt little of him. Here, over his tumbler of Gukguk, he sat reading Journals; sometimes contemplatively looking into the clouds of his tobacco-pipe, without other visible employment: always, from his mild ways, an agreeable phenomenon there; more especially when he opened his lips for speech; on which occasions the whole Coffee-house would hush itself into silence, as if sure to hear something noteworthy. Nay, perhaps to hear a whole series and river of the most memorable utterances; such as, when once thawed, he would for hours indulge in, with fit audience: and the more memorable, as issuing from a head apparently not more interested in them, not more conscious of them, than is the sculptured stone head of some public fountain, which through its brass mouth-tube emits water to the worthy and the unworthy; careless whether it be for cooking victuals or quenching conflagrations; indeed, maintains the same earnest assiduous look, whether any water be flowing or not.

To the Editor of these sheets, as to a young enthusiastic Englishman, however unworthy, Teufelsdröckh opened himself perhaps more than to the most. Pity only that we could not then half guess his importance, and scrutinize him with due power of vision! We enjoyed, what not three men in Weissnichtwo could boast of, a certain degree of access to the Professor's private domicile. It was the attic floor of the highest house in the Wahngasse; and might truly be called the pinnacle of Weissnichtwo, for it rose sheer up above the contiguous roofs, themselves rising from elevated ground. Moreover, with its windows it looked towards all the four *Orte*, or as the Scotch say, and we ought to say, *Airts*: the sitting-room itself commanded three; another came to view in the *Schlafgemach* (bedroom) at the opposite end; to say nothing of the kitchen, which offered two, as it were, *duplicates*, and showing nothing new. So that it was in fact the speculum or watch-tower of Teufelsdröckh; wherefrom, sitting at ease, he might see the whole life-circulation of that considerable City; the streets and lanes of which, with all their doing and driving (*Thun und Treiben*), were for the most part visible there.

"I look down into all that wasp-nest or bee-hive," have we heard him say, "and witness their wax-laying and honey-making, and poison-brewing, and choking by sulphur. From the Palace esplanade, where music plays while Serene Highness is pleased to eat his victuals, down to the low lane, where in her door-sill the aged widow, knitting for a thin livelihood, sits to feel the afternoon sun, I see it all; for, except the Schlosskirche weather-cock, no biped stands so high. Couriers arrive bestrapped and bebooted, bearing Joy and Sorrow bagged-up in pouches of leather: there, topladen, and with four swift horses, rolls-in the country Baron and his household; here, on timber-leg, the lamed Soldier hops painfully along, begging alms: a thousand carriages, and wains and cars, come tumbling-in with Food, with young Rusticity, and other Raw Produce, inanimate or animate, and go tumbling out again with Produce manufactured. That living flood, pouring through these streets, of all qualities and ages, knowest thou whence it is coming, whither it is going? *Aus der Ewigkeit, zu der Ewigkeit hin:* From Eternity, onwards to Eternity! These are Apparitions: what else? Are they not Souls rendered visible: in Bodies, that took shape and will lose it, melting into air? Their solid Pavement is a Picture of the Sense; they walk on the bosom of Nothing, blank Time is behind them and before them. Or fanciest thou, the red and yellow Clothes-screen yonder, with spurs on its heels and feather in its crown, is but of To-day, without a Yesterday or a To-morrow; and had not rather its Ancestor alive when Hengst and Horsa overran thy Island? Friend, thou seest here a living link in that Tissue of History, which inweaves all Being: watch well, or it will be past thee, and seen no more."

"*Ach mein, Lieber!*" said he once, at midnight, when we had returned from the Coffee-house in rather earnest talk, "it is a true sublimity to dwell here. These fringes of lamplight, struggling up through smoke and thousandfold exhalation, some fathoms into the ancient reign of Night, what thinks Boötes of them, as he leads his Hunting-Dogs over the Zenith in their leash of sidereal fire? That stifled hum of Midnight, when Traffic has lain down to rest; and the chariot-wheels of Vanity, still rolling here and there through distant streets, are bearing her to Halls roofed-in, and lighted to the due pitch for her; and only Vice and Misery, to prowl or to moan like nightbirds, are abroad: that hum, I say, like the stertorous, unquiet slumber of sick Life, is heard in Heaven! Oh, under that hideous coverlet of vapors, and putrefactions, and unimaginable gases, what a Fermenting-vat lies simmering and hid! The joyful and the sorrowful are there;

men are dying there, men are being born; men are praying,—on the other side of a brick partition, men are cursing; and around them all is the vast, void Night. The proud Grandee still lingers in his perfumed saloons, or reposes within damask curtains; Wretchedness cowers into truckle-beds, or shivers hunger-stricken into its lair of straw: in obscure cellars, *Rouge-et-Noir* languidly emits its voice-of-destiny to haggard hungry Villains; while Councillors of State sit plotting, and playing their high chess-game, whereof the pawns are Men. The Lover whispers his mistress that the coach is ready; and she, full of hope and fear, glides down, to fly with him over the borders: the Thief, still more silently, sets-to his picklocks and crowbars, or lurks in wait till the watchmen first snore in their boxes. Gay mansions, with supper-rooms and dancing-rooms, are full of light and music and high-swelling hearts; but, in the Condemned Cells, the pulse of life beats tremulous and faint, and bloodshot eyes look-out through the darkness, which is around and within, for the light of a stern last morning. Six men are to be hanged on the morrow: comes no hammering from the *Raben-stein?*—their gallows must even now be a-building. Upwards of five-hundred-thousand two-legged animals without feathers lie round us, in horizontal positions; their heads all in nightcaps, and full of the foolishest dreams. Riot cries aloud, and staggers and swaggers in his rank dens of shame; and the Mother, with streaming hair, kneels over her pallid dying infant, whose cracked lips only her tears now moisten.—All these heaped and huddled together, with nothing but a little carpentry and masonry between them;—crammed in, like salted fish in their barrel;—or weltering, shall I say, like an Egyptian pitcher of tamed vipers, each struggling to get its *head above* the others: *such* work goes on under that smoke-counter-pane!—But I, *mein werther,* sit above it all; I am alone with the Stars."

We looked in his face to see whether, in the utterance of such extraordinary Night-thoughts, no feeling might be traced there; but with the light we had, which indeed was only a single tallow-light, and far enough from the window, nothing save that old calmness and fixedness was visible.

These were the Professor's talking seasons: most commonly he spoke in mere monosyllables, or sat altogether silent and smoked; while the visitor had liberty either to say what he listed, receiving for answer an occasional grunt; or to look round for a space, and then take himself away. It was a strange apartment; full of books and tattered papers, and miscellaneous shreds of all conceivable substances, "united in a common element of dust." Books lay on tables, and below tables; here fluttered a sheet of manuscript, there a torn handkerchief, or nightcap hastily thrown aside; ink-bottles alternated with bread-crusts, coffee-pots, tobacco-boxes, Periodical Literature, and Blücher Boots. Old Lieschen (Lisekin, 'Liza), who was his bed-maker and stove-lighter, his washer and wringer, cook, errand-maid, and general lion's-provider, and for the rest a very orderly creature, had no sovereign authority in this last citadel of Teufelsdröckh; only some once in the month she half-forcibly made her way thither, with broom and duster, and (Teufelsdröckh hastily saving his manuscripts) effected a partial clearance, a jail-delivery of such lumber as was not Literary. These were her *Erdbeben* (earthquakes), which Teufelsdröckh dreaded worse than the pestilence; nevertheless, to such length he had been forced to comply. Glad would he have been to sit here philosophizing forever, or till the litter, by accumulation, drove him out of doors: but Lieschen was his right-arm, and spoon, and necessary of life, and would not be flatly gainsaid. We can still remember the ancient woman; so silent that some thought her dumb; deaf also you would often have supposed her; for Teufelsdröckh, and Teufelsdröckh only, would she serve or give heed to; and with him she seemed to communicate chiefly by signs; if it were not rather by some secret divination that she guessed all his wants, and supplied them. Assiduous old dame! she scoured, and sorted, and swept, in her kitchen, with the least possible violence to the ear; yet all was tight and right there: hot and black came the coffee ever at the due moment; and the speechless Lieschen herself looked out on you, from under her clean white coif with its lappets, through her clean withered face and wrinkles, with a look of helpful intelligence, almost of benevolence.

Few strangers, as above hinted, had admittance hither: the only one we ever saw there, ourselves excepted, was the Hofrath Heuschrecke, already known, by name and expectation, to the readers of these pages. To us, at that period, Herr Heuschrecke seemed one of those purse-mouthed, crane-necked, clean-brushed, pacific individuals, perhaps sufficiently distinguished in society by this fact, that, in dry weather or in wet, "they never appear without their umbrella." Had we not known with what "little wisdom" the world is governed; and how, in Germany as elsewhere, the ninety-and-nine Public Men can for most part be but mute train-bearers to the hundredth, perhaps but stalking-horses and willing or unwilling dupes,—it might have seemed wonderful how Herr Heuschrecke should be named a *Rath*, or Councillor, and Counsellor, even in Weissnichtwo. What counsel to any man, or to any woman, could this particular Hofrath give; in whose loose, zigzag figure; in whose thin visage, as it went jerking to and fro, in minute incessant fluctuation,—you traced rather confusion worse confounded; at most, Timidity and physical Cold? Some indeed said withal, he was "the very Spirit of Love embodied:" blue earnest eyes, full of sadness and kindness; purse ever open, and so forth; the whole of which, we shall now hope, for many reasons, was not quite groundless. Nevertheless friend Teufelsdröckh's outline, who indeed handled the burin like few in these cases, was probably the best: *Er hat Gemüth und Geist, hat wenigstens gehabt, doch ohne Organ, ohne Schicksals-Gunst; ist gegenwärtig aber halb-zerrüttet, halberstarrt,* "He has heart and talent, at least has had such, yet without fit mode of utterance, or favor of Fortune; and so is now half-cracked, half-congealed."—What the Hofrath shall think of this when he sees it, readers may wonder: we, safe in the stronghold of Historical Fidelity, are careless.

The main point, doubtless, for us all, is his love of Teufelsdröckh, which indeed was also by far the most decisive feature of Heuschrecke himself.

We are enabled to assert that he hung on the Professor with the fondness
of a Boswell for his Johnson. And perhaps with the like return; for Teufelsdröckh treated his gaunt admirer with little outward regard, as some
half-rational or altogether irrational friend, and at best loved him out of
gratitude and by habit. On the other hand, it was curious to observe with
what reverent kindness, and a sort of fatherly protection, our Hofrath,
being the elder, richer, and as he fondly imagined far more practically
influential of the two, looked and tended on his little Sage, whom he seemed
to consider as a living oracle. Let but Teufelsdröckh open his mouth,
Heuschrecke's also unpuckered itself into a free doorway, beside his being
all eye and all ear, so that nothing might be lost: and then, at every pause
in the harangue he gurgled out his pursy chuckle of a cough-laugh (for the
machinery of laughter took some time to get in motion, and seemed crank
and slack), or else his twanging nasal *Bravo! Das glaub' ich;* in either case,
by way of heartiest approval. In short, if Teufelsdröckh was Dalai-Lama,
of which, except perhaps in his self-seclusion, and god-like indifference,
there was no symptom, then might Heuschrecke pass for his chief Talapoin,
to whom no dough-pill he could knead and publish was other than medici-
nal and sacred.

In such environment, social, domestic, physical, did Teufelsdröckh, at
the time of our acquaintance, and most likely does he still, live and meditate. Here, perched-up in his high Wahngasse watch-tower, and often, in
solitude, outwatching the Bear, it was that the indomitable Inquirer fought
all his battles with Dulness and Darkness; here, in all probability, that he
wrote this surprising Volume on *Clothes*. Additional particulars: of his
age, which was of that standing middle sort you could only guess at; of
his wide surtout; the color of his trousers, fashion of his broad-brimmed
steeple-hat, and so forth, we might report, but do not.—The Wisest truly
is, in these times, the Greatest; so that an enlightened curiosity, leaving
Kings and such-like to rest very much on their own basis, turns more and
more to the Philosophic Class: nevertheless, what reader expects that, with
all our writing and reporting Teufelsdröckh could be brought home to
him, till once the Documents arrive? His Life, Fortunes, and Bodily Presence, are as yet hidden from us, or matter only of faint conjecture. But,
on the other hand, does not his Soul lie enclosed in this remarkable Volume,
much more truly than Pedro Garcia's did in the buried Bag of Doubloons?
To the soul of Diogenes Teufelsdröckh, to his opinions, namely, on the
"Origin and Influence of Clothes," we for the present gladly return.

CHAPTER IV.

CHARACTERISTICS.

IT WERE a piece of vain flattery to pretend that this Work on Clothes
entirely contents us; that it is not, like all works of genius, like the very

Sun, which, though the highest published creation, or work of genius, has nevertheless black spots and troubled nebulosities amid its effulgence,— a mixture of insight, inspiration, with dulness, double-vision, and even utter blindness.

Without committing ourselves to those enthusiastic praises and prophesyings of the *Weissnichtwo'sche Anzeiger*, we admitted that the Book had in a high degree excited us to self-activity, which is the best effect of any book; that it had even operated changes in our way of thought; nay, that it promised to prove, as it were, the opening of a new mine-shaft, wherein the whole world of Speculation might henceforth dig to unknown depths. More especially it may now be declared that Professor Teufelsdröckh's acquirements, patience of research, philosophic and even poetic vigor, are here made indisputably manifest; and unhappily no less his prolixity and tortuosity and manifold ineptitude; that, on the whole, as in opening new mine-shafts is not unreasonable, there is much rubbish in his Book, though likewise specimens of almost invaluable ore. A paramount popularity in England we cannot promise him. Apart from the choice of such a topic as Clothes, too often the manner of treating it betokens in the Author a rusticity and academic seclusion, unblamable, indeed inevitable in a German, but fatal to his success with our public.

Of good society Teufelsdröckh appears to have seen little, or has mostly forgotten what he saw. He speaks-out with a strange plainness; calls many things by their mere dictionary names. To him the Upholsterer is no Pontiff, neither is any Drawing-room a Temple, were it never so begilt and overhung: "a whole immensity of Brussels carpets, and pier-glasses, and ormolu," as he himself expresses it, "cannot hide from me that such Drawing-room is simply a section of Infinite Space, where so many God-created Souls do for the time meet together." To Teufelsdröckh the highest Duchess is respectable, is venerable; but nowise for her pearl bracelets and Malines laces; in his eyes, the star of a Lord is little less and little more than the broad button of Birmingham spelter in a Clown's smock; "each is an implement," he says, "in its kind; a tag for *hooking-together*; and, for the rest, was dug from the earth, and hammered on a stithy before smith's fingers." Thus does the Professor look in men's faces with a strange impartiality, a strange scientific freedom; like a man unversed in the higher circles, like a man dropped thither from the Moon. Rightly considered, it is in this peculiarity, running through his whole system of thought, that all these short-comings, over-shootings, and multiform perversities, take rise: if indeed they have not a second source, also natural enough, in his Transcendental Philosophies, and humor of looking at all Matter and Material things as Spirit; whereby truly his case were but the more hopeless, the more lamentable.

To the Thinkers of this nation, however, of which class it is firmly believed there are individuals yet extant, we can safely recommend the Work: nay, who knows but among the fashionable ranks too, if it be true, as Teufelsdröckh maintains, that "within the most starched cravat there passes a windpipe and weasand, and under the thickliest embroidered waistcoat beats a heart,"—the force of that rapt earnestness may be felt, and here and there an arrow of the soul pierce through? In our wild Seer, shaggy, unkempt, like a Baptist living on locusts and wild honey, there is an untutored energy, a silent, as it were unconscious, strength, which, except in the higher walks of Literature, must be rare. Many a deep glance, and often with unspeakable precision, has he cast into mysterious Nature, and the still more mysterious Life of Man. Wonderful it is with what cutting words, now and then, he severs asunder the confusion; shears down, were it furlongs deep, into the true center of the matter; and there not only hits the nail on the head, but with crushing force smites it home, and buries it.—On the other hand, let us be free to admit, he is the most unequal writer breathing. Often after some such feat, he will play truant for long pages, and go dawdling and dreaming, and mumbling and maundering the merest commonplaces, as if he were asleep with eyes open, which indeed he is.

Of his boundless Learning, and how all reading and literature in most known tongues, from *Sanchoniathon* to *Dr. Lingard*, from your Oriental *Shasters*, and *Talmuds*, and *Korans*, with Cassini's *Siamese Tables*, and Laplace's *Mécanique Céleste*, down to *Robinson Crusoe* and the *Belfast Town and Country Almanack*, are familiar to him,—we shall say nothing: for unexampled as it is with us, to the Germans such universality of study passes without wonder, as a thing commendable, indeed, but natural, indispensable, and there of course. A man that devotes his life to learning, shall he not be learned?

In respect of style our Author manifests the same genial capability, marred too often by the same rudeness, inequality, and apparent want of intercourse with the higher classes. Occasionally, as above hinted, we find consummate vigor, a true inspiration; his burning thoughts step forth in fit burning words, like so many full-formed Minervas, issuing amid flame and splendor from Jove's head; a rich, idiomatic diction, picturesque allusions, fiery poetic emphasis, or quaint tricksy turns; all the graces and terrors of a wild Imagination, wedded to the clearest Intellect, alternate in beautiful vicissitude. Were it not that sheer sleeping and soporific passages; circumlocutions, repetitions, touches even of pure doting jargon, so often intervene! On the whole, Professor Teufelsdröckh is not a cultivated writer. Of his sentences perhaps not more than nine-tenths stand straight on their legs; the remainder are in quite angular attitudes, buttressed-up by props (of parentheses and dashes), and ever with this or the other tagrag hanging from them; a few even sprawl-out helplessly on all sides, quite broken-backed and dismembered. Nevertheless, in almost his very worst moods, there lies in him a singular attraction. A wild tone pervades the whole utterance of the man, like its keynote and regulator; now screwing itself aloft as into the Song of Spirits, or else the shrill mockery of Fiends; now sinking in cadences, not without melodious heartiness, though sometimes abrupt enough, into the common pitch, when we hear it only as a monotonous hum; of which hum the true character is extremely difficult to fix. Up to this hour we have never fully satisfied ourselves whether it is a tone and hum of real Humor, which we reckon among the very highest qualities of genius, or some echo of mere Insanity and Inanity, which doubtless ranks below the very lowest.

Under a like difficulty, in spite even of our personal intercourse, do we still lie with regard to the Professor's moral feeling. Gleams of an ethereal love burst forth from him, soft wailings of infinite pity; he could clasp the whole Universe into his bosom, and keep it warm; it seems as if under that rude exterior there dwelt a very seraph. Then again he is so sly and still, so imperturbably saturnine; shows such indifference, malign coolness towards all that men strive after; and ever with some half-visible wrinkle of a bitter sardonic humor, if indeed it be not mere stolid callousness,—that you look on him almost with a shudder, as on some incarnate Mephistopheles, to whom this great terrestrial and celestial Round, after all, were but some huge foolish Whirligig, where kings and beggars, and angels and demons, and stars and street-sweepings, were chaotically whirled, in which only children could take interest. His look, as we mentioned, is probably the gravest ever seen: yet it is not of that cast-iron gravity frequent enough among our own Chancery suitors; but rather the gravity as of some silent, high-encircled mountain-pool, perhaps the crater of an extinct volcano; into whose black deeps you fear to gaze: those eyes, those lights that sparkle in it, may indeed be reflexes of the heavenly Stars, but perhaps also glances from the region of Nether Fire!

Certainly a most involved, self-secluded, altogether enigmatic nature, this of Teufelsdröckh! Here, however, we gladly recall to mind that once we saw him *laugh;* once only, perhaps it was the first and last time in his life; but then such a peal of laughter, enough to have awakened the Seven Sleepers! It was of Jean Paul's doings: some single billow in that vast World-Mahlstrom of Humor, with its heaven-kissing coruscations, which is now, alas, all congealed in the frost of death! The large-bodied Poet and the small, both large enough in soul, sat talking miscellaneously together, the present Editor being privileged to listen; and now Paul, in his serious way, was giving one of those inimitable "Extra-harangues;" and, as it chanced, On the Proposal for a *Cast-metal King:* gradually a light kindled in our Professor's eyes and face, a beaming, mantling, loveliest light; through those murky features, a radiant, ever-young Apollo looked; and he burst forth like the neighing of all Tattersall's,—tears streaming down his cheeks, pipe held aloft, foot clutched into the air,—loud, long-continuing, uncontrollable; a laugh not of the face and diaphragm only, but of the whole man from head to heel. The present Editor, who laughed indeed, yet with measure, began to fear all was not right: however, Teufelsdröckh composed himself, and sank into his old stillness; on his inscrutable countenance there was, if anything, a slight look of shame; and Richter himself could not rouse him again. Readers who have any tincture of Psychology know how much is to be inferred from this; and that no man who has once heartily and wholly laughed can be altogether irreclaimably bad. How much lies in laughter: the cipher-key, wherewith we decipher the whole man! Some men wear an everlasting barren simper; in the smile of others lies a cold glitter as of ice: the fewest are able to laugh, what can be called laughing, but only sniff and titter and snigger from the throat outwards; or at best, produce some whiffling husky cachinnation, as if they were laughing through wool: of none such comes good. The man who cannot laugh is not only fit for treasons, stratagems, and spoils; but his whole life is already a treason and a stratagem.

Considered as an Author, Herr Teufelsdröckh has one scarcely pardonable fault, doubtless his worst: an almost total want of arrangement. In this remarkable Volume, it is true, his adherence to the mere course of Time produces, through the Narrative portions, a certain show of outward method; but of true logical method and sequence there is too little. Apart from its multifarious sections and subdivisions, the Work naturally falls into two Parts; a Historical-Descriptive, and a Philosophical-Speculative: but falls, unhappily, by no firm line of demarcation; in that labyrinthic combination, each Part overlaps, and indents, and indeed runs quite through the other. Many sections are of a debatable rubric, or even quite nondescript and unnamable; whereby the Book not only loses in accessibility, but too often distresses us like some mad banquet, wherein all courses had been confounded, and fish and flesh, soup and solid, oyster-sauce, lettuces, Rhine-wine and French mustard, were hurled into one huge tureen or trough, and the hungry Public invited to help itself. To bring what order we can out of this Chaos shall be part of our endeavor.

CHAPTER V.

The World in Clothes.

"As montesquieu wrote a *Spirit of Laws*," observes our Professor, "so could I write a *Spirit of Clothes*; thus, with an *Esprit des Lois*, properly an *Esprit de Coutumes*, we should have an *Esprit de Costumes*. For neither in tailoring nor in legislating does man proceed by mere Accident, but the hand is ever guided on by mysterious operations of the mind. In all his Modes, and habilatory endeavors, an Architectural Idea will be found lurking; his Body and the Cloth are the site and materials whereon and whereby his beautiful edifice, of a Person, is to be built. Whether he flow gracefully out in folded mantles, based on light sandals; tower-up in high headgear, from amid peaks, spangles and bell-girdles; swell-out in starched ruffs, buckram stuffings, and monstrous tuberosities; or girth himself into separate sections, and front the world an Agglomeration of four limbs,—will depend on the nature of such Architectural Idea: whether Grecian, Gothic, Later-Gothic, or altogether Modern, and Parisian or Anglo-Dandiacal. Again, what meaning lies in Color! From the soberest drab to the high-flaming scarlet, spiritual idiosyncrasies unfold themselves in choice of Color: if the Cut betoken Intellect and Talent, so does the Color betoken Temper and Heart. In all which, among nations as among individuals, there is an incessant, indubitable, though infinitely complex working of Cause and Effect: every snip of the Scissors has been regulated and prescribed by ever-active Influences, which doubtless to Intelligences of a superior order are neither invisible nor illegible.

"For such superior Intelligences a Cause-and-Effect Philosophy of Clothes, as of Laws, were probably a comfortable winter-evening entertainment: nevertheless, for inferior Intelligences, like men, such Philosophies have always seemed to me uninstructive enough. Nay, what is your Montesquieu himself but a clever infant spelling Letters from a hieroglyphical prophetic Book, the lexicon of which lies in Eternity, in Heaven?—Let any Cause-and-Effect Philosopher explain, not why I wear such and such a Garment, obey such and such a Law; but even why *I* am *here*, to wear and obey anything!—Much, therefore, if not the whole, of that same *Spirit of Clothes* I shall suppress, as hypothetical, ineffectual, and even impertinent: naked Facts, and Deductions drawn therefrom in quite another than that omniscient style, are my humbler and proper province."

Acting on which prudent restriction, Teufelsdröckh has nevertheless contrived to take-in a well-nigh boundless extent of field; at least, the boundaries too often lie quite beyond our horizon. Selection being indispensable, we shall here glance-over his First Part only in the most cursory manner. This First Part is no doubt, distinguished by omnivorous learning, and utmost patience and fairness: at the same time, in its results and delineations, it is much more likely to interest the Compilers of some *Library* of General, Entertaining, Useful, or even Useless Knowledge than the miscellaneous readers of these pages. Was it this Part of the Book which Heuschrecke had in view, when he recommended us to that joint-stock vehicle of publication, "at present the glory of British Literature"? If so, the Library Editors are welcome to dig in it for their own behoof.

To the First Chapter, which turns on Paradise and Fig-leaves, and leads us into interminable disquisitions of a mythological, metaphorical, cabalistico-sartorial and quite antediluvian cast, we shall content ourselves with giving an unconcerned approval. Still less have we to do with "Lilis, Adam's first wife, whom, according to the Talmudists, he had before Eve, and who bore him, in that wedlock, the whole progeny of aerial, aquatic, and terrestrial Devils,"—very needlessly, we think. On this portion of the Work, with its profound glances into the *Adam-Kadmon*, or primeval Element, here strangely brought into relation with the *Nifl* and *Muspel*, (Darkness and Light) of the antique North, it may be enough to say, that its correctness of deduction, and depth of Talmudic and Rabbinical lore have filled perhaps not the worst Hebraist in Britain with something like astonishment.

But, quitting this twilight region, Teufelsdröckh hastens from the Tower of Babel, to follow the dispersion of Mankind over the whole habitable and habilable globe. Walking by the light of Oriental, Pelasgic, Scandinavian, Egyptian, Otaheitean, Ancient and Modern researches of every conceivable kind, he strives to give us in compressed shape (as the Nürnbergers give an *Orbis Pictus*) an *Orbis Vestitus;* or view of the customs of all mankind, in all countries in all times. It is here that to the Antiquarian, to the Historian, we can triumphantly say: Fall to! Here is learning: an irregular Treasury, if you will; but inexhaustible as the Hoard of King Nibelung, which twelve wagons in twelve days, at the rate of three journeys a day, could not carry off. Sheepskin cloaks and wampum belts; phylacteries, stoles, albs; chlamydes, togas, Chinese silks, Afghan shawls, trunk-hose, leather breeches, Celtic philibegs (though breeches, as the name *Gallia Braccata* indicates, are the more ancient), Hussar cloaks, Vandyke tippets, ruffs, fardingales, are brought vividly before us,—even the Kilmarnock nightcap is not forgotten. For most part, too, we must admit that the Learning, heterogeneous as it is, and tumbled-down quite pellmell, is true concentrated and purified Learning, the drossy parts smelted out and thrown aside.

Philosophical reflections intervene, and sometimes touching pictures of human life. Of this sort the following has surprised us. The first purpose of Clothes, as our Professor imagines, was not warmth or decency, but ornament. "Miserable indeed," says he, "was the condition of the Aboriginal Savage, glaring fiercely from under his fleece of hair, which with the beard reached down to his loins, and hung round him like a matted cloak; the rest of his body sheeted in its thick natural fell. He loitered in the sunny glades of the forest, living on wild-fruits; or, as the ancient Caledonian, squatted himself in morasses, lurking for his bestial or human prey; without implements, without arms, save the ball of heavy Flint, to which, that his sole possession and defence might not be lost, he had attached a long cord of plaited thongs; thereby recovering as well as hurling it with deadly unerring skill. Nevertheless, the pains of Hunger and Revenge once satisfied, his next care was not Comfort but Decoration (*Putz*). Warmth he found in the toils of the chase; or amid dried leaves, in his hollow tree, in his bark shed, or natural grotto: but for Decoration he must have Clothes. Nay, among wild people, we find tattooing and painting even prior to Clothes. The first spiritual want of a barbarous man is Decoration, as indeed we still see among the barbarous classes in civilized countries.

"Reader, the heaven-inspired melodious Singer; loftiest Serene Highness; nay thy own amber-locked, snow-and-rose-bloom Maiden, worthy to glide sylph-like almost on air, whom thou lovest, worshippest as a divine Presence, which, indeed, symbolically taken, she is,—has descended, like thyself, from that same hair-mantled, flint-hurling Aboriginal Anthropophagous! Out of the eater cometh forth meat; out of the strong cometh forth sweetness. What changes are wrought, not by Time, yet in Time! For not Mankind only, but all that Mankind does or beholds, is in continual growth, regenesis and self-perfecting vitality. Cast forth thy Act, thy Word, into the ever-living, ever-working Universe: it is a seed-grain that cannot die; unnoticed to-day (says one), it will be found flourishing as a Banyan grove (perhaps, alas, as a Hemlock-forest!) after a thousand years.

"He who first shortened the labor of Copyists by device of *Movable Types* was disbanding hired Armies, and cashiering most Kings and Senates, and creating a whole new Democratic world: he had invented the Art of Printing. The first ground handful of Nitre, Sulphur, and Charcoal drove Monk Schwartz's pestle through the ceiling: what will the last do? Achieve the final undisputed prostration of Force under Thought, of Animal courage under Spiritual. A simple invention it was in the old-world Grazier,— sick of lugging his slow Ox about the country till he got it bartered for corn or oil,—to take a piece of Leather, and thereon scratch or stamp the mere Figure of an Ox (or *Pecus*); put it in his pocket, and call it *Pecunia*, Money. Yet hereby did Barter grow Sale, the Leather Money is now Golden and Paper, and all miracles have been out-miracled: for there are Rothschilds and English National Debts; and whoso has sixpence is sovereign (to the length of sixpence) over all men; commands cooks to feed him, philosophers to teach him, kings to mount guard over him,—to the length of sixpence.—Clothes too, which began in foolishest love of Ornament, what have they not become! Increased security and pleasurable Heat soon followed: but what of these? Shame, divine Shame (*Scham*, Modesty), as yet a stranger to the Anthropophagous bosom, arose there mysteriously under Clothes; a mystic grove-encircled shrine for the Holy in man. Clothes gave us individuality, distinctions, social polity; Clothes have made Men of us; they are threatening to make Clothes-screens of us.

"But, on the whole," continues our eloquent Professor, "Man is a tool-using Animal (*Handthierendes Thier*). Weak in himself, and of small stature, he stands on a basis, at most for the flattest-soled, of some half-square foot, insecurely enough; has to straddle out his legs, lest the very wind supplant him. Feeblest of bipeds! Three quintals are a crushing load for him; the steer of the meadow tosses him aloft, like a waste rag. Nevertheless he can use Tools, can devise Tools: with these the granite mountain melts into light dust before him; he kneads glowing iron, as if it were soft paste; seas are his smooth highway, winds and fire his unwearying steeds. Nowhere do you find him without Tools; without Tools he is nothing, with Tools he is all."

Here may we not, for a moment, interrupt the stream of Oratory with a remark, that this Definition of the Tool-using Animal appears to us, of all that Animal-sort, considerably the precisest and best? Man is called a Laughing Animal: but do not the apes also laugh, or attempt to do it; and is the manliest man the greatest and oftenest laugher? Teufelsdröckh himself, as we said, laughed only once. Still less do we make of that other French Definition of the Cooking Animal; which, indeed, for rigorous scientific purposes, is as good as useless. Can a Tartar be said to cook, when he only readies his steak by riding on it? Again, what Cookery does the Greenlander use, beyond stowing-up his whale-blubber, as a marmot, in the like case, might do? Or how would Monsieur Ude prosper among those Orinocco Indians who, according to Humboldt, lodge in crow-nests, on the branches of trees; and, for half the year, have no victuals but pipe-clay, the whole country being under water? But, on the other hand, show us the human being of any period or climate, without his Tools: those very Caledonians, as we saw, had their Flint-ball and Thong to it, such as no brute has or can have.

"Man is a Tool-using Animal," concludes Teufelsdröckh in his abrupt way; "of which truth Clothes are but one example: and surely if we consider the interval between the first wooden Dibble fashioned by man, and those Liverpool Steam-carriages, or the British House of Commons, we shall note what progress he has made. He digs up certain black stones from the bosom of the earth, and says to them, *Transport me and this luggage at the rate of five-and-thirty miles an hour;* and they do it: he collects, apparently by lot, six-hundred and fifty-eight miscellaneous individuals, and says to them, *Make this nation toil for us, bleed for us, hunger and sorrow and sin for us;* and they do it."

CHAPTER VI.

Aprons.

One of the most unsatisfactory Sections in the whole Volume is that on *Aprons*. What though stout old Gao, the Persian Blacksmith, "whose Apron, now indeed hidden under jewels, because raised in revolt which proved successful, is still the royal standard of that country;" what though John Knox's Daughter, who threatened Sovereign Majesty that she would catch her husband's head in her Apron, rather than he should lie and be a bishop, what though the Landgravene Elizabeth, with many other Apron worthies,—figure here? An idle wire-drawing spirit, sometimes even a tone of levity, approaching to conventional satire, is too clearly discernible. What, for example, are we to make of such sentences as the following?

"Aprons are Defences; against injury to cleanliness, to safety, to modesty, sometimes to roguery. From the thin slip of notched silk (as it were, the emblem and beatified ghost of an Apron), which some highest-bred housewife, sitting at Nürnberg Work-boxes and Toy-boxes, has gracefully fastened on; to the thick-tanned hide, girt round him with thongs, wherein the Builder builds, and at evening sticks his trowel; or to those jingling sheet-iron Aprons, wherein your otherwise half-naked Vulcans hammer and smelt in their smelt-furnace,—is there not range enough in the fashion and uses of this Vestment? How much has been concealed, how much has been defended in Aprons! Nay, rightfully considered, what is your whole Military and Police Establishment, charged at uncalculated millions, but a huge scarlet-colored, iron-fastened Apron, wherein Society works (uneasily enough); guarding itself from some soil and stithy-sparks, in this Devil's-smithy

(*Teufels-schmiede*) of a world? But of all Aprons the most puzzling to me hitherto has been the Episcopal or Cassock. Wherein consists the usefulness of this Apron? The Overseer (*Episcopus*) of Souls, I notice, has tucked-in the corner of it, as if his day's work were done: what does he shadow forth thereby?" etc., etc.

Or again, has it often been the lot of our readers to read such stuff as we shall now quote?

"I consider those printed Paper Aprons, worn by the Parisian Cooks, as a new vent, though a slight one, for Typography; therefore as an encouragement to modern Literature, and deserving of approval: nor is it without satisfaction that I hear of a celebrated London Firm having in view to introduce the same fashion, with important extensions, in England."—We who are on the spot hear of no such thing; and indeed have reason to be thankful that hitherto there are other vents for our Literature, exuberant as it is.— Teufelsdröckh continues: "If such supply of printed Paper should rise so far as to choke-up the highways and public thoroughfares, new means must of necessity be had recourse to. In a world existing by Industry, we grudge to employ fire as a destroying element, and not as a creating one. However, Heaven is omnipotent, and will find us an outlet. In the meanwhile, is it not beautiful to see five-million quintals of Rags picked annually from the Laystall; and annually, after being macerated, hot-pressed, printed-on, and sold,—returned thither; filling so many hungry mouths by the way? Thus is the Laystall, especially with its Rags or Clothes-rubbish, the grand Electric Battery, and Fountain-of-motion, from which and to which the Social Activities (like vitreous and resinous Electricities) circulate, in larger or smaller circles, through the mighty, billowy, storm-tost Chaos of Life, which they keep alive!"—Such passages fill us, who love the man, and partly esteem him; with a very mixed feeling.

Farther down we meet with this: "The Journalists are now the true Kings and Clergy: henceforth Historians, unless they are fools, must write not of Bourbon Dynasties, and Tudors and Hapsburgs; but of Stamped Broad-sheet Dynasties, and quite new successive Names, according as this or the other Able Editor, or Combination of Able Editors, gains the world's ear. Of the British Newspaper Press, perhaps the most important of all, and wonderful enough in its secret constitution and procedure, a valuable descriptive History already exists, in that language, under the title of *Satan's Invisible World Displayed;* which, however, by search in all the Weissnichtwo Libraries, I have not yet succeeded in procuring (*vermöchte nicht aufzutreiben*)."

Thus does the good Homer not only nod, but snore. Thus does Teufelsdröckh, wandering in regions where he had little business, confound the old authentic Presbyterian Witchfinder with a new, spurious, imaginary Historian of the *Britische Journalistik;* and so stumble on perhaps the most egregious blunder in Modern Literature!

CHAPTER VII.

Miscellaneous-Historical.

Happier is our Professor, and more purely scientific and historic, when he reaches the Middle Ages in Europe, and down to the end of the Seventeenth Century; the true era of extravagance in Costume. It is here that the Antiquary and Student of Modes comes upon his richest harvest. Fantastic garbs, beggaring all fancy of a Teniers or a Callot, succeed each other, like monster devouring monster in a Dream. The whole too in brief authentic strokes, and touched not seldom with that breath of genius which makes even old raiment live. Indeed, so learned, precise, graphical, and everyway interesting have we found these Chapters, that it may be thrown-out as a pertinent question for parties concerned. Whether or not a good English Translation thereof might henceforth be profitably incorporated with Mr. Merrick's valuable Work *On Ancient Armor?* Take, by way of example, the following sketch; as authority for which Paulinus's *Zeitkürzende Lust* (ii. 678) is, with seeming confidence, referred to:

"Did we behold the German fashionable dress of the Fifteenth Century, we might smile; as perhaps those bygone Germans, were they to rise again, and see our haberdashery, would cross themselves, and invoke the Virgin. But happily no bygone German, or man, rises again; thus the Present is not needlessly trammelled with the Past; and only grows out of it, like a Tree, whose roots are not intertangled with its branches, but lie peaceably underground. Nay it is very mournful, yet not useless, to see and know, how the Greatest and Dearest, in a short while, would find his place quite filled-up here, and no room for him; the very Napoleon, the very Byron, in some seven years, has become obsolete, and were now a foreigner to his Europe. Thus is the Law of Progress secured; and in Clothes, as in all other external things whatsoever, no fashion will continue.

"Of the military classes in those old times, whose buff-belts, complicated chains and gorgets, huge churn-boots, and other riding and fighting gear have been bepainted in modern Romance, till the whole has acquired somewhat of a sign-post character,—I shall here say nothing: the civil and pacific classes, less touched upon, are wonderful enough for us.

"Rich men, I find, have *Teusinke*" (a perhaps untranslatable article); "also a silver girdle, whereat hang little bells; so that when a man walks, it is with continual jingling. Some few, of musical turn, have a whole chime of bells (*Glockenspiel*) fastened there; which, especially in sudden whirls, and the other accidents of walking, has a grateful effect. Observe too how fond they are of peaks, and Gothic-arch intersections. The male world wears peaked caps, an ell long, which hang bobbing over the side (*schief*): their shoes are peaked in front, also to the length of an ell, and laced on the side with tags; even the wooden shoes have their ell-long noses: some also clap bells on the peak. Further, according to my authority, the men have breeches without seat (*ohne Gesäss*): these they fasten peakwise to their shirts; and the long round doublet must overlap them.

"Rich maidens, again, flit abroad in gowns scalloped out behind and before, so that back and breast are almost bare. Wives of quality, on the other hand, have train-gowns four or five ells in length; which trains there are boys to carry. Brave Cleopatras, sailing in their silk-cloth Galley, with a Cupid for steersman! Consider their welts, a handbreadth thick, which waver round them by way of hem the long flood of silver buttons, or rather silver shells, from throat to shoe, wherewith these same welt-gowns are buttoned. The maidens have bound silver snoods about their hair, with gold spangles, and pendant flames (*Flammen*), that is, sparkling hair-drops: but of their mother's headgear who shall speak? Neither in love of grace is comfort forgotten. In winter weather you behold the whole fair creation (that can afford it) in long mantles, with skirts wide below, and, for hem, not one but two sufficient handbroad welts; all ending atop in a thick well-starched Ruff, some twenty inches broad: these are their Ruff-mantles (*Kragenmäntel*).

"As yet among the womankind hoop-petticoats are not; but the men have doublets of fustian, under which lie multiple ruffs of cloth, pasted together with batter (*mit Teig zusammengekleistert*), which create protuberance enough. Thus do the two sexes vie with each other in the art of Decoration; and as usual the stronger carries it."

Our Professor, whether he have humor himself or not, manifests a certain feeling of the Ludicrous, a sly observance of it, which, could emotion of any kind be confidently predicated of so still a man, we might call a real love. None of those bell-girdles, bushel-breeches, cornuted shoes, or other the like phenomena, of which the History of Dress offers so many, escape him: more especially the mischances, or striking adventures, incident to the wearers of such, are noticed with due fidelity. Sir Walter Raleigh's fine mantle, which he spread in the mud under Queen Elizabeth's feet, appears to provoke little enthusiasm in him; he merely asks, Whether at that period the Maiden Queen "was red-painted on the nose, and white-painted on the cheeks, as her tirewomen, when from spleen and wrinkles she would no longer look in any glass, were wont to serve her?" We can answer that Sir Walter knew well what he was doing, and had the Maiden Queen been stuffed parchment dyed in verdigris, would have done the same.

Thus too, treating of those enormous habiliments, that were not only slashed and galloned, but artificially swollen-out on the broader parts of the body, by introduction of Bran,—our Professor fails not to comment on that luckless Courtier, who having seated himself on a chair with some projecting nail on it, and therefrom rising, to pay his *devoir* on the entrance of Majesty, instantaneously emitted several pecks of dry wheat-dust: and stood there diminished to a spindle, his galloons and slashes dangling sorrowful and flabby round him. Whereupon the Professor publishes this reflection:

"By what strange chances do we live in History? Erostratus by a torch; Milo by a bullock; Henry Darnley, an unfledged booby and bustard, by his limbs; most Kings and Queens by being born under such and such a bed-tester; Boileau Despréaux (according to Helvetius) by the peck of a turkey; and this ill-starred individual by a rent in his breeches,—for no Memoirist of Kaiser Otto's Court omits him. Vain was the prayer of Themistocles for a talent of Forgetting: my Friends, yield cheerfully to Destiny, and read since it is written."—Has Teufelsdröckh to be put in mind that, nearly related to the impossible talent of Forgetting, stands that talent of Silence, which even travelling Englishmen manifest?

"The simplest costume," observes our Professor, "which I anywhere find alluded to in History, is that used as regimental, by Bolivar's Cavalry, in the late Colombian wars. A square Blanket, twelve feet in diagonal, is provided (some were wont to cut-off the corners, and make it circular): in the centre a slit is effected eighteen inches long; through this the mother-naked Trooper introduces his head and neck; and so rides shielded from all weather, and in battle from many strokes (for he rolls it about his left arm); and not only dressed, but harnessed and draperied."

With which picture of a State of Nature, affecting by its singularity, and Old-Roman contempt of the superfluous, we shall quit this part of our subject.

CHAPTER VIII.

THE WORLD OUT OF CLOTHES.

IF IN THE Descriptive-Historical portion of this Volume, Teufelsdröckh, discussing merely the *Werden* (Origin and successive Improvement) of Clothes, has astonished many a reader, much more will he in the Speculative-Philosophical portion, which treats of their *Wirken* or Influences. It is here that the present Editor first feels the pressure of his task; for here properly the higher and new Philosophy of Clothes commences: an untried almost inconceivable region, or chaos; in venturing upon which, how difficult, yet how unspeakably important, is it to know what course, of survey and conquest, is the true one; where the footing is firm substance and will bear us, where it is hollow, or mere cloud, and may ingulf us! Teufelsdröckh undertakes no less than to expound the moral, political, even religious Influences of Clothes; he undertakes to make manifest, in its thousandfold bearings this grand Proposition, that Man's earthly interests "are all hooked and buttoned together, and held up, by Clothes." He says in so many words, "Society is founded upon Cloth;" and again, "Society sails through the Infinitude on Cloth, as on a Faust's Mantle, or rather like the Sheet of clean and unclean beasts in the Apostle's Dream; and without such Sheet or Mantle, would sink to endless depths, or mount to inane limboes, and in either case be no more."

By what chains, or indeed infinitely complected tissues, of Meditation this grand Theorem is here unfolded, and innumerable practical Corollaries are drawn therefrom, it were perhaps a mad ambition to attempt exhibiting. Our Professor's method is not, in any case, that of common school Logic, where the truths all stand in a row, each holding by the skirts of the other; but at best that of practical Reason, proceeding by large Intuition over whole systematic groups and kingdoms; whereby, we might say, a noble complexity, almost like that of Nature, reigns in his Philosophy, or spiritual Picture of Nature: a mighty maze, yet, as faith whispers, not without a plan. Nay we complained above, that a certain ignoble complexity, what we must call mere confusion, was also discernible. Often, also, we have to exclaim: Would to Heaven those same Biographical Documents were come! For it seems as if the demonstration lay much in the Author's individuality; as if it were not Argument that had taught him, but Experience. At present it is only in local glimpses, and by significant fragments, picked often at wide-enough intervals from the original Volume, and carefully collated, that we can hope to impart some outline or foreshadow of this Doctrine. Readers of any intelligence are once more invited to favor us with their most concentrated attention: let these, after intense consideration, and not till then, pronounce, Whether on the utmost verge of our actual horizon there is not a looming as of Land; a promise of new Fortunate Islands, perhaps whole undiscovered Americas, for such as have canvas to sail thither?—As exordium to the whole, stand here the following long citation:

"With men of a speculative turn," writes Teufelsdröckh, "there come seasons, meditative, sweet, yet awful hours, when in wonder and fear you ask yourself that unanswerable question: Who am I; the thing that can say 'I' (das Wesen das sich Ich nennt)? The world, with its loud trafficking, retires into the distance; and, through the paper-hangings, and stone-walls, and thick-plied tissues of Commerce and Polity, and all the living and lifeless integuments (of Society and a Body), wherewith your Existence sits surrounded,—the sight reaches forth into the void Deep, and you are alone with the Universe, and silently commune with it, as one mysterious Presence with another.

"Who am I; what is this ME? A Voice, a Motion, an Appearance;—some embodied, visualized Idea in the Eternal Mind? Cogito, ergo sum. Alas, poor Cogitator, this takes us but a little way. Sure enough, I am; and lately was not: but Whence? How? Whereto? The answer lies around, written in all colors and motions, uttered in all tones of jubilee and wail, in thousand-figured, thousand-voiced, harmonious Nature: but where is the cunning eye and ear to whom that God-written Apocalypse will yield articulate meaning? We sit as in a boundless Phantasmagoria and Dream-grotto; boundless, for the faintest star, the remotest century, lies not even nearer the verge thereof: sounds and many-colored visions flit round our sense; but Him, the Unslumbering, whose work both Dream and Dreamer are, we see not; except in rare half-waking moments, suspect not. Creation, says one, lies before us, like a glorious Rainbow; but the Sun that made it lies behind us, hidden from us. Then, in that strange Dream, how we clutch at shadows as if they were substances; and sleep deepest while fancying ourselves most awake! Which of your Philosophical Systems is other than a dream-theorem; a net quotient, confidently given out, where divisor and dividend are both unknown? What are all your national Wars, with their Moscow Retreats, and sanguinary hate-filled Revolutions, but the Somnambulism of uneasy Sleepers? This Dreaming, this Somnambulism is what we on Earth call Life; wherein the most indeed undoubtingly wander, as if they knew right hand from left; yet they only are wise who know that they know nothing.

"Pity that all Metaphysics had hitherto proved so inexpressibly unproductive! The secret of Man's Being is still like the Sphinx's secret: a riddle that he cannot rede; and for ignorance of which he suffers death, the worst death, a spiritual. What are your Axioms, and Categories, and Systems, and Aphorisms? Words, words. High Air-castles are cunningly built of Words, the Words well bedded also in good Logic-mortar; wherein however, no Knowledge will come to lodge. *The whole is greater than the part:* how exceedingly true! *Nature abhors a vacuum:* how exceedingly false and calumnious! Again, *Nothing can act but where it is:* with all my heart; only, WHERE is it? Be not the slave of Words: is not the Distant, the Dead, while I love it, and long for it, and mourn for it, Here, in the genuine sense, as truly as the floor I stand on? But that same WHERE, with its brother WHEN, are from the first the master-colors of our Dream-grotto; say rather, the Canvas (the warp and woof thereof) whereon all our Dreams and Life-visions are painted. Nevertheless, has not a deeper meditation taught certain of every climate and age, that the WHERE and WHEN, so mysteriously inseparable from all our thoughts, are but superficial terrestrial adhesions to thought; that the Seer may discern them where they mount up out of the celestial EVERYWHERE and FOREVER: have not all nations conceived their God as Omnipresent and Eternal; as existing in a universal HERE, an everlasting Now? Think well, thou too wilt find that Space is but a mode of our human Sense, so likewise Time; there *is* no Space and no Time: WE are—we know not what; light-sparkles floating in the æther of Deity!

"So that this so solid-seeming World, after all, were but an air-image, our ME the only reality: and Nature, with its thousandfold production and destruction, but the reflex of our own inward Force, the 'phantasy of our Dream;' or what the Earth-Spirit in *Faust* names it, *the living visible Garment of God:*

> " '*In Being's floods, in Action's storm,*
> *I walk and work, above, beneath,*
> *Work and weave in endless motion!*
> *Birth and Death,*
> *An infinite ocean;*
> *A seizing and giving*
> *The fire of Living:*
> *'Tis thus at the roaring Loom of Time I ply,*
> *And weave for God the Garment thou seest Him by.*'

Of twenty millions that have read and spouted this thunder-speech of the *Erdgeist*, are there yet twenty units of us that have learned the meaning thereof?

"It was in some such mood, when wearied and fordone with these high speculations, that I first came upon the question of Clothes. Strange enough, it strikes me, is this same fact of there being Tailors and Tailored. The Horse I ride has his own whole fell: strip him of the girths and flaps and extraneous tags I have fastened round him, and the noble creature is his own sempster and weaver and spinner; nay his own boot-maker, jeweller, and man-milliner; he bounds free through the valleys, with a perennial rain-proof court-suit on his body; wherein warmth and easiness of fit have reached perfection; nay, the graces also have been considered, and frills and fringes, with gay variety of color, featly appended, and ever in the right place, are not wanting. While I—good Heaven!—have thatched myself over with the dead fleeces of sheep, the bark of vegetables, the entrails of worms, the hides of oxen or seals, the felt of furred beasts; and walk abroad a moving Rag-screen, overheaped with shreds and tatters raked from the Charnel-house of Nature, where they would have rotted, to rot on me more slowly! Day after day, I must thatch myself anew; day after day, this despicable thatch must lose some film of its thickness; some film of it, frayed away by tear and wear, must be brushed-off into the Ashpit, into the Laystall; till by degrees the whole has been brushed thither, and I, the dust-making, patent Rag-grinder, get new material to grind down. O subter-brutish! vile! most vile! For have not I too a compact all-enclosing Skin, whiter or dingier? Am I a botched mass of tailors' and cobblers' shreds, then; or a tightly-articulated, homogeneous little Figure, automatic, nay alive?

"Strange enough how creatures of the human-kind shut their eyes to plainest facts; and by the mere inertia of Oblivion and Stupidity, live at ease in the midst of Wonder and Terrors. But indeed man is, and was always, a blockhead and dullard; much readier to feel and digest, than to think and consider. Prejudice, which he pretends to hate, is his absolute lawgiver; mere use-and-wont everywhere leads him by the nose; thus let but a Rising of the Sun, let but a Creation of the World happen *twice* and it ceases to be marvellous, to be noteworthy, or noticeable. Perhaps not once in a lifetime does it occur to your ordinary biped, of any country or generation, be he gold mantled Prince or russet-jerkined Peasant, that his Vestments and his Self are not one and indivisible; that *he* is naked, without vestments, till he buy or steal such, and by forethought sew and button them.

"For my own part, these considerations, of our Clothes-thatch, and how, reaching inwards even to our heart of hearts, it tailorizes and demoralizes us, fill me with a certain horror at myself and mankind; almost as one feels at those Dutch Cows, which, during the wet season, you see grazing deliberately with jackets and petticoats (of striped sacking), in the meadows of Gouda. Nevertheless there is something great in the moment when a man first strips himself of adventitious wrappages; and sees indeed that he is naked, and, as Swift has it, 'a forked straddling animal with handy legs;' yet also a Spirit, and unutterable Mystery of Mysteries."

CHAPTER IX.

ADAMITISM.

LET NO COURTEOUS READER take offence at the opinions broached in the conclusion of the last Chapter. The Editor himself, on first glancing over that singular passage, was inclined to exclaim: What, have we got not only a Sansculottist, but an enemy to Clothes in the abstract? A new Adamite, in this century, which flatters itself that it is the Nineteenth, and destructive both to Superstition and Enthusiasm?

Consider, thou foolish Teufelsdröckh, what benefits unspeakable all ages and sexes derive from Clothes. For example, when thou thyself, a watery, pulpy, slobbery freshman and new-comer in this Planet, sattest muling and puking in thy nurse's arms; sucking thy coral, and looking forth into the world in the blankest manner, what hadst thou been without thy blankets, and bibs, and other nameless hulls? A terror to thyself and mankind! Or hast thou forgotten the day when thou first receivedst breeches, and thy long clothes became short? The village where thou livedst was all apprised of the fact; and neighbor after neighbor kissed thy pudding cheek, and gave thee, as handsel, silver or copper coins, on that the first gala-day of thy existence. Again, wert not thou, at one period of life, a Buck, or Blood, or Macaroni, or Incroyable, or Dandy, or by whatever name, according to year and place, such phenomenon is distinguished? In that one word lie included mysterious volumes. Nay, now when the reign of folly is over, or altered, and thy clothes are not for triumph but for defence, hast thou always worn them perforce, and as a consequence of Man's Fall; never rejoiced in them as in a warm movable House, a Body round thy Body, wherein that strange THEE of thine sat snug, defying all variations of Climate? Girt with thick double-milled kerseys; half-buried under shawls and broadbrims, and overalls and mud-boots, thy very fingers cased in doeskin and mittens, thou hast bestrode that "Horse I ride;" and, though it were in wild winter, dashed through the world, glorying in it as if thou wert its lord. In vain did the sleet beat round thy temples; it lighted only on thy impenetrable, felted or woven, case of wool. In vain did the winds howl,—forests sounding and creaking, deep calling unto deep,—and the storms heap themselves together into one huge Arctic whirlpool: thou flewest through the middle thereof, striking fire from the highway; wild music hummed in thy ears, thou too wert as a "sailor of the air;" the wreck of matter and the crash of worlds was thy element and propitiously wafting tide. Without Clothes, without bit or saddle, what hadst thou been; what had thy fleet quadruped been?—Nature is good, but she is not the best: here truly was the victory of

Art over Nature. A thunderbolt indeed might have pierced thee; all short of this thou couldst defy.

Or, cries the courteous reader, has your Teufelsdröckh forgotten what he said lately about "Aboriginal Savages," and their "condition miserable indeed?" Would he have all this unsaid; and us betake ourselves again to the "matted-cloak," and go sheeted in a "thick natural fell?"

Nowise, courteous reader! The Professor knows full well what he is saying; and both thou and we, in our haste, do him wrong. If Clothes, in these times, "so tailorize and demoralize us," have they no redeeming value; can they not be altered to serve better; must they of necessity be thrown to the dogs? The truth is, Teufelsdröckh, though a Sansculottist, is no Adamite; and much perhaps as he might wish to go forth before this degenerate age "as a Sign," would nowise wish to do it, as those old Adamites did, in a state of Nakedness. The utility of Clothes is altogether apparent to him: nay, perhaps he has an insight into their more recondite, and almost mystic qualities, what we might call the omnipotent virtue of Clothes, such as was never before vouchsafed to any man. For example:

"You see two individuals," he writes, "one dressed in fine Red, the other in coarse threadbare Blue: Red says to Blue, 'Be hanged and anatomized;' Blue hears with a shudder, and (O wonder of wonders!) marches sorrowfully to the gallows; is there noosed-up, vibrates his hour, and the surgeons dissect him, and fit his bones into a skeleton for medical purposes. How is this; or what make ye of your *Nothing can act but where it is?* Red has no physical hold of Blue, no *clutch* of him, is nowise in *contact* with him: neither are those ministering Sheriffs and Lord-Lieutenants and Hangmen and Tipstaves so related to commanding Red, that he can tug them hither and thither; but each stands distinct within his own skin. Nevertheless, as it is spoken, so is it done: the articulated Word sets all hands in Action; and Rope and improved-drop perform their work.

"Thinking reader, the reason seems to me twofold: First, that *Man is a Spirit,* and bound by invisible bonds to *All Men;* secondly, that *he wears Clothes,* which are the visible emblems of that fact. Has not your Red hanging-individual a horsehair wig, squirrel-skins, and a plush-gown; whereby all mortals know that he is a JUDGE?—Society, which the more I think of it astonishes me the more, is founded upon Cloth.

"Often in my atrabiliar moods, when I read of pompous ceremonials, Frankfort Coronations, Royal Drawing-rooms, Levees, Couchees? and how the ushers and macers and pursuivants, are all in waiting; how Duke this is presented by Archduke that, and Colonel A by General B, and innumerable Bishops, Admirals, and miscellaneous Functionaries, are advancing gallantly to the Anointed Presence; and I strive, in my remote privacy, to form a clear picture of that solemnity,—on a sudden, as by some enchanter's wand, the—shall I speak it?—the Clothes fly-off the whole dramatic corps; and Dukes, Grandees, Bishops, Generals, Anointed Presence itself, every mother's son of them, stand straddling there, not a shirt on them; and I know not whether to laugh or weep. This physical or psychical infirmity, in which perhaps I am not singular, I have, after hesitation, thought right to publish, for the solace of those afflicted with the like."

Would to Heaven, say we, thou hadst thought right to keep it secret! Who is there now that can read the five columns of Presentations in his Morning Newspaper without a shudder? Hypochondriac men, and all men are to a certain extent hypochondriac, should be more gently treated. With what readiness our fancy, in this shattered state of the nerves, follows out the consequences which Teufelsdröckh, with a devilish coolness, goes on to draw:

"What would Majesty do, could such an accident befall in reality; should the buttons all simultaneously start, and the solid wool evaporate, in very Deed, as here in Dream? *Ach Gott!* How each skulks into the nearest hiding-place; their high State Tragedy (*Haupt- und Staats-Action*) becomes a Pickleherring-Farce to weep at, which is the worst kind of Farce; *the tables* (according to Horace), and with them, the whole fabric of Government, Legislation, Property, Police, and Civilized Society, *are dissolved,* in wails and howls."

Lives the man that can figure a naked Duke of Windlestraw addressing a naked House of Lords? Imagination, choked as in mephitic air, recoils on itself, and will not forward with the picture. The Woolsack, the Ministerial, the Opposition Benches—*infandum! infandum!* And yet why is the thing impossible? Was not every soul, or rather every body of these Guardians of our Liberties, naked, or nearly so, last night; "a forked Radish with a head fantastically carved"? And why might he not, did our stern fate so order it, walk out to St. Stephen's as well as into bed, in that no-fashion; and there, with other similar Radishes, hold a Bed of Justice? "Solace of those afflicted with the like!" Unhappy Teufelsdröckh, had man ever such a "physical or psychical infirmity" before? And now how many, perhaps, may thy un-paralleled confession (which we, even to the sounder British world, and goaded-on by Critical and Biographical duty, grudge to reimpart) incurably infect therewith! Art thou the malignest of Sansculottists, or only the maddest?

"It will remain to be examined," adds the inexorable Teufelsdröckh, "in how far the Scarecrow, as a Clothed Person, is not also entitled to benefit of clergy, and English trial by jury: nay, perhaps, considering his high function (for is not he too a Defender of Property, and Sovereign armed with the *terrors* of the Law?), to a certain royal Immunity and Inviolability; which, however, misers and the meaner class of persons are not always voluntarily disposed to grant him." . . . . "O my Friends, we are (in Yorick Sterne's words) but as 'turkeys driven, with a stick and red clout to the market:' or if some drivers, as they do in Norfolk, take a dried bladder and put peas in it, the rattle thereof terrifies the boldest!"

CHAPTER X.

Pure Reason.

It must now be apparent enough that our Professor, as above hinted, is a speculative Radical, and of the very darkest tinge; acknowledging, for most part, in the solemnities and paraphernalia of civilized Life, which we make so much of, nothing but so many Cloth-rags, turkey-poles, and "bladders with dried peas." To linger among such speculations, longer than mere Science requires, a discerning public can have no wish. For our purposes the simple fact that such a *Naked World* is possible, nay actually exists (under the Clothed one), will be sufficient. Much, therefore, we omit about "Kings wrestling naked on the green with Carmen," and the Kings being thrown: "dissect them with scalpels," says Teufelsdröckh; "the same viscera, tissues, livers, lights, and other life-tackle, are there: examine their spiritual mechanism; the same great Need, great Greed, and little Faculty; nay ten to one but the Carman, who understands draught-cattle, the rimming of wheels, something of the laws of unstable and stable equilibrium, with other branches of wagon-science, and has actually put forth his hand and operated on Nature, is the more cunningly gifted of the two. Whence, then, their so unspeakable difference? From Clothes." Much also we shall omit about confusion of Ranks, and Joan and My Lady, and how it would be everywhere "Hail fellow well met," and Chaos were come again: all which to any one that has once fairly pictured-out the grand mother-idea, *Society in a state of Nakedness*, will spontaneously suggest itself. Should some sceptical individual still entertain doubts whether in a world without Clothes, the smallest Politeness, Polity, or even Police, could exist, let him turn to the original Volume, and view there the boundless Serbonian Bog of Sansculottism, stretching sour and pestilential: over which we have lightly flown; where not only whole armies but whole nations might sink! If indeed the following argument, in its brief riveting emphasis, be not of itself incontrovertible and final:

"Are we Opossums; have we natural Pouches, like the Kangaroo? Or how, without Clothes, could we possess the master-organ, soul's seat, and true pineal gland of the Body Social: I mean, a Purse?"

Nevertheless it is impossible to hate Professor Teufelsdröckh; at worst, one knows not whether to hate or to love him. For though, in looking at the fair tapestry of human Life, with its royal and even sacred figures, he dwells not on the obverse alone, but here chiefly on the reverse; and indeed turns out the rough seams, tatters, and manifold thrums of that unsightly wrong-side, with an almost diabolic patience and indifference, which must have sunk him in the estimation of most readers,—there is that within which unspeakably distinguishes him from all other past and present Sansculottists. The grand unparalleled peculiarity of Teufelsdröckh is, that with all this

Descendentalism, he combines a Transcendentalism, no less superlative; whereby if on the one hand he degrade man below most animals, except those jacketed Gouda Cows, he, on the other, exalts him beyond the visible Heavens, almost to an equality with the Gods.

"To the eye of vulgar Logic," says he, "what is man? An omnivorous Biped that wears Breeches. To the eye of Pure Reason what is he? A Soul, a Spirit, and divine Apparition. Round his mysterious ME, there lies, under all those wool-rags, a Garment of Flesh (or of Senses), contextured in the Loom of Heaven; whereby he is revealed to his like, and dwells with them in UNION and DIVISION; and sees and fashions for himself a Universe, with azure Starry Spaces, and long Thousands of Years. Deep-hidden is he under that strange Garment; amid Sounds and Colors and Forms, as it were, swathed-in, and inextricably over-shrouded: yet it is sky-woven, and worthy of a God. Stands he not thereby in the center of Immensities, in the conflux of Eternities? He feels; power has been given him to know, to believe; nay does not the spirit of Love, free in its celestial primeval brightness, even here, though but for moments, look through? Well said Saint Chrysostom, with his lips of gold, 'the true SHEKINAH is Man: where else is the GOD's-PRESENCE manifested not to our eyes only, but to our hearts, as in our fellow-man?' "

In such passages, unhappily too rare, the high Platonic Mysticism of our Author, which is perhaps the fundamental element of his nature, bursts forth, as it were, in full flood: and, through all the vapor and tarnish of what is often so perverse, so mean in his exterior and environment, we seem to look into a whole inward Sea of Light and Love;—though, alas, the grim coppery clouds soon roll together again and hide it from view.

Such tendency to Mysticism is everywhere traceable in this man; and indeed, to attentive readers, must have been long ago apparent. Nothing that he sees but has more than a common meaning, but has two meanings: thus if in the highest Imperial Sceptre and Charlemagne-Mantle, as well as in the poorest Ox-goad and Gipsy-Blanket, he finds Prose, Decay, Contemptibility; there is in each sort Poetry also, and a reverend Worth. For Matter, were it never so despicable, is Spirit, the manifestation of Spirit: were it never so honorable, can it be more? The thing Visible, nay the thing Imagined, the thing in any way conceived as Visible, what is it but a Garment, a Clothing of the higher, celestial Invisible, "unimaginable, formless, dark with excess of bright?" Under which point of view the following passage, so strange in purport, so strange in phrase, seems characteristic enough:

"The beginning of all Wisdom is to look fixedly on Clothes, or even with armed eyesight, till they become *transparent*. 'The Philosopher,' says the wisest of this age, 'must station himself in the middle:' how true! The Philosopher is he to whom the Highest has descended, and the Lowest has mounted up; who is the equal and kindly brother of all.

"Shall we tremble before clothwebs and cobwebs, whether woven in Arkwright looms, or by the silent Arachnes that weave unrestingly in our imagination? Or, on the other hand, what is there that we cannot love; since all was created by God?

"Happy he who can look through the Clothes of a Man (the woollen, and fleshly, and official Bankpaper and State-paper Clothes) into the Man himself; and discern, it may be, in this or the other Dread Potentate, a more or less incompetent Digestive-apparatus; yet also an inscrutable venerable Mystery, in the meanest Tinker that sees with eyes!"

For the rest, as is natural to a man of this kind, he deals much in the feeling of Wonder; insists on the necessity and high worth of universal Wonder; which he holds to be the only reasonable temper for the denizen of so singular a Planet as ours. "Wonder," says he, "is the basis of Worship: the reign of wonder is perennial, indestructible in Man; only at certain stages (as the present), it is, for some short season, a reign *in partibus infidelium*." That progress of Science, which is to destroy Wonder, and in its stead substitute Mensuration and Numeration, finds small favor with Teufelsdröckh, much as he otherwise venerates these two latter processes.

"Shall your Science," exclaims he, "proceed in the small chink-lighted, or even oil-lighted, underground workshop of Logic alone; and man's mind become an Arithmetical Mill, whereof Memory is the Hopper, and mere Tables of Sines and Tangents, Codification, and Treatises of what you call Political Economy, are the Meal? And what is that Science, which the scientific head alone, were it screwed off, and (like the Doctor's in the Arabian Tale) set in a basin to keep it alive, could prosecute without shadow of a heart,—but one other of the mechanical and menial handicrafts, for which the Scientific Head (having a Soul in it) is too noble an organ? I mean that Thought without Reverence is barren, perhaps poisonous; at best, dies like cookery with the day that called it forth; does not live, like sowing, in successive tilths and wider-spreading harvests, bringing food and plenteous increase to all time."

In such wise does Teufelsdröckh deal hits, harder or softer, according to ability; yet ever, as we would fain persuade ourselves, with charitable intent. Above all, that class of "Logic-choppers, and treble-pipe Scoffers, and professed Enemies to Wonder; who, in these days, so numerously patrol as night-constables about the Mechanics' Institute of Science, and cackle, like true Old-Roman geese and goslings round their Capitol, on any alarm, or on none; nay who often, as illuminated Sceptics, walk abroad into peaceable society, in full daylight with rattle and lantern, and insist on guiding you and guarding you therewith, though the Sun is shining, and the street populous with mere justice-loving men:" that whole class is inexpressibly wearisome to him. Hear with what uncommon animation he perorates:

"The man who cannot wonder, who does not habitually wonder (and worship), were he President of innumerable Royal Societies, and carried the whole *Mécanique Céleste* and *Hegel's Philosophy*, and the epitome of all Laboratories and Observatories with their results, in his single head,—is but

a Pair of Spectacles behind which there is no Eye. Let those who have Eyes
look through him, then he may be useful.

"Thou wilt have no Mystery and Mysticism; wilt walk through thy world
by the sunshine of what thou callest Truth, or even by the hand-lamp of
what I call Attorney-Logic; and 'explain' all, 'account' for all, or believe
nothing of it? Nay, thou wilt attempt laughter; whoso recognizes the
unfathomable, all-pervading domain of Mystery, which is everywhere under
our feet and among our hands; to whom the Universe is an Oracle and
Temple, as well as a Kitchen and Cattlestall,—he shall be a delirious Mystic;
to him thou, with sniffing charity, wilt protrusively proffer thy hand-lamp,
and shriek, as one injured, when he kicks his foot through it?—*Armer Teufel!*
Doth not thy cow calve, doth not thy bull gender? Thou thyself, wert thou
not born, wilt thou not die? 'Explain' me all this, or do one of two things:
Retire into private places with thy foolish cackle; or, what were better, give
it up, and weep, not that the reign of wonder is done, and God's world all
disembellished and prosaic, but that thou hitherto art a Dilettante and
sand-blind Pedant."

CHAPTER XI.

PROSPECTIVE.

THE PHILOSOPHY of Clothes is now to all readers, as we predicted it would
do, unfolding itself into new boundless expansions, of a cloud-capt, almost
chimerical aspect, yet not without azure loomings in the far distance, and
streaks as of an Elysian brightness; the highly questionable purport and
promise of which it is becoming more and more important for us to ascertain. Is that a real Elysian brightness, cries many a timid wayfarer, or the
reflex of Pandemonian lava? Is it of a truth leading us into beatific Asphodel
meadows, or the yellow-burning marl of a Hell-on-Earth?

Our Professor, like other Mystics, whether delirious or inspired, gives
an Editor enough to do. Ever higher and dizzier are the heights he leads us
to; more piercing, all-comprehending, all-confounding are his views and
glances. For example, this of Nature being not an Aggregate but a Whole:

"Well sang the Hebrew Psalmist: 'If I take the wings of the morning and
dwell in the uttermost parts of the universe, God is there.' Thou thyself, O
cultivated reader, who too probably art no Psalmist, but a Prosaist, knowing
GOD only by tradition, knowest thou any corner of the world where at
least FORCE is not? The drop which thou shakest from thy wet hand, rests
not where it falls, but to-morrow thou findest it swept away; already on the
wings of the Northwind, it is nearing the Tropic of Cancer. How came it
to evaporate, and not lie motionless? Thinkest thou there is aught motionless;
without Force, and utterly dead?

"As I rode through the Schwarzwald, I said to myself: That little fire
which glows star-like across the dark-growing (*nachtende*) moor, where

the sooty smith bends over his anvil, and thou hopest to replace thy lost horse-shoe,—is it a detached, separated speck, cut-off from the whole Universe; or indissolubly joined to the whole? Thou fool, that smithy-fire was (primarily) kindled at the Sun; is fed by air that circulates from before Noah's Deluge, from beyond the Dogstar; therein, with Iron Force, and Coal Force, and the far stranger Force of Man, are cunning affinities and battles and victories of Force brought about; it is a little ganglion, or nervous centre, in the great vital system of Immensity. Call it, if thou wilt, an unconscious Altar, kindled on the bosom of the All; whose iron sacrifice, whose iron smoke and influence reach quite through the All; whose dingy Priest, not by word, yet by brain and sinew, preaches forth the mystery of Force; nay preaches forth (exoterically enough) one little textlet from the Gospel of Freedom, the Gospel of Man's Force, commanding, and one day to be all-commanding.

"Detached, separated! I say there is no such separation: nothing hitherto was ever stranded, cast aside; but all, were it only a withered leaf, works together with all; is borne forth on the bottomless, shoreless flood of Action, and lives through perpetual metamorphoses. The withered leaf is not dead and lost, there are Forces in it and around it, though working in inverse order; else how could it *rot*? Despise not the rag from which man makes Paper, or the litter from which the earth makes Corn. Rightly viewed no meanest object is insignificant; all objects are as windows, through which the philosophic eye looks into Infinitude itself."

Again, leaving that wondrous Schwarzwald Smithy-Altar, what vacant, high-sailing air-ships are these, and whither will they sail with us?

"All visible things are emblems; what thou seest is not there on its own account; strictly taken, is not there at all: Matter exists only spiritually, and to represent some Idea, and *body* it forth. Hence Clothes, as despicable as we think them, are so unspeakably significant. Clothes, from the King's mantle downwards are emblematic, not of want only, but of a manifold cunning Victory over Want. On the other hand, all Emblematic things are properly Clothes, thought-woven or hand-woven: must not the Imagination weave Garments, visible Bodies, wherein the else invisible creations and inspirations of our Reason are, like Spirits, revealed, and first become all-powerful;—the rather if, as we often see, the Hand too aid her, and (by wool Clothes or otherwise) reveal such even to the outward eye?

"Men are properly said to be clothed with Authority, clothed with Beauty, with Curses, and the like. Nay, if you consider it, what is Man himself, and his whole terrestrial Life, but an Emblem; a Clothing or visible Garment for that divine ME of his, cast hither, like a light-particle, down from Heaven? Thus is he said also to be clothed with a Body.

"Language is called the Garment of Thought: however, it should rather be, Language is the Flesh-Garment, the Body, of Thought. I said that Imagination wove this Flesh-Garment; and does not she? Metaphors are her stuff: examine Language; what, if you except some few primitive elements (of natural sound), what is it all but Metaphors, recognized as such, or no longer recognized; still fluid and florid, or now solid-grown and colorless? If those same primitive elements are the osseous fixtures in the Flesh-Garment, Language,—then are Metaphors its muscles and tissues and living integuments. An unmetaphorical style you shall in vain seek for: is not your very *Attention* a *Stretching-to?* The difference lies here: some styles are lean, adust, wiry, the muscle itself seems osseous; some are even quite pallid, hunger-bitten and dead-looking; while others again glow in the flush of health and vigorous self-growth, sometimes (as in my own case) not without an apoplectic tendency. Moreover, there are sham Metaphors, which overhanging that same Thought's-Body (best naked), and deceptively bedizening, or bolstering it out, may be called its false stuffings, superfluous show-cloaks (*Putz-Mäntel*), and tawdry woollen rags: whereof he that runs and reads may gather whole hampers,—and burn them."

Than which paragraph on Metaphors did the reader ever chance to see a more surprisingly metaphorical? However, that is not our chief grievance; the Professor continues:

"Why multiply instances? It is written, the Heavens and the Earth shall fade away like a Vesture; which indeed they are: the Time-vesture of the Eternal. Whatsoever sensibly exists, whatsoever represents Spirit to Spirit, is properly a Clothing, a suit of Raiment, put on for a season, and to be laid off. Thus in this one pregnant subject of CLOTHES, rightly understood, is included all that men have thought, dreamed, done, and been: the whole External Universe and what it holds is but Clothing; and the essence of all Science lies in the PHILOSOPHY OF CLOTHES."

Towards these dim infinitely-expanded regions, close-bordering on the impalpable Inane, it is not without. apprehension, and perpetual difficulties, that the Editor sees himself journeying and struggling. Till lately a cheerful daystar of hope hung before him, in the expected Aid of Hofrath Heuschrecke; which daystar, however, melts now, not into the red of morning, but into a vague, gray half-light, uncertain whether dawn of day or dusk of utter darkness. For the last week, these so-called Biographical Documents are in his hand. By the kindness of a Scottish Hamburg Merchant, whose name, known to the whole mercantile world, he must not mention; but whose honorable courtesy, now and often before spontaneously manifested to him, a mere literary stranger, he cannot soon forget,—the bulky Weissnichtwo Packet, with all its Customhouse seals, foreign hieroglyphs, and miscellaneous tokens of Travel, arrived here in perfect safety, and free of cost. The reader shall now fancy with what hot haste it was broken up, with what breathless expectation glanced over; and, alas, with what unquiet disappointment it has, since then, been often thrown down, and again taken up.

Hofrath Heuschrecke, in a too long-winded Letter, full of compliments, Weissnichtwo politics, dinners, dining repartees, and other ephemeral trivialities, proceeds to remind us of what we knew well already: that however it may be with Metaphysics, and other abstract Science originating in the Head (*Verstand*) alone, no Life-Philosophy (*Lebensphilosophie*), such as this of Clothes pretends to be, which originates equally in the Character

(*Gemüth*) and equally speaks thereto, can attain its significance till the Character itself is known and seen; "till the Author's View of the World (*Weltansicht*), and how he actively and passively came by such view, are clear: in short till a Biography of him has been philosophico-poetically written, and philosophico-poetically read." "Nay," adds he, "were the speculative scientific Truth even known, you still, in this inquiring age, ask yourself, Whence came it, and Why, and How?—and rest not, till, if no better may be, Fancy have shaped-out an answer; and either in the authentic lineaments of Fact, or the forged ones of Fiction, a complete picture and Genetical History of the Man and his spiritual Endeavor lies before you. But why," says the Hofrath, and indeed say we, "do I dilate on the uses of our Teufelsdröckh's Biography? The great Herr Minister von Goethe has penetratingly remarked that 'Man is properly the *only* object that interests man:' thus I too have noted, that in Weissnichtwo our whole conversation is little or nothing else but Biography or Auto-Biography; ever humano-anecdotical (*menschlich-anekdotisch*). Biography is by nature the most universally profitable, universally pleasant of all things: especially Biography of distinguished individuals.

"By this time, *mein Verehrtester* (my Most Esteemed)," continues he, with an eloquence which unless the words be purloined from Teufelsdröckh, or some trick of his, as we suspect, is well-nigh unaccountable, "by this time you are fairly plunged (*vertieft*) in that mighty forest of Clothes-Philosophy; and looking round, as all readers do, with astonishment enough. Such portions and passages as you have already mastered, and brought to paper, could not but awaken a strange curiosity touching the mind they issued from; the perhaps unparalleled psychical mechanism, which manufactured such matter, and emitted it to the light of day. Had Teufelsdröckh also a father and mother; did he, at one time, wear drivel-bibs, and live on spoon-meat? Did he ever, in rapture and tears, clasp a friend's bosom to his; looks he also wistfully into the long burial-aisle of the Past, where only winds, and their low harsh moan, give inarticulate answer? Has he fought duels;—good Heaven! how did he comport himself when in Love? By what singular stair-steps, in short, and subterranean passages, and sloughs of Despair, and steep Pisgah hills, has he reached this wonderful prophetic Hebron (a true Old-Clothes Jewry) where he now dwells?

"To all these natural questions the voice of public History is as yet silent. Certain only that he has been, and is, a Pilgrim, and Traveller from a far Country; more or less footsore and travel-soiled; has parted with road-companions; fallen among thieves, been poisoned by bad cookery, blistered with bugbites; nevertheless, at every stage (for they have let him pass), has had the Bill to discharge. But the whole particulars of his Route, his Weather-observations, the picturesque Sketches he took, though all regularly jotted down (in indelible sympathetic-ink by an invisible interior Penman), are these nowhere forthcoming? Perhaps quite lost: one other leaf of that mighty Volume (of human Memory) left to fly abroad, unprinted, unpublished, unbound up, as waste paper; and to rot, the sport of rainy winds?

"No, *verehrtester Herr Herausgeber*, in no wise! I here, by the unexampled favor you stand in with our Sage, send not a Biography only, but an Autobiography: at least the materials for such; wherefrom, if I misreckon not, your perspicacity will draw fullest insight: and so the whole Philosophy and Philosopher of Clothes will stand clear to the wondering eyes of England, nay thence, through America, through Hindostan, and the antipodal New Holland, finally conquer (*einnehmen*) great part of this terrestrial Planet!"

And now let the sympathizing reader judge of our feeling when, in place of this same Autobiography with "fullest insight," we find—Six considerable PAPER-BAGS, carefully sealed, and marked successively, in gilt China-ink, with the symbols of the Six southern Zodiacal Signs, beginning at Libra; in the inside of which sealed Bags lie miscellaneous masses of Sheets, and oftener Shreds and Snips, written in Professor Teufelsdröckh's scarce legible *cursivschrift;* and treating of all imaginable things under the Zodiac and above it, but of his own personal history only at rare intervals, and then in the most enigmatic manner.

Whole fascicles there are, wherein the Professor, or, as he here, speaking in the third person, calls himself, "the Wanderer," is not once named. Then again, amidst what seems to be a Metaphysico-theological Disquisition, "Detached Thoughts on the Steam-engine," or, "The continued Possibility of Prophecy," we shall meet with some quite private, not unimportant Biographical fact. On certain sheets stand Dreams, authentic or not, while the circumjacent waking Actions are omitted. Anecdotes, oftenest without date of place or time, fly loosely on separate slips, like Sibylline leaves. Interspersed also are long purely Autobiographical delineations; yet without connection, without recognizable coherence; so unimportant, so superfluously minute, they almost remind us of "P. P. Clerk of this Parish." Thus does the famine of intelligence alternate with waste. Selection, order, appears to be unknown to the Professor. In all Bags the same imbroglio; only perhaps in the Bag *Capricorn,* and those near it, the confusion a little worse confounded. Close by a rather eloquent Oration, "On receiving the Doctor's-Hat," lie wash-bills, marked *bezahlt* (settled). His Travels are indicated by the Street-Advertisements of the various cities he has visited; of which Street-Advertisements, in most living tongues, here is perhaps the completest collection extant.

So that if the Clothes-Volume itself was too like a Chaos, we have now instead of the solar Luminary that should still it, the airy Limbo which by intermixture will farther volatilize and discompose it! As we shall perhaps see it our duty ultimately to deposit these Six Paper-Bags in the British Museum, farther description, and all vituperation of them, may be spared. Biography or Autobiography of Teufelsdröckh there is clearly enough, none to be gleaned here: at most some sketchy, shadowy fugitive likeness of him may, by unheard-of efforts, partly of intellect, partly of imagination on the side of Editor and of Reader, rise up between them. Only as a gaseous-chaotic Appendix to that aqueous-chaotic Volume can the contents of the

Six Bags hover round us, and portions thereof be incorporated with our delineation of it.

Daily and nightly does the Editor sit (with green spectacles) deciphering these unimaginable Documents from their perplexed *cursivschrift;* collating them with the almost equally unimaginable Volume, which stands in legible print. Over such a universal medley of high and low, of hot, cold, moist and dry, is he here struggling (by union of like with like, which is Method) to build a firm Bridge for British travellers. Never perhaps since our first Bridge-builders, Sin and Death, built that stupendous Arch from Hell-gate to the Earth, did any Pontifex, or Pontiff, undertake such a task as the present Editor. For in this Arch too, leading, as we humbly presume, far otherwards than that grand primeval one, the materials are to be fished-up from the weltering deep, and down from the simmering air, here one mass, there another, and cunningly cemented, while the elements boil beneath: nor is there any supernatural force to do it with; but simply the Diligence and feeble thinking Faculty of an English Editor, endeavoring to evolve printed Creation out of a German printed and written Chaos, wherein, as he shoots to and fro in it, gathering, clutching, piecing the Why to the far-distant Wherefore, his whole Faculty and Self are like to be swallowed up.

Patiently, under these incessant toils and agitations, does the Editor, dismissing all anger, see his otherwise robust health declining; some fraction of his allotted natural sleep nightly leaving him, and little but an inflamed nervous-system to be looked for. What is the use of health, or of life, if not to do some work therewith? And what work nobler than transplanting foreign Thought into the barren domestic soil; except indeed planting Thought of your own, which the fewest are privileged to do? Wild as it looks, this Philosophy of Clothes, can we ever reach its real meaning, promises to reveal new-coming Eras, the first dim rudiments and already-budding germs of a nobler Era, in Universal History. Is not such a prize worth some striving? Forward with us, courageous reader; be it towards failure, or towards success! The latter thou sharest with us; the former also is not all our own.

BOOK SECOND

CHAPTER I.

GENESIS.

IN A PSYCHOLOGICAL point of view, it is perhaps questionable whether from birth and genealogy, how closely scrutinized soever, much insight is to be gained. Nevertheless, as in every phenomenon the Beginning remains always the most notable moment; so, with regard to any great man, we rest not till, for our scientific profit or not, the whole circumstances of his first appearance in this Planet, and what manner of Public Entry he made, are with utmost completeness rendered manifest. To the Genesis of our Clothes-Philosopher, then, be this First Chapter consecrated. Unhappily, indeed, he seems to be of quite obscure extraction; uncertain, we might almost say, whether of any: so that this Genesis of his can properly be nothing but an Exodus (or transit out of Invisibility into Visibility); whereof the preliminary portion is nowhere forthcoming.

"In the village of Entepfuhl," thus writes he, in the Bag *Libra*, on various Papers, which we arrange with difficulty, "dwelt Andreas Futteral and his wife; childless, in still seclusion, and cheerful though now verging towards old age. Andreas had been grenadier Sergeant, and even regimental Schoolmaster under Frederick the Great; but now, quitting the halbert and ferule for the spade and pruning-hook, cultivated a little Orchard, on the produce of which he, Cincinnatus-like, lived not without dignity. Fruits, the peach, the apple, the grape, with other varieties came in their season; all which Andreas knew how to sell: on evenings he smoked largely, or read (as beseemed a regimental Schoolmaster), and talked to neighbors that would listen about the Victory of Rossbach; and how Fritz the Only (*der Einzige*) had once with his own royal lips spoken to him, had been pleased to say, when Andreas as camp-sentinel demanded the pass-word, 'Schweig, Hund (Peace, hound)!' before any of his staff-adjutants could answer. 'Das nenn' ich mir einen König. There is what I call a King,' would Andreas exclaim: 'but the smoke of Kunersdorf was still smarting his eyes.'

"Gretchen, the housewife, won like Desdemona by the deeds rather than the looks of her now veteran Othello, lived not in altogether military subordination; for, as Andreas said, 'the womankind will not drill (*wer kann die Weiberchen dressiren*):' nevertheless she at heart loved him both for valor and wisdom; to her a Prussian grenadier Sergeant and Regiment's Schoolmaster was little other than a Cicero and Cid: what you see, yet cannot see over, is as good as infinite. Nay, was not Andreas in very deed a man of order, courage, downrightness (*Geradheit*); that understood Büsching's *Geography*, had been in the victory of Rossbach, and left for dead in the camisade of Hochkirch? The good Gretchen, for all her fretting, watched over him and hovered round him as only a true housemother can: assiduously she cooked and sewed and scoured for him; so that not only his old regi-

43

mental sword and grenadier-cap, but the whole habitation and environment where on pegs of honor they hung, looked ever trim and gay: a roomy painted Cottage, enbowered in fruit-trees, and forest-trees, evergreens and honeysuckles; rising many-colored from amid shaven grass-plots, flowers struggling-in through the very windows; under its long projecting eaves nothing but garden-tools in methodic piles (to screen them from rain), and seats where, especially on summer nights, a King might have wished to sit and smoke, and call it his. Such a *Bauergut* (Copyhold) had Gretchen given her veteran; whose sinewy arms, and long-disused gardening talent, had made it what you saw.

"Into this umbrageous Man's-nest, one meek yellow evening or dusk, when the Sun, hidden indeed from terrestrial Entepfuhl, did nevertheless journey visible and radiant along the celestial Balance (*Libra*) it was that a Stranger of reverend aspect entered, and, with grave salutation, stood before the two rather astonished housemates. He was close-muffled in a wide mantle; which without farther parley unfolding, he deposited therefrom what seemed some Basket, overhung with green Persian silk; saying only: *Ihr lieben Leute, hier bringe ein unschätzbares Verleihen; nehmt es in aller Acht, sorgfältigst benützt es: mit hohem Lohn oder wohl mit schweren Zinsen, wird's einst zurückgefordert.* 'Good Christian people here lies for you an invaluable Loan; take all heed thereof, in all carefulness employ it: with high recompense, or else with heavy penalty, will it one day be required back.' Uttering which singular words, in a clear, bell-like, forever memorable tone, the Stranger gracefully withdrew; and before Andreas or his wife, gazing in expectant wonder, had time to fashion either question or answer, was clean gone. Neither out of doors could aught of him be seen or heard; he had vanished in the thickets, in the dusk; the Orchard-gate stood quietly closed: the Stranger was gone once and always. So sudden had the whole transaction been, in the autumn stillness and twilight, so gentle, noiseless, that the Futterals could have fancied it all a trick of Imagination, or some visit from an authentic Spirit. Only that the green-silk Basket, such as neither Imagination nor authentic Spirits are wont to carry, still stood visible and tangible on their little parlor-table. Towards this the astonished couple, now with lit candle, hastily turned their attention. Lifting the green veil, to see what invaluable it hid, they descried there, amid down and rich white wrappages, no Pitt Diamond or Hapsburg Regalia, but, in the softest sleep, a little red-colored Infant! Beside it, lay a roll of gold Friedrichs, the exact amount of which was never publicly known; also a *Taufschein* (baptismal certificate), wherein unfortunately nothing but the Name was decipherable; other document or indication none whatever.

"To wonder and conjecture was unavailing, then and always thenceforth. Nowhere in Entepfuhl, on the morrow or next day, did tidings transpire of any such figure as the Stranger; nor could the Traveller who had passed through the neighboring Town in coach-and-four, be connected with this Apparition except in the way of gratuitous surmise. Meanwhile, for Andreas and his wife, the grand practical problem was: What to do with this little sleeping red-colored Infant? Amid amazements and curiosities, which had to die away without external satisfying, they resolved, as in such circumstances charitable prudent people needs must, on nursing it, though with spoon-meat, into whiteness, and if possible into manhood. The Heavens smiled on their endeavor: thus has that same mysterious Individual ever since had a status for himself in this visible Universe, some modicum of victual and lodging and parade-ground; and now expanded in bulk, faculty and knowledge of good and evil, he, as HERR DIOGENES TEUFELSDRÖCKH, professes or is ready to profess, perhaps not altogether without effect, in the new University of Weissnichtwo, the new Science of Things in General."

Our Philosopher declares here, as indeed we should think he well might, that these facts, first communicated, by the good Gretchen Futteral, in his twelfth year, "produced on the boyish heart and fancy a quite indelible impression. Who this reverend Personage," he says, "that glided into the Orchard Cottage when the Sun was in Libra, and then, as on spirit's wings, glided out again, might be? An inexpressible desire, full of love and of sadness, has often since struggled within me to shape an answer. Ever, in my distresses and my loneliness, has Fantasy turned, full of longing (sehnsuchtsvoll), to that unknown Father, who perhaps far from me, perhaps near, either way invisible, might have taken me to his paternal bosom, there to lie screened from many a woe. Thou beloved Father, dost thou still, shut out from me only by thin penetrable curtains of earthly Space, wend to and fro among the crowd of the living? Or art thou hidden by those far thicker curtains of the Everlasting Night, or rather of the Everlasting Day, through which my mortal eye and outstretched arms need not strive to reach? Alas, I know not, and in vain vex myself to know. More than once, heart-deluded, have I taken for thee this and the other noble-looking Stranger; and approached him wistfully, with infinite regard; but he too had to repel me, he too was not thou.

"And yet, O Man born of Woman," cries the Autobiographer, with one of his sudden whirls, "wherein is my case peculiar? Hadst thou, any more than I, a Father whom thou knowest? The Andreas and Gretchen, or the Adam and Eve, who led thee into Life, and for a time suckled and pap-fed thee there, whom thou namest Father and Mother; these were, like mine, but thy nursing-father and nursing-mother: thy true Beginning and Father is in Heaven, whom with the bodily eye thou shalt never behold, but only with the spiritual."

"The little green veil," adds he, among much similar moralizing, and embroiled discoursing, "I yet keep; still more inseparably the Name, Diogenes Teufelsdröckh. From the veil can nothing be inferred: a piece of now quite faded Persian silk, like thousands of others. On the Name I have many times meditated and conjectured; but neither in this lay there any clew. That it was my unknown Father's name I must hesitate to believe. To no purpose have I searched through all the Herald's Books, in and without the German Empire, and through all manner of Subscriber-Lists (Pränumeranten), Militia-Rolls, and other Name-catalogues; extraordinary names as we have in

Germany, the name Teufelsdröckh, except as appended to my own person, nowhere occurs. Again, what may the unchristian rather than Christian Diogenes mean? Did that reverend Basket-bearer intend, by such designation, to shadow-forth my future destiny, or his own present malign humor? Perhaps the latter, perhaps both. Thou ill-starred Parent, who like an Ostrich hadst to leave thy ill-starred offspring to be hatched into self-support by the mere sky-influences of Chance, can thy pilgrimage have been a smooth one? Beset by Misfortune thou doubtless hast been; or indeed by the worst figure of Misfortune, by Misconduct. Often have I fancied how, in thy hard life-battle, thou wert shot at, and slung at, wounded, hand-fettered, ham-strung, browbeaten and bedevilled by the Time-Spirit (*Zeitgeist*) in thyself and others, till the good soul first given thee was seared into grim rage; and thou hadst nothing for it but to leave in me an indignant appeal to the Future, and living speaking Protest against the Devil, as that same Spirit not of the Time only, but of Time itself, is well named! Which Appeal and Protest, may I now modestly add, was not perhaps quite lost in air.

"For indeed, as Walter Shandy often insisted, there is much, nay almost all, in Names. The Name is the earliest Garment you wrap round the earth-visiting ME; to which it thenceforth cleaves, more tenaciously (for there are Names that have lasted nigh thirty centuries) than the very skin. And now from without, what mystic influences does it not send inwards, even to the centre; especially in those plastic first-times, when the whole soul is yet infantine, soft, and the invisible seedgrain will grow to be an all over-shadowing tree! Names? Could I unfold the influence of Names, which are the most important of all Clothings, I were a second greater Trismegistus. Not only all common Speech, but Science, Poetry itself, is no other, if thou consider it, than a right *Naming*. Adam's first task was giving names to natural Appearances: What is ours still but a continuation of the same; be the Appearances exotic-vegetable, organic, mechanic, stars, or starry movements (as in Science); or (as in Poetry) passions, virtues, calamities, God-attributes, Gods?—In a very plain sense the Proverb says, *Call one a thief, and he will steal;* in an almost similar sense may we not perhaps say, *Call one Diogenes Teufelsdröckh, and he will open the Philosophy of Clothes?*"

"Meanwhile the incipient Diogenes, like others, all ignorant of his Why, his How, or Whereabout, was opening his eyes to the kind Light; sprawling-out his ten fingers and toes; listening, tasting, feeling; in a word, by all his Five Senses, still more by his Sixth Sense of Hunger, and a whole infinitude of inward, spiritual, half-awakened Senses, endeavoring daily to acquire for himself some knowledge of this strange Universe where he had arrived, be his task therein what it might. Infinite was his progress; thus in some fifteen months, he could perform the miracle of—Speech! To breed a fresh Soul, is it not like brooding a fresh (celestial) Egg; wherein as yet all is formless, powerless; yet by degrees organic elements and fibres shoot through the watery albumen; and out of vague Sensation grows Thought, grows Fantasy and Force, and we have Philosophies, Dynasties, nay Poetries and Religions!

"Young Diogenes, or rather young Gneschen, for by such diminutive had they in their fondness named him, travelled forward to those high consummations, by quick yet easy stages. The Futterals, to avoid vain talk, and moreover keep the roll of gold Friedrichs safe, gave-out that he was a grandnephew; the orphan of some sister's daughter, suddenly deceased, in Andreas's distant Prussian birthland; of whom, as of her indigent sorrowing widower, little enough was known at Entepfuhl. Heedless of all which, the Nursling took to his spoon-meat, and throve. I have heard him noted as a still infant, that kept his mind much to himself; above all, that seldom or never cried. He already felt that time was precious; that he had other work cut-out for him than whimpering."

Such, after utmost painful search and collation among these miscellaneous Paper-masses, is all the notice we can gather of Herr Teufelsdröckh's genealogy. More imperfect, more enigmatic it can seem to few readers than to us. The Professor, in whom truly we more and more discern a certain satirical turn, and deep under-currents of roguish whim, for the present stands pledged in honor, so we will not doubt him: but seems it not conceivable that, by the good "Gretchen Futteral," or some other perhaps interested party, he has himself been deceived? Should these sheets, translated or not, ever reach the Entepfuhl Circulating Library, some cultivated native of that district might feel called to afford explanation. Nay, since Books, like invisible scouts, permeate the whole habitable globe, and Timbuctoo itself is not safe from British Literature, may not some Copy find out even the mysterious basket-bearing Stranger, who in a state of extreme senility perhaps still exists; and gently force even him to disclose himself; to claim openly a son, in whom any father may feel pride?

CHAPTER II.

IDYLLIC.

"HAPPY SEASON of Childhood!" exclaims Teufelsdröckh: "Kind Nature, that are to all a bountiful mother; that visitest the poor man's hut with auroral radiance; and for thy Nursling hast provided a soft swathing of Love and infinite Hope, wherein he waxes and slumbers, danced round (*umgaukelt*) by sweetest Dreams! If the paternal Cottage still shuts us in, its roof still screens us; with a Father we have as yet a prophet, priest and king, and an Obedience that makes us free. The young spirit has awakened out of Eternity, and knows not what we mean by Time; as yet Time is no fast-hurrying stream, but a sportful sun-lit ocean; years to the child are as ages: ah! the secret of Vicissitude, of that slower or quicker decay and ceaseless down-rushing of the universal World-fabric, from the granite mountain to the man or day-moth, is yet unknown; and in a motionless Universe, we taste, what afterwards in this quick-whirling Universe is forever denied us, the balm of Rest. Sleep on, thou fair Child, for thy long rough journey is at hand! A little while, and thou too shalt sleep no more, but thy very dreams shall be mimic battles; thou too, with old Arnauld, wilt have to say in stern patience: 'Rest? Rest? Shall I not have all Eternity to rest in?' Celestial Nepenthe! though a Pyrrhus conquer empires, and an Alexander sack the world, he finds thee not; and thou hast once fallen gently, of thy own accord, on the eyelids, on the heart of every mother's child. For as yet, sleep and waking are one: the fair Life-garden rustles infinite around, and everywhere is dewy fragrance, and the building of Hope; which budding, if in youth, too frostnipt, it grow to flowers, will in manhood yield no fruit, but a prickly, bitter-rinded stone-fruit, of which the fewest can find the kernel."

In such rose-colored light does our Professor, as Poets are wont, look back on his childhood; the historical details of which (to say nothing of much other vague oratorical matter) he accordingly dwells on with an almost wearisome minuteness. We hear of Entepfuhl standing "in trustful derangement" among the woody slopes; the paternal Orchard flanking it as extreme outpost from below; the little Kuhbach gushing kindly by, among beech-rows, through river after river, into the Donau, into the Black Sea, into the Atmosphere and Universe; and how "the brave old Linden," stretching like a parasol of twenty ells in radius, over-topping all other rows and clumps, towered-up from the central *Agora* and *Campus Martius* of the Village, like its Sacred Tree; and how the old men sat talking under its shadow (Gneschen often greedily listening), and the wearied laborers reclined, and the unwearied children sported, and the young men and maidens often danced to flute-music. "Glorious summer twilight," cries Teufelsdröckh, "when the Sun, like a proud Conqueror and Imperial Taskmaster, turned his back, with his gold-purple emblazonry, and all his fire-clad body-guard (of Prismatic Colors); and the tired brickmakers of this clay Earth might steal a little frolic, and those few meek Stars would not tell of them!"

Then we have long details of the *Weinlesen* (Vintage), the Harvest-Home, Christmas, and so forth; with a whole cycle of the Entepfuhl Children's-games, differing apparently by mere superficial shades from those of other countries. Concerning all which, we shall here, for obvious reasons, say nothing. What cares the world for our as yet miniature Philosopher's achievements under that "brave old Linden?" Or even where is the use of such practical reflections as the following? "In all the sports of Children, were it only in their wanton breakage and defacements, you shall discern a creative instinct (*schaffenden Trieb*): the Mankin feels that he is a born Man, that his vocation is to work. The choicest present you can make him is a Tool; be it knife or pen-gun, for construction or for destruction; either way it is for Work, for Change. In gregarious sports of skill or strength, the Boy trains himself to Co-operation, for war or peace, as governor or governed: the little Maid again, provident of her domestic destiny, takes with preference to Dolls."

Perhaps, however, we may give this anecdote, considering who it is that relates it: "My first short-clothes were of yellow serge; or rather, I should say, my first short-cloth, for the vesture was one and indivisible, reaching from neck to ankle, a mere body with four limbs: of which fashion how little could I then divine the architectural, how much less the moral significance!"

More graceful is the following little picture: "On fine evenings I was wont to carry-forth my supper (bread-crumb boiled in milk), and eat it out-of-doors. On the coping of the Orchard-wall, which I could reach by climbing, or still more easily if Father Andreas would set-up the pruning-ladder, my porringer was placed: there, many a sunset, have I, looking at the distant western Mountains, consumed, not without relish, my evening meal. Those hues of gold and azure, that hush of World's expectation as Day died, were still a Hebrew Speech for me; nevertheless I was looking at the fair illuminated Letters, and had an eye for their gilding."

With "the little one's friendship for cattle and poultry" we shall not much intermeddle. It may be that hereby he acquired a "certain deeper sympathy with animated Nature:" but when, we would ask, saw any man, in a collection of Biographical Documents, such a piece as this: "Impressive enough (*bedeutungsvoll*) was it to hear, in early morning, the Swineherd's horn; and know that so many hungry happy quadrupeds were, on all sides, starting in hot haste to join him, for breakfast on the Heath. Or to see them at eventide, all marching-in again, with short squeak, almost in military order; and each, topographically correct, trotting-off in succession to the right or left, through its own lane, to its own dwelling; till old Kunz, at the Village-head, now left alone, blew his last blast, and retired for the night. We are wont to love the Hog chiefly in the form of Ham; yet did not these bristly thick-skinned beings here manifest intelligence, perhaps humor of character; at any rate, a touching, trustful submissiveness to Man, —who, were he but a Swineherd, in darned gabardine, and leather breeches more resembling slate or discolored-tin breeches, is still the Hierarch of this lower world?"

It is maintained, by Helvetius and his set, that an infant of genius is quite the same as any other infant, only that certain surprisingly favorable influences accompany him through life, especially through childhood, and expand him, while others lie closefolded and continue dunces. Herein, say they, consists the whole difference between an inspired Prophet and a double-barrelled Game-preserver: the inner man of the one has been fostered into generous development; that of the other, crushed-down perhaps by vigor of animal digestion, and the like, has exuded and evaporated, or at best sleeps now irresuscitably stagnant at the bottom of his stomach. "With which opinion," cries Teufelsdröckh, "I should as soon agree as with this other, that an acorn might, by favorable or unfavorable influences of soil and climate, be nursed into a cabbage, or the cabbage-seed into an oak.

"Nevertheless," continues he, "I too acknowledge the all-but omnipotence of early culture and nurture: hereby we have either a doddered dwarf bush, or a high-towering, wide-shadowing tree; either a sick yellow cabbage, or an edible luxuriant green one. Of a truth, it is the duty of all men, especially of all philosophers, to note-down with accuracy the characteristic circumstances of their Education, what furthered, what hindered, what in any way modified it: to which duty, nowadays so pressing for many a German Autobiographer, I also zealously address myself."—Thou rogue! Is it by short-clothes of yellow serge, and swineherd horns, that an infant of genius is educated? And yet, as usual, it ever remains doubtful whether he is laughing in his sleeve at these Autobiographical times of ours, or writing from the abundance of his own fond ineptitude. For he continues: "If among the ever-streaming currents of Sights, Hearings, Feelings for Pain or Pleasure, whereby, as in a Magic Hall, young Gneschen went about environed, I might venture to select and specify, perhaps these following were also of the number:

"Doubtless, as childish sports call forth Intellect, Activity, so the young creature's Imagination was stirred up, and a Historical tendency given him by the narrative habits of Father Andreas; who, with his battle-reminiscences, and gray austere yet hearty patriarchal aspect, could not but appear another Ulysses and 'much-enduring Man.' Eagerly I hung upon his tales, when listening neighbors enlivened the hearth; from these perils and these travels, wild and far almost as Hades itself, a dim world of Adventure expanded itself within me. Incalculable also was the knowledge I acquired in standing by the Old Men under the Linden-tree: the whole of Immensity was yet new to me; and had not these reverend seniors, talkative enough, been employed in partial surveys thereof for nigh fourscore years? With amazement I began to discover that Entepfuhl stood in the middle of a Country, of a World; that there was such a thing as History, as Biography; to which I also, one day, by hand and tongue, might contribute.

"In a like sense worked the *Postwagen* (Stage-coach), which, slow-rolling under its mountains of men and luggage, wended through our Village: northwards, truly, in the dead of night; yet southwards visibly at eventide. Not till my eighth year did I reflect that this Postwagen could be other than some terrestrial Moon, rising and setting by mere Law of Nature, like the heavenly one; that it came on made highways, from far cities towards far cities; weaving them like a monstrous shuttle into closer and closer union. It was then that, independently of Schiller's *Wilhelm Tell*, I made this not quite insignificant reflection (so true also in spiritual things): *Any road, this simple Entepfuhl road, will lead you to the end of the world!*

"Why mention our Swallows, which, out of far Africa, as I learned, threading their way over seas and mountains, corporate cities and belligerent nations, yearly found themselves, with the month of May, snuglodged in our Cottage Lobby? The hospitable Father (for cleanliness' sake) had fixed a little bracket plumb under their nest: there they built, and caught flies, and twittered, and bred; and all, I chiefly, from the heart loved them. Bright, nimble creatures, who taught *you* the mason-craft; nay, stranger still, gave you a masonic incorporation, almost social police? For if, by ill chance, and when time pressed, your House fell, have I not seen five neighborly Helpers appear next day; and swashing to and fro, with animated, loud, long-drawn chirpings, and activity almost superhirundine, complete it again before nightfall?

"But undoubtedly the grand summary of Entepfuhl child's-culture, where as in a funnel its manifold influences were concentrated and simultaneously poured-down on us, was the annual Cattle-fair. Here, assembling from all the four winds, came the elements of an unspeakable hurlyburly. Nutbrown maids and nutbrown men, all clear-washed, loud-laughing, bedizened and beribanded; who came for dancing, for treating, and if possible, for happiness. Topbooted Graziers from the North; Swiss Brokers, Italian Drovers, also topbooted, from the South; these with their subalterns in leather jerkins, leather skullcaps, and long oxgoads; shouting in half-articulate speech, amid the inarticulate barking and bellowing. Apart stood Potters from far Saxony, with their crockery in fair rows; Nürnberg Pedlers, in booths that to me seemed richer than Ormuz bazaars; Showmen from the Lago Maggiore; detachments of the *Wiener Schub* (Offscourings of Vienna) vociferously superintending games of chance. Ballad-singers brayed, Auctioneers grew hoarse; cheap New Wine (*heuriger*) flowed like water, still worse confounding the confusion; and high over all, vaulted, in ground-and-lofty tumbling, a particolored Merry-Andrew, like the genius of the place and of Life itself.

"Thus encircled by the mystery of Existence; under the deep heavenly Firmament; waited-on by the four golden Seasons, with their vicissitudes of contribution, for even grim Winter brought its skating-matches and shooting-matches, its snow-storms and Christmas-carols,—did the Child sit and learn. These things were the Alphabet, whereby in aftertime he was to syllable and partly read the grand Volume of the World: what matters it whether such Alphabet be in large gilt letters or in small ungilt ones, so you have an eye to read it? For Gneschen, eager to learn, the very act of looking thereon was a blessedness that gilded all: his existence was a bright, soft element of Joy; out of which, as in Prospero's Island, wonder after wonder bodied itself forth, to teach by charming.

"Nevertheless, I were but a vain dreamer to say, that even then my felicity was perfect. I had, once for all, come down from Heaven into the Earth. Among the rainbow colors that glowed on my horizon, lay even in childhood a dark ring of Care, as yet no thicker than a thread, and often quite overshone; yet always it reappeared, nay ever waxing broader and broader; till in after-years it almost over-shadowed my whole canopy, and threatened to ingulf me in final night. It was the ring of Necessity whereby we are all begirt; happy he for whom a kind heavenly Sun brightens it into a ring of Duty, and plays round it with beautiful prismatic diffractions; yet ever, as basis and as bourn for our whole being, it is there.

"For the first few years of our terrestrial Apprenticeship, we have not much work to do; but, boarded and lodged gratis, are set down mostly to look about us over the workshop, and see others work, till we have understood the tools a little, and can handle this and that. If good Passivity alone, and not good Passivity and good Activity together, were the thing wanted, then was my early position favorable beyond the most. In all that respects openness of Sense, affectionate Temper, ingenuous Curiosity, and the fostering of these, what more could I have wished? On the other side, however, things went not so well. My Active Power (*Thatkraft*) was unfavorably hemmed-in; of which misfortune how many traces yet abide with me! In an orderly house, where the litter of children's sports is hateful enough, your training is too stoical; rather to bear and forbear than to make and do. I was forbid much: wishes in any measure bold I had to renounce; everywhere a strait bond of Obedience inflexibly held me down. Thus already Freewill often came in painful collision with Necessity; so that my tears flowed, and at seasons the Child itself might taste that root of bitterness, wherewith the whole fruitage of our life is mingled and tempered.

"In which habituation to Obedience, truly, it was beyond measure safer to err by excess than by defect. Obedience is our universal duty and destiny; wherein whoso will not bend must break: too early and too thoroughly we cannot be trained to know that Would, in this world of ours, is as mere zero to Should, and for most part as the smallest of fractions even to Shall. Hereby was laid for me the basis of worldly Discretion, nay of Morality itself. Let me not quarrel with my upbringing. It was rigorous, too frugal, compressively secluded, everyway unscientific: yet in that very strictness and domestic solitude might there not lie the root of deeper earnestness, of the stem from which all noble fruit must grow? Above all, how unskilful soever, it was loving, it was well-meant, honest; whereby every deficiency was helped. My kind Mother, for as such I must ever love the good Gretchen, did me one altogether invaluable service: she taught me, less indeed by word than by act and daily reverent look and habitude, her own simple version of the Christian Faith. Andreas too attended Church; yet more like a parade-duty, for which he in the other world expected pay with arrears,—as, I trust, he has received; but my Mother, with a true woman's heart, and fine though uncultivated sense, was in the strictest acceptation Religious. How indestructibly the Good grows, and propagates itself, even among the weedy entanglements of Evil! The highest whom I knew on Earth I here saw bowed down, with awe unspeakable, before a Higher in Heaven: such things, especially in infancy, reach inwards to the very core of your being; mysteriously does a Holy of Holies build itself into visibility in the mysterious deeps; and Reverence, the divinest in man, springs forth undying from its mean envelopment of Fear. Wouldst thou rather be a peasant's son that knew, were it never so rudely, there was a God in Heaven and in Man; or a duke's son that only knew there were two-and-thirty quarters on the family coach?"

To which last question we must answer: Beware, O Teufelsdröckh, of spiritual pride!

CHAPTER III.

PEDAGOGY.

HITHERTO we see young Gneschen, in his indivisible case of yellow serge, borne forward mostly on the arms of kind Nature alone; seated, indeed, and much to his mind, in the terrestrial workshop, but (except his soft hazel eyes, which we doubt not already gleamed with a still intelligence) called upon for little voluntary movement there. Hitherto, accordingly, his aspect is rather generic, that of an incipient Philosopher and Poet in the abstract; perhaps it would puzzle Herr Heuschrecke himself to say wherein the special Doctrine of Clothes is as yet foreshadowed or betokened. For with Gneschen, as with others, the Man may indeed stand pictured in the Boy (at least all the pigments are there); yet only some half of the Man stands in the Child, or young Boy, namely, his Passive endowment, not his Active. The more impatient are we to discover what figure he cuts in this latter capacity; how, when, to use his own words, "he understands the tools a little, and can handle this or that," he will proceed to handle it.

Here, however, may be the place to state that, in much of our Philosopher's history, there is something of an almost Hindoo character: nay perhaps in that so well-fostered and everyway excellent "Passivity" of his, which, with no free development of the antagonist Activity, distinguished his childhood, we may detect the rudiments of much that, in after days, and still in these present days, astonishes the world. For the shallow-sighted, Teufelsdröckh is oftenest a man without Activity of any kind, a No-man; for the deep-sighted, again, a man with Activity almost superabundant, yet so spiritual, close-hidden, enigmatic, that no mortal can foresee its explosions, or even when it has exploded, so much as ascertain its significance. A dangerous, difficult temper for the modern European; above all, disadvantageous in the hero of a Biography! Now as heretofore it will behove the Editor of these pages, were it never so unsuccessfully, to do his endeavor.

Among the earliest tools of any complicacy which a man, especially a man of letters, gets to handle, are his Class-books. On this portion of his History, Teufelsdröckh looks down professedly as indifferent. Reading he "cannot remember ever to have learned;" so perhaps had it by nature. He says generally: "Of the insignificant portion of my Education, which depended on Schools, there need almost no notice be taken. I learned what others learn; and kept it stored-by in a corner of my head, seeing as yet no manner of use in it. My Schoolmaster, a downbent, brokenhearted, underfoot martyr, as others of that guild are, did little for me, except discover that he could do little: he, good soul, pronounced me a genius, fit for the learned professions; and that I must be sent to the Gymnasium, and one day to the University. Meanwhile, what printed thing soever I could meet with I read. My very copper pocket-money I laid-out on stall-literature; which, as it accumulated, I with my own hands sewed into volumes. By this means was the young head furnished with a considerable miscellany of things and shadows of things: History in authentic fragments lay mingled with Fabulous chimeras, wherein also was reality; and the whole not as dead stuff, but as living pabulum, tolerably nutritive for a mind as yet so peptic."

That the Entepfuhl Schoolmaster judged well, we now know. Indeed, already in the youthful Gneschen with all his outward stillness, there may have been manifest an inward vivacity that promised much; symptoms of a spirit singularly open, thoughtful, almost poetical. Thus, to say nothing of his Suppers on the Orchard-wall, and other phenomena of that earlier period, have many readers of these pages stumbled, in their twelfth year, on such reflections as the following? "It struck me much, as I sat by the Kuhbach, one silent noontide, and watched it flowing, gurgling, to think how this same streamlet had flowed and gurgled, through all changes of weather and of fortune, from beyond the earliest date of History. Yes, probably on the morning when Joshua forded Jordan; even as at the midday when Cæsar, doubtless with difficulty, swam the Nile, yet kept his *Commentaries* dry,—this little Kuhbach, assiduous as Tiber, Eurotas or Siloa, was murmuring on across the wilderness, as yet unnamed, unseen: here, too, as in the Euphrates and the Ganges, is a vein or veinlet of the grand World-circulation of Waters, which, with its atmospheric arteries, has lasted and lasts simply with the World. Thou fool! Nature alone is antique, and the oldest art a mushroom; that idle crag thou sittest on is six-thousand years of age." In which little thought, as in a little fountain, may there not lie the beginning of those well-nigh unutterable meditations on the grandeur and mystery of Time, and its relation to Eternity, which play such a part in this Philosophy of Clothes?

Over his Gymnastic and Academic years the Professor by no means lingers so lyrical and joyful as over his childhood. Green sunny tracts there are still; but intersected by bitter rivulets of tears, here and there stagnating into sour marshes of discontent. "With my first view of the Hinterschlag Gymnasium," writes he, "my evil days began. Well do I still remember the red sunny Whitsuntide morning, when, trotting full of hope by the side of Father Andreas, I entered the main street of the place, and saw its steeple-clock (then striking Eight) and *Schuldthurm* (Jail), and the aproned or disaproned Burghers moving-in to breakfast: a little dog, in mad terror, was rushing past; for some human imps had tied a tin-kettle to its tail; thus did the agonized creature, loud-jingling, career through the whole length of the Borough, and become notable enough. Fit emblem of many a Conquering Hero, to whom Fate (wedding Fantasy to Sense, as it often elsewhere does) has malignantly appended a tin-kettle of Ambition, to chase him on; which the faster he runs, urges him the faster, the more loudly and more foolishly! Fit emblem also of much that awaited myself, in that mischievous Den; as in the World, whereof it was a portion and epitome!

"Alas, the kind beech-rows of Entepfuhl were hidden in the distance: I was among strangers, harshly, at best indifferently, disposed towards me; the young heart felt, for the first time, quite orphaned and alone." His schoolfellows, as is usual, persecuted him: "They were Boys," he says, "mostly rude Boys, and obeyed the impulse of rude Nature, which bids the deer-herd fall upon any stricken hart, the duck-flock put to death any broken-winged brother or sister, and on all hands the strong tyrannize over the weak." He admits, that though "perhaps in an unusual degree morally courageous," he succeeded ill in battle, and would fain have avoided it; a result, as would appear, owing less to his small personal stature (for in passionate seasons he was "incredibly nimble"), than to his "virtuous principles:" "if it was disgraceful to be beaten," says he, "it was only a shade less disgraceful to have so much as fought; thus was I drawn two ways at once, and in this important element of school-history, the war-element, had little but sorrow." On the whole, that same excellent "Passivity," so notable in Teufelsdröckh's childhood, is here visibly enough again getting nourishment. "He wept often; indeed to such a degree that he was nicknamed *Der Weinende* (the Tearful), which epithet, till towards his thirteenth year, was indeed not quite unmerited. Only at rare intervals did the young soul burst-forth into fire-eyed rage, and, with a stormfulness (*Ungestüm*) under which the boldest quailed, assert that he too had Rights of Man, or at least of Mankin." In all which, who does not discern a fine flower-tree and cinnamon-tree (of genius) nigh choked among pumpkins, reed-grass and ignoble shrubs; and forced if it would live, to struggle upwards only, and not outwards; into a *height* quite sickly, and disproportioned to its *breadth?*

We find, moreover, that his Greek and Latin were "mechanically" taught; Hebrew scarce even mechanically; much else which they called History, Cosmography, Philosophy, and so forth, no better than not at all. So that, except inasmuch as Nature was still busy; and he himself "went about, as was of old his wont, among the Craftsmen's workshops, there learning many things"; and farther lighted on some small store of curious reading, in Hans Wachtel the Cooper's house, where he lodged,—his time, it would appear, was utterly wasted. Which facts the Professor has not yet learned to look upon with any contentment. Indeed, throughout the whole of this Bag *Scorpio,* where we now are, and often in the following Bag, he shows himself unusually animated on the matter of Education, and not without some touch of what we might presume to be anger.

"My Teachers," says he, "were hide-bound Pedants, without knowledge of man's nature, or of boy's; or of aught save their lexicons and quarterly account-books. Innumerable dead Vocables (no dead Language, for they themselves knew no Language) they crammed into us, and called it fostering the growth of mind. How can an inanimate, mechanical Gerundgrinder, the like of whom will, in a subsequent century, be manufactured at Nürnberg out of wood and leather, foster the growth of anything; much more of Mind, which grows, not like a vegetable (by having its roots littered with etymological compost), but like a spirit, by mysterious contact of Spirit; Thought kindling itself at the fire of living Thought? How shall *he* give kindling, in whose own inward man there is no live coal, but all is burnt-out to a dead grammatical cinder? The Hinterschlag Professors knew syntax enough; and of the human soul thus much: that it had a faculty called Memory, and could be acted-on through the muscular integument by appliance of birch-rods.

"Alas, so is it everywhere, so will it ever be; till the Hodman is discharged, or reduced to hodbearing; and an Architect is hired and on all hands fitly encouraged: till communities and individuals discover, not without surprise, that fashioning the souls of a generation by Knowledge can rank on a level with blowing their bodies to pieces by Gunpowder; that with Generals and Fieldmarshals for killing, there should be world-honored Dignitaries, and were it possible, true God-ordained Priests, for teaching. But as yet, though the Soldier wears openly, and even parades, his butchering-tool, nowhere, far as I have travelled, did the Schoolmaster make show of his instructing-tool: nay, were he to walk abroad with birch girt on thigh, as if he therefrom expected honor, would there not, among the idler class, perhaps a certain levity be excited?"

In the third year of this Gymnasic period, Father Andreas seems to have died: the young Scholar, otherwise so maltreated, saw himself for the first time clad outwardly in sables, and inwardly in quite inexpressible melancholy. "The dark bottomless Abyss, that lies under our feet, had yawned open; the pale kingdoms of Death, with all their innumerable silent nations and generations, stood before him; the inexorable word, NEVER! now first showed its meaning. My Mother wept, and her sorrow got vent; but in my heart lay a whole lake of tears, pent-up in silent desolation. Nevertheless the unworn Spirit is strong; Life is so healthful that it even finds nourishment in Death: these stern experiences, planted down by Memory in my Imagination, rose there to a whole cypress-forest, sad but beautiful; waving, with not unmelodious sighs, in dark luxuriance, in the hottest sunshine, through long years of youth:—as in manhood also it does, and will do; for I have now pitched my tent under a Cypress-tree; the Tomb is now my inexpugnable Fortress, ever close by the gate of which I look upon the hostile armaments, and pains and penalties of tyrannous Life placidly enough, and listen to its loudest threatenings with a still smile. O ye loved ones, that already sleep in the noiseless Bed of Rest, whom in life I could only weep for and never help; and ye, who wide-scattered still toil lonely in the monster-bearing Desert, dyeing the flinty ground with your blood, —yet a little while, and we shall all meet THERE, and our Mother's bosom will screen us all; and Oppression's harness, and Sorrow's fire-whip, and all the Gehenna Bailiffs that patrol and inhabit ever-vexed Time, cannot thenceforth harm us any more!"

Close by which rather beautiful apostrophe, lies a labored Character of the deceased Andreas Futteral; of his natural ability, his deserts in life (as Prussian Sergeant); with long historical inquiries into the genealogy of the Futteral Family, here traced back as far as Henry the Fowler: the whole of which we pass over, not without astonishment. It only concerns us to add, that now was the time when Mother Gretchen revealed to her foster-son that he was not at all of this kindred; or indeed of any kindred, having come into historical existence in the way already known to us. "Thus was I doubly orphaned," says he; "bereft not only of Possession, but even of Remembrance. Sorrow and Wonder, here suddenly united, could not but produce abundant fruit. Such a disclosure, in such a season, struck its roots through my whole nature: ever till the years of mature manhood, it mingled with my whole thoughts, was as the stem whereon all my day-dreams and night-dreams grew. A certain poetic elevation, yet also a corresponding civic depression, it naturally imparted: *I was like no other;* in which fixed-idea, leading sometimes to highest, and oftener to frightfullest results, may there not lie the first spring of tendencies, which in my Life have become remarkable enough? As in birth, so in action, speculation, and social position, my fellows are perhaps not numerous."

In the Bag *Sagittarius,* as we at length discover, Teufelsdröckh has become a University man; though how, when, or of what quality, will nowhere disclose itself with the smallest certainty. Few things, in the way of confusion and capricious indistinctness, can now surprise our readers; not even the total want of dates, almost without parallel in a Biographical work. So enigmatic, so chaotic we have always found, and must always look to find, these scattered Leaves. In *Sagittarius,* however, Teufelsdröckh begins to show himself even more than usually Sibylline: fragments of all sorts; scraps of regular Memoir, College-Exercises, Programmes, Professional Testimoniums, Milkscores, torn Billets, sometimes to appearance of an amatory cast; all blown together as if by merest chance, henceforth bewilder the sane Historian. To combine any picture of these University, and the subsequent, years; much more, to decipher therein any illustrative primordial elements of the Clothes-Philosophy becomes such a problem as the reader may imagine.

So much we can see; darkly, as through the foliage of some wavering thicket: a youth of no common endowment, who has passed happily through Childhood, less happily yet still vigorously through Boyhood, now at length perfect in "dead vocables," and set down, as he hopes, by the living Fountain, there to superadd Ideas and Capabilities. From such Fountain he draws, diligently, thirstily, yet never or seldom with his whole heart, for the water nowise suits his palate; discouragements, entanglements, aberrations are discoverable or supposable. Nor perhaps are even pecuniary distresses wanting; for "the good Gretchen, who in spite of advices from not disinterested relatives has sent him hither, must after a time withdraw her willing but too feeble hand." Nevertheless in an atmosphere of Poverty and manifold Chagrin, the Humor of that young Soul, what character is in him, first decisively reveals itself; and, like strong sunshine in weeping skies, gives out variety of colors, some of which are prismatic. Thus, with the aid of Time and of what Time brings, has the stripling Diogenes Teufelsdröckh waxed into manly stature; and into so questionable an aspect, that we ask with new eagerness, How he specially came by it, and regret anew that there is no more explicit answer. Certain of the intelligible and partially significant fragments, which are few in number, shall be extracted from that Limbo of a Paper-bag and presented with the usual preparation.

As if, in the Bag *Scorpio,* Teufelsdröckh had not already expectorated his antipedagogic spleen; as if, from the name *Sagittarius,* he had thought himself called upon to shoot arrows, we here again fall-in with such matter as this: "The University where I was educated still stands vivid enough in my remembrance, and I know its name well; which name, however, I, from tenderness to existing interests and persons, shall in nowise divulge. It is my painful duty to say that, out of England and Spain, ours was the worst of all hitherto discovered Universities. This is indeed a time when right Education is, as nearly as may be, impossible: however, in degrees of wrongness there is no limit: nay, I can conceive a worse system than that of the Nameless itself; as poisoned victual may be worse than absolute hunger.

"It is written, When the blind lead the blind, both shall fall into the ditch: wherefore, in such circumstances, may it not sometimes be safer, if both leader and led simply—sit still? Had you, anywhere in Crim Tartary, walled-in a square enclosure; furnished it with a small, ill-chosen Library; and then turned loose into it eleven-hundred Christian striplings, to tumble about as they listed, from three to seven years: certain persons, under the title of Professors, being stationed at the gates, to declare aloud that it was a University, and exact considerable admission-fees,—you had, not indeed in mechanical structure, yet in spirit and result, some imperfect resemblance of our High Seminary. I say, imperfect; for if our mechanical structure was quite other, so neither was our result altogether the same: unhappily, we were not in Crim Tartary, but in a corrupt European city, full of smoke and sin; moreover, in the middle of a Public, which, without far costlier apparatus than that of the Square Enclosure, and Declaration aloud, you could not be sure of gulling.

"Gullible, however, by fit apparatus, all Publics are; and gulled, with the most surprising profit. Towards anything like a *Statistics of Imposture,* indeed, little as yet has been done: with a strange indifference, our Economists, nigh buried under Tables for minor Branches of Industry, have altogether overlooked the grand all-overtopping Hypocrisy Branch; as if our whole arts of Puffery, of Quackery, Priestcraft, Kingcraft, and the innumerable other crafts and mysteries of that genus, had not ranked in Productive Industry at all! Can any one, for example, so much as say, What moneys, in Literature and Shoeblacking, are realized by actual Instruction and actual jet Polish; what by fictitious-persuasive Proclamation of such; specifying, in distinct items, the distributions, circulations, disbursements, incomings of said moneys, with the smallest approach to accuracy? But to ask, How far, in all the several infinitely-complected departments of social business, in government, education, in manual, commercial, intellectual fabrication of every sort, man's Want is supplied by true Ware; how far by the mere Appearance of true Ware:—in other words, To what extent, by what methods, with what effects, in various times and countries, Deception takes the place of wages of Performance: here truly is an Inquiry big with results for the future time, but to which hitherto only the vaguest answer can be given. If for the present, in our Europe, we estimate the ratio of Ware to Appearance of Ware so high even as at One to a Hundred (which, considering the Wages of a Pope, Russian Autocrat, or English Game-Preserver, is probably not far from the mark),—what almost prodigious saving may there not be anticipated, as the *Statistics of Imposture* advances, and so the manufacturing of Shams (that of Realities rising into clearer and clearer distinction therefrom) gradually declines, and at length becomes all but wholly unnecessary!

"This for the coming golden ages. What I had to remark, for the present brazen one, is, that in several provinces, as in Education, Polity, Religion, where so much is wanted and indispensable, and so little can as yet be furnished, probably Imposture is of sanative, anodyne nature, and man's Gullibility not his worst blessing. Suppose your sinews of war quite broken; I mean your military chest insolvent, forage all but exhausted; and that the whole army is about to mutiny, disband, and cut your and each other's throat,—then were it not well could you, as if by miracle, pay them in any sort of fairy-money, feed them on coagulated water, or mere imagination of meat; whereby, till the real supply came up, they might be kept together and quiet? Such perhaps was the aim of Nature, who does nothing without aim, in furnishing her favorite, Man, with this his so omnipotent or rather omnipatient Talent of being Gulled.

"How beautifully it works, with a little mechanism; nay, almost makes mechanism for itself! These Professors in the Nameless lived with ease, with safety, by a mere Reputation, constructed in past times, and then too with no great effort, by quite another class of persons. Which Reputation, like a strong, brisk-going undershot wheel, sunk into the general current, bade fair, with only a little annual repainting on their part, to hold long together, and of its own accord assiduously grind for them. Happy that it was so, for the Millers! They themselves needed not to work; their attempts at working, at what they called Educating, now when I look back on it, fill me with a certain mute admiration.

"Besides all this, we boasted ourselves a Rational University; in the highest degree hostile to Mysticism; thus was the young vacant mind furnished with much talk about Progress of the Species, Dark Ages, Prejudice, and the like; so that all were quickly enough blown out into a state of windy argumentativeness; whereby the better sort had soon to end in sick, impotent Scepticism; the worser sort explode (*crepiren*) in finished Self-conceit, and to all spiritual intents become dead.—But this too is portion of mankind's lot. If our era is the Era of Unbelief, why murmur under it; is there not a better coming, nay come? As in long-drawn systole and long-drawn diastole, must the period of Faith alternate with the period of Denial; must the vernal growth, the summer luxuriance of all Opinions, Spiritual Representations and Creations, be followed by, and again follow, the autumnal decay, the winter dissolution. For man lives in Time, has his whole earthly being, endeavor and destiny shaped for him by Time: only in the transitory Time-Symbol is the ever-motionless Eternity we stand on made manifest. And yet, in such winter-seasons of Denial, it is for the nobler-minded perhaps a comparative misery to have been born, and to be awake and work; and for the duller a felicity, if, like hibernating animals, safe-lodged in some Salamanca University, or Sybaris City, or other superstitious or voluptuous Castle of Indolence, they can slumber-through, in stupid dreams, and only awaken when the loud-roaring hailstorms have all done their work, and to our prayers and martyrdoms the new Spring has been vouchsafed."

That in the environment here mysteriously enough shadowed forth, Teufelsdröckh must have felt ill at ease, cannot be doubtful. "The hungry young," he says, "looked up to their spiritual Nurses; and, for food, were bidden eat the east-wind. What vain jargon of controversial Metaphysic, Etymology, and mechanical Manipulation falsely named Science, was current there, I indeed learned, better perhaps than the most. Among eleven-hundred Christian youths, there will not be wanting some eleven eager to learn. By collision with such, a certain warmth, a certain polish was communicated; by instinct and happy accident, I took less to rioting (renommiren) than to thinking and reading, which latter also I was free to do. Nay from the chaos of that Library, I succeeded in fishing-up more books perhaps than had been known to the very keepers thereof. The foundation of a Literary Life was hereby laid: I learned, on my own strength, to read fluently in almost all cultivated languages, on almost all subjects and sciences; farther, as man is ever the prime object to man, already it was my favorite employment to read character in speculation, and from the Writing to construe the Writer. A certain groundplan of Human Nature and Life began to fashion itself in me; wondrous enough, now when I look back on it; for my whole Universe, physical and spiritual, was as yet a Machine! However such a conscious, recognized groundplan, the truest I had, was beginning to be there, and by additional experiments might be corrected and indefinitely extended."

Thus from poverty does the strong educe nobler wealth; thus in the destitution of the wild desert does our young Ishmael acquire for himself the highest of all possessions, that of Self-help. Nevertheless a desert this was, waste, and howling with savage monsters. Teufelsdröckh gives us long details of his "fever-paroxysms of Doubt;" his Inquiries concerning Miracles, and the Evidences of religious Faith; and how "in the silent night-watches, still darker in his heart than over sky and earth, he has cast himself before the All-seeing, and with audible prayers cried vehemently for

Light, for deliverance from Death and the Grave. Not till after long years, and unspeakable agonies, did the believing heart surrender; sink into spell-bound sleep, under the nightmare, Unbelief; and, in this hag-ridden dream, mistake God's fair living world for a pallid, vacant Hades and extinct Pande-monium. But through such Purgatory pain," continues he, "it is appointed us to pass; first must the dead Letter of Religion own itself dead, and drop piecemeal into dust, if the living Spirit of Religion, freed from this its charnal-house, is to arise on us, newborn of Heaven, and with new healing under its wings."

To which Purgatory pains, seemingly severe enough, if we add a liberal measure of Earthly distresses, want of practical guidance, want of sympathy, want of money, want of hope; and all this in the fervid season of youth, so exaggerated in imagining, so boundless in desires, yet here so poor in means,—do we not see a strong incipient spirit oppressed and overloaded from without and from within; the fire of genius struggling-up among fuel-wood of the greenest, and as yet with more of bitter vapor than of clear flame?

From various fragments of Letters and other documentary scraps, it is to be inferred that Teufelsdröckh, isolated, shy, retiring as he was, had not altogether escaped notice: certain established men are aware of his exist-ence; and, if stretching-out no helpful hand, have at least their eyes on him. He appears, though in dreary enough humor, to be addressing himself to the Profession of Law;—whereof, indeed, the world has since seen him a public graduate. But omitting these broken, unsatisfactory thrums of Eco-nomical relation, let us present rather the following small thread of Moral relation; and therewith, the reader for himself weaving it in at the right place, conclude our dim arras-picture of these University years.

"Here also it was that I formed acquaintance with Herr Towgood, or, as it is perhaps better written, Herr Toughgut; a young person of quality (von Adel), from the interior parts of England. He stood connected, by blood and hospitality, with the Counts von Zähdarm, in this quarter of Germany; to which noble Family I likewise was, by his means, with all friendliness, brought near. Towgood had a fair talent, unspeakably ill-cultivated; with considerable humor of character: and, bating his total ig-norance, for he knew nothing except Boxing and a little Grammar, showed less of that aristocratic impassivity, and silent fury, than for most part belongs to Travellers of his nation. To him I owe my first practical knowl-edge of the English and their ways; perhaps also something of the partiality with which I have ever since regarded that singular people. Towgood was not without an eye, could have come at any light. Invited doubtless by the presence of the Zähdarm Family, he had travelled hither, in the almost frantic hope of perfecting his studies; he, whose studies had as yet been those of infancy, hither to a University where so much as the notion of perfection, not to say the effort after it, no longer existed! Often we would condole over the hard destiny of the Young in this era: how, after all our toil, we were to be turned-out into the world, with beards on our chins indeed, but with few other attributes of manhood; no existing thing that we were trained to Act on, nothing that we could so much as Believe. 'How has our head on the outside a polished Hat,' would Towgood exclaim, 'and in the inside Vacancy, or a froth of Vocables and Attorney-Logic! At a small cost men are educated to make leather into shoes; but at a great cost, what am I educated to make? By Heaven, Brother! what I have already eaten and worn, as I came thus far, would endow a considerable Hospital of Incurables.'—'Man, indeed,' I would answer, 'has a Digestive Faculty, which must be kept working, were it even partly by stealth. But as for our Mis-education, make not bad worse; waste not the time yet ours, in trampling on thistles because they have yielded us no figs. *Frisch zu, Bruder!* Here are Books, and we have brains to read them; here is a whole Earth and a whole Heaven, and we have eyes to look on them: *Frisch zu!*'

"Often also our talk was gay; not without brilliancy, and even fire. We looked-out on Life, with its strange scaffolding, where all at once harlequins dance, and men are beheaded and quartered: motley, not unterrific was the aspect; but we looked on it like brave youths. For myself, these were perhaps my most genial hours. Towards this young warmhearted, strongheaded and wrongheaded Herr Towgood I was even near experiencing the now obsolete sentiment of Friendship. Yes, foolish Heathen that I was, I felt that, under certain conditions, I could have loved this man, and taken him to my bosom, and been his brother once and always. By degrees, however, I understood the new time, and its wants. If man's *Soul* is indeed, as in the Finnish Language, and Utilitarian Philosophy, a kind of *Stomach*, what else is the true meaning of Spiritual Union but an Eating together? Thus we, instead of Friends, are Dinner-guests; and here as elsewhere have cast away chimeras."

So ends, abruptly as is usual, and enigmatically, this little incipient romance. What henceforth becomes of the brave Herr Towgood, or Toughgut? He has dived-under, in the Autobiographical Chaos, and swims we see not where. Does any reader "in the interior parts of England" know of such a man?

CHAPTER IV.

Getting under Way.

"Thus nevertheless," writes our Autobiographer, apparently as quitting College, "was there realized Somewhat; namely, I, Diogenes Teufelsdröckh: a visible Temporary Figure (*Zeitbild*), occupying some cubic feet of Space and containing within it Forces both physical and spiritual; hopes, passions, thoughts; the whole wondrous furniture, in more or less perfection, belonging to that mystery, a Man. Capabilities there were in me to give battle, in some small degree, against the great Empire of Darkness: does not the very Ditcher and Delver, with his spade, extinguish many a thistle and puddle, and so leave a little Order, where he found the opposite? Nay, your very

Daymoth has capabilities in this kind; and ever organizes something (into its own Body, if no otherwise); which was before Inorganic; and of mute dead air makes living music, though only of the faintest, by humming.

"How much more, one whose capabilities are spiritual; who has learned, or begun learning, the grand thaumaturgic art of Thought! Thaumaturgic I name it; for hitherto all Miracles have been wrought thereby, and henceforth innumerable will be wrought; whereof we, even in these days, witness some. Of the Poet's and Prophet's inspired Message, and how it makes and unmakes whole worlds, I shall forbear mention: but cannot the dullest hear Steam-engines clanking around him? Has he not seen the Scottish Brassmith's IDEA (and this but a mechanical one) travelling on fire-wings round the Cape, and across two Oceans; and stronger than any other Enchanter's Familiar, on all hands unweariedly fetching and carrying: at home, not only weaving Cloth; but rapidly enough overturning the whole old system of Society; and, for Feudalism and Preservation of the Game, preparing us, by indirect but sure methods, Industrialism and the Government of the Wisest? Truly a Thinking Man is the worst enemy the Prince of Darkness can have; every time such a one announces himself, I doubt not, there runs a shudder through the Nether Empire; and new Emissaries are trained, with new tactics, to, if possible, entrap him, and hoodwink and handcuff him.

"With such high vocation had I too, as denizen of the Universe, been called. Unhappy it is, however, that though born to the amplest Sovereignty, in this way, with no less than sovereign right of Peace and War against the Time-Prince (*Zeitfürst*), or Devil, and all his Dominions, your coronation-ceremony costs such trouble, your sceptre is so difficult to get at, or even to get eye on!"

By which last wiredrawn similitude does Teufelsdröckh mean no more than that young men find obstacles in what we call "getting under way?" "Not what I Have," continues he, "but what I Do is my Kingdom. To each is given a certain inward Talent, a certain outward Environment of Fortune; to each, by wisest combination of these two, a certain maximum of Capability. But the hardest problem were ever this first: To find by study of yourself, and of the ground you stand on, what your combined inward and outward Capability specially is. For, alas, our young soul is all budding with Capabilities, and we see not yet which is the main and true one. Always too the new man is in a new time, under new conditions; his course can be the *facsimile* of no prior one, but is by its nature original. And then how seldom will the outward Capability fit the inward: though talented wonderfully enough, we are poor, unfriended, dyspeptical, bashful; nay what is worse than all, we are foolish. Thus, in a whole imbroglio of Capabilities, we go stupidly groping about, to grope which is ours, and often clutch the wrong one: in this mad work must several years of our small term be spent, till the purblind Youth, by practice, acquire notions of distance, and become a seeing Man. Nay, many so spend their whole term, and in ever-new expectation, ever-new disappointment, shift from enterprise to enterprise, and from side to side: till at length, as exasperated striplings of threescore-and-ten, they shift into their last enterprise, that of getting buried.

"Such, since the most of us are too ophthalmic, would be the general fate; were it not that one thing saves us: our Hunger. For on this ground, as the prompt nature of Hunger is well known, must a prompt choice be made: hence have we, with wise foresight, Indentures and Apprenticeships for our irrational young; whereby, in due season, the vague universality of a Man shall find himself ready-moulded into a specific Craftsman; and so thenceforth work, with much or with little waste of Capability as it may be; yet not with the worst waste, that of time. Nay even in matters spiritual, since the spiritual artist too is born blind, and does not, like certain other creatures, receive sight in nine days, but far later, sometimes never,—is it not well that there should be what we call Professions, or Bread-studies (*Brodzwecke*), preappointed us? Here, circling like the gin horse, for whom partial or total blindness is no evil, the Bread-artist can travel contentedly round and round, still fancying that it is forward and forward; and realize much: for himself victuals; for the world an additional horse's power in the grand corn-mill or hemp-mill of Economic Society. For me too had such a leading-string been provided; only that it proved a neck-halter, and had nigh throttled me, till I broke it off. Then, in the words of Ancient Pistol, did the world generally become mine oyster, which I, by strength or cunning, was to open, as I would and could. Almost had I deceased (*fast wär ich umgekommen*), so obstinately did it continue shut."

We see here, significantly foreshadowed, the spirit of much that was to befall our Autobiographer; the historical embodiment of which, as it painfully takes shape in his Life, lies scattered, in dim disastrous details, through this Bag *Pisces*, and those that follow. A young man of high talent, and high though still temper, like a young mettled colt, "breaks-off his neck-halter," and bounds forth, from his peculiar manger, into the wide world; which, alas, he finds all rigorously fenced-in. Richest clover-fields tempt his eye; but to him they are forbidden pasture: either pining in progressive starvation, he must stand; or, in mad exasperation, must rush to and fro, leaping against sheer stone-walls, which he cannot leap over, which only lacerate and lame him; till at last, after thousand attempts and endurances, he, as if by miracle, clears his way; not indeed into luxuriant and luxurious clover, yet into a certain bosky wilderness where existence is still possible, and Freedom, though waited on by Scarcity, is not without sweetness. In a word, Teufelsdröckh having thrown-up his legal Profession, finds himself without landmark of outward guidance; whereby his previous want of decided Belief, or inward guidance, is frightfully aggravated. Necessity urges him on; Time will not stop, neither can he, a Son of Time; wild passions without solacement, wild faculties without employment, ever vex and agitate him. He too must enact that stern Monodrama, *No Object and no Rest;* must front its successive destinies, work through to its catastrophe, and deduce therefrom what moral he can.

Yet let us be just to him, let us admit that his "neck-halter" sat nowise easy on him; that he was in some degree forced to break it off. If we look at the young man's civic position, in this Nameless capital, as he emerges from its Nameless University, we can discern well that it was far from enviable. His first Law-Examination he has come through triumphantly; and can even boast that the *Examen Rigorosum* need not have frightened him: but though he is hereby "an *Auscultator* of respectability," what avails it? There is next to no employment to be had. Neither, for a youth without connections, is the process of Expectation very hopeful in itself; nor for one of his disposition much cheered from without. "My fellow Auscultators," he says, "were Auscultators: they dressed, and digested, and talked articulate words; other vitality showed they almost none. Small speculation in those eyes, that they did glare withal! Sense neither for the high nor for the deep, nor for aught human or divine, save only for the faintest scent of coming Preferment." In which words, indicating a total estrangement on the part of Teufelsdröckh, may there not also lurk traces of bitterness as from wounded vanity? Doubtless these prosaic Auscultators may have sniffed at him, with his strange ways; and tried to hate, and what was much more impossible, to despise him. Friendly communion, in any case, there could not be: already has the young Teufelsdröckh left the other young geese; and swims apart, though as yet uncertain whether he himself is cygnet or gosling.

Perhaps, too, what little employment he had was performed ill, at best unpleasantly. "Great practical method and expertness" he may brag of; but is there not also great practical pride, though deep-hidden, only the deeper seated? So shy a man can never have been popular. We figure to ourselves, how in those days he may have played strange freaks with his independence, and so forth: do not his own words betoken as much? "Like a very young person, I imagined it was with Work alone, and not also with Folly and Sin, in myself and others, that I had been appointed to struggle." Be this as it may, his progress from the passive Auscultatorship, towards any active Assessorship, is evidently of the slowest. By degrees, those same established men, once partially inclined to patronize him, seem to withdraw their countenance, and give him up as "a man of genius:" against which procedure he, in these Papers, loudly protests. "As if," says he, "the higher did not presuppose the lower; as if he who can fly into heaven, could not also walk post if he resolved on it! But the world is an old woman, and mistakes any gilt farthing for a gold coin; whereby being often cheated, she will thenceforth trust nothing but the common copper."

How our winged sky-messenger, unaccepted as a terrestrial runner, contrived, in the meanwhile, to keep himself from flying skyward without return, is not too clear from these Documents. Good old Gretchen seems to have vanished from the scene, perhaps from the Earth; other Horn of Plenty, or even of Parsimony, nowhere flows for him; so that "the prompt nature of Hunger being well known," we are not without our anxiety. From private Tuition, in never so many languages and sciences, the aid derivable is small; neither, to use his own words, "does the young Adventurer hitherto suspect in himself any literary gift; but at best earns bread-and-water wages, by his wide faculty of Translation. Nevertheless," continues he, "that I subsisted is clear, for you find me even now alive." Which fact, however, except upon the principle of our true-hearted, kind old Proverb, that "there is always life for a living one," we must profess ourselves unable to explain.

Certain Landlords' Bills, and other economic Documents, bearing the mark of Settlement, indicate that he was not without money; but, like an independent Hearth-holder, if not House-holder, paid his way. Here also occur, among many others, two little mutilated Notes, which perhaps throw light on his condition. The first has now no date, or writer's name, but a huge Blot; and runs to this effect: "The (*Inkblot*), tied-down by previous promise, cannot, except by best wishes, forward the Herr Teufelsdröckh's views on the Assessorship in question; and sees himself under the cruel necessity of forbearing, for the present, what were otherwise his duty and joy, to assist in opening the career for a man of genius, on whom far higher triumphs are yet waiting." The other is on gilt paper; and interests us like a sort of epistolary mummy now dead, yet which once lived and beneficently worked. We give it in the original: "*Herr Teufelsdröckh wird von der Frau Gräfin, auf Donnerstag, zum ÆSTHETISCHEN THEE schönstens eingeladen.*"

Thus, in answer to a cry for solid pudding, whereof there is the most urgent need, comes, epigrammatically enough, the invitation to a wash of quite fluid *Æsthetic Tea!* How Teufelsdröckh, now at actual handgrips with Destiny herself, may have comported himself among these Musical and Literary Dilettanti of both sexes, like a hungry lion invited to a feast of chicken-weed, we can only conjecture. Perhaps in expressive silence, and abstinence: otherwise if the lion, in such case, is to feast at all, it cannot be on the chicken-weed, but only on the chickens. For the rest, as this Frau Gräfin dates from the *Zähdarm House,* she can be no other than the Countess and mistress of the same; whose intellectual tendencies, and good-will to Teufelsdröckh, whether on the footing of Herr Towgood, or on his own footing, are hereby manifest. That some sort of relation, indeed, continued, for a time, to connect our Autobiographer, though perhaps feebly enough, with this noble House, we have elsewhere express evidence. Doubtless, if he expected patronage, it was in vain; enough for him if he here obtained occasional glimpses of the great world, from which we at one time fancied him to have been always excluded. "The Zähdarms," says he, "lived in the soft, sumptuous garniture of Aristocracy; whereto Literature and Art, attracted and attached from without, were to serve as the handsomest fringing. It was to the *Gnädigen Frau* (her Ladyship) that this latter improvement was due: assiduously she gathered, dextrously she fitted-on, what fringing was to be had; lace or cobweb, as the place yielded." Was Teufelsdröckh also a fringe, of lace or cobweb; or promising to be such? "With his *Excellenz* (the Count)," continues he, "I have more than once had the honor to converse; chiefly on general affairs, and the aspect of the world, which he, though now past middle life, viewed in no unfavorable light; finding indeed, except the Outrooting of Journalism (*die auszurottende Journalsitik*), little to desiderate therein. On some points, as his *Excellenz* was not uncholeric, I found it more pleasant to keep silence. Besides, his occupation being that of Owning Land, there might be faculties enough, which, as superfluous for such use, were little developed in him."

That to Teufelsdröckh the aspect of the world was nowise so faultless, and many things besides "the Outrooting of Journalism" might have seemed improvements, we can readily conjecture. With nothing but a barren Auscultatorship from without, and so many mutinous thoughts and wishes from within, his position was no easy one. "The Universe," he says, "was as a mighty Sphinx-riddle, which I knew so little of, yet must rede, or be devoured. In red streaks of unspeakable grandeur, yet also in the blackness of darkness, was Life, to my too-unfurnished Thought, unfolding itself. A strange contradiction lay in me; and I as yet knew not the solution of it; knew not that spiritual music can spring only from discords set in harmony; that but for Evil there were no Good, as victory is only possible by battle."

"I have heard affirmed (surely in jest)," observes he elsewhere, "by not unphilanthropic persons, that it were a real increase of human happiness, could all young men from the age of nineteen be covered under barrels, or rendered otherwise invisible; and there left to follow their lawful studies and callings, till they emerged, sadder and wiser, at the age of twenty-five. With which suggestion, at least as considered in the light of a practical scheme, I need scarcely say that I nowise coincide. Nevertheless it is plausibly urged that, as young ladies (*Mädchen*) are, to mankind, precisely the most delightful in those years; so young gentlemen (*Bübchen*) do then attain their maximum of detestability. Such gawks (*Gecken*) are they, and foolish peacocks, and yet with such a vulturous hunger for self-indulgence; so obstinate, obstreperous, vain-glorious; in all senses, so froward and so forward. No mortal's endeavor or attainment will, in the smallest, content the as yet unendeavoring, unattaining young gentleman; but he could make it all infinitely better, were it worthy of him. Life everywhere is the most manageable matter, simple as a question in the Rule-of-Three: multiply your second and third term together, divide the product by the first, and your quotient will be the answer,—which you are but an ass if you cannot come at. The booby has not yet found-out, by any trial, that, do what one will, there is ever a cursed fraction, oftenest a decimal repeater, and no net integer quotient so much as to be thought of."

In which passage does not there lie an implied confession that Teufelsdröckh himself, besides his outward obstructions, had an inward, still greater, to contend with; namely, a certain temporary, youthful, yet still afflictive derangement of head? Alas, on the former side alone, his case was hard enough. "It continues ever true," says he, "that Saturn, or Chronos, or what we call TIME, devours all his children: only by incessant Running, by incessant Working, may you (for some three-score-and-ten years) escape him; and you too he devours at last. Can any Sovereign, or Holy Alliance of Sovereigns, bid Time stand still; even in thought, shake themselves free of Time? Our whole terrestrial being is based on Time, and built of Time; it is wholly a Movement, a Time-impulse; Time is the author of it, the material of it. Hence also our Whole Duty, which is to move, to work,—in the right direction. Are not our Bodies and our Souls in continual movement, whether we will or not; in a continual Waste, requiring a continual Repair? Utmost satisfaction of our whole outward and inward Wants were but satisfaction for a space of Time; Thus, whatso we have done, is done, and for us annihilated, and ever must we go and do anew. O Time-Spirit, how hast thou environed and imprisoned us, and sunk us so deep in thy troublous dim Time-Element, that only in lucid moments can so much as glimpses of our upper Azure Home be revealed to us! Me, however, as a Son of Time, unhappier than some others, was Time threatening to eat quite prematurely; for, strive as I might, there was no good Running, so obstructed was the path, so gyved were the feet." That is to say, we presume, speaking in the dialect of this lower world, that Teufelsdröckh's whole duty and necessity was, like other men's, "to work,—in the right direction," and that no work was to be had; whereby he became wretched enough. As was natural: with haggard Scarcity threatening him in the distance; and so vehement a soul languishing in restless inaction, and forced thereby, like Sir Hudibras's sword by rust,

> *To eat into itself, for lack*
> *Of something else to hew and hack!*

But on the whole, the same "excellent Passivity," as it has all along done, is here again vigorously flourishing; in which circumstance may we not trace the beginnings of much that now characterizes our Professor; and perhaps, in faint rudiments, the origin of the Clothes-Philosophy itself? Already the attitude he has assumed toward the World is too defensive; not, as would have been desirable, a bold attitude of attack. "So far hitherto," he says, "as I had mingled with mankind, I was notable, if for anything, for a certain stillness of manner, which, as my friends often rebukingly declared, did but ill express the keen ardor of my feelings. I, in truth, regarded men with an excess both of love and of fear. The mystery of a Person, indeed, is ever divine to him that has a sense for the Godlike. Often, notwithstanding, was I blamed, and by half-strangers hated, for my so-called Hardness (*Härte*), my indifferentism towards men; and the seemingly ironic tone I had adopted, as my favorite dialect in conversation. Also, the panoply of Sarcasm was but as a buckram case, wherein I had striven to envelope myself; that so my own poor Person might live safe there, and in all friendliness, being no longer exasperated by wounds. Sarcasm I now see to be, in general, the language of the Devil; for which reason I have long since as good as renounced it. But how many individuals did I, in those days, provoke into some degree of hostility thereby! An ironic man, with his sly stillness, and ambuscading ways, more especially an ironic young man, from whom it is least expected, may be viewed as a pest to society. Have we not seen persons of weight and name coming forward, with gentlest indifference, to tread such a one out of sight, as an insignificancy and worm, start ceiling-high (*balkenhoch*), and thence fall shattered and supine, to be borne home on shutters, not without indignation, when he proved electric and a torpedo!"

Alas, how can a man with this devilishness of temper make way for himself in Life; where the first problem, as Teufelsdröckh too admits, is "to unite yourself with some one and with somewhat (*sich anzuschliessen*)?" Division, not union, is written on most part of his procedure. Let us add to that, in no great length of time, the only important connection he had ever succeeded in forming, his connection with the Zähdarm Family, seems to have been paralyzed, for all practical uses, by the death of the "not uncholeric" old Count. This fact stands recorded, quite incidentally, in a certain *Discourse on Epitaphs*, huddled into the present Bag, among so much else; of which Essay the learning and curious penetration are more to be approved of than the spirit. His grand principle is, that lapidary inscriptions, of what sort soever, should be Historical rather than Lyrical. "By request of that worthy Nobleman's survivors," says he, "I undertook to compose his Epitaph; and not unmindful of my own rules, produced the following; which however, for an alleged defect of Latinity, a defect never yet fully visible to myself, still remains unengraven;"—wherein we may predict, there is more than the Latinity that will surprise an English reader:

HIC JACET
PHILIPPUS ZAEHDARM COGNOMINE MAGNUS,
ZAEHDARMI COMES,
EX IMPERII CONCILIO,
VELLERIS AUREI, PERISCELIDIS, NECNON VULTURIS NIGRI EQUES.

QUI DUM SUB LUNA AGEBAT,
QUINQUIES MILLE PERDICES
PLUMBO CONFECIT:
VARII CIBI
CENTUMPONDIA MILLIES CENTENA MILLIA,
PER SE, PERQUE SERVOS QUADRUPEDES BIPEDESVE,
HAUD SINE TUMULTU DEVOLVENS,
IN STERCUS
PALAM CONVERTIT.

NUNC A LABORE REQUIESCENTEM
OPERA SEQUUNTUR.

SI MONUMENTUM QUÆRIS,
FIMETUM ADSPICE.

PRIMUM IN ORBE DEJECIT [*sub dato*]; POSTREMUM
[*sub dato*].

CHAPTER V.

ROMANCE.

"FOR LONG YEARS," writes Teufelsdröckh, "had the poor Hebrew, in this Egypt of an Auscultatorship, painfully toiled, baking bricks without stubble, before ever the question once struck him with entire force: For what?— *Beym Himmel!* For Food and Warmth! And are Food and Warmth nowhere else, in the whole wide Universe, discoverable?—Come of it what might, I resolved to try."

Thus then are we to see him in a new independent capacity, though perhaps far from an improved one. Teufelsdröckh is now a man without Profession. Quitting the common Fleet of herring-busses and whalers, where indeed his leeward, laggard condition was painful enough, he desperately steers off, on a course of his own, by sextant and compass of his own. Unhappy Teufelsdröckh! Though neither Fleet nor Traffic, nor Commodores pleased thee, still was it not *a Fleet,* sailing in prescribed track, for fixed objects; above all, in combination, wherein, by mutual guidance, by all manner of loans and borrowings, each could manifoldly aid the other? How wilt thou sail in unknown seas; and for thyself find that shorter Northwest Passage to thy fair Spice-country of a Nowhere?—A solitary rover, on such a voyage, with such nautical tactics, will meet with adventures. Nay, as we forthwith discover, a certain Calypso-Island detains him at the very outset; and as it were falsifies and oversets his whole reckoning.

"If in youth," writes he once, "the Universe is majestically unveiling, and everywhere Heaven revealing itself on Earth, nowhere to the Young Man does this Heaven on Earth so immediately reveal itself as in the Young Maiden. Strangely enough, in this strange life of ours, it has been so appointed. On the whole, as I have often said, a Person (*Persönlichkeit*) is ever holy to us; a certain orthodox Anthropomorphism connects my *Me* with all *Thees* in bonds of Love: but it is in this approximation of the Like and Unlike, that such heavenly attraction, as between Negative and Positive, first burns-out into a flame. Is the pitifullest mortal Person, think you, indifferent to us? Is it not rather our heartfelt wish to be made one with him; to unite him to us, by gratitude, by admiration, even by fear; or failing all these, unite ourselves to him? But how much more, in this case of the Like-Unlike! Here is conceded us the higher mystic possibility of such a union, the highest in our Earth; thus, in the conducting medium of Fantasy, flames-forth that *fire*-development of the universal Spiritual Electricity, which, as unfolded between man and woman, we first emphatically denominate LOVE.

"In every well-conditioned stripling, as I conjecture, there already blooms a certain prospective Paradise, cheered by some fairest Eve; nor, in the stately vistas, and flowerage and foliage of that Garden, is a Tree of Knowledge, beautiful and awful in the midst thereof, wanting. Perhaps too the whole is but the lovelier, if Cherubim and a Flaming Sword divide it from all footsteps of men; and grant him, the imaginative stripling, only the view, not the entrance. Happy season of virtuous youth, when shame is still an impassable celestial barrier; and the sacred air-cities of Hope have not shrunk into the mean clay-hamlets of Reality; and man, by his nature, is yet infinite and free.

"As for our young Forlorn," continues Teufelsdröckh, evidently meaning himself, "in his secluded way of life, and with his glowing Fantasy, the more fiery that it burnt under cover, as in a reverberating furnace, his feeling towards the Queens of this Earth was, and indeed is, altogether unspeakable. A visible Divinity dwelt in them; to our young Friend all women were holy, were heavenly. As yet he but saw them flitting past, in their many-colored angel-plumage; or hovering mute and inaccessible on the outskirts of *Æsthetic Tea:* all of air they were, all Soul and Form; so lovely, like mysterious priestesses, in whose hand was the invisible Jacob's-ladder, whereby man might mount into very Heaven. That he, our poor Friend, should ever win for himself one of these Gracefuls (*Holden*)—*Ach Gott!* how could he hope it; should he not have died under it? There was a certain delirious vertigo in the thought.

"Thus was the young man, if all-sceptical of Demons and Angels such as the vulgar had once believed in, nevertheless not unvisited by hosts of true Sky-born, who visibly and audibly hovered round him wheresoever he went; and they had that religious worship in his thought, though as yet it was by their mere earthly and trivial name that he named them. But now, if on a soul so circumstanced, some actual Air-maiden, incorporated into tangibility and reality, should cast any electric glance of kind eyes, saying thereby 'Thou too mayest love and be loved;' and so kindle him,—good Heaven, what a volcanic, earthquake-bringing, all-consuming fire were probably kindled!"

Such a fire, it afterwards appears, did actually burst-forth, with explosions more or less Vesuvian, in the inner man of Herr Diogenes; as indeed how could it fail? A nature, which, in his own figurative style, we might say, had now not a little carbonized tinder, of Irritability; with so much nitre of latent Passion, and sulphurous Humor enough; the whole lying in such hot neighborhood, close by "a reverberating furnace of Fantasy:" have we not here the components of driest Gunpowder, ready, on occasion of the smallest spark, to blaze-up? Neither, in this our Life-element, are sparks anywhere wanting. Without doubt, some Angel, whereof so many hovered round, would one day, leaving "the outskirts of *Æsthetic Tea,*" flit nigher; and, by electric Promethean glance, kindle no despicable firework. Happy, if it indeed proved a Firework, and flamed-off rocketwise, in successive beautiful bursts of splendor, each growing naturally from the other, through the several stages of a happy Youthful Love; till the whole were safely burnt-out; and the young soul relieved with little damage! Happy, if it did not rather prove a Conflagration and mad Explosion; painfully lacerating the heart itself; nay perhaps bursting the heart in pieces (which were Death); or at best, bursting the thin walls of your "reverberating furnace," so that it rage thenceforth all unchecked among the contiguous combustibles (which were Madness): till of the so fair and manifold internal world of our Diogenes, there remained Nothing, or only the "crater of an extinct volcano!"

From multifarious Documents in this Bag *Capricornus*, and in the adjacent ones on both sides thereof, it becomes manifest that our philosopher, as stoical and cynical as he now looks, was heartily and even frantically in Love: here therefore may our old doubts whether his heart were of stone or of flesh give way. He loved once; not wisely but too well. And once only: for as your Congreve needs a new case or wrappage for every new rocket, so each human heart can properly exhibit but one Love, if even one; the "First Love which is infinite" can be followed by no second like unto it. In more recent years, accordingly, the Editor of these Sheets was led to regard Teufelsdröckh as a man not only who would never wed, but who would never even flirt; whom the grand-climacteric itself, and *St. Martin's Summer* of incipient Dotage, would crown with no new myrtle-garland. To the Professor, women are henceforth Pieces of Art; of Celestial Art, indeed; which celestial pieces he glories to survey in galleries but has lost thought of purchasing.

Psychological readers are not without curiosity to see how Teufelsdröckh, in this for him unexampled predicament, demeans himself; with what specialties of successive configuration, splendor, and color, his Firework blazes-off. Small, as usual, is the satisfaction that such can meet with here. From amid these confused masses of Eulogy and Elegy, with their mad Petrarchan and Werterean ware lying madly scattered among all sorts of quite extraneous matter, not so much as the fair one's name can be deciphered. For, without doubt, the title *Blumine*, whereby she is here designated, and which means simply Goddess of Flowers, must be fictitious. Was her real name Flora, then? But what was her surname, or had she none? Of what station in Life was she; of what parentage, fortune, aspect? Specially, by what Pre-established Harmony of occurrences did the Lover and the Loved meet one another in so wide a world; how did they behave in such meeting? To all which questions, not unessential in a Biographic work, mere Conjecture must for most part return answer. "It was appointed," says our Philosopher, "that the high celestial orbit of Blumine should intersect the low sublunary one of our Forlorn; that he, looking in her empyrean eyes, should fancy the upper Sphere of Light was come down into this nether Sphere of Shadows; and finding himself mistaken, make noise enough."

We seem to gather that she was young, hazel-eyed, beautiful and some one's Cousin; highborn, and of high spirit; but unhappily dependent and insolvent; living, perhaps, on the not too gracious bounty of moneyed relatives. But how came "the Wanderer" into her circle? Was it by the humid vehicle of *Æsthetic Tea*, or by the arid one of mere Business? Was it on the hand of Herr Towgood; or of the Gnädige Frau, who, as an ornamental Artist, might sometimes like to promote flirtation, especially for young cynical Nondescripts? To all appearance, it was chiefly by Accident, and the grace of Nature.

"Thou fair Waldschloss," writes our Autobiographer, "what stranger ever saw thee, were it even an absolved Auscultator, officially bearing in his pocket the last *Relatio ex Actis* he would ever write, but must have paused to wonder! Noble Mansion! There stoodest thou, in deep Mountain Amphitheatre, on umbrageous lawns, in thy serene solitude; stately, massive, all of granite; glittering in the western sunbeams, like a palace of El Dorado, overlaid with precious metal. Beautiful rose up, in wavy curvature, the slope of thy guardian Hills; of the greenest was their sward, embossed with its dark-brown frets of crag, or spotted by some spreading solitary Tree and its shadow. To the unconscious Wayfarer thou wert also as an Ammon's Temple in the Libyan Waste; where, for joy and woe, the tablet of his Destiny lay written. Well might he pause and gaze; in that glance of his were prophecy and nameless forebodings."

But now let us conjecture that the so presentient Auscultator has handed-in his *Relatio ex Actis;* been invited to a glass of Rhine-wine; and so, instead of returning dispirited and athirst to his dusty Town-home, is ushered into the Gardenhouse, where sit the choicest party of dames and cavaliers: if not engaged in Æsthetic Tea, yet in trustful evening conversation, and perhaps Musical Coffee, for we hear of "harps and pure voices making the stillness live." Scarcely, it would seem, is the Gardenhouse inferior in respectability to the noble Mansion itself. "Embowered amid rich foliage, rose-clusters, and the hues and odors of thousand flowers, here sat that brave company; in front, from the wide-opened doors, fair outlook over blossom and bush, over grove and velvet green, stretching, undulating onwards to the remote Mountain peaks: so bright, so mild, and everywhere the melody of birds and happy creatures: it was all as if man had stolen a shelter from the Sun in the bosom-vesture of Summer herself. How came it that the Wanderer advanced thither with such forecasting heart (*ahn-dungsvoll*), by the side of his gay host? Did he feel that to these soft influences his hard bosom ought to be shut; that here, once more, Fate had it in view to try him; to mock him, and see whether there were Humor in him?

"Next moment he finds himself presented to the party; and especially by name to—Blumine! Peculiar among all dames and damosels glanced Blumine, there in her modesty, like a star among earthly lights. Noblest maiden! whom he bent to, in body and in soul; yet scarcely dared look at, for the presence filled him with painful yet sweetest embarrassment.

"Blumine's was a name well known to him; far and wide was the fair one heard of, for her gifts, her graces, her caprices: from all which vague color-ings of Rumor, from the censures no less than from the praises, had our friend painted for himself a certain imperious Queen of Hearts, and bloom-ing warm Earth-angel, much more enchanting than your mere white Heaven-angels of women, in whose placid veins circulates too little naphtha-fire. Herself also he had seen in public places; that light yet so stately form; those dark tresses, shading a face where smiles and sunlight played over earnest deeps: but all this he had seen only as a magic vision, for him inaccessible, almost without reality. Her sphere was too far from his; how should she ever think of him; O Heaven! how should they so much as once meet together? And now that Rose-goddess sits in the same circle with him; the light of *her* eyes has smiled on him; if he speak, she will hear it! Nay, who knows, since the heavenly Sun looks into lowest valleys, but Blumine herself might have aforetime noted the so unnotable; perhaps, from his very gainsayers, as he had from hers, gathered wonder, gathered favor for him. Was the attraction, the agitation mutual, then; pole and pole trembling towards contact, when once brought into neighborhood? Say rather, heart swelling in presence of the Queen of Hearts; like the Sea swelling when once near its Moon! With the Wanderer it was even so: as in heavenward gravitation, suddenly as at the touch of a Seraph's wand, his whole soul is roused from its deepest recesses; and all that was painful and that was blissful there, dim images, vague feelings of a whole Past and a whole Future, are heaving in unquiet eddies within him.

"Often, in far less agitating scenes, had our still Friend shrunk forcibly together; and shrouded-up his tremors and flutterings, of what sort soever, in a safe cover of silence, and perhaps of seeming Stolidity. How was it, then, that here, when trembling to the core of his heart, he did not sink into swoons, but rose into strength, into fearlessness and clearness? It was his guiding Genius (*Dämon*) that inspired him; he must go forth and meet his Destiny. Show thyself now, whispered it, or be forever hid. Thus sometimes it is even when your anxiety becomes transcendental, that the soul first feels herself able to transcend it; that she rises above it, in fiery victory; and borne on new-found wings of victory, moves so calmly, even because so rapidly, so irresistibly. Always must the Wanderer remember, with a certain satisfaction and surprise, how in this case he sat not silent, but struck adroitly into the stream of conversation; which thenceforth, to speak with an apparent not a real vanity, he may say that he continued to lead. Surely, in those hours, a certain inspiration was imparted him, such inspiration as is still possible in our late era. The self-secluded unfolds himself in noble thoughts, in free, glowing words; his soul is as one sea of light, the peculiar home of Truth and Intellect; wherein also Fantasy bodies-forth form after form, radiant with all prismatic hues."

It appears, in this otherwise so happy meeting, there talked one "Philistine;" who even now, to the general weariness, was dominantly pouring-forth Philistinism (*Philistriositäten*); little witting what hero was here entering to demolish him! We omit the series of Socratic, or rather Diogenic utterances, not unhappy in their way, whereby the monster, "persuaded into silence," seems soon after to have withdrawn for the night. "Of which dialectic marauder," writes our hero, "the discomfiture was visibly felt as a benefit by most: but what were all applauses to the glad smile, threatening every moment to become a laugh, wherewith Blumine herself repaid the victor? He ventured to address her, she answered with attention: nay what if there were a slight tremor in that silver voice; what if the red glow of evening were hiding a transient blush!

"The conversation took a higher tone, one fine thought called forth another: it was one of those rare seasons, when the soul expands with full freedom, and man feels himself brought near to man. Gayly in light, graceful abandonment, the friendly talk played round that circle; for the burden was rolled from every heart; the barriers of Ceremony, which are indeed the laws of polite living, had melted as into vapor; and the poor claims of *Me* and *Thee*, no longer parted by rigid fences, now flowed softly into one another; and Life lay all harmonious, many-tinted, like some fair royal champaign, the sovereign and owner of which were Love only. Such music springs from kind hearts, in a kind environment of place and time. And yet as the light grew more aërial on the mountain-tops, and the shadows fell longer over the valley, some faint tone of sadness may have breathed through the heart; and, in whispers more or less audible, reminded every one that as this bright day was drawing towards its close, so likewise must the day of Man's Existence decline into dust and darkness; and with all its sick toilings, and joyful and mournful noises, sink in the still Eternity.

"To our Friend the hours seemed moments; holy was he and happy: the words from those sweetest lips came over him like dew on thirsty grass; all better feelings in his soul seemed to whisper, It is good for us to be here. At parting, the Blumine's hand was in his: in the balmy twilight, with the kind stars above them, he spoke something of meeting again, which was not contradicted; he pressed gently those small soft fingers, and it seemed as if they were not hastily, not angrily withdrawn."

Poor Teufelsdröckh! it is clear to demonstration thou art smit: the Queen of Hearts would see a "man of genius" also sigh for her; and there, by art-magic, in that preternatural hour, has she bound and spell-bound thee. "Love is not altogether a Delirium," says he elsewhere; "yet has it many points in common therewith. I call it rather a discerning of the Infinite in the Finite, of the Idea made Real; which discerning again may be either true or false, either seraphic or demoniac Inspiration or Insanity. But in the former case too, as in common Madness, it is Fantasy that superadds itself to sight; on the so petty domain of the Actual plants its Archimedes-lever, whereby to move at will the infinite Spiritual. Fantasy I might call the true Heaven-gate and Hell-gate of man: his sensuous life is but the small temporary stage (*Zeitbühne*), whereon thick-streaming influences from both these far yet near regions meet visibly, and act tragedy and melodrama. Sense can support herself handsomely, in most countries, for some eighteen pence a day; but for Fantasy planets and solar-systems will not suffice. Witness your Pyrrhus conquering the world, yet drinking no better red wine than he had before." Alas! witness also your Diogenes, flame-clad, scaling the upper Heaven and verging towards Insanity, for prize of a "high-souled Brunette," as if the earth held but one and not several of these!

He says that, in Town, they met again: "day after day, like his heart's sun, the blooming Blumine shone on him. Ah! a little while ago, and he was yet in all darkness: him what Graceful (*Holde*) would ever love? Disbelieving all things, the poor youth had never learned to believe in himself. Withdrawn, in proud timidity, within his own fastnesses; solitary from men, yet baited by night-spectres enough, he saw himself, with a sad indignation, constrained to renounce the fairest hopes of existence. And now, O now! 'She looks on thee,' cried he: 'she the fairest, noblest; do not her dark eyes tell thee, thou art not despised? The Heaven's-Messenger! All Heaven's blessings be hers!' Thus did soft melodies flow through his heart; tones of an infinite gratitude: sweetest intimations that he also was a man, that for him also unutterable joys had been provided.

"In free speech, earnest or gay, amid lambent glances, laughter, tears, and often with the inarticulate mystic speech of Music: such was the element they now lived in; in such a many-tinted, radiant Aurora, and by this fairest of Orient Light-bringers must our Friend be blandished, and the new Apocalypse of Nature unrolled to him. Fairest Blumine! And, even as a Star, all Fire and humid Softness, a very Light-ray incarnate! Was there so much as a fault, a 'caprice,' he could have dispensed with? Was she not to him in very deed a Morning-Star; did not her presence bring with it airs from Heaven? As from Æolian Harps in the breath of dawn, as from the Memnon's Statue struck by the rosy finger of Aurora, unearthly music was around him, and lapped him into untried balmy Rest. Pale Doubt fled away to the distance; Life bloomed-up with happiness and hope. The past, then, was all a haggard dream; he had been in the Garden of Eden, then, and could not discern it! But lo now! the black walls of his prison melt away; the captive is alive, is free. If he loved his Disenchantress? *Ach Gott!* His whole heart and soul and life were hers, but never had he named it Love: existence was all a Feeling, not yet shaped into a thought."

Nevertheless, into a Thought, nay into an Action, it must be shaped; for neither Disenchanter nor Disenchantress, mere "Children of Time," can abide by Feeling alone. The Professor knows not, to this day, "how in her soft, fervid bosom the Lovely found determination, even on hest of Necessity, to cut asunder these so blissful bonds." He even appears surprised at the "Duenna Cousin," whoever she may have been, "in whose meagre, hunger-bitten philosophy, the religion of young hearts was, from the first, faintly approved of." We, even at such distance, can explain it without necromancy. Let the philosopher answer this one question. What figure, at that period, was a Mrs. Teufelsdröckh likely to make in polished society? Could she have driven so much as a brass-bound Gig, or even a simple iron-spring one? Thou foolish "absolved Auscultator," before whom lies no prospect of capital, will any yet known "religion of young hearts" keep the human kitchen warm? Pshaw! thy divine Blumine, when she "resigned herself to wed some richer," shows more philosophy, though but "a woman of genius," than thou, a pretended man.

Our readers have witnessed the origin of this Love-mania, and with what royal splendor it waxes, and rises. Let no one ask us to unfold the glories of its dominant state; much less the horrors of its almost instantaneous dissolution. How from such inorganic masses, henceforth madder than ever, as lie in these Bags, can even fragments of a living delineation be organized? Besides, of what profit were it? We view, with a lively pleasure, the gay silk Montgolfier start from the ground, and shoot upwards, cleaving the liquid deeps, till it dwindle to a luminous star: but what is there to look longer on, when once, by natural elasticity, or accident of fire, it has exploded? A hapless air-navigator, plunging, amid torn parachutes, sand-bags, and confused wreck, fast enough into the jaws of the Devil? Suffice it to know that Teufelsdröckh rose into the highest regions of the Empyrean, by a natural parabolic track, and returned thence in a quick perpendicular one. For the rest, let any feeling reader, who has been unhappy enough to do the like, paint it out for himself: considering only that if he, for his perhaps comparatively insignificant mistress, underwent such agonies and frenzies, what must Teufelsdröckh's have been, with a fire-heart, and for a nonpareil Blumine! We glance merely at the final scene:

"One morning, he found his Morning-star all dimmed and dusky-red; the fair creature was silent, absent, she seemed to have been weeping. Alas, no longer a Morning-star, but a troublous skyey Portent, announcing that the Doomsday had dawned! She said, in a tremulous voice, They were to meet no more." The thunderstruck Air-sailor is not wanting to himself in this dread hour: but what avails it? We omit the passionate expostulations, entreaties, indignations, since all was vain, and not even an explanation was conceded him; and hasten to the catastrophe. " Farewell, then, Madam!' said he, not without sternness, for his stung pride helped him. She put her hand in his, she looked in his face, tears started to her eyes; in wild audacity he clasped her to his bosom; their lips were joined, their two souls, like two dew-drops, rushed into one,—for the first time, and for the last!" Thus was Teufelsdröckh made immortal by a kiss. And then? Why, then—"thick curtains of Night rushed over his soul, as rose the immeasurable Crash of Doom; and through the ruins as of a shivered Universe was he falling, falling, towards the Abyss."

CHAPTER VI.

Sorrows of Teufelsdröckh.

We have long felt that, with a man like our Professor, matters must often be expected to take a course of their own; that in so multiplex, intricate a nature, there might be channels, both for admitting and emitting, such as the Psychologist had seldom noted; in short, that on no grand occasion and convulsion, neither in the joy-storm nor in the woe-storm, could you predict his demeanor.

To our less philosophical readers, for example, it is now clear that the so passionate Teufelsdröckh, precipitated through "a shivered Universe" in this extraordinary way, has only one of three things which he can next do:

Establish himself in Bedlam; begin writing Satanic poetry; or blow-out his brains. In the progress towards any of which consummations, do not such readers anticipate extravagance enough; breast-beating, brow-beating (against walls), lion-bellowings of blasphemy and the like, stampings, smitings, breakages of furniture, if not arson itself?

Nowise so does Teufelsdröckh deport him. He quietly lifts his *Pilgerstab* (Pilgrim-staff), "old business being soon wound-up;" and begins a perambulation and circumambulation of the terraqueous Globe! Curious it is, indeed, how with such vivacity of conception, such intensity of feeling, above all, with these unconscionable habits of Exaggeration in speech, he combines that wonderful stillness of his, that stoicism in external procedure. Thus, if his sudden bereavement, in this matter of the Flower-goddess, is talked of as a real Doomsday and Dissolution of Nature, in which light doubtless it partly appeared to himself, his own nature is nowise dissolved thereby; but rather is compressed closer. For once, as we might say, a Blumine by magic appliances has unlocked that shut heart of his, and its hidden things rush-out tumultuous, boundless, like genii enfranchised from their glass phial: but no sooner are your magic appliances withdrawn, than the strange casket of a heart springs-to again; and perhaps there is now no key extant that will open it; for a Teufelsdröckh, as we remarked, will not love a second time. Singular Diogenes! No sooner has that heart-rending occurrence fairly taken place, than he affects to regard it as a thing natural, of which there is nothing more to be said. "One highest hope, seemingly legible in the eyes of an Angel, had recalled him as out of Death-shadows into celestial Life: but a gleam of Tophet passed over the face of his Angel; he was rapt away in whirlwinds, and heard the laughter of Demons. It was a Calenture," adds he, "whereby the Youth saw green Paradise-groves in the waste Ocean-waters:" a lying vision, yet not wholly a lie, for *he* saw it. But what things soever passed in him, when he ceased to see it; what ragings and despairings soever Teufelsdröckh's soul was the scene of, he has the goodness to conceal under a quite opaque cover of Silence. We know it well; the first mad paroxysm past, our brave Gneschen collected his dismembered philosophies, and buttoned himself together; he was meek, silent, or spoke of the weather and the Journals: only by a transiently knitting of those shaggy brows, by some deep flash of those eyes, glancing one knew not whether with tear-dew or with fierce fire,—might you have guessed what a Gehenna was within; that a whole Satanic School were spouting, though inaudibly, there. To consume your own choler, as some chimneys consume their own smoke; to keep a whole Satanic School spouting, if it must spout, inaudibly, is a negative yet no slight virtue, nor one of the commonest in these times.

Nevertheless, we will not take upon us to say, that in the strange measure he fell upon, there was not a touch of latent Insanity; whereof indeed the actual condition of these Documents in *Capricornus* and *Aquarius* is no bad emblem. His so unlimited Wanderings, toilsome enough, are without assigned or perhaps assignable aim; internal Unrest seems his sole guidance; he wanders, wanders, as if that curse of the Prophet had fallen on him, and he were "made like unto a wheel." Doubtless, too, the chaotic nature of these Paper-bags aggravates our obscurity. Quite without note of preparation, for example, we come upon the following slip: "A peculiar feeling it is that will rise in the Traveller, when turning some hill-range in his desert road, he descries lying far below, embosomed among its groves and green natural bulwarks, and all diminished to a toybox, the fair Town, where so many souls, as it were seen and yet unseen, are driving their multifarious traffic. Its white steeple is then truly a starward-pointing finger; the canopy of blue smoke seems like a sort of Life-breath: for always, of its own unity, the soul gives unity to whatsoever it looks on with love; thus does the little Dwelling-place of men, in itself a congeries of houses and huts, become for us an individual, almost a person. But what thousand other thoughts unite thereto, if the place has to ourselves been the arena of joyous or mournful experiences; if perhaps the cradle we were rocked in still stands there, if our Loving ones still dwell there, if our Buried ones there slumber!" Does Teufelsdröckh, as the wounded eagle is said to make for its own eyrie, and indeed military deserters, and all hunted outcast creatures, turn as if by instinct in the direction of their birthland,—fly first, in this extremity, towards his native Entepfuhl; but reflecting that there no help awaits him, take only one wistful look from the distance, and then wend elsewhither?

Little happier seems to be his next flight: into the wilds of Nature; as if in her mother-bosom he would seek healing. So at least we incline to interpret the following Notice, separated from the former by some considerable space, wherein, however, is nothing noteworthy:

"Mountains were not new to him; but rarely are Mountains seen in such combined majesty and grace as here. The rocks are of that sort called Primitive by the mineralogists, which always arrange themselves in masses of a rugged, gigantic character; which ruggedness, however, is here tempered by a singular airiness of form, and softness of environment: in a climate favorable to vegetation, the gray cliff, itself covered with lichens, shoots-up through a garment of foliage or verdure; and white, bright cottages, tree-shaded, cluster around the everlasting granite. In fine vicissitude, Beauty alternates with Grandeur: you ride through stony hollows, along strait passes, traversed by torrents, overhung by high walls of rock; now winding amid broken shaggy chasms, and huge fragments; now suddenly emerging into some emerald valley, where the streamlet collects itself into a Lake, and man has again found a fair dwelling, and it seems as if Peace had established herself in the bosom of Strength.

"To Peace, however, in this vortex of existence can the Son of Time not pretend: still less if some Spectre haunt him from the Past; and the Future is wholly a Stygian Darkness, spectre-bearing. Reasonably might the Wanderer exclaim to himself: Are not the gates of this world's Happiness inexorably shut against thee; hast thou a hope that is not mad? Nevertheless, one may still murmur audibly, or in the original Greek if that suit thee better: 'Whoso can look on death will start no shadows.'

"From such meditations is the Wanderer's attention called outwards;

for now the Valley closes-in abruptly, intersected by a huge mountain mass, the stony water-worn ascent of which is not to be accomplished on horse-back. Arrived aloft, he finds himself again lifted into the evening sunset light; and cannot but pause, and gaze round him, some moments there. An upland irregular expanse of wold, where valleys in complex branchings are sud-denly or slowly arranging their descent towards every quarter of the sky. The mountain-ranges are beneath your feet, and folded together: only the loftier summits look down here and there as on a second plain; lakes also lie clear and earnest in their solitude. No trace of man now visible; unless in-deed it were he who fashioned that little visible link of Highway, here, as would seem, scaling the inaccessible, to unite Province with Province. But sunwards, lo you! how it towers sheer up, a world of Mountains, the diadem and centre of the mountain region! A hundred and a hundred savage peaks, in the last light of Day; all glowing, of gold and amethyst, like giant spirits of the wilderness; there in their silence, in their solitude, even as on the night when Noah's Deluge first dried! Beautiful, nay solemn, was the sudden aspect to our Wanderer. He gazed over those stupendous masses with wonder, almost with longing desire; never till this hour had he known Nature, that she was One, that she was his Mother and divine. And as the ruddy glow was fading into clearness in the sky, and the Sun had now departed, a murmur of Eternity and Immensity, of Death and of Life, stole through his soul; and he felt as if Death and Life were one, as if the Earth were not dead, as if the Spirit of the Earth had its throne in that splendor, and his own spirit were therewith holding communion.

"The spell was broken by a sound of carriage-wheels. Emerging from the hidden Northward, to sink soon into the hidden Southward, came a gay Barouche-and-four: it was open; servants and postillions wore wedding-favors: that happy pair, then, had found each other, it was their marriage evening! Few moments brought them near: *Du Himmel!* It was Herr Tow-good and—Blumine! With slight unrecognizing salutation they passed me; plunged down amid the neighboring thickets, onwards, to Heaven, and to England; and I, in my friend Richter's words, *I remained alone, behind them, with the Night.*"

Were it not cruel in these circumstances, here might be the place to insert an observation, gleaned long ago from the great *Clothes-Volume*, where it stands with quite other intent: "Some time before Small-pox was extirpated," says the Professor, "there came a new malady of the spiritual sort on Europe: I mean the epidemic, now endemical, of View-hunting. Poets of old date, being privileged with Senses, had also enjoyed external Nature; but chiefly as we enjoy the crystal cup which holds good or bad liquor for us; that is to say, in silence, or with slight incidental commentary: never, as I compute, till after the *Sorrows of Werter*, was there man found who would say: Come let us make a Description! Having drunk the liquor, come let us eat the glass! Of which endemic the Jenner is unhappily still to seek." Too true!

We reckon it more important to remark that the Professor's Wanderings, so far as his stoical and cynical envelopment admits us to clear insight, here first take their permanent character, fatuous or not. That Basilisk-glance of the Barouche-and-four seems to have withered-up what little remnant of a purpose may have still lurked in him: Life has become wholly a dark labyrinth; wherein, through long years, our Friend, flying from spectres, has to stumble about at random, and naturally with more haste than progress.

Foolish were it in us to attempt following him, even from afar, in this extraordinary world-pilgrimage of his; the simplest record of which, were clear record possible, would fill volumes. Hopeless is the obscurity, unspeakable the confusion. He glides from country to country, from condition to condition; vanishing and re-appearing, no man can calculate how or where. Through all quarters of the world he wanders, and apparently through all circles of society. If in any scene, perhaps difficult to fix geographically, he settles for a time, and forms connections, be sure he will snap them abruptly asunder. Let him sink out of sight as Private Scholar (*Privatisirender*), living by the grace of God in some European capital, you may next find him as Hadjee in the neighborhood of Mecca. It is an inexplicable Phantasmagoria, capricious, quick-changing; as if our Traveller, instead of limbs and high-ways, had transported himself by some wishing-carpet, or Fortunatus' Hat. The whole, too, imparted emblematically, in dim multifarious tokens (as that collection of Street-Advertisements); with only some touch of direct his-torical notice sparingly interspersed: little light-islets in the world of haze! So that, from this point, the Professor is more of an enigma than ever. In figurative language, we might say he becomes, not indeed a spirit, yet spiritualized, vaporized. Fact unparalleled in Biography: The river of his History, which we have traced from its tiniest fountains, and hoped to see flow onward, with increasing current, into the ocean, here dashes itself over that terrific Lover's Leap; and, as a mad-foaming cataract, flies wholly into tumultuous clouds of spray! Low down it indeed collects again into pools and plashes; yet only at a great distance, and with difficulty, if at all, into a general stream. To cast a glance into certain of those pools and plashes, and trace whither they run, must, for a chapter or two, form the limit of our endeavor.

For which end doubtless those direct historical Notices, where they can be met with, are the best. Nevertheless, of this sort too there occurs much, which, with our present light, it were questionable to emit. Teufelsdröckh, vibrating everywhere between the highest and the lowest levels, comes into contact with public History itself. For example, those conversations and relations with illustrous Persons, as Sultan Mahmoud, the Emperor Napoleon, and others, are they not as yet rather of a diplomatic character than of a biographic? The Editor, appreciating the sacredness of crowned heads, nay perhaps suspecting the possible trickeries of a Clothes-Philosopher, will eschew this province for the present; a new time may bring new insight and a different duty.

If we ask now, not indeed with what ulterior Purpose, for there was none, yet with what immediate outlooks; at all events, in what mood of mind, the Professor undertook and prosecuted this world-pilgrimage,—the answer is more distinct than favorable. "A nameless Unrest," says he, "urged me forward; to which the outward motion was some momentary lying solace. Whither should I go? My Loadstars were blotted out; in that canopy of grim fire shone no star. Yet forward must I; the ground burnt under me; there was no rest for the sole of my foot. I was alone, alone! Ever too the strong inward longing shaped Fantasms for itself: towards these, one after the other, must I fruitlessly wander. A feeling I had, that for my fever-thirst there was and must be somewhere a healing Fountain. To many fondly imagined Fountains, the Saints' Wells of these days, did I pilgrim; to great Men, to great Cities, to great Events: but found there no healing. In strange countries, as in the well-known, in savage deserts, and in the press of corrupt civilization, it was ever the same: how could your wanderer escape from—*his own Shadow?* Nevertheless still Forward! I felt as if in great haste; to do I saw not what. From the depths of my own heart, it called to me, Forwards! The winds and the streams, and all Nature sounded to me, Forwards! *Ach Gott,* I was even, once for all, a Son of Time."

From which is it not clear that the internal Satanic School was still active enough? He says elsewhere: "The *Enchiridion of Epictetus* I had ever with me, often as my sole rational companion; and regret to mention that the nourishment it yielded was trifling." Thou foolish Teufelsdröckh! How could it else? Hadst thou not Greek enough to understand thus much: *The end of Man is an action, and not a Thought,* though it were the noblest?

"How I lived?" writes he once: "Friend, hast thou considered the 'rugged all-nourishing Earth,' as Sophocles well names her; how she feeds the sparrows on the house-top, much more her darling, man? While thou stirrest and livest, thou hast a probability of victual. My breakfast of tea has been cooked by a Tartar woman, with water of the Amur, who wiped her earthen kettle with a horse-tail. I have roasted wild-eggs in the sand of Sahara; I have awakened in Paris *Estrapades* and Vienna *Malzleins*, with no prospect of breakfast beyond elemental liquid. That I had my Living to seek saved me from Dying,—by suicide. In our busy Europe, is there not an everlasting demand for Intellect, in the chemical, mechanical, political, religious, educational, commercial departments? In Pagan countries, cannot one write Fetiches? Living! Little knowest thou what alchemy is in an inventive Soul; how, as with its little finger, it can create provision enough for the body (of a Philosopher); and then, as with both hands, create quite other than provision; namely, spectres to torment itself withal."

Poor Teufelsdröckh! Flying with Hunger always parallel to him; and a whole Infernal Chase in his rear; so that the countenance of Hunger is comparatively a friend's! Thus must he, in the temper of ancient Cain, or of the modern Wandering Jew,—save only that he feels himself not guilty and but suffering the pains of guilt,—wend to and fro with aimless speed. Thus must he, over the whole surface of the Earth (by footprints), write his *Sorrows of Teufelsdröckh;* even as the great Goethe, in passionate words, had to write his *Sorrows of Werter,* before the spirit freed herself, and he could become a Man. Vain truly is the hope of your swiftest Runner to escape "from his own Shadow!" Nevertheless, in these sick days, when the Born of Heaven first descries himself (about the age of twenty) in a world such as ours, richer than usual in two things, in Truths grown obsolete, and Trades grown obsolete,—what can the fool think but that it is all a Den of Lies, wherein whoso will not speak Lies and act Lies, must stand idle and despair? Whereby it happens that, for your nobler minds, the publishing of some such Work of Art, in one or the other dialect, becomes almost a necessity. For what is it properly but an Altercation with the Devil, before you begin honestly Fighting him? Your Byron publishes his *Sorrows of Lord George*, in verse and in prose, and copiously otherwise: your Bonaparte represents his *Sorrows of Napoleon* Opera, in an all-too stupendous style; with music of cannon-volleys, and murder-shrieks of a world; his stage-lights are the fires of Conflagration; his rhyme and recitative are the tramp of embattled Hosts and the sound of falling Cities.—Happier is he who, like our Clothes-Philosopher, can write such matter, since it must be written, on the insensible Earth, with his shoe-soles only; and also survive the writing thereof!

CHAPTER VII.

The Everlasting No.

UNDER the strange nebulous envelopment, wherein our Professor has now shrouded himself, no doubt but his spiritual nature is nevertheless progressive, and growing: for how can the "Son of Time," in any case, stand still? We behold him, through those dim years, in a state of crisis, of transition: his mad Pilgrimings, and general solution into aimless Discontinuity, what is all this but a mad Fermentation; wherefrom, the fiercer it is, the clearer product will one day evolve itself?

Such transitions are ever full of pain: thus the Eagle when he moults is sickly; and, to attain his new beak, must harshly dash-off the old one upon rocks. What Stoicism soever our Wanderer, in his individual acts and motions, may affect, it is clear that there is a hot fever of anarchy and misery raging within; coruscations of which flash out: as, indeed, how could there be other? Have we not seen him disappointed, bemocked of Destiny, through long years? All that the young heart might desire and pray for has been denied; nay, as in the last worst instance, offered and then snatched away. Ever an "excellent Passivity;" but of useful, reasonable Activity essential to the former as Food to Hunger, nothing granted: till at length, in this wild Pilgrimage, he must forcibly seize for himself an Activity, though useless, unreasonable. Alas, his cup of bitterness, which had been filling drop by drop, ever since that first "ruddy morning" in the Hinterschlag Gymnasium, was at the very lip; and then with that poison-drop, of the Towgood-and-Blumine business, it runs over, and even hisses over in a deluge of foam.

He himself says once, with more justice than originality: Man is, properly speaking, based upon Hope, he has no other possession but Hope; this world of his is emphatically the "Place of Hope." What, then, was our Professor's possession? We see him, for the present, quite shut-out from Hope; looking not into the golden orient, but vaguely all round into a dim copper firmament, pregnant with earthquake and tornado.

Alas, shut-out from Hope, in a deeper sense than we yet dream of! For, as he wanders wearisomely through this world, he has now lost all tidings of another and higher. Full of religion, or at least of religiosity, as our Friend has since exhibited himself, he hides not that, in those days, he was wholly irreligious: "Doubt had darkened into Unbelief," says he; "shade after shade goes grimly over your soul, till you have the fixed, starless, Tartarean black." To such readers as have reflected, what can be called reflecting, on man's life, and happily discovered, in contradiction to much Profit-and-Loss Philosophy, speculative and practical, that Soul is *not* synonymous with Stomach; who understand, therefore, in our Friend's words, "that, for man's well-being, Faith is properly the one thing needful; how, with it, Martyrs, otherwise weak, can cheerfully endure the shame and the cross; and without it, Worldlings puke-up their sick existence, by suicide, in the midst of luxury:" to such it will be clear that, for a pure moral nature, the loss of his religious Belief was the loss of everything. Unhappy young man! All wounds, the crush of long-continued Destitution, the stab of false Friendship and of false Love, all wounds in thy so genial heart, would have healed again, had not its life-warmth been withdrawn. Well might he exclaim, in his wild way: "Is there no God, then; but at best an absentee God, sitting idle, ever since the first Sabbath, at the outside of his Universe, and *seeing* it go? Has the word Duty no meaning; is what we call Duty no divine Messenger and Guide, but a false earthly Fantasm, made-up of Desire and Fear, of emanations from the Gallows and from Doctor Graham's Celestial-Bed? Happiness of an approving Conscience! Did not Paul of Tarsus, whom admiring men have since named Saint, feel that *he* was "the chief of sinners;" and Nero of Rome, jocund in spirit (*wohlgemuth*), spend much of his time in fiddling? Foolish Word-monger and Motive-grinder, who in thy Logic-mill hast an earthly mechanism for the Godlike itself, and wouldst fain grind me out Virtue from the husks of Pleasure,—I tell thee, Nay! To the unregenerate Prometheus Vinctus of a man, it is ever the bitterest aggravation of his wretchedness that he is conscious of Virtue, that he feels himself the victim not of suffering only, but of injustice. What then? Is the heroic inspiration we name Virtue but some Passion; some bubble of the blood, bubbling in the direction others *profit* by? I know not: only this I know, If what thou namest Happiness be our true aim, then are we all astray. With Stupidity and sound Digestion man may front much. But what, in these dull unimaginative days, are the terrors of Conscience to the diseases of the Liver! Not on Morality, but on Cookery, let us build our stronghold: there brandishing our frying-pan, as censer, let us offer sweet incense to the Devil, and live at ease on the fat things *he* has provided for his Elect!"

Thus has the bewildered Wanderer to stand, as so many have done, shouting question after question into the Sibyl-cave of Destiny, and receive no

Answer but an Echo. It is all a grim Desert, this once fair world of his; wherein is heard only the howling of wild-beasts, or the shrieks of despairing, hate-filled men; and no Pillar of Cloud by day, and no Pillar of Fire by night, any longer guides the Pilgrim. To such length has the spirit of Inquiry carried him. "But what boots it (*was thut's*)?" cries he: "it is but the common lot in this era. Not having come to spiritual majority prior to the *Siècle de Louis Quinze*, and not being born purely a Loghead (*Dummkopf*), thou hadst no other outlook. The whole world is, like thee, soul to Unbelief; their old Temples of the Godhead, which for long have not been rainproof, crumble down; and men ask now: Where is the Godhead; our eyes never saw him?"

Pitiful enough were it, for all these wild utterances, to call our Diogenes wicked. Unprofitable servants as we all are, perhaps at no era of his life was he more decisively the Servant of Goodness, the Servant of God, than even now when doubting God's existence. "One circumstance I note," says he: "after all the nameless woe that Inquiry, which for me, what it is not always, was genuine Love of Truth, had wrought me, I nevertheless still loved Truth, and would bate no jot of my allegiance to her. 'Truth!' I cried, 'though the Heavens crush me for following her: no Falsehood! though a whole celestial Lubberland were the price of Apostasy.' In conduct it was the same. Had a divine Messenger from the clouds, or miraculous Handwriting on the wall, convincingly proclaimed to me *This thou shalt do*, with what passionate readiness, as I often thought, would I have done it, had it been leaping into the infernal Fire. Thus, in spite of all Motive-grinders, and Mechanical Profit-and-Loss Philosophies, with the sick ophthalmia and hallucination they had brought on, was the Infinite nature of Duty still dimly present to me: living without God in the world, of God's light I was not utterly bereft; if my as yet sealed eyes, with their unspeakable longing, could nowhere see Him, nevertheless in my heart He was present, and His heaven-written Law still stood legible and sacred there."

Meanwhile, under all these tribulations, and temporal and spiritual destitutions, what must the Wanderer, in his silent soul, have endured! "The painfullest feeling," writes he, "is that of your own Feebleness (*Unkraft*); ever, as the English Milton says, to be weak is the true misery. And yet of your Strength there is and can be no clear feeling, save by what you have prospered in, by what you have done. Between vague wavering Capability and fixed undubitable Performance, what a difference! A certain inarticulate Self-consciousness dwells dimly in us; which only our Works can render articulate and decisively discernible. Our Works are the mirror wherein the spirit first sees its natural lineaments. Hence, too, the folly of that impossible Precept, *Know thyself;* till it be translated into this partially possible one, *Know what thou canst work at.*

"But for me, so strangely unprosperous had I been, the net-result of my Workings amounted as yet simply to—Nothing. How then could I believe in my Strength, when there was as yet no mirror to see it in? Ever did this agitating, yet, as I now perceive, quite frivolous question, remain to me insoluble: Hast thou a certain Faculty, a certain Worth, such even as the most have not; or art thou the completest Dullard of these modern times? Alas, the fearful Unbelief is unbelief in yourself; and how could I believe? Had not my first, last Faith in myself, when even to me the Heavens seemed laid open, and I dared to love, been all-too cruelly belied? The Speculative Mystery of Life grew ever more mysterious to me: neither in the practical Mystery had I made the slightest progress, but been everywhere buffeted, foiled, and contemptuously cast out. A feeble unit in the middle of a threatening Infinitude, I seemed to have nothing given me but eyes, whereby to discern my own wretchedness. Invisible yet impenetrable walls, as of Enchantment, divided me from all living: was there, in the wide world, any true bosom I could press trustfully to mine? O Heaven, No, there was none! I kept a lock upon my lips: why should I speak much with that shifting variety of so-called Friends, in whose withered, vain and too-hungry souls Friendship was but an incredible tradition? In such cases, your resource is to talk little, and that little mostly from the Newspapers. Now when I look back, it was a strange isolation I then lived in. The men and women around me, even speaking with me, were but Figures; I had, practically, forgotten that they were alive, that they were not merely automatic. In the midst of their crowded streets and assemblages, I walked solitary; and (except as it was my own heart, not another's, that I kept devouring) savage also, as the tiger in his jungle. Some comfort it would have been, could I, like a Faust, have fancied myself tempted and tormented of the Devil; for a Hell, as I imagine, without Life, though only diabolic Life, were more frightful: but in our age of Down-pulling and Disbelief, the very Devil has been pulled down, you cannot so much as believe in a Devil. To me the Universe was all void of Life, of Purpose, of Volition, even of Hostility: it was one huge, dead, immeasurable Steam-engine, rolling on, in its dead indifference, to grind me limb from limb. O, the vast, gloomy, solitary Golgotha, and Mill of Death! Why was the Living banished thither companionless, conscious? Why, if there is no Devil; nay, unless the Devil is your God?"

A prey incessantly to such corrosions, might not, moreover, as the worst aggravation to them, the iron constitution even of a Teufelsdröckh threaten to fail? We conjecture that he has known sickness; and, in spite of his locomotive habits, perhaps sickness of the chronic sort. Hear this, for example: "How beautiful to die of broken-heart, on Paper! Quite another thing in practice; every window of your Feeling, even of your Intellect, as it were, begrimed and mud-bespattered, so that no pure ray can enter; a whole Drugshop in your inwards; the fordone soul drowning slowly in quagmires of Disgust!"

Putting all which external and internal miseries together, may we not find in the following sentences, quite in our Professor's still vein, significance enough? "From Suicide a certain aftershine (*Nachschein*) of Christianity withheld me: perhaps also a certain indolence of character; for, was not that a remedy I had at any time within reach? Often, however, was there a question present to me: Should some one now, at the turning of that corner, blow thee suddenly out of Space, into the other World, or other No-world, by pistol-shot,—how were it? On which ground, too, I have often, in sea-storms and sieged cities and other death-scenes, exhibited an imperturbability, which passed, falsely enough, for courage.

"So had it lasted," concludes the Wanderer, "so had it lasted, as in bitter protracted Death-agony, through long years. The heart within me, unvisited by any heavenly dewdrop, was smouldering in sulphurous, slow-consuming fire. Almost since earliest memory I had shed no tear; or once only when I, murmuring half-audibly, recited Faust's Deathsong, that wild *Selig der den er im Siegesglanze findet* (Happy whom *he* finds in Battle's splendor), and thought that of this last Friend even I was not forsaken, that Destiny itself could not doom me not to die. Having no hope, neither had I any definite fear, were it of Man or of Devil: nay, I often felt as if it might be solacing, could the Arch-Devil himself, though in Tartarean terrors, but rise to me, that I might tell him a little of my mind. And yet, strangely enough, I lived in a continual, indefinite, pining fear; tremulous, pusillanimous, apprehensive of I knew not what: it seemed as if all things in the Heavens above and the Earth beneath would hurt me; as if the Heavens and the Earth were but boundless jaws of a devouring monster, wherein I, palpitating, waited to be devoured.

"Full of such humor, and perhaps the miserablest man in the whole French Capital or Suburbs, was I, one sultry Dogday, after much perambulation, toiling along the dirty little *Rue Saint-Thomas de l'Enfer*, among civic rubbish enough, in a close atmosphere, and over pavements hot as Nebuchadnezzar's Furnace; whereby doubtless my spirits were little cheered; when, all at once, there rose a Thought in me, and I asked myself: 'What *art* thou afraid of? Wherefore, like a coward, dost thou forever pip and whimper, and go cowering and trembling? Despicable biped! what is the sum-total of the worst that lies before thee? Death? Well, Death; and say the pangs of Tophet too, and all that the Devil and Man may, will or can do against thee! Hast thou not a heart; canst thou not suffer whatsoever it be; and, as a Child of Freedom, though outcast, trample Tophet itself under thy feet, while it consumes thee? Let it come, then; I will meet it and defy it!' And as I so thought, there rushed like a stream of fire over my whole soul; and I shook base Fear away from me forever. I was strong, of unknown strength; a spirit, almost a god. Ever from that time, the temper of my misery was changed: not Fear or whining Sorrow was it, but Indignation and grim fire-eyed Defiance.

"Thus had the EVERLASTING No (*das ewige Nein*) pealed authoritatively through all the recesses of my Being, of my ME; and then was it that my whole ME stood up, in native God-created majesty, and with emphasis recorded its Protest. Such a Protest, the most important transaction in Life, may that same Indignation and Defiance, in a psychological point of view, be fitly called. The Everlasting No had said: 'Behold, thou art fatherless, outcast, and the Universe is mine (the Devil's);' to which my whole ME now made answer: '*I* am not thine, but Free, and forever hate thee!'

"It is from this hour that I incline to date my Spiritual New-birth, or Baphometic Fire-baptism; perhaps I directly thereupon began to be a Man."

CHAPTER VIII.

CENTRE OF INDIFFERENCE.

THOUGH, after this "Baphometic Fire-baptism" of his, our Wanderer signifies that his Unrest was but increased; as, indeed, "Indignation and Defiance," especially against things in general, are not the most peaceable inmates; yet can the Psychologist surmise that it was no longer a quite hopeless Unrest; that henceforth it had at least a fixed centre to revolve round. For the fire-baptized soul, long so scathed and thunder-driven, here feels its own Freedom, which feeling is its Baphometic Baptism; the citadel of its whole kingdom it has thus gained by assault, and will keep inexpugnable; outwards from which the remaining dominions, not indeed without hard battling, will doubt-less by degrees be conquered and pacificated. Under another figure, we might say, if in that great moment, in the *Rue Saint-Thomas de l'Enfer*, the old inward Satanic School was not yet thrown out of doors, it received peremptory judicial notice to quit;—whereby, for the rest, its howl-chant-ings, Ernulphus-cursings, and rebellious gnashings of teeth, might, in the meanwhile, become only the more tumultuous, and difficult to keep secret.

Accordingly, if we scrutinize these Pilgrimings well, there is perhaps discernible henceforth a certain incipient method in their madness. Not wholly as a Spectre does Teufelsdröckh now storm through the world; at worst as a spectre-fighting Man, nay who will one day be a Spectre-queller. If pilgriming restlessly to so many "Saints' Wells," and ever without quench-ing of his thirst, he nevertheless finds little secular wells, whereby from time to time some alleviation is ministered. In a word, he is now, if not ceasing, yet intermitting to "eat his own heart;" and clutches round him outwardly on the NOT-ME for wholesomer food. Does not the following glimpse exhibit him in a much more natural state?

"Towns also and Cities, especially the ancient, I failed not to look upon with interest. How beautiful to see thereby, as through a long vista, into the remote Time; to have as it were, an actual section of almost the earliest Past brought safe into the Present, and set before your eyes! There, in that old City, was a live ember of Culinary Fire put down, say only two thousand years ago; and there, burning more or less triumphantly, with such fuel as the region yielded, it has burnt, and still burns, and thou thyself seest the very smoke thereof! Ah! and the far more mysterious live ember of Vital Fire was then also put down there; and still miraculously burns and spreads; and the smoke and ashes thereof (in these Judgment-Halls and Church-yards), and its bellows-engines (in these Churches), thou still seest; and its flame, looking out from every kind countenance, and every hateful one, still warms thee or scorches thee.

"Of Man's Activity and Attainment the chief results are aeriform, mystic, and preserved in Tradition only: such are his Forms of Government, with the Authority they rest on; his Customs, or Fashions both of Cloth-habits and of Soul-habits; much more his collective stock of Handicrafts, the whole Faculty he has acquired of manipulating Nature: all these things, as indispensable and priceless as they are, cannot in any way be fixed under lock and key, but must flit, spirit-like, on impalpable vehicles, from Father to Son; if you demand sight of them, they are nowhere to be met with. Visible Ploughmen and Hammermen there have been ever, from Cain and Tubalcain downwards: but where does your accumulated Agricultural, Metallurgic, and other Manufacturing SKILL lie warehoused? It transmits itself on the atmospheric air, on the sun's rays (by Hearing and by Vision); it is a thing aeriform, impalpable, of quite spiritual sort. In like manner, ask me not, Where are the LAWS; where is the GOVERNMENT? In vain wilt thou go to Schönbrunn, to Downing Street, to the Palais Bourbon: thou findest nothing there but brick or stone houses, and some bundles of Papers tied with tape. Where, then, is that same cunningly-devised almighty GOVERNMENT of theirs to be laid hands on? Everywhere, yet nowhere: seen only in its works, this too is a thing aeriform, invisible; or if you will, mystic and miraculous. So spiritual (*geistig*) is our whole daily Life: all that we do springs out of Mystery, Spirit, invisible Force; only like a little Cloud-image, or Armida's Palace, air-built, does the Actual body itself forth from the great mystic Deep.

"Visible and tangible products of the Past, again, I reckon-up to the extent of three: Cities, with their Cabinets and Arsenals; then tilled Fields, to either or to both of which divisions Roads with their Bridges may belong; and thirdly——Books. In which third truly, the last invented, lies a worth far surpassing that of the two others. Wondrous indeed is the virtue of a true Book. Not like a dead city of stones, yearly crumbling, yearly needing repair; more like a tilled field, but then a spiritual field: like a spiritual tree, let me rather say, it stands from year to year, and from age to age (we have Books that already number some hundred-and-fifty human ages); and yearly comes its new produce of leaves (Commentaries, Deductions, Philosophical, Political Systems; or were it only Sermons, Pamphlets, Journalistic Essays), every one of which is talismanic and thaumaturgic, for it can persuade men. O thou who art able to write a Book, which once in the two centuries or oftener there is a man gifted to do, envy not him whom they name City-builder, and inexpressibly pity him whom they name Conqueror or City-burner! Thou too art a Conqueror and Victor; but of the true sort, namely over the Devil: thou too hast built what will outlast all marble and metal, and be a wonder-bringing City of the Mind, a Temple and Seminary and Prophetic Mount, whereto all kindreds of the Earth will pilgrim.—Fool! why journeyest thou wearisomely, in thy antiquarian fervor, to gaze on the stone pyramids of Geeza, or the clay ones of Sacchara? These stand there, as I can tell thee, idle and inert, looking over the Desert, foolishly enough, for the last three-thousand years: but canst thou not open thy Hebrew BIBLE, then, or even Luther's Version thereof?"

No less satisfactory is his sudden appearance not in Battle, yet, on some Battle-field; which, we soon gather, must be that of Wagram; so that here, for once, is a certain approximation to distinctness of date. Omitting much, let us impart what follows:

"Horrible enough! A whole Marchfeld strewed with shell-splinters, cannon shot, ruined tumbrils, and dead men and horses; stragglers still remaining not so much as buried. And those red mould heaps: ay, there lie the Shells of Men, out of which all the Life and Virtue has been blown; and now are they swept together, and crammed-down out of sight, like blown Egg-shells!— Did Nature, when she bade the Donau bring down his mould-cargoes from the Carinthian and Carpathian Heights, and spread them out here into the softest, richest level,—intend thee, O Marchfeld, for a corn-bearing Nursery, whereon her children might be nursed; or for a Cockpit, wherein they might the more commodiously be throttled and tattered? Were thy three broad Highways, meeting here from the ends of Europe, made for Ammunition-wagons, then? Were thy Wagrams and Stillfrieds but so many ready-built Casemates, wherein the house of Hapsburg might batter with artillery, and with artillery be battered? König Ottokar, amid yonder hillocks, dies under Rodolf's truncheon; here Kaiser Franz falls a-swoon under Napoleon's: within which five centuries, to omit the others, how has thy breast fair Plain, been defaced and defiled! The green-sward is torn-up and trampled-down; man's fond care of it, his fruit-trees, hedge-rows, and pleasant dwellings, blown-away with gunpowder; and the kind seedfield lies a desolate, hideous Place of Skulls.—Nevertheless, Nature is at work; neither shall these Powder-Devilkins with their utmost devilry gainsay her: but all that gore and carnage will be shrouded-in, absorbed into manure; and next year the Marchfeld will be green, nay greener. Thrifty unwearied Nature, ever out of our great waste educing some little profit of thy own,—how dost thou, from the very carcass of the Killer, bring Life for the Living!

"What, speaking in quite unofficial language, is the net-purport and upshot of war? To my own knowledge, for example, there dwell and toil, in the British village of Dumdrudge, usually some five-hundred souls. From these, by certain 'Natural Enemies' of the French there are successfully selected, during the French war, say thirty able-bodied men: Dumdrudge, at her own expense, has suckled and nursed them: she has, not without difficulty and sorrow, fed them up to manhood, and even trained them to crafts, so that one can weave, another build, another hammer, and the weakest can stand under thirty stone avoirdupois. Nevertheless, amid much weeping and swearing, they are selected; all dressed in red; and shipped away, at the public charges, some two-thousand miles, or say only to the south of Spain; and fed there till wanted. And now to that same spot, in the south of Spain, are thirty similar French artisans, from a French Dumdrudge, in like manner wending: till at length, after infinite effort, the two parties come into actual juxtaposition; and Thirty stands fronting Thirty, each with a gun in his hand. Straightway the word 'Fire!' is given: and they blow the souls out of one another; and in place of sixty brisk useful craftsmen, the world has sixty dead carcasses, which it must bury, and anew shed tears for. Had these men any quarrel? Busy as the Devil is, not the smallest! They lived far enough apart; were the entirest strangers; nay, in so wide a Universe, there was even, unconsciously, by Commerce, some mutual helpfulness between them. How then? Simpleton! their Governors had fallen-out; and, instead of shooting one another, had the cunning to make these poor blockheads shoot.—Alas, so is it in Deutschland, and hitherto in all other lands; still as of old, 'what devilry soever Kings do, the Greeks must pay the piper!'—In that fiction of the English Smollet, it is true, the final Cessation of War is perhaps prophetically shadowed forth; where the two Natural Enemies, in person, take each a Tobacco-pipe, filled with Brimstone; light the same, and smoke in one another's faces, till the weaker gives in: but from such predicted Peace-Era, what blood-filled trenches, and contentious centuries, may still divide us!"

Thus can the Professor, at least in lucid intervals, look away from his own sorrows, over the many-colored world, and pertinently enough note what is passing there. We may remark, indeed, that for the matter of spiritual culture, if for nothing else, perhaps few periods of his life were richer than this. Internally, there is the most momentous instructive Course of Practical Philosophy, with Experiments, going on; towards the right comprehension of which his Peripatetic habits, favorable to Meditation, might help him rather than hinder. Externally, again, as he wanders to and fro, there are, if for the longing heart little substance, yet for the seeing eye sights enough: in these so boundless Travels of his, granting that the Satanic School was even partially kept down, what an incredible knowledge of our Planet, and its Inhabitants and their Works, that is to say, of all knowable things, might not Teufelsdröckh acquire!

"I have read in most Public Libraries," says he, "including those of Constantinople and Samarcand: in most Colleges, except the Chinese Mandarin ones, I have studied, or seen that there was no studying. Unknown Languages have I oftenest gathered from their natural repertory, the Air, by my organ of Hearing; Statistics, Geographics, Topographics came, through the Eye, almost of their own accord. The ways of Man, how he seeks food, and warmth, and Protection for himself, in most regions, are ocularly known to me. Like the great Hadrian, I meted-out much of the terraqueous Globe with a pair of Compasses that belonged to myself only.

"Of great Scenes why speak? Three summer days, I lingered reflecting, and even composing (*dichtete*), by the Pine-chasms of Vaucluse; and in that clear Lakelet moistened my bread. I have sat under the Palm-trees of Tadmor; smoked a pipe among the ruins of Babylon. The great Wall of China I have seen; and can testify that it is of gray brick, coped and covered with granite, and only shows second-rate masonry.—Great events, also, have not I witnessed? Kings sweated-down (*ausgemergelt*) into Berlin-and-Milan Customhouse-Officers; the World well won, and the World well lost; oftener than once a hundred-thousand individuals shot (by each other) in one day. All kindreds and peoples and nations dashed together, and shifted and shovelled into heaps that they might ferment there, and in time unite.

The birth-pangs of Democracy, wherewith convulsed Europe was groaning in cries that reached Heaven, could not escape me.

"For great Men I have ever had the warmest predilection; and can perhaps boast that few such in this era have wholly escaped me. Great Men are the inspired (speaking and acting) Text of that divine BOOK OF REVELATIONS, whereof a Chapter is completed from epoch to epoch, and by some named HISTORY; to which inspired Texts your numerous talented men, and your innumerable untalented men, are the better or worse exegetic Commentaries, and wagonload of too-stupid, heretical or orthodox, weekly Sermons. For my study, the inspired Texts themselves! Thus did not I, in very early days, having disguised me as tavern-waiter, stand behind the field-chairs, under that shady Tree at Treisnitz by the Jena Highway; waiting upon the great Schiller and greater Goethe; and hearing what I have not forgotten. For——"

——But at this point the Editor recalls his principle of caution, some time ago laid down, and must suppress much. Let not the sacredness of Laurelled, still more, of Crowned Heads, be tampered with. Should we, at a future day, find circumstances altered, and the time come for Publication, then may these glimpses into the privacy of the Illustrious be conceded; which for the present were little better than treacherous, perhaps traitorous Eavesdroppings. Of Lord Byron, therefore, of Pope Pius, Emperor Tarakwang, and the "White Water-roses" (Chinese Carbonari), with their mysteries, no notice here! Of Napoleon himself we shall only, glancing from afar, remark that Teufelsdröckh's relation to him seems to have been of very varied character. At first we find our poor Professor on the point of being shot as a spy; then taken into private conversation, even pinched on the ear, yet presented with no money; at last indignantly dismissed, almost thrown out of doors, as an "Ideologist." "He himself," says the Professor, "was among the completest Ideologists, at least Ideopraxists: in the Idea (*in der Idee*) he lived, moved and fought. The man was a Divine Missionary, though unconscious of it; and preached, through the cannon's throat, that great doctrine, *La carrière ouverte aux talens* (The Tools to him that can handle them), which is our ultimate Political Evangel, wherein alone can liberty lie. Madly enough he preached, it is true, as Enthusiasts and first Missionaries are wont, with imperfect utterance, amid much frothy rant; yet as articulately perhaps as the case admitted. Or call him, if you will, an American Backwoodsman, who had to fell unpenetrated forests, and battle with innumerable wolves, and did not entirely forbear strong liquor, rioting, and even theft; whom, notwithstanding, the peaceful Sower will follow, and, as he cuts the boundless harvest, bless."

More legitimate and decisively authentic is Teufelsdröckh's appearance and emergence (we know not well whence) in the solitude of the North Cape on that June Midnight. He has a "light-blue Spanish cloak" hanging round him, as his "most commodious principal, indeed sole upper-garment;" and stands there, on the World-promontory, looking over the infinite Brine, like a little blue Belfry (as we figure), now motionless indeed, yet ready, if stirred, to ring quaintest changes.

"Silence as of death," writes he; "for Midnight, even in the Arctic latitudes, has its character: nothing but the granite cliffs ruddy-tinged, the peaceable gurgle of that slow-heaving Polar Ocean, over which in the utmost North the great Sun hangs low and lazy, as if he too were slumbering. Yet is his cloud-couch wrought of crimson and cloth-of-gold; yet does his light stream over the mirror of waters, like a tremulous fire-pillar, shooting downwards to the abyss, and hide itself under my feet. In such moments, Solitude also is invaluable; for who would speak, or be looked on, when behind him lies all Europe and Africa, fast asleep, except the watchmen; and before him the silent Immensity, and Palace of the Eternal, whereof our Sun is but a porch-lamp?

"Nevertheless, in this solemn moment comes a man, or monster, scrambling from among the rock-hollows; and, shaggy, huge as the Hyperborean Bear, hails me in Russian speech: most probably, therefore, a Russian Smuggler. With courteous brevity, I signify my indifference to contraband trade, my humane intentions, yet strong wish to be private. In vain: the monster, counting doubtless on his superior stature, and minded to make sport for himself, or perhaps profit, were it with murder, continues to advance; ever assailing me with his importunate train-oil breath; and now has advanced, till we stand both on the verge of the rock, the deep Sea rippling greedily down below. What argument will avail? On the thick Hyperborean, cherubic reasoning, seraphic eloquence were lost. Prepared for such extremity, I, deftly enough, whisk aside one step; draw out, from my interior reservoirs, a sufficient Birmingham Horse-pistol, and say, 'Be so obliging as retire, Friend (*Erziehe sich zurück, Freund*), and with promptitude!' This logic even the Hyperborean understands: fast enough, with apologetic, petitionary growl, he sidles off; and, except for suicidal as well as homicidal purposes, need not return.

"Such I hold to be the genuine use of Gunpowder: that it makes all men alike tall. Nay, if thou be cooler, cleverer than I, if thou have more *Mind*, though all but no *Body* whatever, then canst thou kill me first, and art the taller. Hereby, at last, is the Goliath powerless, and the David resistless; savage Animalism is nothing, inventive Spiritualism is all.

"With respect to Duels, indeed, I have my own ideas. Few things, in this so surprising world, strike me with more surprise. Two little visual Spectra of men, hovering with insecure enough cohesion in the midst of the UN-FATHOMABLE, and to dissolve therein, at any rate, very soon,—make pause at the distance of twelve paces asunder; whirl round; and, simultaneously by the cunningest mechanism, explode one another into Dissolution; and off-hand become Air, and Non-extant! Deuce on it (*verdammt*), the little spit-fires!—Nay, I think with old Hugo von Trimberg: 'God must needs laugh outright, could such a thing be, to see his wondrous Manikins here below.'"

But amid these specialties, let us not forget the great generality, which is our chief quest here: How prospered the inner man of Teufelsdröckh under so much outward shifting? Does Legion still lurk in him, though repressed;

or has he exorcised that Devil's Brood? We can answer that the symptoms continue promising. Experience is the grand spiritual Doctor; and with him Teufelsdröckh has now been long a patient, swallowing many a bitter bolus. Unless our poor Friend belong to the numerous class of Incurables, which seems not likely, some cure will doubtless be effected. We should rather say that Legion, or the Satanic School, was now pretty well extirpated and cast out, but next to nothing introduced in its room; whereby the heart remains, for the while, in a quiet but no comfortable state.

"At length, after so much roasting," thus writes our Autobiographer, "I was what you might name calcined. Pray only that it be not rather, as is the more frequent issue, reduced to a *caput-mortuum!* But in any case, by mere dint of practice, I had grown familiar with many things. Wretchedness was still wretched; but I could now partly see through it, and despise it. Which highest mortal, in this inane Existence, had I not found a Shadow-hunter, or Shadow-hunted; and, when I looked through his brave garnitures, miserable enough? Thy wishes have all been sniffed aside, thought I: but what, had they even been all granted! Did not the Boy Alexander weep because he had not two Planets to conquer; or a whole Solar System; or after that, a whole Universe? *Ach Gott*, when I gazed into these Stars, have they not looked-down on me as if with pity, from their serene spaces; like Eyes glistening with heavenly tears over the little lot of man! Thousands of human generations, all as noisy as our own, have been swallowed-up of Time, and there remains no wreck of them any more; and Arcturus and Orion and Sirius and the Pleiades are still shining in their courses, clear and young, as when the Shepherd first noted them in the plain of Shinar. Pshaw! what is this paltry little Dog-cage of an Earth; what art thou that sittest whining there? Thou art still Nothing, Nobody? true; but who, then, is Something, Somebody? For thee the Family of Man has no use; it rejects thee; thou art wholly as a dissevered limb: so be it; perhaps it is better so!"

Too-heavy-laden Teufelsdröckh! Yet surely his bands are loosening; one day he will hurl the burden far from him, and bound forth free and with a second youth.

"This," says our Professor, "was the CENTRE OF INDIFFERENCE I had now reached; through which whoso travels from the Negative Pole to the Positive must necessarily pass."

CHAPTER IX.

THE EVERLASTING YEA.

"TEMPTATIONS in the Wilderness!" exclaims Teufelsdröckh: "Have we not all to be tried with such? Not so easily can the old Adam, lodged in us by birth, be dispossessed. Our Life is compassed round with Necessity; yet is the meaning of Life itself no other than Freedom, than Voluntary Force: thus have we a warfare; in the beginning, especially, a hard-fought battle. For the God-given mandate, *Work thou in Welldoing*, lies mysteriously

written, in Promethean Prophetic Characters, in our hearts; and leaves us
no rest, night or day, till it be deciphered and obeyed; till it burn forth, in
our conduct, a visible, acted Gospel of Freedom. And as the clay-given
mandate, *Eat thou and be filled,* at the same time persuasively proclaims
itself through every nerve,—must not there be a confusion, a contest, before
the better Influence can become the upper?

"To me nothing seems more natural than that the Son of Man, when such
God-given mandate first prophetically stirs within him, and the Clay must
now be vanquished or vanquish,—should be carried of the spirit into grim
Solitudes, and there fronting the Tempter do grimmest battle with him;
defiantly setting him at naught, till he yield and fly. Name it as we choose:
with or without visible Devil, whether in the natural Desert of rocks and
sands, or in the populous moral Desert of selfishness and baseness,—to such
Temptation are we all called. Unhappy if we are not! Unhappy if we are
but Half-men, in whom that divine handwriting has never blazed forth,
all-subduing, in true sun-splendor; but quivers dubiously amid meaner
lights: or smoulders, in dull pain, in darkness, under earthly vapors!—Our
Wilderness is the wide World in an Atheistic Century; our Forty Days are
long years of suffering and fasting: nevertheless, to these also comes an
end. Yes, to me also was given, if not Victory, yet the consciousness of
Battle, and the resolve to persevere therein while life or faculty is left. To
me also, entangled in the enchanting forests, demon-peopled, doleful of
sight and of sound, it was given, after weariest wanderings, to work out my
way into the higher sunlit slopes—of that Mountain which has no summit,
or whose summit is in Heaven only!"

He says elsewhere, under a less ambitious figure; as figures are, once for
all, natural to him: "Has not thy Life been that of most sufficient men
(*tüchtigen Männer*) thou hast known in this generation? An outflush of
foolish young Enthusiasm, like the first fallow-crop, wherein are as many
weeds as valuable herbs: this all parched away, under the Droughts of
practical and spiritual Unbelief, as Disappointment, in thought and act,
often-repeated gave rise to Doubt, and Doubt gradually settled into Denial!
If I have had a second-crop, and now see the perennial green-sward, and sit
under umbrageous cedars, which defy all Drought (and Doubt); herein too,
be the Heavens praised, I am not without examples, and even exemplars."

So that, for Teufelsdröckh also, there has been a "glorious revolution:"
these mad shadow-hunting and shadow-hunted Pilgrimings of his were but
some purifying "Temptation in the Wilderness," before his apostolic work
(such as it was) could begin; which Temptation is now happily over, and
the Devil once more worsted! Was "that high moment in the *Rue de l'
Enfer,*" then, properly the turning-point of the battle; when the Fiend said,
Worship me or be torn in shreds; and was answered valiantly with an
Apage Satana?—Singular Teufelsdröckh, would thou hadst told thy singular
story in plain words! But it is fruitless to look there, in those Paper-bags,
for such. Nothing but innuendoes, figurative crotchets: a typical Shadow,
fitfully wavering, prophetico-satiric; no clear logical Picture. "How paint to

the sensual eye," asks he once, "what passes in the Holy-of-Holies of Man's Soul; in what words, known to these profane times, speak even afar-off of the unspeakable? We ask in turn: Why perplex these times, profane as they are, with needless obscurity by omission and by commission? Not mystical only is our Professor, but whimsical; and involves himself, now more than ever, in eye-bewildering *chiaroscuro*. Successive glimpses, here faithfully imparted, our more gifted readers must endeavor to combine for their own behoof.

He says: "The hot Harmattan wind had raged itself out; its howl went silent within me; and the long-deafened soul could now hear. I paused in my wild wanderings; and sat me down to wait, and consider; for it was as if the hour of change drew nigh. I seemed to surrender, to renounce utterly, and say: Fly, then, false shadows of Hope; I will chase you no more, I will believe you no more. And ye too, haggard spectres of Fear, I care not for you; ye too are all shadows and a lie. Let me rest here: for I am way-weary and life-weary; I will rest here, were it but to die: to die or to live is alike to me; alike insignificant."—And again: "Here, then, as I lay in that CENTRE OF INDIFFERENCE; cast, doubtless by benignant upper Influence, into a healing sleep, the heavy dreams rolled gradually away, and I woke to a new Heaven and a new Earth. The first preliminary moral Act, Annihilation of Self (*Selbst-tödtung*), had been happily accomplished; and my mind's eyes were now unsealed, and its hands ungyved."

Might we not also conjecture that the following passage refers to his Locality, during this same "healing sleep;" that his Pilgrim-staff lies cast aside here, on "the high table-land;" and indeed that the repose is already taking wholesome effect on him? If it were not that the tone, in some parts, has more of riancy, even of levity, than we could have expected? However, in Teufelsdröckh, there is always the strangest Dualism: light dancing, with guitar-music, will be going on in the fore-court, while by fits from within comes the faint whimpering of woe and wail. We transcribe the piece entire.

"Beautiful it was to sit there, as in my skyey Tent, musing and meditating; on the high table-land, in front of the Mountains; over me, as roof, the azure Dome, and around me, for walls, four azure-flowing curtains,—namely, of the Four azure Winds, on whose bottom-fringes also I have seen gilding. And then to fancy the fair Castles that stood sheltered in these Mountain hollows; with their green flower-lawns, and white dames and damosels, lovely enough: or better still, the straw-roofed Cottages, wherein stood many a Mother baking bread, with her children round her:—all hidden and protectingly folded-up in the valley-folds; yet there and alive, as sure as if I beheld them. Or to see, as well as fancy, the nine Towns and Villages, that lay round my mountain-seat, which, in still weather, were wont to speak to me (by their steeple-bells) with metal tongue; and, in almost all weather, proclaimed their vitality by repeated Smoke-clouds; whereon, as on a culinary horologe, I might read the hour of the day. For it was the smoke of cookery, as kind housewives at morning, midday, eventide, were boiling their husbands' kettles; and ever a blue pillar rose up into the air, successively or simultaneously, from each of the nine, saying, as plainly as smoke could say: Such and such a meal is getting ready here. Not uninteresting! For you have the whole Borough, with all its love-makings and scandal-mongeries, contentions and contentments, as in miniature, and could cover it all with your hat.—If, in my wide Wayfarings, I had learned to look into the business of the World in its details, here perhaps was the place for combining it into general propositions, and deducing inferences therefrom.

"Often also could I see the black Tempest marching in anger through the Distance: round some Schreckhorn, as yet grim-blue, would the eddying vapor gather, and there tumultuously eddy, and flow down like a mad witch's hair; till, after a space, it vanished, and, in the clear sunbeam, your Schreckhorn stood smiling grim-white, for the vapor had held snow. How thou fermentest and elaboratest, in thy great fermenting-vat and laboratory of an Atmosphere, of a World, O Nature!—Or what is Nature? Ha! why do I not name thee GOD? Art not thou the 'Living Garment of God'? O Heavens, is it, in very deed, HE, then, that ever speaks through thee; that lives and loves in thee, that lives and loves in me?

"Fore-shadows, call them rather fore-splendors, of that Truth, and Beginning of Truths, fell mysteriously over my soul. Sweeter than Day-spring to the Shipwrecked in Nova Zembla; ah, like the mother's voice to her little child that strays bewildered, weeping, in unknown tumults; like soft streamings of celestial music to my too-exasperated heart, came that Evangel. The Universe is not dead and demoniacal, a charnel-house with spectres; but god-like, and my Father's!

"With other eyes, too, could I now look upon my fellow-man: with an infinite Love, an infinite Pity-Poor, wandering, wayward man! Art thou not tried, and beaten with stripes, even as I am? Ever, whether thou bear the royal mantle or the beggar's gabardine, art thou not so weary, so heavy-laden; and thy Bed of Rest is but a Grave. O my Brother, my Brother, why cannot I shelter thee in my bosom, and wipe away all tears from thine eyes! —truly, the din of many-voiced Life, which, in this solitude, with the mind's organ, I could hear, was no longer a maddening discord, but a melting one; like inarticulate cries, and sobbings of a dumb creature, which in the ear of Heaven are prayers. The poor Earth, with her poor joys, was now my needy Mother, not my cruel Stepdame; Man, with his so mad Wants and so mean Endeavors, had become the dearer to me; and even for his suffer-ings and his sins, I now first named him Brother. Thus was I standing in the porch of that 'Sanctuary of Sorrow;' by strange, steep ways had I too been guided thither; and ere long its sacred gates would open, and the 'Divine Depth of Sorrow' lie disclosed to me."

The Professor says, he here first got eye on the Knot that had been strangling him, and straightway could unfasten it, and was free. "A vain interminable controversy," writes he, "touching what is at present called Origin of Evil, or some such thing, arises in every soul, since the beginning of the world; and in every soul, that would pass from idle Suffering into actual Endeavoring, must first be put an end to. The most, in our time, have to go content with a simple, incomplete enough Suppression of this controversy; to a few some Solution of it is indispensable. In every new era, too, such Solution comes-out in different terms; and ever the Solution of the last era has become obsolete, and is found unserviceable. For it is man's nature to change his Dialect from century to century; he cannot help it though he would. The authentic *Church-Catechism* of our present century has not yet fallen into my hands: meanwhile, for my own private behoof, I attempt to elucidate the matter so. Man's Unhappiness, as I construe, comes of his Greatness; it is because there is an Infinite in him, which with all his cunning he cannot quite bury under the Finite. Will the whole Finance Ministers and Upholsterers and Confectioners of modern Europe undertake, in joint-stock company, to make one Shoeblack HAPPY? They cannot accomplish it, above an hour or two: for the Shoeblack also has a Soul quite other than his Stomach; and would require, if you consider it, for his permanent satisfaction and saturation, simply this allotment, no more, and no less; *God's infinite Universe altogether to himself*, therein to enjoy infinitely, and fill every wish as fast as it rose. Oceans of Hochheimer, a Throat like that of Ophiuchus: speak not of them; to the infinite Shoeblack they are as nothing. No sooner is your ocean filled, than he grumbles that it might have been of better vintage. Try him with half of a Universe, of an Omnipotence, he sets to quarrelling with the proprietor of the other half, and declares himself the most maltreated of men.—Always there is a black spot in our sunshine: it is even, as I said, the *Shadow of Ourselves*.

"But the whim we have of Happiness is somewhat thus. By certain valuations, and averages, of our own striking, we come upon some sort of average terrestrial lot; this we fancy belongs to us by nature, and of indefeasible right. It is simple payment of our wages, of our deserts; requires neither thanks nor complaint; only such *overplus* as there may be do we account Happiness; any *deficit* again is Misery. Now consider that we have the valuation of our own deserts ourselves, and what a fund of Self-conceit there is in each of us,—do you wonder that the balance should so often dip the wrong way, and many a Blockhead cry: See there, what a payment; was ever worthy gentleman so used!—I tell thee, Blockhead, it all comes of thy Vanity; of what thou *fanciest* those same deserts of thine to be. Fancy that thou deservest to be hanged (as is most likely), thou wilt feel it happiness to be only shot: fancy that thou deservest to be hanged in a hair-halter, it will be a luxury to die in hemp.

"So true is it, what I then said, that *the Fraction of Life can be increased in value not so much by increasing your Numerator as by lessening your Denominator*. Nay, unless my Algebra deceive me, *Unity* itself divided by Zero will give *Infinity*. Make thy claim of wages a zero, then; thou hast the world under thy feet. Well did the Wisest of our time write: 'It is only with Renunciation (*Entsagen*) that Life, properly speaking, can be said to begin.'

"I asked myself: What is this that, ever since earliest years, thou hast been fretting and fuming, and lamenting and self-tormenting, on account of? Say it in a word: is it not because thou art not HAPPY? Because the THOU (sweet gentleman) is not sufficiently honored, nourished, soft-bedded, and lovingly cared-for? Foolish soul! What Act of Legislature was there that *thou* shouldst be Happy? A little while ago thou hadst no right to *be* at all. What if thou wert born and predestined not to be happy, but to be Unhappy! Art thou nothing other than a Vulture, then, that fliest through the Universe seeking after somewhat to *eat;* and shrieking dolefully because carrion enough is not given thee? Close thy *Byron;* open thy *Goethe.*"

"*Es leuchtet mir ein,* I see a glimpse of it!" cries he elsewhere: "there is in man a HIGHER than Love of Happiness: he can do without Happiness, and instead thereof find Blessedness! Was it not to preach-forth this same HIGHER that sages and martyrs, the Poet and the Priest, in all times, have spoken and suffered; bearing testimony, through life and through death, of the Godlike that is in Man, and how in the Godlike only has he Strength and Freedom? Which God-inspired Doctrine art thou also honored to be taught; O Heavens! and broken with manifold merciful Afflictions, even till thou become contrite, and learn it! O, thank thy Destiny for these; thankfully bear what yet remain: thou hadst need of them; the Self in thee needed to be annihilated. By benignant fever-paroxysms is Life rooting out the deep-seated chronic Disease, and triumphs over Death. On the roaring billows of Time, thou art not ingulfed, but borne aloft into the azure of Eternity. Love not Pleasure; love God. This is the EVERLASTING YEA, wherein all contradiction is solved: wherein whoso walks and works, it is well with him."

And again: "Small is it that thou canst trample the Earth with its injuries under thy feet, as old Greek Zeno trained thee: thou canst love the Earth while it injures thee, and even because it injures thee; for this a Greater than Zeno was needed, and he too was sent. Knowest thou that '*Worship of Sorrow*'? The Temple thereof, founded some eighteen centuries ago, now lies in ruins, overgrown with jungle, the habitation of doleful creatures: nevertheless, venture forward; in a low crypt, arched out of falling fragments, thou findest the Altar still there, and its sacred Lamp perennially burning."

Without pretending to comment on which strange utterances, the Editor will only remark, that there lies beside them much of a still more questionable character; unsuited to the general apprehension; nay wherein he himself does not see his way. Nebulous disquisitions on Religion, yet not without bursts of splendor; on the "perennial continuance of Inspiration;" on Prophecy; that there are "true Priests, as well as Baal-Priests, in our own day:" with more of the like sort. We select some fractions, by way of finish to this farrago.

"Cease, my much-respected Herr von Voltaire," thus apostrophizes the Professor: "shut thy sweet voice; for the task appointed thee seems finished. Sufficiently hast thou demonstrated this proposition, considerable or otherwise: That the Mythus of the Christian Religion looks not in the eighteenth century as it did in the eighth. Alas, were thy six-and-thirty quartos, and the six-and-thirty thousand other quartos and folios, and flying sheets or reams, printed before and since on the same subject, all needed to convince us of so little! But what next? Wilt thou help us to embody the divine Spirit of that Religion in a new Mythus, in a new vehicle and vesture, that our Souls, otherwise too like perishing, may live? What! thou hast no faculty in that kind? Only a torch for burning, no hammer for building? Take our thanks, then, and——thyself away.

"Meanwhile what are antiquated Mythuses to me? Or is the God present, felt in my own heart, a thing which Herr von Voltaire will dispute out of me; or dispute into me? To the '*Worship of Sorrow*' ascribe what origin and genesis thou pleasest, *has* not that Worship originated, and been generated; is it not *here*? Feel it in thy heart, and then say whether it is of God! This is Belief; all else is Opinion,—for which latter whoso will, let him worry and be worried."

"Neither," observes he elsewhere, "shall ye tear-out one another's eyes, struggling over 'Plenary Inspiration,' and suchlike: try rather to get a little even Partial Inspiration, each of you for himself. One BIBLE I know, of whose Plenary Inspiration doubt is not so much as possible; nay with my own eyes I saw the God's-Hand writing it: thereof all other Bibles are but Leaves,—say, in Picture-Writing to assist the weaker faculty."

Or, to give the wearied reader relief, and bring it to an end, let him take the following perhaps more intelligible passage:

"To me in this our life," says the Professor, "which is an internecine warfare with the Time-spirit, other warfare seems questionable. Hast thou in any way a Contention with thy brother, I advise thee, think well what the meaning thereof is. If thou gauge it to the bottom, it is simply this: 'Fellow, see! thou art taking more than thy share of Happiness in the world, something from *my* share, which, by the Heavens, thou shalt not; nay I will fight thee rather.'—Alas, and the whole lot to be divided is such a beggarly matter, truly a 'feast of shells,' for the substance has been spilled out: not enough to quench one Appetite; and the collective human species clutching at them!—Can we not, in all such cases, rather say: 'Take it, thou too-ravenous individual: take that pitiful additional fraction of a share, which I reckoned mine, but which thou so wantest: take it with a blessing: would to Heaven I had enough for thee!'—If Fichte's *Wissenschaftslehre* be, 'to a certain extent, Applied Christianity,' surely to a still greater extent, so is this. We have here not a Whole Duty of Man, yet a Half Duty, namely the Passive half: could we but do it, as we can demonstrate it!

"But indeed Conviction, were it never so excellent, is worthless till it convert itself into Conduct. Nay properly Conviction is not possible till then; inasmuch as all Speculation is by nature endless, formless, a vortex amid vortices: only by a felt indubitable certainty of Experience does it find any centre to revolve round, and so fashion itself into a system. Most true is it, as a wise man teaches us, that 'Doubt of any sort cannot be

removed except by Action.' On which ground,
painfully in darkness or uncertain light, and pr
dawn may ripen into day, lay this other precept w
was of invaluable service: '*Do the Duty which lies*
knowest to be a Duty! Thy second Duty will alre

"May we not say, however, that the hour of Sp
even this: When your Ideal World, wherein the v
struggling inexpressibly languishing to work, beco
open; and you discover, with amazement enou
Wilhelm Meister, that your 'America is here or
that has not its Duty, its Ideal, was never yet ot...
in this poor, miserable, hampered, despicable Actual, wherein thou even
now standest, here or nowhere is thy Ideal: work it out therefrom; and
working, believe, live, be free. Fool! the Ideal is in thyself, the impediment
too is in thyself: thy Condition is but the stuff thou art to shape that same
Ideal out of: what matters whether such stuff be of this sort or that, so the
Form thou give it be heroic, be poetic? O thou that pinest in the imprisonment of the Actual, and criest bitterly to the gods of a kingdom wherein
to rule and create, know this of a truth: the thing thou seekest is already
with thee, 'here or nowhere,' couldst thou only see!

"But it is with man's Soul as it was with Nature: the beginning of Creation is—Light. Till the eye have vision, the whole members are in bonds.
Divine moment, when over the tempest-tost Soul, as once over the wild-
weltering Chaos, it is spoken: Let there be Light! Ever to the greatest that
has felt such moment is it not miraculous and God-announcing; even as,
under simpler figures, to the simplest and least. The mad primeval Discord
is hushed; the rudely-jumbled conflicting elements bind themselves into
separate Firmaments: deep silent rock foundations are built beneath; and the
skyey vault with its everlasting Luminaries above: instead of a dark wasteful Chaos, we have a blooming, fertile, heaven-encompassed World.

"I too could now say to myself: Be no longer a Chaos, but a World, or
even Worldkin. Produce! Produce! Were it but the pitifullest, infinitesimal
fraction of a Product, produce it, in God's name! 'Tis the utmost thou hast
in thee: out with it, then. Up, up! Whatsoever thy hand findeth to do, do
it with thy whole might. Work while it is called To-day; for the Night
cometh, wherein no man can work."

CHAPTER X.

Pause.

THUS HAVE WE, as closely and perhaps satisfactorily as, in such circumstances, might be, followed Teufelsdröckh through the various successive
states and stages of Growth, Entanglement, Unbelief, and almost Reprobation, into a certain clearer state of what he himself seems to consider as

lame not the word," says he; "rejoice rather that such a
ing such a thing, has come to light in our modern Era, though
m the wisest Ancients. The Old World knew nothing of Con-
instead of an *Ecce Homo,* they had only some *Choice of Hercules.*
a new-attained progress in the Moral Development of man: hereby
the Highest come home to the bosoms of the most Limited; what to
lato was but a hallucination, and to Socrates a chimera, is now clear and
certain to your Zinzendorfs, your Wesleys, and the poorest of their Pietists
and Methodists."

It is here, then, that the spiritual majority of Teufelsdröckh commences.
we are henceforth to see him "work in well-doing," with the spirit and clear
aims of a Man. He has discovered that the Ideal Workshop he so panted
for is even this same Actual ill-furnished Workshop he has so long been
stumbling in. He can say to himself: "Tools? Thou hast no Tools? Why,
there is not a Man, or a Thing, now alive but has tools. The basest of
created animalcules, the Spider itself, has a spinning-jenny, and warping-
mill, and power-loom within its head: the stupidest of Oysters has a Papin's-
Digester, with stone-and-lime house to hold it in: every being that can live
can do something: this let him *do.*—Tools? Hast thou not a Brain, furnished,
furnishable with some glimmerings of Light; and three fingers to hold a
Pen withal? Never since Aaron's Rod went out of practice, or even before
it, was there such a wonder-working Tool: greater than all recorded
miracles have been performed by Pens. For strangely in this so solid-seeming World, which nevertheless is in continual restless flux, it is appointed
that *Sound,* to appearance the most fleeting, should be the most continuing
of all things. The WORLD is well said to be omnipotent in this world; man,
thereby divine, can create as by a *Fiat.* Awake, arise! Speak forth what is
in thee; what God has given thee, what the Devil shall not take away.
Higher task than that of Priesthood was allotted to no man: wert thou but
the meanest in that sacred Hierarchy, is it not honor enough therein to
spend and be spent?

"By this Art, which whoso will may sacrilegiously degrade into a handi-
craft," adds Teufelsdröckh, "have I thenceforth abidden. Writings of mine,
not indeed known as mine (for what am *I?*), have fallen, perhaps not altogether void, into the mighty seed-field of Opinion; fruits of my unseen
sowing, gratifyingly meet me here and there. I thank the Heavens that I have
now found my Calling; wherein, with or without perceptible result, I am
minded diligently to persevere.

"Nay how knowest thou," cries he, "but this and the other pregnant
Device, now grown to be a world-renowned far-working Institution; like a
grain of right mustard-seed once cast into the right soil, and now stretching-out strong boughs to the four winds, for the birds of the air to lodge in,
—may have been properly my doing? Some one's doing, it without doubt
was; from some Idea, in some single Head, it did first of all take beginning:
why not from some Idea in mine?" Does Teufelsdröckh here glance at that
"SOCIETY FOR THE CONSERVATION OF PROPERTY (*Eigenthums-conservirende*

Gesellschaft)," of which so many ambiguous notices glide spectre-like through these inexpressible Paper-bags? "An institution," hints he, "not unsuitable to the wants of the time; as indeed such sudden extension proves: for already can the Society number, among its office-bearers or corresponding members, the highest Names, if not the highest Persons, in Germany, England, France; and contributions, both of money and of meditation, pour in from all quarters; to, if possible, enlist the remaining Integrity of the world, and, defensively and with forethought, marshal it round this Palladium." Does Teufelsdröckh mean, then, to give himself out as the originator of that so notable *Eigenthums-conservirende* ("Owndom-conserving") *Gesellschaft;* and if so, what, in the Devil's name, is it? He again hints: "At a time when the divine Commandment, *Thou shalt not steal*, wherein truly, if well understood, is comprised the whole Hebrew Decalogue, with Solon's and Lycurgus's Constitutions; Justinian's Pandects, the Code Napoléon, and all Codes, Catechisms, Divinities, Moralities whatsoever, that man has hitherto devised (and enforced with Altar-fire and Gallows-ropes) for his social guidance: at a time, I say, when this divine Commandment has all-but faded away from the general remembrance; and, with little disguise, a new opposite Commandment, *Thou shalt steal*, is everywhere promulgated,—it perhaps behooved, in this universal dotage and deliration, the sound portion of mankind to bestir themselves and rally. When the widest and wildest violations of that divine right of Property, the only divine right now extant or conceivable, are sanctioned and recommended by a vicious Press, and the world has lived to hear it asserted that *we have no Property in our very Bodies, but only an accidental Possession and Life-rent*, what is the issue to be looked for?—Hangmen and Catchpoles may, by their noose-gins and baited fall-traps, keep down the smaller sort of vermin; but what, except perhaps some such Universal Association, can protect us against whole meat-devouring, and man-devouring hosts of Boa-constrictors? If, therefore, the more sequestered Thinker have wondered, in his privacy, from what hand that perhaps not ill-written *Program* in the Public Journals, with its high *Prize-Questions* and so liberal *Prizes*, could have proceeded,—let him now cease such wonder; and, with undivided faculty, betake himself to the *Concurrenz* (Competition)."

We ask: Has this same "perhaps not ill-written *Program*," or any other authentic Transaction of that Property-conserving Society, fallen under the eye of the British Reader, in any Journal foreign or domestic? If so, what are those *Prize-Questions;* what are the terms of Competition, and when and where? No printed Newspaper-leaf, no farther light of any sort, to be met with in these Paper-bags! Or is the whole business one other of those whimsicalities and perverse inexplicabilities, whereby Herr Teufelsdröckh, meaning much or nothing, is pleased so often to play fast-and-loose with us?

Here, indeed, at length, must the Editor give utterance to a painful suspicion, which, through late Chapters, has begun to haunt him; paralyzing any little enthusiasm that might still have rendered his thorny Biographical task a labor of love. It is a suspicion grounded perhaps on trifles, yet confirmed almost into certainty by the more and more discernible humoristico-satirical tendency of Teufelsdröckh, in whom underground humors and intricate sardonic rogueries, wheel within wheel, defy all reckoning: a suspicion, in one word, that these Autobiographical Documents are partly a mystification! What if many so-called Fact were little better than a Fiction; if here we had no direct Camera-obscura Picture of the Professor's History; but only some more or less fantastic Adumbration, symbolically, perhaps significantly enough, shadowing-forth the same! Our theory begins to be that, in receiving as literally authentic what was but hieroglyphically so, Hofrath Heuschrecke, whom in that case we scruple not to name Hofrath Nose-of-Wax, was made a fool of, and set adrift to make fools of others. Could it be expected, indeed, that a man so known for impenetrable reticence as Teufelsdröckh, would all at once frankly unlock his private citadel to an English Editor and a German Hofrath; and not rather deceptively *in*-lock both Editor and Hofrath in the labyrinthic tortuosities and covered-ways of said citadel (having enticed them thither), to see, in his half-devilish way, how the fools would look?

Of one fool, however, the Herr Professor will perhaps find himself short. On a small slip, formerly thrown aside as blank, the ink being all-but invisible, we lately notice, and with effort decipher, the following: "What are your historical Facts; still more your biographical? Wilt thou know a Man, above all a Mankind, by stringing-together beadrolls of what thou namest Facts? The Man is the spirit he worked in; not what he did, but what he became. Facts are engraved Hierograms, for which the fewest have the key. And then how your Blockhead (*Dummkopf*) studies not their Meaning; but simply whether they are well or ill cut, what he calls Moral or Immoral! Still worse is it with your Bungler (*Pfuscher*): such I have seen reading some Rousseau, with pretences of interpretation; and mistaking the ill-cut Serpent-of-Eternity for a common poisonous reptile." Was the Professor apprehensive lest an Editor, selected as the present boasts himself, might mistake the Teufelsdröckh Serpent-of-Eternity in like manner? For which reason it was to be altered, not without underhand satire, into a plainer Symbol? Or is this merely one of his half-sophisms, half-truisms, which if he can but set on the back of a Figure, he cares not whither it gallop? We say not with certainty; and indeed, so strange is the Professor, can never say. If our suspicion be wholly unfounded, let his own questionable ways, not our necessary circumspectness, bear the blame.

But be this as it will, the somewhat exasperated and indeed exhausted Editor determines here to shut these Paper-bags for the present. Let it suffice that we know of Teufelsdröckh, so far, if "not what he did, yet what he became:" the rather, as his character has now taken its ultimate bent, and no new revolution, of importance, is to be looked for. The imprisoned Chrysalis is now a winged Psyche: and such, wheresoever be its flight, it will continue. To trace by what complex gyrations (flights or involuntary waftings) through the mere external Life element, Teufelsdröckh reaches his University Professorship, and the Psyche clothes herself in civic Titles, without altering her now fixed nature,—would be comparatively an unproductive task, were we even unsuspicious of its being, for us at least, a false and impossible one. His outward Biography, therefore, which, at the Blumine Lover's-Leap, we saw churned utterly into spray-vapor, may hover in that condition, for aught that concerns us here. Enough that by survey of certain "pools and plashes," we have ascertained its general direction; do we not already know that, by one way and other, it *has* long since rained-down again into a stream; and even now, at Weissnichtwo, flows deep and still, fraught with the *Philosophy of Clothes*, and visible to whoso will cast eye thereon? Over much invaluable matter, that lies scattered, like jewels among quarry-rubbish, in those Paper-catacombs, we may have occasion to glance back, and somewhat will demand insertion at the right place: meanwhile be our tiresome diggings therein suspended.

If now, before reopening the great *Clothes-Volume*, we ask what our degree of progress, during these Ten Chapters, has been, towards right understanding of the *Clothes-Philosophy*, let not our discouragement become total. To speak in that old figure of the Hell-gate Bridge over Chaos, a few flying pontoons have perhaps been added, though as yet they drift straggling on the Flood; how far they will reach, when once the chains are straightened and fastened, can, at present, only be matter of conjecture.

So much we already calculate: Through many a little loop-hole, we have had glimpses into the internal world of Teufelsdröckh; his strange mystic, almost magic Diagram of the Universe, and how it was gradually drawn, is not henceforth altogether dark to us. Those mysterious ideas on TIME, which merit consideration, and are not wholly unintelligible with such, may by and by prove significant. Still more may his somewhat peculiar view of Nature, the decisive Oneness he ascribes to Nature. How all Nature and Life are but one *Garment*, a "Living Garment," woven and ever aweaving in the "Loom of Time;" is not here, indeed, the outline of a whole *Clothes-Philosophy;* at least the arena it is to work in? Remark, too, that the Character of the Man, nowise without meaning in such a matter, becomes less enigmatic: amid so much tumultuous obscurity, almost like diluted madness, do not a certain indomitable Defiance and yet a boundless Reverence seem to loom forth, as the two mountain-summits, on whose rock-strata all the rest were based and built?

Nay further, may we not say that Teufelsdröckh's Biography, allowing it even, as suspected, only a hieroglyphical truth, exhibits a man, as it were pre-appointed for Clothes-Philosophy? To look through the Shows of things into Things themselves he is led and compelled. The "Passivity" given him by birth is fostered by all turns of his fortune. Everywhere cast out, like oil out of water, from mingling in any Employment, in any public Communion, he has no portion but Solitude, and a life of Meditation. The whole energy of his existence is directed, through long years, on one task: that of enduring pain, if he cannot cure it. Thus everywhere do the Shows of things oppress him, withstand him, threaten him with fearfullest destruction: only by victoriously penetrating into Things themselves can he find peace and a stronghold. But is not this same looking-through the Shows, or Vestures, into the Things, even the first preliminary to a *Philosophy of Clothes?* Do we not, in all this, discern some beckonings towards the true, higher purport of such a Philosophy; and what shape it must assume with such a man, in such an era?

Perhaps in entering on Book Third, the courteous Reader is not utterly without guess whither he is bound: nor, let us hope, for all the fantastic Dream-Grottoes through which, as is our lot with Teufelsdröckh, he must wander, will there be wanting between whiles some twinkling of a steady Polar Star.

BOOK THIRD

CHAPTER I.

INCIDENT IN MODERN HISTORY.

As a wonder-loving and wonder-seeking man, Teufelsdröckh, from an early part of this Clothes-Volume, has more and more exhibited himself. Striking it was, amid all his perverse cloudiness, with what force of vision and of heart he pierced into the mystery of the World; recognizing in the highest sensible phenomena, so far as Sense went, only fresh or faded Raiment; yet ever, under this, a celestial Essence thereby rendered visible: and while, on the one hand, he trod the old rags of Matter, with their tinsels, into the mire, he on the other everywhere exalted Spirit above all earthly principalities and powers, and worshipped it, though under the meanest shapes, with a true Platonic mysticism. What the man ultimately purposed by thus casting his Greek-fire into the general Wardrobe of the Universe; what such, more or less complete, rending and burning of Garments, throughout the whole compass of Civilized Life and Speculation, should lead to; the rather as he was no Adamite, in any sense, and could not, like Rousseau, recommend either bodily or intellectual Nudity, and a return to the savage state: all this our readers are now bent to discover; this is, in fact, properly the gist and purport of Professor Teufelsdröckh's Philosophy of Clothes.

Be it remembered, however, that such purport is here not so much evolved, as detected to lie ready for evolving. We are to guide our British Friends into the new Gold-country, and show them the mines; nowise to dig-out and exhaust its wealth, which indeed remains for all time inexhaustible. Once there, let each dig for his own behoof, and enrich himself.

Neither, in so capricious inexpressible a Work as this of the Professor's can our course now more than formerly be straightforward, step by step, but at best leap by leap. Significant Indications stand-out here and there; which for the critical eye, that looks both widely and narrowly, shape themselves into some ground-scheme of a Whole: to select these with judgment, so that a leap from one to the other be possible, and (in our old figure) by chaining them together, a passable Bridge be effected: this, as heretofore, continues our only method. Among such light-spots, the following, floating in much wild matter about *Perfectibility*, has seemed worth clutching at:

"Perhaps the most remarkable incident in Modern History," says Teufelsdröckh, "is not the Diet of Worms, still less the Battle of Austerlitz, Waterloo, Peterloo, or any other Battle; but an incident passed carelessly over by most Historians, and treated with some degree of ridicule by others: namely, George Fox's making to himself a suit of Leather. This man, the first of the Quakers, and by trade a Shoemaker, was one of those, to whom, under ruder or purer form, the Divine Idea of the Universe is pleased to

107

manifest itself; and, across all the hulls of Ignorance and earthly Degradation, shine through, in unspeakable Awfulness, unspeakable Beauty, on their souls: who therefore are rightly accounted Prophets, God-possessed; or even Gods, as in some periods it has chanced. Sitting in his stall; working on tanned hides, amid pincers, paste, horns, rosin, swine-bristles, and a nameless flood of rubbish, this youth had, nevertheless, a Living Spirit belonging to him; also an antique Inspired Volume, through which, as through a window, it could look upwards, and discern its celestial Home. The task of a daily pair of shoes, coupled even with some prospect of victuals, and an honorable Mastership in Cordwainery, and perhaps the post of Third-borough in his hundred, as the crown of long faithful sewing,—was nowise satisfaction enough to such a mind: but ever amid the boring and hammering came tones from that far country, came Splendors and Terrors; for this poor Cordwainer, as we said, was a Man and the Temple of Immensity, wherein as Man he had been sent to minister, was full of holy mystery to him.

"The Clergy of the neighborhood, the ordained Watchers and Interpreters of that same holy mystery, listened with unaffected tedium to his consultations, and advised him, as the solution of such doubts, to 'drink beer and dance with the girls.' Blind leaders of the blind! For what end were their tithes levied and eaten; for what were their shovel-hats scooped out, and their surplices and cassock-aprons girt-on; and such a church-repairing, and chaffering, and organing, and other racketing, held over that spot of God's Earth,—if Man were but a Patent Digester, and the Belly with its adjuncts the grand Reality? Fox turned from them, with tears and a sacred scorn, back to his Leather-parings and his Bible. Mountains of encumbrance, higher than Ætna, had been heaped over that Spirit: but it was a Spirit, and would not lie buried there. Through long days and nights of silent agony, it struggled and wrestled, with a man's force, to be free: how its prison-mountains heaved and swayed tumultuously, as the giant spirit shook them to this hand and that, and emerged into the light of Heaven! That Leicester shoeshop, had men known it, was a holier place than any Vatican or Loretto-shrine.—'So bandaged, and hampered and hemmed in,' groaned he, 'with thousand requisitions, obligations, straps, tatters, and tagrags, I can neither see nor move: not my own am I, but the World's; and Time flies fast, and Heaven is high, and Hell is deep: Man! bethink thee, if thou hast power of Thought! Why not; what binds me here? Want, want!—Ha, of what? Will all the shoe-wages under the Moon ferry me across into that far Land of Light? Only Meditation can, and devout Prayer to God. I will to the woods: the hollow of a tree will lodge me, wild-berries feed me; and for Clothes, cannot I stitch myself one perennial suit of Leather!'

"Historical Oil-painting," continues Teufelsdröckh, "is one of the Arts I never practiced; therefore shall I not decide whether this subject were easy of execution on the canvas. Yet often has it seemed to me as if such first outflashing of man's Freewill, to lighten, more and more into Day, the Chaotic Night that threatened to ingulf him in its hindrances and its horrors, were properly the only grandeur there is in History. Let some living Angelo or Rosa, with seeing eye and understanding heart, picture George Fox on that morning, when he spreads-out his cutting-board for the last time, and cuts cowhides by unwonted patterns, and stitches them together into one continuous all-including Case, the farewell service of his awl! Stitch away, thou noble Fox: every prick of that little instrument is pricking into the heart of Slavery, and World-worship, and the Mammon-god. Thy elbows jerk, as in strong swimmer-strokes, and every stroke is bearing thee across the Prison-ditch, within which Vanity holds her Work-house and Ragfair, into lands of true Liberty; were the work done, there is in broad Europe one Free Man, and thou art he!

"Thus from the lowest depth there is a path to the loftiest height; and for the Poor also a Gospel has been published. Surely if, as D'Alembert asserts, my illustrious namesake, Diogenes, was the greatest man of Antiquity, only that he wanted Decency, then by stronger reason is George Fox the greatest of the Moderns, and greater than Diogenes himself: for he too stands on the adamantine basis of his Manhood, casting aside all props and shores; yet not, in half-savage Pride, undervaluing the Earth; valuing it rather, as a place to yield him warmth and food, he looks Heavenward from his Earth, and dwells in an element of Mercy and Worship, with a still Strength, such as the Cynic's Tub did nowise witness. Great, truly, was that Tub; a temple from which man's dignity and divinity was scornfully preached abroad: but greater is the Leather Hull, for the same sermon was preached there, and not in Scorn but in Love."

George Fox's "perennial suit," with all that it held, has been worn quite into ashes for nigh two centuries; why, in a discussion on the *Perfectibility of Society*, reproduce it now? Not out of blind sectarian partisanship: Teufelsdröckh himself is no Quaker; with all his pacific tendencies, did not we see him, in that scene at the North Cape, with the Archangel Smuggler, exhibit fire-arms?

For us, aware of his deep Sansculottism, there is more meant in this passage than meets the ear. At the same time, who can avoid smiling at the earnestness and Bœotian simplicity (if indeed there be not an underhand satire in it), with which that "Incident" is here brought forward; and, in the Professor's ambiguous way, as clearly perhaps as he durst in Weissnichtwo, recommended to imitation! Does Teufelsdröckh anticipate that, in this age of refinement, any considerable class of the community, by way of testifying against the "Mammon-god," and escaping from what he calls "Van-ity's Workhouse and Ragfair," where doubtless some of them are toiled and whipped and hoodwinked sufficiently,—will sheathe themselves in close-fitting cases of Leather? The idea is ridiculous in the extreme. Will Majesty lay aside its robes of state, and Beauty its frills and train-gowns, for a second-skin of tanned hide? By which change Huddersfield and Man-chester, and Coventry and Paisley, and the Fancy-Bazaar, were reduced to hungry solitudes; and only Day and Martin could profit. For neither would

Teufelsdröckh's mad daydream, here as we presume covertly intended, of levelling Society (*levelling* it indeed with a vengeance, into one huge drowned marsh!), and so attaining the political effects of Nudity without its frigorific or other consequences,—be thereby realized. Would not the rich man purchase a waterproof suit of Russia Leather; and the high-born Belle step-forth in red or azure morocco, lined with shamoy: the black cowhide being left to the Drudges and Gibeonites of the world; and so all the old Distinctions be re-established?

Or has the Professor his own deeper intention; and laughs in his sleeve at our strictures and glosses, which indeed are but a part thereof?

CHAPTER II.

CHURCH-CLOTHES.

NOT LESS QUESTIONABLE is his Chapter on *Church-Clothes*, which has the farther distinction of being the shortest in the Volume. We here translate it entire:

"By Church-Clothes, it need not be premised that I mean infinitely more than Cassocks and Surplices; and do not at all mean the mere haberdasher Sunday Clothes that men go to Church in. Far from it! Church-Clothes are, in our vocabulary, the Forms, the *Vestures*, under which men have at various periods embodied and represented for themselves the Religious Principle; that is to say, invested the Divine Idea of the World with a sensible and practically active Body, so that it might dwell among them as a living and life-giving WORD.

"These are unspeakably the most important of all the vestures and garnitures of Human Existence. They are first spun and woven, I may say, by that wonder of wonders, SOCIETY; for it is still only when 'two or three are gathered together,' that Religion, spiritually existent, and indeed indestructible, however latent, in each, first outwardly manifests itself (as with 'cloven tongues of fire'), and seeks to be embodied in a visible Communion and Church Militant. Mystical, more than magical, is that Communing of Soul with Soul, both looking heavenward: here properly Soul first speaks with Soul; for only in looking heavenward, take it in what sense you may, not in looking earthward, does what we can call Union, mutual Love, Society, begin to be possible. How true is that of Novalis: 'It is certain, my Belief gains quite *infinitely* the moment I can convince another mind thereof!' Gaze thou in the face of thy Brother, in those eyes where plays the lambent fire of Kindness, or in those where rages the lurid conflagration of Anger; feel how thy own so quiet Soul is straightway involuntarily kindled with the like, and ye blaze and reverberate on each other, till it is all one limitless confluent flame (of embracing Love, or of deadly-grappling Hate); and then say what miraculous virtue goes out of man into man. But if so, through all the thick-plied hulls of our Earthly Life; how much more when it is of the

Divine Life we speak, and inmost ME is, as it were, brought into contact with inmost ME!

"Thus was it that I said, the Church-Clothes are first spun and woven by Society; outward Religion originates by Society, Society becomes possible by Religion. Nay, perhaps, every conceivable Society, past and present, may well be figured as properly and wholly a Church, in one or other of these three predicaments: an audibly preaching and prophesying Church, which is the best; second, a Church that struggles to preach and prophesy, but cannot as yet, till its Pentecost come; and third and worst, a Church gone dumb with old age, or which only mumbles delirium prior to dissolution. Whoso fancies that by Church is here meant Chapterhouses and Cathedrals, or by preaching and prophesying, mere speech and chanting, let him," says the oracular Professor, "read on, light of heart (*getrosten Muthes*).

"But with regard to your Church proper, and the Church-Clothes specially recognized as Church-Clothes, I remark, fearlessly enough, that without such Vestures and sacred Tissues Society has not existed, and will not exist. For if Government is, so to speak, the outward SKIN of the Body Politic, holding the whole together and protecting it; and all your Craft-Guilds, and Associations for Industry, of hand or of head, are the Fleshly Clothes, the muscular and osseous Tissues (lying *under* such SKIN), whereby Society stands and works;—then is Religion the inmost Pericardial and Nervous Tissue, which ministers Life and warm Circulation to the whole. Without which Pericardial Tissue the Bones and Muscles (of Industry) were inert, or animated only by a Galvanic vitality; the SKIN would become a shrivelled pelt, or fast-rotting raw-hide; and Society itself a dead carcass,—deserving to be buried. Men were no longer Social, but Gregarious; which latter state also could not continue, but must gradually issue in universal selfish discord, hatred, savage isolation, and dispersion;—whereby, as we might continue to say, the very dust and dead body of Society would have evaporated and become abolished. Such, and so all-important, all-sustaining, are the Church-Clothes to civilized or even to rational men.

"Meanwhile, in our era of the World, those same Church-Clothes have gone sorrowfully out-at-elbows: nay, far worse, many of them have become mere hollow Shapes, or Masks, under which no living Figure or Spirit any longer dwells; but only spiders and unclean beetles, in horrid accumulation, drive their trade; and the mask still glares on you with its glass-eyes, in ghastly affectation of Life,—some generation-and-half after Religion has quite withdrawn from it, and in unnoticed nooks is weaving for herself new Vestures, wherewith to reappear, and bless us, or our sons or grandsons. As a Priest, or Interpreter of the Holy, is the noblest and highest of all men, so is a Sham-priest (*Schein-priester*) the falsest and basest; neither is it doubtful that his Canonicals, were they Popes' Tiaras, will one day be torn from him, to make bandages for the wounds of mankind; or even to burn into tinder, for general scientific or culinary purposes.

"All which, as out of place here, falls to be handled in my Second

Volume, *On the Palingenesia, or New-birth of Society;* which volume, as treating practically of the Wear, Destruction, and Retexture of Spiritual Tissues, or Garments, forms, properly speaking, the Transcendental or ultimate Portion of this my work *on Clothes,* and is already in a state of forwardness."

And herewith, no farther exposition, note, or commentary being added, does Teufelsdröckh and must his Editor now, terminate the singular chapter on Church-Clothes!

CHAPTER III.

SYMBOLS.

PROBABLY it will elucidate the draft of these foregoing obscure utterances, if we here insert somewhat of our Professor's speculations on *Symbols.* To state his whole doctrine, indeed, were beyond our compass: nowhere is he more mysterious, impalpable, than in this of "Fantasy being the organ of the Godlike;" and how "Man thereby, though based, to all seeming, on the small Visible, does nevertheless extend down into the infinite deeps of the Invisible, of which Invisible, indeed, his Life is properly the bodying forth." Let us, omitting these high transcendental aspects of the matter, study to glean (whether from the Paper-bags or the Printed Volume) what little seems logical and practical, and cunningly arrange it into such degree of coherence as it will assume. By way of proem, take the following not injudicious remarks:

"The benignant efficacies of Concealment," cries our Professor, "who shall speak or sing? SILENCE and SECRECY! Altars might still be raised to them (were this an altar-building time) for universal worship. Silence is the element in which great things fashion themselves together; that at length they may emerge, full-formed and majestic, into the daylight of Life, which they are thenceforth to rule. Not William the Silent only, but all the considerable men I have known, and the most undiplomatic and unstrategic of these, forbore to babble of what they were creating and projecting. Nay, in thy own mean perplexities, do thou thyself but *hold thy tongue for one day:* on the morrow, how much clearer are the purposes and duties; what wreck and rubbish have those mute workmen within these swept away, when intrusive noises were shut out! Speech is too often not, as the Frenchmen defined it, the art of concealing Thought; but of quite stifling and suspending Thought, so that there is none to conceal. Speech too is great, but not the greatest. As the Swiss Inscription says: *Sprechen ist silbern, Schweigen ist golden* (Speech is silvern, Silence is golden); or as I might rather express it: Speech is of Time, Silence is of Eternity.

"Bees will not work except in darkness; Thought will not work except in Silence: neither will Virtue work except in Secrecy. Let not thy left hand know what thy right hand doeth! Neither shalt thou prate even to thy own heart of 'those secrets known to all.' Is not Shame (*Scham*) the soil of all

Virtue, of all good manners and good morals? Like other plants, Virtue will not grow unless its root be hidden, buried from the eye of the sun. Let the sun shine on it, nay do but look at it privily thyself, the root withers, and no flower will glad thee. O my Friends, when we view the fair clustering flowers that overwreathe, for example, the Marriage-bower, and encircle man's life with the fragrance and hues of heaven, what hand will not smite the foul plunderer that grubs them up by the roots, and with grinning, grunting satisfaction, shows us the dung they flourish in! Men speak much of the Printing-Press with its Newspapers: *du Himmel!* what are these to Clothes and the Tailor's Goose?"

"Of kin to the so incalculable influences of Concealment, and connected with still greater things, is the wondrous agency of *Symbols*. In a Symbol there is concealment and yet revelation: here therefore, by Silence and by Speech acting together, comes a double significance. And if both the Speech be itself high, and the Silence fit and noble, how expressive will their union be! Thus in many a painted Device, or simple Seal-emblem, the commonest Truth stands out to us proclaimed with quite new emphasis.

"For it is here that Fantasy with her mystic wonderland plays into the small prose domain of Sense, and becomes incorporated therewith. In the Symbol proper, what we can call a Symbol, there is ever, more or less distinctly and directly, some embodiment and revelation of the Infinite; the Infinite is made to blend itself with the Finite, to stand visible, and as it were, attainable there. By Symbols, accordingly, is man guided and commanded, made happy, made wretched. He everywhere finds himself encompassed with Symbols, recognized as such or not recognized: the Universe is but one vast Symbol of God; nay if thou wilt have it, what is man himself but a Symbol of God; is not all that he does symbolical; a revelation to Sense of the mystic god-given force that is in him; a 'Gospel of Freedom,' which he, the 'Messias of Nature,' preaches, as he can, by act and word? Not a Hut he builds but is the visible embodiment of a Thought; but bears visible record of invisible things; but is, in the transcendental sense, symbolical as well as real."

"Man," says the Professor elsewhere, in quite antipodal contrast with these high-soaring delineations, which we have here cut-short on the verge of the inane. "Man is by birth somewhat of an owl. Perhaps, too, of all the owleries that ever possessed him, the most owlish, if we consider it, is that of your actually existing Motive-Millwrights. Fantastic tricks enough man has played, in his time; has fancied himself to be most things, down even to an animated heap of Glass: but to fancy himself a dead iron-Balance for weighing Pains and Pleasures on, was reserved for this his latter era. There stands he, his Universe one huge Manger, filled with hay and thistles to be weighed against each other; and looks long-eared enough. Alas, poor devil! spectres are appointed to haunt him: one age he is hagridden, bewitched; the next, priest-ridden, befooled; in all ages, bedevilled. And now the Genius of Mechanism smothers him worse than any Nightmare did; till the Soul is nigh choked out of him, and only a kind of Digestive, Mechanic life remains. In Earth and in Heaven he can see nothing but Mechanism; has fear for nothing else, hope in nothing else: the world would indeed grind him to pieces; but cannot he fathom the Doctrine of Motives, and cunningly compute these, and mechanize them to grind the other way?

"Were he not, as has been said, purblinded by enchantment, you had but to bid him open his eyes and look. In which country, in which time, was it hitherto that man's history, or the history of any man, went-on by calculated or calculable 'Motives'? What make ye of your Christianities, and Chivalries, and Reformations, and Marseilles Hymns, and Reigns of Terror? Nay, has not perhaps the Motive-grinder himself been *in Love?* Did he never stand so much as a contested Election? Leave him to Time, and the medicating virtue of Nature."

"Yes, Friends," elsewhere observes the Professor, "not our Logical, Mensurative faculty, but our Imaginative one is King over us; I might say, Priest and Prophet to lead us heavenward; or Magician and Wizard to lead us hellward. Nay, even for the basest Sensualist, what is Sense but the implement of Fantasy; the vessel it drinks out of? Ever in the dullest existence there is a sheen either of Inspiration or of Madness (thou partly hast it in thy choice, which of the two), that gleams-in from the circumambient Eternity, and colors with its own hues our little islet of Time. The Understanding is indeed thy window, too clear thou canst not make it; but Fantasy is thy eye, with its color-giving retina, healthy or diseased. Have not I myself known five-hundred living soldiers sabred into crows'-meat for a piece of glazed cotton, which they called their Flag; which, had you sold it at any market-cross, would not have brought above three groschen? Did not the whole Hungarian Nation rise, like some tumultuous moon-stirred Atlantic, when Kaiser Joseph pocketed their Iron Crown; an implement, as was sagaciously observed, in size and commercial value little differing from a horseshoe? It is in and through *Symbols* that man, consciously or unconsciously, lives, works, and has his being: those ages, moreover, are accounted the noblest which can the best recognize symbolical worth, and prize it the highest. For is not a Symbol ever, to him who has eyes for it, some dimmer or clearer revelation of the Godlike?

"Of Symbols, however, I remark farther, that they have both an extrinsic and intrinsic value; oftenest the former only. What, for instance, was in that clouted Shoe, which the Peasants bore aloft with them as ensign in their *Bauernkrieg* (Peasants' War)? Or in the Wallet-and-staff round which the Netherland *Gueux*, glorying in that nickname of Beggars, heroically rallied and prevailed, though against King Philip himself? Intrinsic significance these had none: only extrinsic; as the accidental Standards of multitudes more or less sacredly uniting together; in which union itself, as above noted, there is ever something mystical and borrowing of the Godlike. Under a like category, too, stand, or stood, the stupidest heraldic Coats-of-arms; military Banners everywhere; and generally all national or other sectarian Costumes and Customs: they have no intrinsic, necessary divineness, or even worth; but have acquired an extrinsic one. Nevertheless through all these there glimmers something of a Divine Idea; as through military Banners themselves, the Divine Idea of Duty, of heroic Daring; in some instances of Freedom, of Right. Nay the Highest ensign that men ever met and embraced under, the Cross itself, had no meaning save an accidental extrinsic one.

"Another matter it is, however, when your Symbol has intrinsic meaning, and is of itself *fit* that men should unite round it. Let but the Godlike manifest itself to Sense; let but Eternity look, more or less visibly, through the Time-Figure (*Zeitbild*)! Then is it fit that men unite there; and worship together before such Symbol; and so from day to day, and from age to age, superadd to it new divineness.

"Of this latter sort are all true Works of Art: in them (if thou know a Work of Art from a Daub of Artifice) wilt thou discern Eternity looking through Time; the Godlike rendered visible. Here too may an extrinsic value gradually superadd itself: thus certain *Iliads*, and the like, have, in three-thousand years, attained quite new significance. But nobler than all in this kind are the Lives of heroic god-inspired Men; for what other Work of Art is so divine? In Death too, in the Death of the Just, as the last perfection of a Work of Art, may we not discern symbolic meaning? In that divinely transfigured Sleep, as of Victory, resting over the beloved face which now knows thee no more, read (if thou canst for tears) the confluence of Time with Eternity, and some gleam of the latter peering through.

"Highest of all Symbols are those wherein the Artist or Poet has risen into Prophet, and all men can recognize a present God, and worship the same: I mean religious Symbols. Various enough have been such religious Symbols, what we call *Religions;* as men stood in this stage of culture or the other, and could worse or better body-forth the Godlike: some Symbols with a transient intrinsic worth; many with only an extrinsic. If thou ask to what height man has carried it in this manner, look on our divinest Symbol: on Jesus of Nazareth, and his Life, and his Biography, and what followed there-from. Higher has the human Thought not yet reached: this is Christianity and Christendom; a Symbol of quite perennial, infinite character; whose significance will ever demand to be anew inquired into, and anew made manifest.

"But, on the whole, as Time adds much to the sacredness of Symbols, so likewise in his progress he at length defaces, or even desecrates them; and Symbols, like all terrestrial Garments, wax old. Homer's Epos, has not ceased to be true; yet it is no longer *our* Epos, but shines in the distance, if clearer and clearer, yet also smaller and smaller, like a receding Star. It needs a scientific telescope, it needs to be reinterpreted and artificially brought near us, before we can so much as know that it *was* a Sun. So likewise a day comes when the Runic Thor, with his Eddas, must withdraw into dimness; and many an African Mumbo-Jumbo and Indian Pawaw be utterly abolished. For all things, even Celestial Luminaries, much more atmospheric meteors, have their rise, their culmination, their decline."

"Small is this which thou tellest me, that the Royal Sceptre is but a piece of gilt-wood; that the Pyx has become a most foolish box, and truly, as

Ancient Pistol thought, 'of little price.' A right Conjurer might I name thee, couldst thou conjure back into these wooden tools the divine virtue they once held."

"Of this thing, however, be certain: wouldst thou plant for Eternity, then plant into the deep infinite faculties of man, his Fantasy and Heart; wouldst thou plant for Year and Day, then plant into his shallow superficial faculties, his Self-love and Arithmetical Understanding, what will grow there. A Hierarch, therefore, and Pontiff of the World will we call him, the Poet and inspired Maker; who, Prometheus-like, can shape new Symbols, and bring new Fire from Heaven to fix it there. Such too will not always be wanting; neither perhaps now are. Meanwhile, as the average of matters goes, we account him Legislator and wise who can so much as tell when a Symbol has grown old, and gently remove it.

"When, as the last English Coronation[1] was preparing," concludes this wonderful Professor, "I read in their Newspapers that the 'Champion of England,' he who has to offer battle to the Universe for his new King, had brought it so far that he could now 'mount his horse with little assistance,' I said to myself: Here also we have a Symbol well-nigh superannuated. Alas, move whithersoever you may, are not the tatters and rags of superannuated worn-out Symbols (in this Ragfair of a World) dropping off everywhere, to hoodwink, to halter, to tether you; nay, if you shake them not aside, threatening to accumulate, and perhaps produce suffocation?"

CHAPTER IV.

HELOTAGE.

AT THIS POINT we determine on adverting shortly, or rather reverting, to a certain Tract of Hofrath Heuschrecke's, entitled *Institute for the Repression of Population;* which lies, dishonorably enough (with torn leaves, and a perceptible smell of aloetic drugs) stuffed into the Bag *Pisces.* Not indeed for the sake of the Tract itself, which we admire little; but of the marginal Notes, evidently in Teufelsdröckh's hand, which rather copiously fringe it. A few of these may be in their right place here.

Into the Hofrath's *Institute,* with its extraordinary schemes and machinery of Corresponding Boards and the like, we shall not so much as glance. Enough for us to understand that Heuschrecke is a disciple of Malthus; and so zealous for the doctrine, that his zeal almost literally eats him up. A deadly fear of Population possesses the Hofrath; something like a fixed-idea; undoubtedly akin to the more diluted forms of Madness. Nowhere, in that quarter of his intellectual world, is there light; nothing but a grim shadow of Hunger; open mouths opening wider and wider; a world to terminate by the frightfullest consummation: by its too dense inhabitants, famished into delirium, universally eating one another. To make air for himself in which

[1]That of George IV.—ED.

strangulation, choking enough to a benevolent heart, the Hofrath founds, or proposes to found, this *Institute* of his, as the best he can do. It is only with our Professor's comments thereon that we concern ourselves.

First, then, remark that Teufelsdröckh, as a speculative Radical, has his own notions about human dignity; that the Zähdarm palaces and courtesies have not made him forgetful of the Futteral cottages. On the blank cover of Heuschrecke's Tract we find the following indistinctly engrossed:

"Two men I honor, and no third. First, the toilworn Craftsman that with earth-made Implement laboriously conquers the Earth, and makes her man's. Venerable to me is the hard Hand; crooked, coarse; wherein notwithstanding lies a cunning virtue, indefeasibly royal, as of the Sceptre of this Planet. Venerable too is the rugged face, all weather-tanned, besoiled, with its rude intelligence; for it is the face of a man living manlike. O, but the more venerable for thy rudeness, and even because we must pity as well as love thee! Hardly-entreated Brother! For us was thy back so bent, for us were thy straight limbs and fingers so deformed: thou wert our Conscript, on whom the lot fell, and fighting our battles wert so marred. For in thee too lay a god-created Form, but it was not to be unfolded; incrusted must it stand with the thick adhesions and defacements of Labor: and thy body, like thy soul, was not to know freedom. Yet toil on, toil on, *thou* art in thy duty, be out of it who may; thou toilest for the altogether indispensable, for daily bread.

"A second man I honor, and still more highly: Him who is seen toiling for the spiritually indispensable; not daily bread, but the bread of Life. Is not he too in his duty; endeavoring towards inward Harmony; revealing this, by act or by word, through all his outward endeavors, be they high or low? Highest of all, when his outward and his inward endeavor are one: when we can name him Artist; not earthly Craftsman only, but inspired Thinker, who with heaven-made Implement conquers Heaven for us! If the poor and humble toil that we have Food, must not the high and glorious toil for him in return, that he have Light, have Guidance, Freedom, Immortality?—These two, in all their degrees, I honor: all else is chaff and dust, which let the wind blow whither it listeth.

"Unspeakably touching is it, however, when I find both dignities united; and he that must toil outwardly for the lowest of man's wants, is also toiling inwardly for the highest. Sublimer in this world know I nothing than a Peasant Saint, could such now anywhere be met with. Such a one will take thee back to Nazareth itself; thou wilt see the splendor of Heaven spring forth from the humblest depths of Earth, like a light shining in great darkness."

And again: "It is not because of his toils that I lament for the poor: we must all toil, or steal (howsoever we name our stealing), which is worse; no faithful workman finds his task a pastime. The poor is hungry and athirst; but for him also there is food and drink: he is heavy laden and weary; but for him also the Heavens send Sleep, and of the deepest; in his smoky cribs, a clear dewy heaven of Rest envelops him, and fitful glitterings of cloudskirted Dreams. But what I do mourn over is, that the lamp of his soul should go out; that no ray of heavenly, or even of earthly knowledge, should visit him; but only, in the haggard darkness, like two spectres, Fear and Indignation bear him company. Alas, while the Body stands so broad and brawny, must the Soul lie blinded, dwarfed, stupefied, almost annihilated! Alas, was this too a Breath of God; bestowed in Heaven, but on earth never to be unfolded!—That there should one Man die ignorant who had capacity for Knowledge, this I call a tragedy, were it to happen more than twenty times in the minute, as by some computations it does. The miserable fraction of Science which our united Mankind, in a wide Universe of Nescience, has acquired, why is not this, with all diligence, imparted to all?"

Quite in an opposite strain is the following: "The old Spartans had a wiser method; and went out and hunted-down their Helots, and speared and spitted them, when they grew too numerous. With our improved fashions of hunting, Herr Hofrath, now after the invention of fire-arms, and standing-armies, how much easier were such a hunt! Perhaps in the most thickly-peopled country, some three days annually might suffice to shoot all the able-bodied Paupers that had accumulated within the year. Let Governments think of this. The expense were trifling: nay the very carcasses would pay it. Have them salted and barrelled; could not you victual therewith, if not Army and Navy, yet richly such infirm Paupers, in workhouses and else-where, as enlightened Charity, dreading no evil of them, might see good to keep alive?"

"And yet," writes he farther on, "there must be something wrong. A full-formed Horse will, in any market, bring from twenty to as high as two-hundred Friedrichs d'or: such is his worth to the world. A full-formed Man is not only worth nothing to the world, but the world could afford him a round sum would he simply engage to go and hang himself. Nevertheless, which of the two was the more cunningly-devised article, even as an Engine? Good Heavens! A white European Man, standing on his two Legs, with his two five-fingered Hands at his shackle-bones, and miraculous Head on his shoulders, is worth, I should say, from fifty to a hundred Horses!"

"True, thou Gold-Hofrath," cries the Professor elsewhere: "too crowded indeed! Meanwhile, what portion of this inconsiderable terraqueous Globe have ye actually tilled and delved, till it will grow no more? How thick stands your Population in the Pampas and Savannas of America; round ancient Carthage, and in the interior of Africa; on both slopes of the Altaic chain, in the central Platform of Asia; in Spain, Greece, Turkey, Crim Tartary, the Curragh of Kildare? One man, in one year, as I have understood it, if you lend him Earth, will feed himself and nine others. Alas, where now are the Hengsts and Alarics of our still-glowing, still-expanding Europe; who, when their home is grown too narrow, will enlist, and, like Fire-pillars, guide onwards those superfluous masses of indomitable living Valor; equipped, not now with the battle-axe and war chariot, but with the steam-engine and plough-share? Where are they?—Preserving their Game!"

CHAPTER V.

THE PHOENIX.

PUTTING which four singular Chapters together, and alongside of them numerous hints, and even direct utterances, scattered over these Writings of his, we come upon the startling yet not quite unlooked for conclusion, that Teufelsdröckh is one of those who consider Society, properly so called, to be as good as extinct; and that only the gregarious feelings, and old inherited habitudes, at this juncture, hold us from Dispersion, and universal national, civil, domestic and personal war! He says expressly: "For the last three centuries, above all for the last three quarters of a century, that same Peri-cardial Nervous Tissue (as we named it) of Religion, where lies the Life-essence of Society, has been smote-at and perforated, needfully and needlessly; till now it is quite rent into shreds; and Society, long pining, diabetic, consumptive, can be regarded as defunct; for those spasmodic, galvanic sprawlings are not life; neither indeed will they endure, galvanize as you may, beyond two days."

"Call ye that a Society," cries he again, "where there is no longer any Social Idea extant; not so much as the Idea of a common Home, but only of a common over-crowded Lodging-house? Where each, isolated, regard-less of his neighbor, turned against his neighbor, clutches what he can get, and cries 'Mine!' and calls it Peace, because, in the cut-purse and cut-throat Scramble, no steel knives, but only a far cunninger sort, can be employed? Where Friendship, Communion, has become an incredible tradition; and your holiest Sacramental Supper is a smoking Tavern Dinner, with Cook for Evangelist? Where your Priest has no tongue but for plate-licking: and your high Guides and Governors cannot guide; but on all hands hear it pas-sionately proclaimed: *Laissez faire;* Leave us alone of *your* guidance, such light is darker than darkness; eat you your wages, and sleep!

"Thus, too," continues he, "does an observant eye discern everywhere that saddest spectacle: The Poor perishing, like neglected, foundered Draught-Cattle, of Hunger and Overwork; the Rich, still more wretchedly of Idle-ness, Satiety, and Overgrowth. The Highest in rank, at length, without honor from the Lowest; scarcely, with a little mouth-honor, as from tavern-waiters who expect to put it in the bill. Once-sacred Symbols fluttering as empty Pageants, whereof men grudge even the expense; a World becoming dismantled: in one word, the CHURCH fallen speechless, from obesity and apoplexy; the STATE shrunken into a Police-Office, straitened to get its pay!"

We might ask, are there many "observant eyes," belonging to practical men in England or elsewhere, which have descried these phenomena; or is it only from the mystic elevation of a German *Wahngasse* that such wonders are visible? Teufelsdröckh contends that the aspect of a "deceased or expiring

Society" fronts us everywhere, so that whoso runs may read. "What, for example," says he, "is the universally-arrogated Virtue, almost the sole remaining Catholic Virtue, of these days? For some half century, it has been the thing you name 'Independence.' Suspicion of 'Servility,' of reverence for Superiors, the very dog-leech is anxious to disavow. Fools! Were your Superiors worthy to govern, and you worthy to obey, reverence for them were even your only possible freedom. Independence, in all kinds, is rebellion; if unjust rebellion, why parade it, and everywhere prescribe it?"

But what then? Are we returning, as Rousseau prayed, to the state of Nature? "The Soul Politic having departed," says Teufelsdröckh, "what can follow but that the Body Politic be decently interred, to avoid putrescence? Liberals, Economists, Utilitarians enough I see marching with its bier, and chanting loud pæans, towards the funeral-pile, where, amid wailings from some, and saturnalian revelries from the most, the venerable Corpse is to be burnt. Or, in plain words, that these men, Liberals, Utilitarians, or whatsoever they are called, will ultimately carry their point, and dissever and destroy most existing Institutions of Society, seems a thing which has some time ago ceased to be doubtful.

"Do we not see a little subdivision of the grand Utilitarian Armament come to light even in insulated England? A living nucleus, that will attract and grow, does at length appear there also; and under curious phasis; properly as the inconsiderable fag-end, and so far in the rear of the others as to fancy itself the van. Our European Mechanizers are a sect of boundless diffusion, activity, and co-operative spirit: has not Utilitarianism flourished in high places of Thought, here among ourselves, and in every European country, at some time or other, within the last fifty years? If now in all countries, except perhaps England, it has ceased to flourish, or indeed to exist, among Thinkers, and sunk to Journalists and the popular mass,—who sees not that, as hereby it no longer preaches, so the reason is, it now needs no Preaching, but is in full universal Action, the doctrine everywhere known, and enthusiastically laid to heart? The fit pabulum, in these times, for a certain rugged workshop intellect and heart, nowise without their corresponding workshop strength and ferocity, it requires but to be stated in such scenes to make proselytes enough.—Admirably calculated for destroying, only not for rebuilding! It spreads like a sort of Dog-madness; till the whole World-kennel will be rabid: then woe to the Huntsmen, with or without their whips! They should have given the quadrupeds water," adds he; "the water, namely, of Knowledge and of Life, while it was yet time."

Thus, if Professor Teufelsdröckh can be relied on, we are at this hour in a most critical condition; beleaguered by that boundless "Armament of Mechanizers" and Unbelievers, threatening to strip us bare! "The World," says he, "as it needs must, is under a process of devastation and waste, which, whether by silent assiduous corrosion, or open quicker combustion, as the case chances, will effectually enough annihilate the past Forms of Society; replace them with what it may. For the present, it is contemplated that when man's whole Spiritual Interests are once *divested*, these innumerable stript-off

Garments shall mostly be burnt; but the sounder Rags among them be quilted together into one huge Irish watch-coat for the defence of the Body only!" —This, we think, is but Job's-news to the humane reader.

"Nevertheless," cries Teufelsdröckh, "who can hinder it; who is there that can clutch into the wheel-spokes of Destiny, and say to the Spirit of the Time: Turn back, I command thee?—Wiser were it that we yielded to the Inevitable and Inexorable, and accounted even this the best."

Nay, might not an attentive Editor, drawing his own inferences from what stands written, conjecture that Teufelsdröckh individually had yielded to this same "Inevitable and Inexorable" heartily enough; and now sat waiting the issue, with his natural diabolico-angelical Indifference, if not even Placidity? Did we not hear him complain that the World was a "huge Ragfair," and the "rags and tatters of old Symbols" were raining-down everywhere, like to drift him in, and suffocate him? What with those "unhunted Helots" of his; and the uneven *sic vos non vobis* pressure and hard-crashing collision he is pleased to discern in existing things; what with the so hateful "empty Masks," full of beetles and spiders, yet glaring out on him, from their glass eyes, "with a ghastly affectation of life,"—we feel entitled to conclude him even willing that much should be thrown to the Devil, so it were but done gently! Safe himself in that "Pinnacle of Weissnichtwo," he would consent, with a tragic solemnity, that the monster UTILITARIA, held back, indeed, and moderated by nose-rings, halters, foot-shackles, and every conceivable modification of rope, should go forth to do her work;—to tread down old ruinous Palaces and Temples with her broad hoof, till the whole were trodden down; that new and better might be built! Remarkable in this point of view are the following sentences.

"Society," says he, "is not dead: that Carcass, which you call dead Society, is but her mortal coil which she has shuffled-off, to assume a nobler; she herself, through perpetual metamorphoses, in fairer and fairer development, has to live till Time also merge in Eternity. Wheresoever two or three Living Men are gathered together, there is Society; or there it will be, with its cunning mechanisms and stupendous structures, overspreading this little Globe, and reaching upwards to Heaven and downwards to Gehenna: for always, under one or the other figure, it has two authentic Revelations, of a God and of a Devil; the Pulpit, namely, and the Gallows."

Indeed, we already heard him speak of "Religion, in unnoticed nooks, weaving for herself new Vestures;"—Teufelsdröckh himself being one of the loom-treadles? Elsewhere he quotes without censure that strange aphorism of Saint-Simon's concerning which and whom so much were to be said: *"L'age d'or, qu'une aveugle tradition a placé jusqu'ici dans le passe est devant nous;* The golden age, which a blind tradition has hitherto placed in the Past, is Before us."—But listen again:

"When the Phœnix is fanning her funeral pyre, will there not be sparks flying! Alas, some millions of men, and among them such as a Napoleon, have already been licked into that high-eddying Flame, and like moths consumed there. Still also have we to fear that incautious beards will get singed.

"For the rest, in what year of grace such Phœnix-cremation will be completed, you need not ask. The law of Perseverance is among the deepest in man: by nature he hates change; seldom will he quit his old house till it has actually fallen about his ears. Thus have I seen Solemnities linger as Ceremonies, sacred Symbols as idle Pageants, to the extent of three-hundred years and more after all life and sacredness had evaporated out of them. And then, finally, what time the Phœnix Death-Birth itself will require, depends on unseen contingencies.—Meanwhile, would Destiny offer Mankind, that after, say two centuries of convulsion and conflagration, more or less vivid, the fire-creation should be accomplished, and we to find ourselves again in a Living Society, and no longer fighting but working,—were it not perhaps prudent in Mankind, to strike the bargain?"

Thus is Teufelsdröckh content that old sick Society should be deliberately burnt (alas, with quite other fuel than spice-wood); in the faith that she is a Phœnix; and that a new heavenborn young one will rise out of her ashes! We ourselves, restricted to the duty of Indicator, shall forbear commentary. Meanwhile, will not the judicious reader shake his head, and reproachfully, yet more in sorrow than in anger, say or think: From a *Doctor utriusque Juris*, titular Professor in a University, and man to whom hitherto, for his services, Society, bad as she is, has given not only food and raiment (of a kind), but books, tobacco and gukguk, we expected more gratitude to his benefactress; and less of a blind trust in the future, which resembles that rather of a philosophical Fatalist and Enthusiast, than of a solid householder paying scot-and-lot in a Christian country.

CHAPTER VI.

OLD CLOTHES.

As MENTIONED ABOVE, Teufelsdröckh, though a Sansculottist, is in practice probably the politest man extant: his whole heart and life are penetrated and informed with the spirit of politeness; a noble natural Courtesy shines through him, beautifying his vagaries; like sunlight, making a rosy-fingered, rainbow-dyed Aurora out of mere aqueous clouds; nay, brightening London-smoke itself into gold vapor, as from the crucible of an alchemist. Hear in what earnest though fantastic wise he expresses himself on this head:

"Shall Courtesy be done only to the rich, and only by the rich? In Good-breeding, which differs, if at all, from High-breeding, only as it gracefully remembers the rights of others, rather than gracefully insists on its own rights, I discern no special connection with wealth or birth: but rather that it lies in human nature itself, and is due from all men towards all men. Of a truth, were your Schoolmaster at his post, and worth anything when there, this, with so much else, would be reformed. Nay, each man were then also his neighbor's schoolmaster; till at length a rude-visaged, unmannered Peasant could no more be met with, than a Peasant unacquainted with botanical Physiology, or who felt not that the clod he broke was created in Heaven.

"For whether thou bear a sceptre or a sledge-hammer, art not thou ALIVE; is not this thy brother ALIVE? 'There is but one temple in the world,' says Novalis, 'and that temple is the Body of Man. Nothing is holier than this high Form. Bending before men is a reverence done to this Revelation in the Flesh. We touch Heaven, when we lay our hands on a human Body.'

"On which ground, I would fain carry it farther than most do; and whereas the English Johnson only bowed to every Clergyman, or man with a shovel-hat, I would bow to every Man with any sort of hat, or with no hat whatever. Is not he a temple, then; the visible Manifestation and Imper- sonation of the Divinity? And yet, alas, such indiscriminate bowing serves not. For there is a Devil dwells in man, as well as a Divinity; and too often the bow is but pocketed by the *former*. It would go to the pocket of Vanity (which is your clearest phasis of the Devil, in these times); therefore must we withhold it.

"The gladder am I, on the other hand, to do reverence to those Shells and outer Husks of the Body, wherein no devilish passion any longer lodges, but only the pure emblem and effigies of Man: I mean, to Empty, or even to Cast Clothes. Nay, is it not to Clothes that most men do reverence: to the fine frogged broadcloth, nowise to the 'straddling animal with bandy legs' which it holds, and makes a Dignitary of? Who ever saw any Lord my- lorded in tattered blanket fastened with wooden skewer? Nevertheless, I say, there is in such worship a shade of hypocrisy, a practical deception: for how often does the Body appropriate what was meant for the Cloth only! Whoso would avoid falsehood, which is the essence of all Sin, will perhaps see good to take a different course. That reverence which cannot act without obstruc- tion and perversion when the Clothes are full, may have free course when they are empty. Even as, for Hindoo Worshippers, the Pagoda is not less sacred than the God; so do I too worship the hollow cloth Garment with equal fervor, as when it contained the Man: nay, with more, for I now fear no deception, of myself or of others.

"Did not King *Toomtabard*, or, in other words, John Baliol, reign long over Scotland; the man John Baliol being quite gone, and only the 'Toom Tabard' (Empty Gown) remaining? What still dignity dwells in a suit of Cast Clothes! How meekly it bears its honors! No haughty looks, no scornful gesture: silent and serene, it fronts the world; neither demanding worship, nor afraid to miss it. The Hat still carries the physiognomy of its Head: but the vanity and the stupidity, and goose-speech which was the sign of these two, are gone. The Coat-arm is stretched out, but not to strike; the Breeches, in modest simplicity, depend at ease, and now at last have a graceful flow; the Waistcoat hides no evil passion, no riotous desire; hunger or thirst now dwells not in it. Thus all is purged from the grossness of sense, from the carking cares and foul vices of the World; and rides there, on its Clothes- Horse; as, on a Pegasus, might some skyey Messenger, or purified Apparition, visiting our low Earth.

"Often, while I sojourned in that monstrous tuberosity of Civilized Life, the Capital of England; and meditated, and questioned Destiny, under that ink-sea of vapor, black, thick, and multifarious as Spartan broth; and was one lone soul amid those grinding millions;—often have I turned into their Old-Clothes Market to worship. With awe-struck heart I walk through that Monmouth Street, with its empty Suits, as through a Sanhedrim of stainless Ghosts. Silent are they, but expressive in their silence: the past witnesses and instruments of Woe and Joy, of Passions, Virtues, Crimes, and all the fathomless tumult of Good and Evil in 'the Prison men call Life.' Friends! trust not the heart of that man for whom Old Clothes are not venerable. Watch, too, with reverence, that bearded Jewish High-priest, who with hoarse voice, like some Angel of Doom, summons them from the four winds! On his head, like the Pope, he has three Hats,—a real triple tiara; on either hand are the similitude of wings, whereon the summoned Garments come to alight; and ever as he slowly cleaves the air, sounds forth his deep fateful note, as if through a trumpet he were proclaiming: 'Ghosts of Life, come to Judgment!' Reck not, ye fluttering Ghosts: he will purify you in his Purgatory, with fire and with water; and, one day, new-created ye shall reappear. O, let him in whom the flame of Devotion is ready to go out, who has never worshipped, and knows not what to worship, pace and repace, with austerest thought, the pavement of Monmouth Street, and say whether his heart and his eyes still continue dry. If Field Lane, with its long fluttering rows of yellow handkerchiefs, be a Dionysius' Ear, where, in stifled jarring hubbub, we hear the Indictment which Poverty and Vice bring against lazy Wealth, that it has left them there cast-out and trodden under foot of Want, Darkness and the Devil,—then is Monmouth Street a Mirza's Hill, where, in motley vision, the whole Pageant of Existence passes awfully before us; with its wail and jubilee, mad loves and mad hatreds, church-bells and gallows-ropes, farce-tragedy, beast-godhood,—the Bedlam of creation!"

To most men, as it does to ourselves, all this will seem overcharged. We too have walked through Monmouth Street; but with little feeling of "Devotion:" probably in part because the contemplative process is so fatally broken in upon by the brood of money-changers who nestle in that Church, and importune the worshipper with merely secular proposals. Whereas Teufelsdröckh might be in that happy middle state, which leaves to the Clothes-broker no hope either of sale or of purchase, and so be allowed to linger there without molestation.—Something we would have given to see the little philosophical figure, with its steeple-hat and loose flowing skirts, and eyes in a fine frenzy, "pacing and repacing in austerest thought" that foolish Street; which to him was a true Delphic avenue, and supernatural Whispering-gallery, where the "Ghosts of Life" rounded strange secrets in his ear. O thou philosophic Teufelsdröckh, that listenest while others only gabble, and with thy quick tympanum hearest the grass grow!

At the same time, is it not strange that, in Paper-bag Documents destined for an English work, there exists nothing like an authentic diary of this his sojourn in London; and of his Meditations among the Clothes-shops only the obscurest emblematic shadows? Neither, in conversation (for, indeed, he was not a man to pester you with his Travels), have we heard him more than allude to the subject.

For the rest, however, it cannot be uninteresting that we here find how early the significance of Clothes had dawned on the now so distinguished Clothes-Professor. Might we but fancy it to have been even in Monmouth Street, at the bottom of our own English "ink-sea," that this remarkable Volume first took being, and shot forth its salient point in his soul,—as in Chaos did the Egg of Eros, one day to be hatched into a Universe!

CHAPTER VII.

Organic Filaments.

For us, who happen to live while the World-Phœnix is burning herself, and burning so slowly that, as Teufelsdröckh calculates, it were a handsome bargain would she engage to have done "within two centuries," there seems to lie but an ashy prospect. Not altogether so, however, does the Professor figure it. "In the living subject," says he, "change is wont to be gradual: thus, while the serpent sheds its old skin, the new is already formed beneath. Little knowest thou of the burning of a World-Phœnix, who fanciest that she must first burn-out, and lie as a dead cinereous heap; and therefrom the young one start-up by miracle, and fly heavenward. Far otherwise! In that Fire-whirlwind, Creation and Destruction proceed together; ever as the ashes of the Old are blown about, do organic filaments of the New mysteriously spin themselves: and amid the rushing and the waving of the Whirlwind-element come tones of a melodious Deathsong, which end not but in tones of a more melodious Birthsong. Nay, look into the Fire-whirlwind with thy own eyes, and thou wilt see." Let us actually look, then: to poor individuals, who cannot expect to live two centuries, those same organic filaments, mysteriously spinning themselves, will be the best part of the spectacle. First, therefore, this of Mankind in general:

"In vain thou deniest it," says the Professor; "thou *art* my Brother. Thy very Hatred, thy very Envy, those foolish Lies thou tellest of me in thy splenetic humor: what is all this but an inverted Sympathy? Were I a Steam-engine, wouldst thou take the trouble to tell lies of me? Not thou! I should grind all unheeded, whether badly or well.

"Wondrous truly are the bonds that unite us one and all; whether by the soft binding of Love, or the iron chaining of Necessity, as we like to choose it. More than once have I said to myself, of some perhaps whimsically strutting Figure, such as provokes whimsical thoughts: 'Wert thou, my little Brotherkin, suddenly covered-up within the largest imaginable Glass-bell,—what a thing it were, not for thyself only, but for the world! Post Letters, more or fewer, from all the four winds, impinge against thy

Glass walls, but have to drop unread: neither from within comes there question or response into any Postbag; thy Thoughts fall into no friendly ear or heart, thy Manufacture into no purchasing hand: thou art no longer a circulating venous-arterial Heart, that, taking and giving, circulatest through all Space and all Time: there has a Hole fallen-out in the immeasurable, universal World-tissue, which must be darned up again!"

"Such venous-arterial circulation, of Letters, verbal Messages, paper and other Packages, going out from him and coming in, are a blood-circulation, visible to the eye: but the finer nervous-circulation, by which all things, the minutest that he does, minutely influence all men, and the very look of his face blesses or curses whomso it lights on, and so generates ever new blessing or new cursing: all this you cannot see, but only imagine. I say, there is not a red Indian, hunting by Lake Winnipic, can quarrel with his squaw, but the whole world must smart for it: will not the price of beaver rise? It is a mathematical fact that the casting of this pebble from my hand alters the center of gravity of the Universe.

"If now an existing generation of men stand so woven together, not less indissolubly does generation with generation. Hast thou ever meditated on that word, Tradition: how we inherit not Life only, but all the garniture and form of Life; and work, and speak, and even think and feel, as our Fathers, and primeval grandfathers, from the beginning, have given it us?— Who printed thee, for example, this unpretending Volume on the Philosophy of Clothes? Not the Herren Stillschweigen and Company; but Cadmus of Thebes, Faust of Mentz, and innumerable others whom thou knowest not. Had there been no Mœsogothic Ulfila, there had been no English Shakespeare, or a different one. Simpleton! it was Tubal-cain that made thy very Tailor's needle, and sewed that court-suit of thine.

"Yes, truly, if Nature is one, and a living indivisible whole, much more is Mankind, the Image that reflects and creates Nature, without which Nature were not. As palpable life-streams in that wondrous Individual Mankind, among so many life-streams that are not palpable, flow on those main-currents of what we call Opinion; as preserved in Institutions, Polities, Churches, above all in Books. Beautiful it is to understand and know that a Thought did never yet die; that as thou, the originator thereof, hast gathered it and created it from the whole Past, so thou wilt transmit it to the whole Future. It is thus that the heroic heart, the seeing eye of the first times, still feels and sees in us of the latest; that the Wise Man stands ever encompassed, and spiritually embraced, by a cloud of witnesses and brothers; and there is a living, literal *Communion of Saints*, wide as the World itself, and as the History of the World.

"Noteworthy also, and serviceable for the progress of this same Individual, wilt thou find his subdivision into Generations. Generations are as the Days of toilsome Mankind; Death and Birth are the vesper and the matin bells that summon Mankind to sleep, and to rise refreshed for new advancement. What the Father has made, the Son can make and enjoy; but has also work of his own appointed him. Thus all things wax, and roll onwards;

Arts, Establishments, Opinions, nothing is completed, but ever completing. Newton has learned to see what Kepler saw; but there is also a fresh heaven-derived force in Newton; he must mount to still higher points of vision. So too the Hebrew Lawgiver is, in due time, followed by an Apostle of the Gentiles. In the business of Destruction, as this also is from time to time a necessary work, thou findest a like sequence and perseverance: for Luther it was as yet hot enough to stand by that burning of the Pope's Bull; Voltaire could not warm himself at the glimmering ashes, but required quite other fuel. Thus likewise, I note, the English Whig has, in the second generation, become an English Radical; who, in the third again, it is to be hoped, will become an English Rebuilder. Find Mankind where thou wilt, thou findest it in living movement, in progress faster or slower: the Phœnix soars aloft, hovers with outstretched wings, filling Earth with her music; or, as now, she sinks, and with spheral swan-song immolates herself in flame, that she may soar the higher and sing the clearer."

Let the friends of social order, in such a disastrous period, lay this to heart, and derive from it any little comfort they can. We subjoin another passage, concerning Titles:

"Remark, not without surprise," says Teufelsdröckh, "how all high Titles of Honor come hitherto from Fighting. Your *Herzog* (Duke, *Dux*) is Leader of Armies; your Earl (*Jarl*) is Strong Man; your Marshal cavalry Horse-shoer. A Millennium, or reign of Peace and Wisdom, having from of old been prophesied, and becoming now daily more and more indubitable, may it not be apprehended that such Fighting-titles will cease to be palatable, and new and higher need to be devised?

"The only Title wherein I, with confidence, trace eternity, is that of King. *König* (King), anciently *Könning,* means Ken-ning (Cunning), or which is the same thing, Can-ning. Ever must the Sovereign of Mankind be fitly entitled King."

"Well, also," says he elsewhere, "was it written by Theologians: a King rules by divine right. He carries in him an authority from God, or man will never give it him. Can I choose my own King? I can choose my own King Popinjay, and play what farce or tragedy I may with him: but he who is to be my Ruler, whose will is to be higher than my will, was chosen for me in Heaven. Neither except in such Obedience to the Heaven-chosen is Freedom so much as conceivable."

The Editor will here admit that, among all the wondrous provinces of Teufelsdröckh's spiritual world, there is none he walks in with such astonishment, hesitation, and even pain, as in the Political. How, with our English love of Ministry and Opposition, and that generous conflict of Parties, mind warming itself against mind in their mutual wrestle for the Public Good, by which wrestle, indeed, is our invaluable Constitution kept warm and alive; how shall we domesticate ourselves in this spectral Necropolis, or rather City both of the Dead and of the Unborn, where the Present seems little other than an inconsiderable Film dividing the Past and the Future? In those dim longdrawn expanses, all is so immeasurable; much so disastrous, ghastly; your very radiances and straggling light-beams have a supernatural character. And then with such an indifference, such a prophetic peacefulness (accounting the inevitably coming as already here, to him all one whether it be distant by centuries or only by days), does he sit;—and live, you would say, rather in any other age than in his own! It is our painful duty to announce, or repeat, that, looking into this man, we discern a deep, silent, slow-burning, inextinguishable Radicalism, such as fills us with shuddering admiration.

Thus, for example, he appears to make little even of the Elective Franchise; at least so we interpret the following: "Satisfy yourselves," he says, "by universal, indubitable experiment, even as ye are now doing or will do, whether FREEDOM, heaven-born and leading heavenward, and so vitally essential for us all, cannot peradventure be mechanically hatched and brought to light in that same Ballot-Box of yours; or at worst, in some other discoverable or devisable Box, Edifice, or Steam-mechanism. It were a mighty convenience; and beyond all feats of manufacture witnessed hitherto." Is Teufelsdröckh acquainted with the British Constitution, even slightly?—He says, under another figure: "But after all, were the problem, as indeed it now everywhere is, To rebuild your old House from the top downwards (since you must live in it the while), what better, what other, than the Representative Machine will serve your turn? Meanwhile, however, mock me not with the name of Free, 'when you have but knit-up my chains into ornamental festoons.' "—Or what will any member of the Peace Society make of such an assertion as this: "The lower people everywhere desire War. Not so unwisely; there is then a demand for lower people—to be shot!"

Gladly, therefore, do we emerge from those soul-confusing labyrinths of speculative Radicalism, into somewhat clearer regions. Here, looking round, as was our hest, for "organic filaments," we ask, may not this, touching "Hero-worship," be of the number? It seems of a cheerful character; yet so quaint, so mystical, one knows not what, or how little, may lie under it. Our readers shall look with their own eyes:

"True is it that, in these days, man can do almost all things, only not obey. True likewise that whoso cannot obey cannot be free, still less bear rule; he that is the inferior of nothing, can be the superior of nothing, the equal of nothing. Nevertheless, believe not that man has lost his faculty of Reverence; that if it slumber in him it has gone dead. Painful for man is that same rebellious Independence, when it has become inevitable; only in loving companionship with his fellows does he feel safe; only in reverently bowing down before the Higher does he feel himself exalted.

"Or what if the character of our so troublous Era lay even in this: that man had forever cast away Fear, which is the lower; but not yet risen into perennial Reverence, which is the higher and highest?

"Meanwhile, observe with joy, so cunningly has Nature ordered it, that whatsoever man ought to obey, he cannot but obey. Before no faintest

revelation of the Godlike did he ever stand irreverent; least of all, when
the Godlike showed itself revealed in his fellow-man. Thus is there a true
religious Loyalty forever rooted in his heart; nay, in all ages, even in ours,
it manifests itself as a more or less orthodox *Hero-worship*. In which fact,
that Hero-worship exists, has existed, and will forever exist, universally
among Mankind, mayest thou discern the corner-stone of living-rock,
whereon all Polities for the remotest time may stand secure."

Do our readers discern any such corner-stone, or even so much as what
Teufelsdröckh is looking at? He exclaims, "Or hast thou forgotten Paris
and Voltaire? How the aged, withered man, though but a Sceptic, Mocker,
and millinery Court-poet, yet because even he seemed the Wisest, Best,
could drag mankind at his chariot-wheels, so that princes coveted a smile
from him, and the loveliest of France would have laid their hair beneath
his feet! All Paris was one vast Temple of Hero-worship; though their
Divinity, moreover, was of feature too apish.

"But if such things," continues he, "were done in the dry tree, what
will be done in the green? If, in the most parched season of Man's History,
in the most parched spot of Europe, when Parisian life was at best but a
scientific *Hortus Siccus*, bedizened with some Italian Gumflowers, such
virtue could come out of it; what is to be looked for when Life again waves
leafy and bloomy, and your Hero-Divinity shall have nothing apelike, but
be wholly human? Know that there is in man a quite indestructible Reverence for whatsoever holds of Heaven, or even plausibly counterfeits such
holding. Show the dullest clodpole, show the haughtiest featherhead, that
a soul higher than himself is actually here; were his knees stiffened into
brass, he must down and worship."

Organic filaments, of a more authentic sort, mysteriously spinning themselves, some will perhaps discover in the following passage:

"There is no Church, sayest thou? The voice of Prophecy has gone
dumb? This is even what I dispute: but in any case, hast thou not still
Preaching enough? A Preaching Friar settles himself in every village; and
builds a pulpit, which he calls Newspaper. Therefrom he preaches what
most momentous doctrine is in him, for man's salvation; and dost not
thou listen, and believe? Look well, thou seest everywhere a new Clergy
of the Mendicant Orders, some bare-footed, some almost bare-backed,
fashion itself into shape, and teach and preach, zealously enough, for
copper alms and the love of God. These break in pieces the ancient idols;
and, though themselves too often reprobate, as idol-breakers are wont to
be, mark out the sites of new Churches, where the true God-ordained,
that are to follow, may find audience, and minister. Said I not, Before the
old skin was shed, the new had formed itself beneath it?"

Perhaps also in the following; wherewith we now hasten to knit-up
this ravelled sleeve:

"But there is no Religion?" reiterates the Professor. "Fool! I tell thee,
there is. Hast thou well considered all that lies in this immeasurable froth-
ocean we name LITERATURE? Fragments of a genuine Church-*Homiletic*

lie scattered there, which Time will assort: nay, fractions even of a *Liturgy* could I point out. And knowest thou no Prophet, even in the vesture, environment, and dialect of this age? None to whom the Godlike had revealed itself, through all meanest and highest forms of the Common; and by him been again prophetically revealed: in whose inspired melody, even in these rag-gathering and rag-burning days, Man's Life again begins, were it but afar off, to be divine? Knowest thou none such? I know him, and name him—Goethe.

"But thou as yet standest in no Temple; joinest in no Psalm-worship: feelest well that, where there is no ministering Priest, the people perish? Be of comfort! Thou art not alone, if thou have Faith. Spake we not of a Communion of Saints, unseen, yet not unreal, accompanying and brotherlike embracing thee, so thou be worthy? Their heroic Sufferings rise up melodiously together to Heaven, out of all lands, and out of all times, as a sacred *Miserere;* their heroic Actions also, as a boundless everlasting Psalm of Triumph. Neither say that thou hast now no Symbol of the Godlike. Is not God's Universe a Symbol of the Godlike; is not Immensity a Temple; is not Man's History, and Men's History, a perpetual Evangel? Listen, and for organ-music thou wilt ever, as of old, hear the Morning Stars sing together."

CHAPTER VIII.

Natural Supernaturalism.

It is in his stupendous Section, headed *Natural Supernaturalism,* that the Professor first becomes a Seer; and, after long effort, such as we have witnessed, finally subdues under his feet this refractory Clothes-Philosophy, and takes victorious possession thereof. Phantasms enough he has had to struggle with; "Cloth-webs and Cob-webs," of Imperial Mantles, Superannuated Symbols, and what not: yet still did he courageously pierce through. Nay, worst of all, two quite mysterious, world-embracing Phantasms, Time and Space, have ever hovered round him, perplexing and bewildering: but with these also he now resolutely grapples, these also he victoriously rends asunder. In a word, he has looked fixedly on Existence, till, one after the other, its earthly hulls and garnitures have all melted away; and now, to his rapt vision, the interior celestial Holy of Holies lies disclosed.

Here, therefore, properly it is that the Philosophy of Clothes attains to Transcendentalism; this last leap, can we but clear it, takes us safe into the promised land, where *Palingenesia,* in all senses, may be considered as beginning. "Courage, then!" may our Diogenes exclaim, with better right than Diogenes the First once did. This stupendous Section we, after long painful meditation, have found not to be unintelligible; but, on the contrary, to grow clear, nay radiant, and all-illuminating. Let the reader, turning on it what utmost force of speculative intellect is in him, do his art; as we, by judicious selection and adjustment, shall study to do ours: "Deep has been, and is, the significance of Miracles," thus quietly begins he Professor; "far deeper perhaps than we imagine. Meanwhile, the question of questions were: What specially is a Miracle? To that Dutch King of Siam, an icicle had been a miracle; whoso had carried with him an airpump, and vial of vitriolic ether, might have worked a miracle. To my Horse, again, who unhappily is still more unscientific, do not I work a miracle, and magical 'Open sesame!' every time I please to pay two-pence, nd open for him an impassable Schlagbaum, or shut Turnpike?

" 'But is not a real Miracle simply a violation of the Laws of Nature?' ask everal. Whom I answer by this new question: What are the Laws of Nature? To me perhaps the rising of one from the dead were no violation of these Laws, but a confirmation; were some far deeper Law, now first penetrated into, and by Spiritual Force, even as the rest have all been, brought to bear on us with its Material Force.

"Here too may some inquire, not without astonishment: On what ground shall one, that can make Iron swim, come and declare that therefore he can teach Religion? To us, truly, of the Nineteenth Century, such declaration were inept enough; which nevertheless to our fathers, of the First Century, was full of meaning.

" 'But is it not the deepest Law of Nature that she be constant?' cries an illuminated class: 'Is not the Machine of the Universe fixed to move by unalterable rules?' Probable enough, good friends: nay I, too, must believe hat the God, whom ancient inspired men assert to be 'without variableness or shadow of turning,' does indeed never change; that Nature, that the Universe, which no one whom it so pleases can be prevented from calling a Machine, does move by the most unalterable rules. And now of you, oo, I make the old inquiry: What those same unalterable rules, forming he complete Statute-Book of Nature, may possibly be?

"They stand written in our Works of Science, say you; in the accumulated records of Man's Experience?—Was Man with his Experience present at the Creation, then, to see how it all went on? Have any deepest scientific individuals yet dived down to the foundations of the Universe, and gauged everything there? Did the Maker take them into His counsel; that they read His groundplan of the incomprehensible All; and can say, This stands marked therein, and no more than this? Alas, not in anywise! These scientific individuals have been nowhere but where we also are; have seen some handbreadths deeper than we see into the Deep that is infinite, without bottom as without shore.

"Laplace's Book on the Stars, wherein he exhibits that certain Planets, with their Satellites, gyrate round our worthy Sun, at a rate and in a course, which, by greatest good fortune, he and the like of him have succeeded in detecting,—is to me as precious as to another. But is this what thou namest 'Mechanism of the Heavens,' and 'System of the World;' this, wherein Sirius and the Pleiades, and all Herschel's Fifteen-thousand Suns per minute, being left out, some paltry handful of Moons, and inert Balls, had been—

looked at, nicknamed, and marked in the Zodiacal Way-bill; so that w
can now prate of their Whereabout; their How, their Why, their Wha
being hid from us, as in the signless Inane?

"System of Nature! To the wisest man, wide as is his vision, Natur
remains the quite *infinite* depth, of quite infinite expansion; and all Experi
ence thereof limits itself to some few computed centuries and measure
square-miles. The course of Nature's phases, on this our little fraction of
Planet, is partially known to us: but who knows what deeper course
these depend on; what infinitely larger Cycle (of causes) our little Epicycl
revolves on? To the Minnow every cranny and pebble, and quality an
accident, of its little native Creek may have become familiar: but doe
the Minnow understand the Ocean Tides and periodic Currents, th
Trade-winds, and Monsoons, and Moon's Eclipses; by all which the con
dition of its little Creek is regulated, and may, from time to time (*un*miracu
lously enough), be quite overset and reversed? Such a minnow is Man
his Creek this Planet Earth; his Ocean the immeasurable All; his Monsoon
and periodic Currents the mysterious Course of Providence through Æon
of Æons.

"We speak of the Volume of Nature: and truly a Volume it is,—whos
Author and Writer is God. To read it! Dost thou, does man, so much a
well know the Alphabet thereof? With its Words, Sentences, and gran
descriptive Pages, poetical and philosophical, spread out through Sola
Systems, and Thousand of Years, we shall not try thee. It is a Volume writ
ten in celestial hieroglyphs, in the true Sacred-writing; of which ever
Prophets are happy that they can read here a line and there a line. A
for your Institutes, and Academies of Science, they strive bravely; and
from amid the thick-crowded, inextricably intertwisted hieroglyphic writ
ing, pick out, by dextrous combination, some Letters in the vulgar Charac
ter, and therefrom put together this and the other economic Recipe, o
high avail in Practice. That Nature is more than some boundless Volume o
such Recipes, or huge, well-nigh inexhaustible Domestic-Cookery Book
of which the whole secret will in this manner one day evolve itself, the
fewest dream.

"Custom," continues the Professor, "doth make dotards of us all. Con
sider well, thou wilt find that Custom is the greatest of Weavers; and
weaves air-raiment for all the Spirits of the Universe; whereby, indeed
these dwell with us visibly, as ministering servants, in our houses and work
shops; but their spiritual nature becomes, to the most, forever hidden
Philosophy complains that Custom has hoodwinked us from the first; that
we do everything by Custom, even Believe by it; that our very Axioms
let us boast of Free-thinking as we may, are oftenest simply such Beliefs
as we have never heard questioned. Nay, what is Philosophy throughou
but a continual battle against Custom; an ever-renewed effort to *transcen*
the sphere of blind Custom, and so become Transcendental?

"Innumerable are the illusions and legerdemain-tricks of Custom: but o
all these, perhaps the cleverest is her knack of persuading us that the

Miraculous, by simple repetition, ceases to be Miraculous. True, it is by this means we live; for man must work as well as wonder: and herein is Custom so far a kind nurse, guiding him to his true benefit. But she is a fond, foolish nurse, or rather we are false, foolish nurslings, when, in our resting and reflecting hours, we prolong the same deception. Am I to view the Stupendous with stupid indifference, because I have seen it twice, or two-hundred, or two-million times? There is no reason in Nature or in Art why I should: unless, indeed, I am a mere Work-Machine, for whom the divine gift of Thought were no other than the terrestrial gift of Steam is to the Steam-engine; a power whereby cotton might be spun, and money and money's worth realized.

"Notable enough too, here as elsewhere, wilt thou find the potency of Names; which indeed are but one kind of such custom-woven, wonder-hiding Garments. Witchcraft, and all manner of Spectre-work, and Demon-ology, we have now named Madness, and Diseases of the Nerves. Seldom reflecting that still the new question comes upon us: What is Madness, what are Nerves? Ever, as before, does Madness remain a mysterious-terrific, altogether *infernal* boiling-up of the Nether Chaotic Deep, through this fair painted Vision of Creation, which swims thereon, which we name the Real. Was Luther's Picture of the Devil less a Reality, whether it were formed within the bodily eye, or without it? In every the wisest Soul lies a whole world of internal Madness, an authentic Demon-Empire; out of which, indeed, his world of Wisdom has been creatively built together, and now rests there, as on its dark foundations does a habitable flowery Earth-rind.

"But deepest of all illusory Appearances, for hiding Wonder, as for many other ends, are your two grand fundamental world-enveloping Ap-pearances, SPACE and TIME. These, as spun and woven for us from before Birth itself, to clothe our Celestial ME for dwelling here, and yet to blind it,—lie all-embracing, as the universal canvas, or warp and woof, whereby all minor Illusions, in this Phantasm Existence, weave and paint themselves. In vain, while here on Earth, shall you endeavor to strip them off; you can, at best, but rend them asunder for moments, and look through.

"Fortunatus had a wishing Hat, which when he put on, and wished himself Anywhere, behold he was There. By this means had Fortunatus triumphed over Space, he had annihilated Space; for him there was no Where, but all was Here. Were a Hatter to establish himself, in the Wahn-gasse of Weissnichtwo, and make felts of this sort for all mankind, what a world we should have of it! Still stranger, should, on the opposite side of the street, another Hatter establish himself; and, as his fellow-craftsman made Space-annihilating Hats, make Time-annihilating! Of both would I purchase, were it with my last groschen; but chiefly of this latter. To clap-on your felt, and, simply by wishing that you were Any*where*, straightway to be *There!* Next to clap-on your other felt, and, simply by wishing that you were Any*when*, straightway to be *Then!* This were indeed the grander: shooting at will from the Fire-Creation of the World to its Fire-Consummation; here historically present in the First Century, conversing face to face with Paul and Seneca; there prophetically in the Thirty-first, conversing also face to face with other Pauls and Senecas, who as yet stand hidden in the depth of that late Time!

"Or thinkest thou it were impossible, unimaginable? Is the Past annihilated, then, or only past; is the Future nonextant, or only future? Those mystic faculties of thine, Memory and Hope, already answer: already through those mystic avenues, thou the Earth-blinded summonest both Past and Future, and communest with them, though as yet darkly, and with mute beckonings. The curtains of Yesterday drop down, the curtains of To-morrow roll up; but Yesterday and To-morrow both *are*. Pierce through the Time-element, glance into the Eternal. Believe what thou findest written in the sanctuaries of Man's Soul, even as all Thinkers, in all ages, have devoutly read it there: that Time and Space are not God, but creations of God; that with God as it is a universal HERE, so it is an everlasting Now.

"And seest thou therein any glimpse of IMMORTALITY?—O Heaven! Is the white Tomb of our Loved One, who died from our arms, and had to be left behind us there, which rises in the distance, like a pale, mournfully receding Milestone, to tell how many toilsome uncheered miles we have journeyed on alone,—but a pale spectral Illusion! Is the lost Friend still mysteriously Here, even as we are Here mysteriously, with God!—Know of a truth that only the Time-shadows have perished, or are perishable; that the real Being of whatever was, and whatever is, and whatever will be, *is* even now and forever. This, should it unhappily seem new, thou mayest ponder at thy leisure; for the next twenty years, or the next twenty centuries: believe it thou must; understand it thou canst not.

"That the Thought-forms, Space and Time, wherein, once for all, we are sent into this Earth to live, should condition and determine our whole Practical reasonings, conceptions, and imagings or imaginings, seems altogether fit, just, and unavoidable. But that they should, furthermore, usurp such sway over pure spiritual Meditation, and blind us to the wonder everywhere lying close on us, seems nowise so. Admit Space and Time to their due rank as Forms of Thought; nay, even, if thou wilt, to their quite undue rank of Realities: and consider, then, with thyself how their thin disguises hide from us the brightest God-effulgences! Thus, were it not miraculous, could I stretch forth my hand and clutch the Sun? Yet thou seest me daily stretch forth my hand and therewith clutch many a thing, and swing it hither and thither. Art thou a grown baby, then, to fancy that the Miracle lies in miles of distance, or in pounds avoirdupois of weight: and not to see that the true inexplicable God-revealing Miracle lies in this, that I can stretch forth my hand at all; that I have free Force to clutch aught therewith? Innumerable other of this sort are the deceptions and wonder-hiding stupefactions, which Space practises on us.

"Still worse is it with regard to Time. Your grand anti-magician, and universal wonder-hider, is this same lying Time. Had we but the Time-annihilating Hat, to put on for once only, we should see ourselves in a World of Miracles, wherein all fabled or authentic Thaumaturgy, and feats of Magic, were outdone. But unhappily we have not such a Hat; and man, poor fool that he is, can seldom and scantily help himself without one.

"Were it not wonderful, for instance, had Orpheus, or Amphion, built the walls of Thebes by the mere sound of his Lyre? Yet tell me, Who built these walls of Weissnichtwo; summoning out all the sandstone rocks, to dance along from the *Steinbruch* (now a huge Troglodyte Chasm, with frightful green-mantled pools); and shape themselves into Doric and Ionic pillars, squared ashlar houses and noble streets? Was it not the still higher Orpheus, or Orpheuses, who, in past centuries, by the divine Music of Wisdom, succeeded in civilizing Man? Our highest Orpheus walked in Judea, eighteen-hundred years ago: his sphere-melody, flowing in wild native tones, took captive the ravished souls of men; and, being of a truth sphere-melody, still flows and sounds, though now with thousandfold accompaniments, and rich symphonies, through all our hearts; and modulates, and divinely leads them. Is that a wonder, which happens in two hours; and does it cease to be wonderful if happening in two million? Not only was Thebes built by the music of an Orpheus; but without the music of some inspired Orpheus was no city ever built, no work that man glories in ever done.

"Sweep away the illusion of Time; glance, if thou have eyes, from the near moving-cause to its far-distant Mover: The stroke that came transmitted through a whole galaxy of elastic balls, was it less a stroke than if the last ball only had been struck, and sent flying? O, could I (with the Time-annihilating Hat) transport thee direct from the Beginnings to the Endings, how were thy eyesight unsealed, and thy heart set flaming in the Light-sea of celestial wonder! Then sawest thou that this fair Universe, were it in the meanest province thereof, is in very deed the star-domed City of God; that through every star, through every grass-blade, and most through every Living Soul, the glory of a present God still beams. But Nature, which is the Time-vesture of God, and reveals Him to the wise, hides Him from the foolish.

"Again, could anything be more miraculous than an actual authentic Ghost? The English Johnson longed, all his life, to see one; but could not, though he went to Cock Lane, and thence to the church-vaults, and tapped on coffins. Foolish Doctor! Did he never, with the mind's eye as well as with the body's, look round him into that full tide of human Life he so loved; did he never so much as look into Himself? The good Doctor was a Ghost, as actual and authentic as heart could wish; well-nigh a million of Ghosts were travelling the streets by his side. Once more I say, sweep away the illusion of Time; compress the threescore years into three minutes: what else was he, what else are we? Are we not Spirits, that are shaped into a body, into an Appearance; and that fade away again into air and Invisibility? This is no metaphor, it is a simple scientific *fact:* we start out of Nothingness, take figure, and are Apparitions; round us, as round the veriest spectre, is Eternity; and to Eternity minutes are as years and æons. Come there not tones of Love and Faith, as from celestial harp-strings, like the Song of beatified Souls? And again, do not we squeak and jibber (in our discordant, screech-owlish debatings and recriminatings); and glide bodeful, and feeble, and fearful; or uproar (*poltern*), and revel in our mad Dance of the Dead,—till the scent of the morning air summons us to our still Home; and dreamy Night, becomes awake and Day? Where now is Alexander of Macedon: does the steel Host, that yelled in fierce battle-shouts at Issus and Arbela, remain behind him; or have they all vanished utterly, even as perturbed Goblins must? Napoleon too, and his Moscow Retreats and Austerlitz Campaigns? Was it all other than the veriest Spectre-hunt; which has now, with its howling tumult that made Night hideous, flitted away?—Ghosts! There are nigh a thousand-million walking the Earth openly at noontide; some half-hundred have vanished from it, some half-hundred have arisen in it, ere thy watch ticks once.

"O Heaven, it is mysterious, it is awful to consider that we only carry each a future Ghost within him; but are, in very deed, Ghosts! These Limbs, whence had we them; this stormy Force; this life-blood with its burning Passion? They are dust and shadow; a Shadow-system gathered round our ME; wherein, through some moments or years, the Divine Essence is to be revealed in the Flesh. That warrior on his strong war-horse, fire flashes through his eyes; force dwells in his arm and heart: but warrior and war-horse are a vision; a revealed Force, nothing more. Stately they tread the Earth, as if it were a firm substance: fool! the Earth is but a film; it cracks in twain, and warrior and war-horse sink beyond plummet's sounding. Plummet's? Fantasy herself will not follow them. A little while ago, they were not; a little while, and they are not, their very ashes are not.

"So has it been from the beginning, so will it be to the end. Generation after generation takes to itself the Form of a Body; and forth-issuing from Cimmerian Night, on Heaven's mission APPEARS. What Force and Fire is in each he expends: one grinding in the mill of Industry; one hunter-like climbing the giddy Alpine heights of Science; one madly dashed in pieces on the rocks of Strife, in war with his fellow:—and then the Heaven-sent is recalled; his earthly Vesture falls away, and soon even to Sense becomes a vanished Shadow. Thus, like some wild-flaming, wild-thundering train of Heaven's Artillery, does this mysterious MANKIND thunder and flame, in long-drawn, quick-succeeding grandeur, through the unknown Deep. Thus, like a God-created, fire-breathing Spirit-host, we emerge from the Inane; haste stormfully across the astonished Earth; then plunge again into the Inane. Earth's mountains are levelled, and her seas filled up, in our passage: can the Earth, which is but dead and a vision, resist Spirits which have reality and are alive? On the hardest adamant some footprint of us is stamped-in; the last Rear of the host will read traces of the earliest

Van. But whence?—O Heaven, whither? Sense knows not; Faith knows not;
only that it is through Mystery to Mystery, from God and to God.

> "*We* are such stuff
> *As dreams are made of, and our little Life,*
> *Is rounded with a sleep!*"

CHAPTER IX.

CIRCUMSPECTIVE.

HERE, then, arises the so momentous question: Have many British Readers
actually arrived with us at the new promised country; is the Philosophy
of Clothes now at last opening around them? Long and adventurous has
the journey been: from those outmost vulgar, palpable Woollen Hulls of
Man; through his wondrous Flesh-Garments, and his wondrous Social Garnitures; inwards to the Garments of his very Soul's Soul, to Time and
Space themselves! And now does the spiritual, eternal Essence of Man, and
of Mankind, bared of such wrappages, begin in any measure to reveal
itself? Can many readers discern, as through a glass darkly, in huge wavering outlines, some primeval rudiments of Man's Being, what is changeable
divided from what is unchangeable? Does that Earth-Spirit's speech in
Faust,—

> "'Tis thus at the roaring Loom of Time I ply,
> And weave for God the Garment thou see'st Him by;"

or that other thousand-times repeated speech of the Magician, Shakespeare,—

> "And like the baseless fabric of this vision,
> The cloudcapt Towers, the gorgeous Palaces,
> The solemn Temples, the great Globe itself,
> And all which it inherit, shall dissolve;
> And like this unsubstantial pageant faded,
> Leave not a wrack behind;"

begin to have some meaning for us? In a word, do we at length stand safe
in the far region of Poetic Creation and Palingenesia, where that Phoenix
Death-Birth of Human Society, and of all Human Things, appears possible,
is seen to be inevitable?

Along this most insufficient, unheard-of Bridge, which the Editor, by
Heaven's blessing, has now seen himself enabled to conclude if not complete, it cannot be his sober calculation, but only his fond hope, that many
have travelled without accident. No firm arch, overspanning the Impassable
with paved highway, could the Editor construct; only, as was said, some
zigzag series of rafts floating tumultuously thereon. Alas, and the leaps
from raft to raft were too often of a breakneck character; the darkness,
the nature of the element, all was against us!

Nevertheless, may not here and there one of a thousand, provided with a discursiveness of intellect rare in our day, have cleared the passage, in spite of all? Happy few! little band of Friends! be welcome, be of courage. By degrees, the eye grows accustomed to its new Whereabout; the hand can stretch itself forth to work there: it is in this grand and indeed highest work of Palingenesia that ye shall labor, each according to ability. New laborers will arrive; new Bridges will be built; nay, may not our own poor rope-and-raft Bridge, in your passings and repassings, be mended in many a point, till it grow quite firm, passable even for the halt?

Meanwhile, of the innumerable multitude that started with us, joyous and full of hope, where now is the innumerable remainder, whom we see no longer by our side? The most have recoiled, and stand gazing afar off in unsympathetic astonishment, at our career: not a few, pressing forward with more courage, have missed footing, or leaped short, and now swim weltering in the Chaos-flood, some towards this shore, some towards that. To these also a helping hand should be held out; at least some word of encouragement be said.

Or, to speak without metaphor, with which mode of utterance Teufelsdröckh unhappily has somewhat infected us,—can it be hidden from the Editor that many a British Reader sits reading quite bewildered in head, and afflicted rather than instructed by the present Work? Yes, long ago has many a British Reader been, as now, demanding with something like a snarl: Whereto does all this lead; or what use is in it?

In the way of replenishing thy purse, or otherwise aiding thy digestive faculty, O British Reader, it leads to nothing, and there is no use in it; but rather the reverse, for it costs thee somewhat. Nevertheless, if through this unpromising Horn-gate, Teufelsdröckh, and we by means of him, have led thee into the true Land of Dreams; and through the Clothes-screen, as through a magical *Pierre-Pertuis*, thou lookest, even for moments, into the region of the Wonderful, and seest and feelest that thy daily life is girt with Wonder, and based on Wonder, and thy very blankets and breeches are Miracles,—then art thou profited beyond money's worth: and hast a thankfulness towards our Professor; nay, perhaps in many a literary Tea-circle wilt open thy kind lips, and audibly express that same.

Nay farther, art not thou too perhaps by this time made aware that all Symbols are properly Clothes; that all Forms whereby Spirit manifests itself to sense, whether outwardly or in the imagination, are Clothes; and thus not only the parchment Magna Charta, which a Tailor was nigh cutting into measures, but the Pomp and Authority of Law, the sacredness of Majesty, and all inferior Worships (Worthships) are properly a Vesture and Raiment; and the Thirty-nine Articles themselves are articles of wearing-apparel (for the Religious Idea)? In which case, must it not also be admitted that this Science of Clothes is a high one, and may with infinitely deeper study on thy part yield richer fruit: that it takes scientific rank beside Codification and Political Economy and the Theory of the British Constitution; nay rather, from its prophetic height looks down on all these as on so many weaving-shops, and spinning-mills, where the Vestures which *it* has to fashion, and consecrate, and distribute, are, too often by haggard hungry operatives who see no farther than their nose, mechanically woven and spun?

But omitting all this, much more all that concerns Natural Supernaturalism, and indeed whatever has reference to the Ulterior or Transcendental portion of the Science, or bears never so remotely on that promised Volume of the *Palingenesie der menschlichen Gesellschaft* (Newbirth of Society),— we humbly suggest that no province of Clothes-Philosophy, even the lowest, is without its direct value, but that innumerable inferences of a practical nature may be drawn therefrom. To say nothing of those pregnant considerations, ethical, political, symbolical, which crowd on the Clothes-Philosopher from the very threshold of his Science; nothing even of those "architectural ideas," which, as we have seen, lurk at the bottom of all Modes, and will one day, better unfolding themselves, lead to important revolutions,—let us glance for a moment, and with the faintest light of Clothes Philosophy, on what may be called the Habilatory Class of our fellow-men. Here too overlooking, where so much were to be looked on, the million spinners, weavers, fullers, dyers, washers, and wringers, that puddle and muddle in their dark recesses, to make us Clothes, and die that we may live,—let us but turn the reader's attention upon two small divisions of mankind, who, like moths, may be regarded as Cloth-animals, creatures that live, move and have their being in Cloth: we mean, Dandies and Tailors.

In regard to both which small divisions it may be asserted without scruple, that the public feeling, unenlightened by Philosophy, is at fault; and even that the dictates of humanity are violated. As will perhaps abundantly appear to readers of the two following Chapters.

CHAPTER X.

The Dandiacal Body.

First, touching Dandies, let us consider, with some scientific strictness, what a Dandy specially is. A Dandy is a Clothes-wearing Man, a Man whose trade, office and existence consists in the wearing of Clothes. Every faculty of his soul, spirit, purse and person is heroically consecrated to this one object, the wearing of Clothes wisely and well: so that as others dress to live, he lives to dress. The all-importance of Clothes, which a German Professor, of unequalled learning and acumen, writes his enormous Volume to demonstrate, has sprung up in the intellect of the Dandy without effort, like an instinct of genius; he is inspired with Cloth, a Poet of Cloth. What Teufelsdröckh would call a "Divine Idea of Cloth" is born with him; and this, like other such Ideas, will express itself outwardly, or wring his heart asunder with unutterable throes.

But, like a generous, creative enthusiast, he fearlessly makes his Idea an

Action; shows himself in peculiar guise to mankind; walks forth, a witness and living Martyr to the eternal worth of Clothes. We called him a Poet: is not his body the (stuffed) parchment-skin whereon he writes, with cunning Huddersfield dyes, a Sonnet to his mistress' eyebrow? Say, rather, an Epos, and *Clotha Virumque cano,* to the whole world, in Macaronic verses, which he that runs may read. Nay, if you grant, what seems to be admissible, that the Dandy has a Thinking-principle in him, and some notions of Time and Space, is there not in this Life-devotedness to Cloth, in this so willing sacrifice of the Immortal to the Perishable, something (though in reverse order) of that blending and identification of Eternity with Time, which, as we have seen, constitutes the Prophetic character?

And now, for all this perennial Martyrdom, and Poesy, and even Prophecy, what is it that the Dandy asks in return? Solely, we may say, that you would recognize his existence; would admit him to be a living object; or even failing this, a visual object, or thing that will reflect rays of light. Your silver or your gold (beyond what the niggardly Law has already secured him) he solicits not; simply the glance of your eyes. Understand his mystic significance, or altogether miss and misinterpret it; do but look at him, and he is contented. May we not well cry shame on an ungrateful world, which refuses even this poor boon; which will waste its optic faculty on dried Crocodiles, and Siamese Twins; and over the domestic wonderful wonder of wonders, a live Dandy, glance with hasty indifference, and a scarcely concealed contempt! Him no Zoölogist classes among the Mammalia, no Anatomist dissects with care: when did we see any injected Preparation of the Dandy in our Museums; any specimen of him preserved in spirits? Lord Herringbone may dress himself in a snuff-brown suit, with snuff-brown shirt and shoes: it skills not; the undiscerning public, occupied with grosser wants, passes by regardless on the other side.

The age of Curiosity, like that of Chivalry, is indeed, properly speaking, gone. Yet perhaps only gone to sleep: for here arises the Clothes-Philosophy, to resuscitate, strangely enough both the one and the other! Should sound views of this Science come to prevail, the essential nature of the British Dandy, and the mystic significance that lies in him, cannot always remain hidden under laughable and lamentable hallucination. The following long Extract from Professor Teufelsdröckh may set the matter, if not in its true light, yet in the way towards such. It is to be regretted, however, that here, as so often elsewhere, the Professor's keen philosophic perspicacity is somewhat marred by a certain mixture of almost owlish purblindness, or else of some perverse, ineffectual, ironic tendency; our readers shall judge which:

"In these distracted times," writes he, "when the Religious Principle, driven out of most Churches, either, lies unseen in the hearts of good men, looking and longing and silently working there towards some new Revelation; or else wanders homeless over the world, like a disembodied soul seeking its terrestrial organization,—into how many strange shapes of Superstition and Fanaticism, does it not tentatively and errantly cast itself! The higher Enthusiasm of man's nature is for the while without Exponent: yet does it continue indestructible, unweariedly active, and work blindly in the great chaotic deep: thus Sect after Sect, and Church after Church, bodies itself forth, and melts again into new metamorphosis.

"Chiefly is this observable in England, which, as the wealthiest and worst-instructed of European nations, offers precisely the elements (of Heat, namely, and of Darkness), in which such moon-calves and monstrosities are best generated. Among the newer Sects of that country, one of the most notable, and closely connected with our present subject, is that of the *Dandies;* concerning which, what little information I have been able to procure may fitly stand here.

"It is true, certain of the English Journalists, men generally without sense for the Religious Principle, or judgment for its manifestations, speak, in their brief enigmatic notices, as if this were perhaps rather a Secular Sect, and not a Religious one; nevertheless, to the psychologic eye its devotional and even sacrificial character plainly enough reveals itself. Whether it belongs to the class of Fetish-worships, or of Hero-worships or Poly-theisms, or to what other class, may in the present state of our intelligence remain undecided (*schweben*). A certain touch of Manicheism, not indeed in the Gnostic shape, is discernible enough: also (for human Error walks in a cycle, and reappears at intervals) a not-inconsiderable resemblance to that superstition of the Athos Monks, who by fasting from all nourishment, and looking intensely for a length of time in their own navels, came to discern therein the true Apocalypse of Nature and Heaven Unveiled. To my own surmise, it appears as if this Dandiacal-sect were but a new modifi-cation, adapted to the new time of that primeval Superstition, *Self-worship;* which Zerdusht, Quangfoutchee, Mohammed, and others, strove rather to subordinate and restrain than to eradicate; and which only in the purer forms of Religion has been altogether rejected. Wherefore, if any one chooses to name it revived Ahrimanism, or a new figure of Demon-Worship, I have, so far as is yet visible, no objection.

"For the rest, these people, animated with the zeal of a new Sect, display courage and perseverance, and what force there is in man's nature, though never so enslaved. They affect great purity and separatism; distinguish themselves by a particular costume (whereof some notices were given in the earlier part of this Volume); likewise, so far as possible, by a particular speech (apparently some broken *Lingua-franca,* or English-French); and, on the whole, strive to maintain a true Nazarene deportment, and keep themselves unspotted from the world.

"They have their Temples, whereof the chief, as the Jewish Temple did, stands in their metropolis; and is named *Almack's,* a word of uncertain etymology. They worship principally by night; and have their Highpriests and Highpriestesses, who, however, do not continue for life. The rites, by some supposed to be of the Menadic sort, or perhaps with an Eleusinian or Cabiric character, are held strictly secret. Nor are Sacred Books wanting to the Sect; these they call *Fashionable Novels:* however, the Canon is not completed, and some are canonical and others not.

"Of such Sacred Books, I, not without expense, procured myself some samples; and in hope of true insight, and with the zeal which beseems an Inquirer into Clothes, sent to interpret and study them. But wholly to no purpose: that tough faculty of reading, for which the world will not refuse me credit, was here for the first time foiled and set at naught. In vain that I summoned my whole energies (*mich weidlich anstrengte*), and did my very utmost; at the end of some short space, I was uniformly seized with not so much what I can call a drumming in my ears, as a kind of infinite, unsufferable Jew's-harping and scrannel-piping there; to which the frightfullest species of Magnetic Sleep soon supervened. And if I strove to shake this away, and absolutely would not yield, there came a hitherto unfelt sensation, as of *Delirium Tremens,* and a melting into total deliquium: till at last, by order of the Doctor, dreading ruin to my whole intellectual and bodily faculties, and a general breaking-up of the constitution, I reluctantly but determinedly forbore. Was there some miracle at work here; like those Fire-balls, and supernal and infernal prodigies, which, in the case of the Jewish Mysteries, have also more than once scared-back the Alien? Be this as it may, such failure on my part, after best efforts, must excuse the imperfection of this sketch; altogether incomplete, yet the completest I could give of a Sect too singular to be omitted.

"Loving my own life and senses as I do, no power shall induce me, as a private individual, to open another *Fashionable Novel.* But luckily, in this dilemma, comes a hand from the clouds; whereby if not victory, deliverance is held out to me. Round one of those Book-packages, which the *Stillschweigen'sche Buchhandlung* is in the habit of importing from England, come, as is usual, various waste printed-sheets (*Maculatur-blätter*), by way of interior wrappage: into these the Clothes-Philosopher, with a certain Mohamedan reverence even for waste-paper, where curious knowledge will sometimes hover, disdains not to cast his eye. Readers may judge of his astonishment when on such a defaced stray-sheet, probably the outcast fraction of some English Periodical, such as they name *Magazine,* appears something like a Dissertation on this very subject of *Fashionable Novels!* It sets out, indeed, chiefly from a Secular point of view; directing itself, not without asperity, against some to me unknown individual named *Pelham,* who seems to be a Mystagogue, and leading Teacher and Preacher of the Sect; so that, what indeed otherwise was not to be expected in such a fugitive fragmentary sheet, the true secret, the Religious physiognomy and physiology of the Dandiacal Body, is nowise laid fully open there. Nevertheless, scattered lights do from time to time sparkle out, whereby I have endeavored to profit. Nay, in one passage selected from the Prophecies, or Mythic Theogonies, or whatever they are (for the style seems very mixed) of this Mystagogue, I find what appears to be a Confession of Faith, or Whole Duty of Man, according to the tenets of that Sect. Which Confession or Whole Duty, therefore, as proceeding from a source so authentic, I shall here arrange under Seven distinct Articles, and in very abridged shape lay before the German world; therewith taking leave of this matter. Observe also, that to avoid possibility of error, I, as far as may be, quote literally from the Original.

"ARTICLES OF FAITH.

'1. Coats should have nothing of the triangle about them; at the same time, wrinkles behind should be carefully avoided.

'2. The collar is a very important point: it should be low behind, and slightly rolled.

'3. No license of fashion can allow a man of delicate taste to adopt the posterial luxuriance of a Hottentot.

'4. There is safety in a swallow-tail.

'5. The good sense of a gentleman is nowhere more finely developed than in his rings.

'6. It is permitted to mankind, under certain restrictions, to wear white waistcoats.

'7. The trousers must be exceedingly tight across the hips.'

"All which Propositions I, for the present, content myself with modestly but peremptorily and irrevocably denying.

"In strange contrast with this Dandiacal Body stands another British Sect, originally, as I understand, of Ireland, where its chief seat still is; but known also in the main Island, and indeed everywhere rapidly spreading. As this Sect has hitherto emitted no Canonical Books, it remains to me in the same state of obscurity as the Dandiacal, which has published Books that the unassisted human faculties are inadequate to read. The members appear to be designated by a considerable diversity of names, according to their various places of establishment: in England they are generally called the *Drudge* Sect; also, unphilosophically enough, the *White Negroes;* and, chiefly in scorn by those of other communions, the *Ragged-Beggar* Sect. In Scotland, again, I find them entitled *Hallanshakers,* or the *Stook of Duds* Sect; any individual communicant is name *Stook of Duds* (that is, Shock of Rags), in allusion, doubtless, to their professional Costume. While in Ireland, which, as mentioned, is their grand parent hive, they go by a perplexing multiplicity of designations, such as *Bogtrotters, Redshanks, Ribbonmen, Cottiers, Peep-of-Day Boys, Babes of the Wood, Rockites, Poor-Slaves:* which last, however, seems to be the primary and generic name; whereto, probably enough, the others are only subsidiary species, or slight varieties; or, at most, propagated offsets from the parent stem, whose minute subdivisions, and shades of difference, it were here loss of time to dwell on. Enough for us to understand, what seems indubitable, that the original Sect is that of the *Poor-Slaves:* whose doctrines, practices, and fundamental characteristics pervade and animate the whole Body, howsoever denominated or outwardly diversified.

"The precise speculative tenets of this Brotherhood: how the Universe, and Man, and Man's Life, picture themselves to the mind of an Irish Poor-Slave; with what feelings and opinions he looks forward on the Future, round on the Present, back on the Past, it were extremely difficult to specify. Something Monastic there appears to be in their Constitution: we find them bound by the two Monastic Vows, of Poverty and Obedience; which Vows, especially the former, it is said, they observe with great strictness; nay, as I have understood it, they are pledged, and be it by any solemn Nazarene ordination or not, irrevocably consecrated thereto even *before* birth. That the third Monastic Vow, of Chastity, is rigidly enforced among them, I find no ground to conjecture.

"Furthermore, they appear to imitate the Dandiacal Sect in their grand principle of wearing a peculiar Costume. Of which Irish Poor-Slave Costume no description will indeed be found in the present Volume; for this reason, that by the imperfect organ of Language it did not seem describable. Their raiment consists of innumerable skirts, lappets and irregular wings, of all cloths and of all colors; through the labyrinthic intricacies of which their bodies are introduced by some unknown process. It is fastened together by a multiplex combination of buttons, thrums and skewers; to which frequently is added a girdle of leather, of hempen or even of straw rope, round the loins. To straw rope, indeed, they seem partial, and often wear it by way of sandals. In head-dress they affect a certain freedom: hats with partial brim, without crown, or with only a loose, hinged, or valved crown; in the former case, they sometimes invert the hat, and wear it brim uppermost, like a University-cap, with what view is unknown.

"The name Poor-Slaves seems to indicate a Slavonic, Polish, or Russian origin: not so, however, the interior essence and spirit of their Superstition, which rather displays a Teutonic or Druidical character. One might fancy them worshippers of Hertha, or the Earth: for they dig and affectionately work continually in her bosom; or else, shut-up in private Oratories, meditate and manipulate the substances derived from her; seldom looking-up towards the Heavenly Luminaries, and then with comparative indifference. Like the Druids, on the other hand, they live in dark dwellings; often even breaking their glass-windows, where they find such, and stuffing them up with pieces of raiment, or other opaque substances, till the fit obscurity is restored. Again, like all followers of Nature-Worship, they are liable to outbreakings of an enthusiasm rising to ferocity; and burn men, if not in wicker idols, yet in sod cottages.

"In respect of diet, they have also their observances. All Poor-Slaves are Rhizophagous (or Root-eaters); a few are Ichthyophagous, and use Salted Herrings: other animal food they abstain from; except indeed, with perhaps some strange inverted fragment of a Brahminical feeling, such animals as die a natural death. Their universal sustenance is the root named Potato, cooked by fire alone; and generally without condiment or relish of any kind, save an unknown condiment named *Point*, into the meaning of which I have vainly inquired; the victual *Potatoes-and-Point* not appearing, at least not with specific accuracy of description, in any European Cookery-

Book whatever. For drink, they use, with an almost epigrammatic counter-poise of taste, Milk, which is the mildest of liquors, and *Potheen*, which is the fiercest. This latter I have tasted, as well as the English *Blue-Ruin*, and the Scotch *Whisky*, analogous fluids used by the Sect in those countries: it evidently contains some form of alcohol, in the highest state of concentration, though disguised with acrid oils; and is, on the whole, the most pungent substance known to me,—indeed, a perfect liquid fire. In all their Religious Solemnities, Potheen is said to be an indispensable requisite, and largely consumed.

"An Irish Traveller, of perhaps common veracity, who presents himself under the to me unmeaning title of *The Late John Bernard*, offers the following sketch of a domestic establishment, the inmates whereof, though such is not stated expressly, appear to have been of that faith. Thereby shall my German readers now behold an Irish Poor-Slave, as it were with their own eyes; and even see him at meat. Moreover, in the so precious waste-paper sheet above mentioned, I have found some corresponding picture of a Dandiacal Household painted by that same Dandiacal Mystagogue, or Theogonist; this also, by way of counterpart and contrast, the world shall look into.

"First, therefore, of the Poor-Slave, who appears likewise to have been a species of Innkeeper. I quote from the original:

Poor-Slave Household.

"'The furniture of this Caravansera consisted of a large iron Pot, two oaken Tables, two Benches, two Chairs, and a Potheen Noggin. There was a Loft above (attainable by a ladder), upon which the inmates slept; and the space below was divided by a hurdle into two Apartments; the one for their cow and pig, the other for themselves and guests. On entering the house we discovered the family, eleven in number, at dinner; the father sitting at the top, the mother at the bottom, the children on each side, of a large oaken Board, which was scooped-out in the middle, like a trough, to receive the contents of their Pot of Potatoes. Little holes were cut at equal distances to contain Salt; and a bowl of Milk stood on the table: all the luxuries of meat and beer, bread, knives and dishes were dispensed with.' The Poor-Slave himself, our Traveller found, as he says, broad-backed, black-browed, of great personal strength, and mouth from ear to ear. His Wife was a sun-browned but well-featured woman; and his young ones, bare and chubby, had the appetite of ravens. Of their Philosophical or Religious tenets or observances, no notice or hint.

"But now, secondly, of the Dandiacal Household; in which, truly, that often-mentioned Mystagogue and inspired Penman himself has his abode:

Dandiacal Household.

"'A Dressing-room splendidly furnished; violet-colored curtains, chairs and ottomans of the same hue. Two full-length Mirrors are placed, one on each side of a table, which supports the luxuries of the Toilet. Several Bottles of Perfumes, arranged in a peculiar fashion, stand upon a smaller table of mother-of-pearl: opposite to these are placed the appurtenances of Lavation, richly wrought in frosted silver. A Wardrobe of Buhl is on the left; the doors of which, being partly open, discover a profusion of Clothes; Shoes of a singularly small size monopolize the lower shelves. Fronting the wardrobe a door ajar gives some slight glimpse of a Bathroom. Folding-doors in the background.—Enter the Author,' our Theogonist in person, 'obsequiously preceded by a French Valet, in white silk Jacket and cambric Apron.'

"Such are the two Sects which, at this moment, divide the more unsettled portion of the British People; and agitate that ever-vexed country. To the eye of the political Seer, their mutual relation, pregnant with the elements of discord and hostility, is far from consoling. These two principles of Dandiacal Self-worship, or Demon-worship, and Poor-Slavish or Drudgical Earth-worship, or whatever that same Drudgism may be, do as yet indeed manifest themselves under distant and nowise considerable shapes: nevertheless, in their roots and subterranean ramifications, they extend through the entire structure of Society, and work unweariedly in the secret depths of English national Existence; striving to separate and isolate it into two contradictory, uncommunicating masses.

"In numbers, and even individual strength, the Poor-Slaves or Drudges, it would seem, are hourly increasing. The Dandiacal, again, is by nature no proselytizing Sect; but it boasts of great hereditary resources, and is strong by union; whereas the Drudges, split into parties, have as yet no rallying-point; or at best only co-operate by means of partial secret affiliations. If, indeed, there were to arise a *Communion of Drudges*, as there is already a Communion of Saints, what strangest effects would follow therefrom! Dandyism as yet affects to look-down on Drudgism: but perhaps the hour of trial, when it will be practically seen which ought to look down, and which up, is not so distant.

"To me it seems probable that the two Sects will one day part England between them; each recruiting itself from the intermediate ranks, till there be none left to enlist on either side. Those Dandiacal Manicheans, with the host of Dandyizing Christians, will form one body: the Drudges, gathering round them whosoever is Drudgical, be he Christian or Infidel Pagan; sweeping-up likewise all manner of Utilitarians, Radicals, refractory Pot-wallopers, and so forth, into their general mass, will form another. I could liken Dandyism and Drudgism to two bottomless boiling Whirlpools that had broken-out on opposite quarters of the firm land: as yet they appear only disquieted, foolishly bubbling wells, which man's art might cover-in; yet mark them, their diameter is daily widening: they are hollow Cones that boil-up from the infinite Deep, over which your firm land is but a thin crust or rind! Thus daily is the intermediate land crumbling-in, daily the empire of the two Buchan-Bullers extending; till now there is but a footplank, a mere film of Land between them; this too is washed away: and then—we have the true Hell of Waters, and Noah's Deluge is outdeluged!

"Or better, I might call them two boundless, and indeed unexampled Electric Machines (turned by the 'Machinery of Society'), with batteries of opposite quality; Drudgism the Negative, Dandyism the Positive: one attracts hourly towards it and appropriates all the Positive Electricity of the nation (namely, the Money thereof); the other is equally busy with the Negative (that is to say the Hunger), which is equally potent. Hitherto you see only partial transient sparkles and sputters: but wait a little, till the entire nation is in an electric state; till your whole vital Electricity, no longer healthfully Neutral, is cut into two isolated portions of Positive and Negative (of Money and of Hunger); and stands there bottled-up in two World-Batteries! The stirring of a child's finger brings the two together; and then—What then? The Earth is but shivered into impalpable smoke by that Doom's-thunderpeal; the Sun misses one of his Planets in Space, and thenceforth there are no eclipses of the Moon.—Or better still, I might liken—"

O, enough, enough of likenings and similitudes; in excess of which, truly, it is hard to say whether Teufelsdröckh or ourselves sin the more.

We have often blamed him for a habit of wire-drawing and over-refining; from of old we have been familiar with his tendency to Mysticism and Religiosity, whereby in everything he was still scenting-out Religion: but never perhaps did these amaurosis-suffusions so cloud and distort his otherwise most piercing vision, as in this of the *Dandiacal Body!* Or was there something of intended satire; is the Professor and Seer not quite the blinkard he affects to be? Of an ordinary mortal we should have decisively answered in the affirmative; but with a Teufelsdröckh there ever hovers some shade of doubt. In the meanwhile, if satire were actually intended, the case is little better. There are not wanting men who will answer: Does your Professor take us for simpletons? His irony has overshot itself: we see through it, and perhaps through him.

CHAPTER XI.

TAILORS.

THUS, HOWEVER, has our first Practical Inference from the Clothes-Philosophy, that which respects Dandies, been sufficiently drawn; and we come now to the second, concerning Tailors. On this latter our opinion happily quite coincides with that of Teufelsdröckh himself, as expressed in the concluding page of his Volume, to whom, therefore, we willingly give place. Let him speak his own last words, in his own way:

"Upwards of a century," says he, "must elapse, and still the bleeding fight of Freedom be fought, whoso is noblest perishing in the van, and thrones be hurled on altars like Pelion on Ossa, and the Moloch of Iniquity have his victims, and the Michael of Justice his martyrs, before Tailors can be admitted to their true prerogatives of manhood, and this last wound of suffering Humanity be closed.

"If aught in the history of the world's blindness could surprise us, here might we indeed pause and wonder. An idea has gone abroad, and fixed itself down into a wide-spreading rooted error, that Tailors are a distinct species in Physiology, not Men, but fractional Parts of a Man. Call any one a *Schneider* (Cutter, Tailor), is it not, in our dislocated, hoodwinked, and indeed delirious condition of Society, equivalent to defying his perpetual fellest enmity? The epithet *schneider-mässig* (tailor-like) betokens an otherwise unapproachable degree of pusillanimity: we introduce a *Tailor's Melancholy*, more opprobrious than any Leprosy, into our Books of Medicine; and fable I know not what of his generating it by living on Cabbage. Why should I speak of Hans Sachs (himself a Shoemaker, or kind of Leather-Tailor), with his *Schneider mit dem Panier?* Why of Shakespeare, in his *Taming of the Shrew*, and elsewhere? Does it not stand on record that the English Queen Elizabeth, receiving a deputation of Eighteen Tailors, addressed them with a 'Good morning, gentlemen both!' Did not the same virago boast that she had a Cavalry Regiment, whereof neither horse nor man could be injured; her Regiment, namely, of Tailors on Mares? Thus everywhere is the falsehood taken for granted, and acted on as an indisputable fact.

"Nevertheless, need I put the question to any Physiologist, whether it is disputable or not? Seems it not at least presumable, that, under his Clothes, the Tailor has bones and viscera, and other muscles than the sartorious? Which function of manhood is the Tailor not conjectured to perform? Can he not arrest for debt? Is he not in most countries a tax-paying animal?

"To no reader of this Volume can it be doubtful which conviction is mine. Nay if the fruit of these long vigils, and almost preternatural Inquiries, is not to perish utterly, the world will have approximated towards a higher Truth; and the doctrine, which Swift, with the keen forecast of genius, dimly anticipated, will stand revealed in clear light: that the Tailor is not only a Man, but something of a Creator or Divinity. Of Franklin it was said, that 'he snatched the Thunder from Heaven and the Sceptre from Kings:' but which is greater, I would ask, he that lends, or he that snatches? For, looking away from individual cases, and how a man is by the Tailor new-created into a Nobleman, and clothed not only with Wool but with Dignity and a Mystic Dominion,—is not the fair fabric of Society itself, with all its royal mantles and pontifical stoles, whereby, from nakedness and dismemberment, we are organized into Polities, into nations, and a whole co-operating Mankind, the creation, as has here been often irrefragably evinced, of the Tailor alone?—What too are all Poets and moral Teachers, but a species of Metaphorical Tailors? Touching which high Guild the greatest living Guild-brother has triumphantly asked us: 'Nay if thou wilt have it, who but the Poet first made Gods for men; brought them down to us; and raised us up to them?'

"And this is he, whom sitting downcast, on the hard basis of his Shopboard, the world treats with contumely, as the ninth part of a man! Look up, thou much-injured one, look up with the kindling eye of hope, and prophetic bodings of a noble better time. Too long hast thou sat there, on crossed legs, wearing thy ankle-joints to horn; like some sacred Anchorite, or Catholic Fakir, doing penance, drawing down Heaven's richest blessings, for a world that scoffed at thee. Be of hope! Already streaks of blue peer through our clouds; the thick gloom of Ignorance is rolling asunder, and it will be Day. Mankind will repay with interest their long-accumulated debt: the Anchorite that was scoffed at will be worshipped; The Fraction will become not an Integer only, but a Square and Cube. With astonishment the world will recognize that the Tailor is its Hierophant and Hierarch, or even its God.

"As I stood in the Mosque of St. Sophia, and looked upon these Four-and-Twenty Tailors, sewing and embroidering that rich Cloth, which the Sultan sends yearly for the Caaba of Mecca, I thought within myself: How many other Unholies has your covering Art made holy, besides this Arabian Whinstone!

"Still more touching was it when, turning the corner of a lane, in the Scottish Town of Edinburgh, I came upon a Signpost, whereon stood written that such and such a one was 'Breeches-Maker to his Majesty;' and stood painted the Effigies of a Pair of Leather Breeches, and between the knees these memorable words, SIC ITUR AD ASTRA. Was not this the martyr prison-speech of a Tailor sighing indeed in bonds, yet sighing towards deliverance, and prophetically appealing to a better day? A day of justice when the worth of Breeches would be revealed to man, and the Scissors become forever venerable.

"Neither, perhaps, may I now say, has his appeal been altogether in vain. It was in this high moment, when the soul, rent, as it were, and shed asunder, is open to inspiring influence, that I first conceived this Work on Clothes: the greatest I can ever hope to do; which has already, after long retardations, occupied, and will yet occupy, so large a section of my Life; and of which the Primary and simpler Portion may here find its conclusion."

CHAPTER XII.

FAREWELL.

SO HAVE WE ENDEAVORED, from the enormous, amorphous Plum-pudding, more like a Scottish Haggis, which Herr Teufelsdröckh had kneaded for his fellow mortals, to pick out the choicest Plums, and present them separately on a cover of our own. A laborious, perhaps a thankless enterprise; in which, however, something of hope has occasionally cheered us, and of which we can now wash our hands not altogether without satisfaction. If hereby, though in barbaric wise, some morsel of spiritual nourishment have been added to the scanty ration of our beloved British world, what nobler recompense could the Editor desire? If it prove otherwise, why should he murmur? Was not this a Task which Destiny, in any case, had appointed him; which having now done with, he sees his general Day's-work so much the lighter, so much the shorter?

Of Professor Teufelsdröckh it seems impossible to take leave without a mingled feeling of astonishment, gratitude and disapproval. Who will not regret that talents, which might have profited in the higher walks of Philosophy, or in Art itself, have been so much devoted to a rummaging among lumber-rooms; nay, too often to a scraping in kennels, where lost rings and diamond-necklaces are nowise the sole conquest? Regret is unavoidable; yet censure were loss of time. To cure him of his mad humors British Criticism would essay in vain: enough for her if she can, by vigilance, prevent the spreading of such among ourselves. What a result, should this piebald, entangled, hyper-metaphorical style of writing, not to say of thinking, become general among our Literary men! As it might so easily do. Thus has not the Editor himself, working over Teufelsdröckh's German, lost much of his own English purity? Even as the smaller whirlpool is sucked into the larger, and made to whirl along with it, so has the lesser mind, in this instance, been forced to become portion of the greater, and, like it, see all things figuratively: which habit, time and assiduous effort will be needed to eradicate.

Nevertheless, wayward as our professor shows himself, is there any reader that can part with him in declared enmity? Let us confess, there is that in the wild, much-suffering, much-inflicting man, which almost attaches us. His attitude, we will hope and believe, is that of a man who had said to Cant, Begone; and to Dilettantism, Here thou canst not be; and to Truth, Be thou in place of all to me: a man who had manfully defied the "Time-prince," or Devil, to his face; nay perhaps, Hannibal-like, was mysteriously consecrated from birth to that warfare, and now stood minded to wage the same, by all weapons, in all places, at all times. In such a cause, any soldier, were he but a Polack Scythe-man, shall be welcome.

Still the question returns on us: How could a man occasionally of keen insight, not without keen sense of propriety, who had real Thoughts to communicate, resolve to emit them in a shape bordering so closely on the absurd? Which question he were wiser than the present Editor who should satisfactorily answer. Our conjecture has sometimes been, that perhaps Necessity as well as Choice was concerned in it. Seems it not conceivable that, in a Life like our Professor's, where so much bountifully given by Nature had in Practice failed and misgone, Literature also would never rightly prosper: that striving with his characteristic vehemence to paint this and the other Picture, and ever without success, he at last desperately dashes his sponge, full of all colors, against the canvas, to try whether it will paint Foam? With all his stillness, there were perhaps in Teufelsdröckh desperation enough for this.

A second conjecture we hazard with even less warranty. It is, that Teufelsdröckh is not without some touch of the universal feeling, a wish to proselytize. How often already have we paused, uncertain whether the basis of this so enigmatic nature were really Stoicism and Despair, or Love and Hope only seared into the figure of these! Remarkable, moreover, is this saying of his: "How were Friendship possible? In mutual devotedness to the Good and True: otherwise impossible; except as Armed Neutrality, or hollow Commercial League. A man, be the Heavens ever praised, is sufficient for himself; yet were ten men, united in Love, capable of being and of doing what ten thousand singly would fail in. Infinite is the help man can yield to man." And now in conjunction therewith consider this other: "It is the Night of the World, and still long till it be Day: we wander amid the glimmer of smoking ruins, and the Sun and the Stars of Heaven are as if blotted out for a season and two immeasurable Phantoms, HYPOCRISY and ATHEISM, with the Gowl SENSUALITY, stalk abroad over the Earth, and call it theirs: well at ease are the Sleepers for whom Existence is a shallow Dream."

But what of the awestruck Wakeful who find it a Reality? Should not these unite; since even an authentic Spectre is not visible to Two?—In which case were this enormous Clothes-Volume properly an enormous pitchpan, which our Teufelsdröckh in his lone watchtower had kindled, that it might flame far and wide through the Night, and many a disconsolately wandering spirit be guided thither to a Brother's bosom!—We say as before, with all his malign Indifference, who knows what mad Hopes this man may harbor?

Meanwhile there is one fact to be stated here, which harmonizes ill with such conjectures; and, indeed, were Teufelsdröckh made like other men, might as good as altogether subvert it. Namely, that while the Beacon-fire blazed its brightest, the Watchman had quitted it; that no pilgrim could now ask him: Watchman, what of the Night? Professor Teufelsdröckh, be it known, is no longer visibly present at Weissnichtwo, but again to all appearance lost in space! Some time ago, the Hofrath Heuschrecke was pleased to favor us with another copious Epistle; wherein much is said about the "Population-Institute;" much repeated in praise of the Paper-bag Documents, the hieroglyphic nature of which our Hofrath still seems not to have surmised; and lastly, the strangest occurrence communicated, to us for the first time, in the following paragraph:

"Ew. Wohlgeboren will have seen from the public Prints, with what affectionate and hitherto fruitless solicitude Weissnichtwo regards the disappearance of her Sage. Might but the united voice of Germany, prevail on him to return; nay, could we but so much as elucidate for ourselves by what mystery he went away! But, alas, old Lieschen experiences or affects the profoundest deafness, the profoundest ignorance: in the Wahngasse all lies swept, silent, sealed up; the Privy Council itself can hitherto elicit no answer.

"It had been remarked that while the agitating news of those Parisian Three Days flew from mouth to mouth, and dinned every ear in Weissnichtwo, Herr Teufelsdröckh was not known at the Gans or elsewhere, to have spoken, for a whole week, any syllable except once these three: Es geht *an* (It is beginning). Shortly after, as *Ew. Wohlgeboren* knows, was the public tranquillity here, as in Berlin, threatened by a Sedition of the Tailors. Nor did there want Evil-wishers, or perhaps mere desperate Alarmists, who asserted that the closing Chapter of the Clothes-Volume was to blame. In this appalling crisis, the serenity of our Philosopher was indescribable; nay, perhaps through one humble individual, something thereof might pass into the *Rath* (Council) itself, and so contribute to the country's deliverance. The Tailors are now entirely pacificated.—

"To neither of these two incidents can I attribute our loss: yet still comes there the shadow of a suspicion out of Paris and its Politics. For example when the *Saint-Simonian Society* transmitted its Proposition hither, and the whole *Gans* was one vast cackle of laughter, lamentation and astonishment, our Sage sat mute; and at the end of the third evening said merely: 'Here also are men who have discovered, not without amazement, that Man is still Man; of which high, long-forgotten Truth you already see them make a false application.' Since then, as has been ascertained by examination of the Post-Director, there passed at least one Letter with its Answer between the Messieurs Bazard-Enfantin and our Professor himself; of what tenor can now only be conjectured. On the fifth night following, he was seen for the last time!

"Has this invaluable man, so obnoxious to most of the hostile Sects that convulse our Era, been spirited away by certain of their emissaries; or did he go forth voluntarily to their headquarters to confer with them and confront them? Reason we have, at least of a negative sort, to believe the Lost still living; our widowed heart also whispers that ere long he will himself give a sign. Otherwise, indeed, his archives must, one day, be opened by Authority; where much, perhaps the *Palingenesie* itself, is thought to be reposited."

Thus far the Hofrath: who vanishes, as is his wont, too like an Ignis Fatuus, leaving the dark still darker.

So that Teufelsdröckh's public History were not done, then, or reduced to an even, unromantic, tenor: nay, perhaps the better part thereof were only beginning? We stand in a region of conjectures, where substance has melted into shadow, and one cannot be distinguished from the other. May time, which solves or suppresses all problems, throw glad light on this also! Our own private conjecture, now amounting almost to certainty, is that, safe-moored in some stillest obscurity, not to lie always still, Teufelsdröckh is actually in London!

Here, however, can the present Editor, with an ambrosial joy as of over-weariness falling into sleep, lay down his pen. Well does he know, if human testimony be worth aught, that to innumerable British readers likewise, this is a satisfying consummation; that innumerable British readers consider him, during these current months, but as an uneasy interruption to their ways of thought and digestion; and indicate so much, not without a certain irritancy and even spoken invective. For which, as for other mercies, ought not he to thank the Upper Powers? To one and all of you, O irritated readers, he, with outstretched arms and open heart, will wave a kind farewell. Thou too, miraculous Entity, who namest thyself YORKE and OLIVER, and with thy vivacities and genialities, with thy all-too Irish mirth and madness, and odor of palled punch, makes such strange work, farewell; long as thou canst fare-*well!* Have we not, in the course of Eternity, travelled some months of our Life-journey in partial sight of one another; have we not existed together, though in a state of quarrel?

APPENDIX.

THIS questionable little Book was undoubtedly written among the mountain solitudes, in 1831; but, owing to impediments natural and accidental, could not, for seven years more, appear as a Volume in England;—and had at last to clip itself in pieces, and be content to struggle out, bit by bit, in some courageous *Magazine* that offered. Whereby now, to certain idly curious readers, and even to myself till I make study, the insignificant but at last irritating question, What its real history and chronology are, is, if not insoluble, considerably involved in haze.

To the first English Edition, 1838, which an American, or two Americans, had now opened the way for, there was slightingly prefixed, under the title *"Testimonies of Authors,"* some straggle of real documents, which, now that I find it again, sets the matter into clear light and sequence;—and shall here, for removal of idle stumbling-blocks and nugatory guessings from the path of every reader, be reprinted as it stood. (*Author's Note of* 1868.)

TESTIMONIES OF AUTHORS.

I. HIGHEST CLASS, BOOKSELLER'S TASTER.

Taster to Bookseller.—"The Author of *Teufelsdröckh* is a person of talent; his work displays here and there some felicity of thought and expression, considerable fancy and knowledge: but whether or not it would take with the public seems doubtful. For a *jeu d'esprit* of that kind it is too long; it would have suited better as an essay or article than as a volume. The Author has no great tact; his wit is frequently heavy; and reminds one of the German Baron who took to leaping on tables, and answered that he was learning to be lively. *Is* the work a translation?"

Bookseller to Editor.—"Allow me to say that such a writer requires only a little more tact to produce a popular as well as an able work. Directly on receiving your permission, I sent your MS. to a gentleman in the highest class of men of letters, and an accomplished German scholar: I now enclose you his opinion, which, you may rely upon it, is a just one; and I have too high an opinion of your good sense to" etc., etc.—MS. (*penes nos*), London, 17th September, 1831.

II. CRITIC OF THE SUN.

"*Fraser's Magazine* exhibits the usual brilliancy, and also the" etc. "*Sartor Resartus* is what old Dennis used to call 'a heap of clotted nonsense,' mixed, however, here and there, with passages marked by thought and striking poetic vigor. But what does the writer mean by 'Baphometic fire-baptism'? Why cannot he lay aside his pedantry, and write so as to make himself generally intelligible? We quote by way of curiosity a sentence from the *Sartor Resartus;* which may be read either backwards or forwards, for it is equally intelligible either way: indeed, by beginning at the tail, and so working up to the head, we think the reader will stand the fairest chance of getting at its meaning: 'The fire-baptized soul, long so scathed and thunder-riven, here feels its own freedom; which feeling is its Baphometic baptism: the citadel of its whole kingdom it has thus gained by assault, and will keep inexpugnable; outwards from which the remaining dominions, not indeed without hard battering, will doubtless by degrees be conquered and pacificated.' Here is a"—*Sun Newspaper, 1st April,* 1834.

III. NORTH-AMERICAN REVIEWER.

. . . "After a careful survey of the whole ground, our belief is that no such persons as Professor Teufelsdröckh or Counselor Heuschrecke ever existed; that the six Paper-bags, with their China-ink inscriptions and multifarious contents, are a mere figment of the brain; that the 'present Editor' is the only person who has ever written upon the Philosophy of Clothes; and that the *Sartor Resartus* is the only treatise that has yet appeared upon that subject;—in short, that the whole account of the origin of the work before us, which the supposed Editor relates with so much gravity, and of which we have given a brief abstract, is, in plain English, a *hum.*

"Without troubling our readers at any great length with our reasons for entertaining these suspicions, we may remark, that the absence of all other information on the subject, except what is contained in the work, is itself a fact of a most significant character. The whole German press, as well as the particular one where the work purports to have been printed, seems to be under the control of *Stillschweigen and Co.*—Silence and Company. If the Clothes-Philosophy and its author are making so great a sensation throughout Germany as is pretended, how happens it that the only notice we have of the fact is contained in a few numbers of a monthly Magazine published at London? How happens it that no intelligence about the matter has come out directly to this country? We pique ourselves here in New England upon knowing at least as much of what is going on in the literary way in the old Dutch Mother-land as our brethren of the fast-anchored Isle; but thus far we have no tidings whatever of the 'extensive close-printed close-meditated volume,' which forms the subject of this pretended commentary. Again, we would respectfully inquire of the 'present Editor' upon what part of the map of Germany we are to look for the city of *Weissnichtwo*—'Know-not-where,' —at which place the work is supposed to have been printed, and the Author to have resided. It has been our fortune to visit several portions of the German territory, and to examine pretty carefully, at different times and for various purposes, maps of the whole; but we have no recollection of any such place. We suspect that the city of *Know-not-where* might be called, with at least as much propriety, *Nobody-knows-where,* and is to be found in the kingdom of *Nowhere.* Again, the village of *Entepfuhl*—'Duck-pond'—where the supposed Author of the work is said to have passed his youth, and that of *Hinterschlag,* where he had his education, are equally foreign to our geography. Duck-ponds enough there undoubtedly are in almost every village in Germany, as the traveler in that country knows too well to his cost, but any particular village denominated Duck-pond is to us altogether *terra incognita.* The names of the personages are not less singular than those of the places. Who can refrain from a smile at the yoking together of such a pair of appellatives as Diogenes Teufelsdröckh? The supposed bearer of this strange title is represented as admitting, in his pretended auto-biography, that 'he had searched to no purpose through all the Heralds' books in and without the German empire, and through all manner of Subscribers'-lists, Militia-rolls, and other Name-catalogues,' but had nowhere been able to find 'the name Teufelsdröckh, except as appended to his own person.' We can readily believe this, and we doubt very much whether any Christian parent would think of condemning a son to carry through life the burden of so unpleasant a title. That of Counselor Heuschrecke—'Grasshopper'—though not offensive, looks much more like a piece of fancy work than a 'fair business transaction.' The same may be said of Blumine—'Flower-Goddess'—the heroine of the fable; and so of the rest.

"In short, our private opinion is, as we have remarked, that the whole story of a correspondence with Germany, a university of Nobody-knows-where, a Pro-fessor of Things in General, a Counselor Grasshopper, a Flower-Goddess Blumine, and so forth, has about as much foundation in truth as the late enter-taining account of Sir John Herschel's discoveries in the moon. Fictions of this kind are, however, not uncommon, and ought not, perhaps, to be condemned with too much severity; but we are not sure that we can exercise the same indulgence in regard to the attempt, which seems to be made to mislead the public as to the substance of the work before us, and its pretended German original. Both purport, as we have seen, to be upon the subject of Clothes, or dress. Clothes, their Origin and Influence, is the title of the supposed German treatise of Pro-fessor Teufelsdröckh, and the rather odd name of Sartor Resartus—the Tailor Patched—which the present Editor has affixed to his pretended commentary, seems to look the same way. But though there is a good deal of remark through-out the work in a half-serious, half-comic style upon dress, it seems to be in reality a treatise upon the great science of Things in General, which Teufels-dröckh is supposed to have professed at the university of Nobody-knows-where. Now, without intending to adopt a too rigid standard of morals, we own that we doubt a little the propriety of offering to the public a treatise on Things in Gen-eral, under the name and in the form of an Essay on Dress. For ourselves, ad-vanced as we unfortunately are in the journey of life, far beyond the period when dress is practically a matter of interest, we have no hesitation in saying, that the real subject of the work is to us more attractive than the ostensible one. But this is probably not the case with the mass of readers. To the younger portion of the community, which constitutes everywhere the very great majority, the sub-ject of dress is one of intense and paramount importance. An author who treats it, appeals like the poet, to the young men and maidens—virginibus puerisque—and calls upon them, by all the motives which habitually operate most strongly upon their feelings, to buy his book. When, after opening their purses for this purpose, they have carried home the work in triumph, expecting to find in it some particu-lar instruction in regard to the tying of their neckcloths, or the cut of their corsets, and meet with nothing better than a dissertation on Things in General, they will—to use the mildest term—not be in very good humor. If the last im-provements in legislation, which we have made in this country, should have found their way to England, the author, we think, would stand some chance of being Lynched. Whether his object in this piece of supercherie be merely pecuniary profit, or whether he takes a malicious pleasure in quizzing the Dandies, we shall not undertake to say. In the latter part of the work, he devotes a separate chapter to this class of persons, from the tenor of which we should be disposed to conclude, that he would consider any mode of divesting them of their property very much in the nature of a spoiling of the Egyptians.

"The only thing about the work, tending to prove that it is what it purports to be, a commentary on a real German treatise, is the style, which is a sort of Babylonish dialect, not destitute, it is true, of richness, vigor, and at times a sort of singular felicity of expression, but very strongly tinged throughout with the peculiar idiom of the German language. This quality in the style, however, may be a mere result of a great familiarity with German literature; and we cannot, therefore, look upon it as in itself decisive, still less as outweighing so much evidence of an opposite character."—*North-American Review, No. 89, October,* 1835.

IV. NEW-ENGLAND EDITORS.

"The Editors have been induced, by the express desire of many persons, to collect the following sheets out of the ephemeral pamphlets[1] in which they first appeared, under the conviction that they contain in themselves the assurance of a longer date.

"The Editors have no expectation that this little Work will have a sudden and general popularity. They will not undertake, as there is no need, to justify the gay costume in which the Author delights to dress his thoughts, or the German idioms with which he has sportively sprinkled his pages. It is his humor to advance the gravest speculations upon the gravest topics in a quaint and burlesque style. If his masquerade offend any of his audience, to that degree that they will not hear what he has to say, it may chance to draw others to listen to his wisdom; and what work of imagination can hope to please all? But we will venture to remark that the distaste excited by these peculiarities in some readers is greatest at first, and is soon forgotten; and that the foreign dress and aspect of the Work are quite superficial, and cover a genuine Saxon heart. We believe, no book has been published for many years, written in a more sincere style of idiomatic English, or which discovers an equal mystery over all the riches of the language. The Author makes ample amends for the occasional eccentricity of his genius, not only by frequent bursts of pure splendor, but by the wit and sense which never fail him.

"But what will chiefly commend the Book to the discerning reader is the manifest design of the work, which is, a Criticism upon the Spirit of the Age—we had almost said, of the hour—in which we live; exhibiting in the most just and novel light the present aspects of Religion, Politics, Literature, Arts, and Social Life. Under all his gayety the Writer has an earnest meaning, and discovers an insight into the manifold wants and tendencies of human nature, which is very rare among our popular authors. The philanthropy and the purity of moral sentiment, which inspire the work, will find their way to the heart of every lover of virtue." *Preface to Sartor Resartus; Boston,* 1835, 1837.

SUNT, FUERUNT VEL FUERE.

London, 30th June, 1838.

[1]*Fraser's* (London) *Magazine,* 1833–4.

HEROES, HERO–WORSHIP,
AND
THE HEROIC IN HISTORY

HEROES, HERO-WORSHIP,
AND
THE HEROIC IN HISTORY

LECTURE I.[1]

THE HERO AS DIVINITY—ODIN—PAGANISM—SCANDINAVIAN MYTHOLOGY.

WE HAVE undertaken to discourse here for a little on great men, their manner of appearance in our world's business, how they have shaped themselves in the world's history, what ideas men formed of them, what work they did; on heroes, namely, and on their reception and performance; what I call hero-worship and the heroic in human affairs. Too evidently this is a large topic; deserving quite other treatment then we can expect to give it at present. A large topic; indeed, an illimitable one; wide as universal history itself. For, as I take it, universal history, the history of what man has accomplished in this world, is at bottom the history of the great men who have worked here. They are the leaders of men, these great ones; the modelers, patterns, and in a wide sense creators, of whatsoever the general mass of men contrived to do or to attain; all things that we see standing accomplished in the world are properly the outer material result, the practical realization and embodiment of thoughts that dwelt in the great men sent into the world: the soul of the whole world's history, it may justly be considered, were the history of these. Too clearly it is a topic we shall do no justice to in this place!

One comfort is, that great men taken up in any way, are profitable company. We cannot look, however imperfectly, upon a great man without gaining something by him. He is the living light-fountain, which it is good and pleasant to be near. The light which enlightens, which has enlightened the darkness of the world; and this not as a kindled lamp only, but rather as a natural luminary shining by the gift of Heaven; a flowing light-fountain, as I say, of native original insight, of manhood and heroic nobleness—in whose radiance all souls feel that it is well with them. On any terms whatsoever, you will not grudge to wander in such neighborhood for a while. These six classes of heroes, chosen out of widely-distant countries and epochs, and in mere external figure differing altogether, ought, if we look faithfully at them, to illustrate several things for us. Could we see *them* well, we should get some glimpses into the very marrow of the world's history. How happy, could I but in any measure, in such times as these, make manifest to you the meanings of heroism; the divine relation (for I may well call it such) which in all times unites a great man to other men; and thus, as it were, not exhaust my subject, but so much as break ground on it! At all events I must make the attempt.

[1]Delivered Tuesday, May 5, 1840.

It is well said, in every sense, that a man's religion is the chief fact with regard to him. A man's, or a nation of men's. By religion I do not mean the church-creed which he professes, the articles of faith which he will sign, and, in words or otherwise, assert; not this wholly, in many cases not this at all. We see men of all kinds of professed creeds attain to almost all degrees of worth or worthlessness under each or any of them. This is not what I call religion, this profession and assertion; which is often only a profession and assertion from the outworks of the man, from the mere argumentative region of him, if even so deep as that. But the thing a man does practically believe (and this is often enough *without* asserting it even to himself, much less to others); the thing a man does practically lay to heart and know for certain, concerning his vital relations to this mysterious universe, and his duty and destiny there, that is in all cases the primary thing for him, and creatively determines all the rest. That is his *religion;* or, it may be, his mere skepticism and *no-religion:* the manner it is in which he feels himself to be spiritually related to the unseen world or no-world; and I say, if you tell me what that is, you tell me to a very great extent what the man is, what the kind of things he will do. Of a man or of a nation we inquire, therefore, first of all. What religion they had? Was it Heathenism—plurality of gods, mere sensuous representation of this mystery of life, and for chief recognized element therein physical force? Was it Christianism; faith in an invisible, not as real only, but as the only reality; time, through every meanest moment of it, resting on eternity; pagan empire of force displaced by a nobler supremacy that of holiness? Was it skepticism, uncertainty and inquiry whether there was an unseen world, and mystery of life except a mad one— doubt as to all this, or unbelief and flat denial? Answering of this question is giving us the soul of the history of the man or nation. The thoughts they had were the parents of the actions they did; their feelings were parents of their thoughts: it was the unseen and spiritual in them that determined the outward and actual; their religion, as I say, was the great fact about them. In these discourses limited as we are, it will be good to direct our survey chiefly to that religious phasis of the matter. That once known well, all is known. We have chosen as the first hero in our series, Odin the central figure of Scandinavian paganism; an emblem to us of a most extensive province of things. Let us look for a little at the hero as divinity, the oldest primary form of heroism.

Surely it seems a very strange-looking thing this paganism; almost inconceivable to us in these days. A bewildering, inextricable jungle of delusions, confusions, falsehoods and absurdities, covering the whole field of life! A thing that fills us with astonishment, almost, if it were possible, with incredulity—for truly it is not easy to understand that sane men could ever calmly, with their eyes open, believe and live by such a set of doctrines. That men should have worshiped their poor fellow-man as a god, and not him only, but stocks and stones, and all manner of animate and inanimate objects; and fashioned for themselves such a distracted chaos of hallucinations by way of theory of the universe: all this looks like an incredible fable.

Nevertheless it is a clear fact that they did it. Such hideous inextricable jungle of misworships, misbeliefs, men, made as we are, did actually hold by, and live at home in. This is strange. Yes, we may pause in sorrow and silence over the depths of darkness that are in man; if we rejoice in the heights of purer vision he has attained to. Such things were and are in man; in all men; in us too.

Some speculators have a short way of accounting for the pagan religion: mere quackery, priestcraft and dupery, say they; no sane man ever did believe it—merely contrived to persuade other men, not worthy of the name of sane, to believe it! It will be often our duty to protest against this sort of hypothesis about men's doings and history; and I here, on the very threshold, protest against it in reference to paganism, and to all other *isms* by which man has ever for a length of time striven to walk in this world. They have all had a truth in them, or men would not have taken them up. Quackery and dupery do abound; in religions, above all in the more advanced decaying stages of religions, they have fearfully abounded: but quackery was never the originating influence in such things; it was not the health and life of such things, but their disease, their sure precursor of their being about to die! Let us never forget this. It seems to me a most mournful hypothesis, that of quackery giving birth to any faith even in savage men. Quackery gives birth to nothing; gives death to all things. We shall not see into the true heart of anything, if we look merely at the quackeries of it; if we do not reject the quackeries altogether; as mere diseases, corruptions, with which our and all men's sole duty is to have done with them, to sweep them out of our thoughts as out of our practice. Man everywhere is the born enemy of lies. I find grand Lamaism itself to have a kind of truth in it. Read the candid, clear-sighted, rather skeptical Mr. Turner's "Account of his Embassy" to that country and see. They have their belief, these poor Thibet people, that Providence sends down always an incarnation of Himself into every generation. At bottom some belief in a kind of pope! At bottom still better, belief that there is a *greatest* man; that *he* is discoverable; that, once discovered, we ought to treat him with an obedience which knows no bounds. This is the truth of grand Lamaism; the "discoverability" is the only error here. The Thibet priests have methods of their own of discovering what man is greatest, fit to be supreme over them. Bad methods: but they are so much worse than our methods—of understanding him to be always the eldest-born of a certain genealogy? Alas, it is a difficult thing to find good methods for! We shall begin to have a chance of understanding paganism, when we first admit that to its followers it was, at one time, earnestly true. Let us consider it very certain that men did believe in paganism; men with open eyes, sound senses, men made altogether like ourselves; that we, had we been there, should have believed in it. Ask now, What paganism could have been?

Another theory, somewhat more respectable, attributes such things to allegory. It was a play of poetic minds, say these theorists; a shadowing-forth, in allegorical fable, in personification and visual form, of what such poetic minds had known and felt of this universe. Which agrees, add they, with a primary law of human nature, still everywhere observably at work, though in less important things. That what a man feel intensely, he struggles to speak-out of him, to see represented before him in visual shape, and as if with a kind of life and historical reality in it. Now doubtless there is such a law, and it is one of the deepest in human nature; neither need we doubt that it did operate fundamentally in this business. The hypothesis which ascribes paganism wholly or mostly to this agency, I call a little more respectable; but I cannot yet call it the true hypothesis. Think, would *we* believe, and take with us as our life-guidance, an allegory, a poetic sport? Not sport but earnest is what we should require. It is a most earnest thing to be alive in this world; to die is not sport for a man. Man's life never was a sport to him; it was a stern reality, altogether a serious matter to be alive!

I find therefore, that though these allegory theorists are on the way toward truth in this matter, they have not reached it either. Pagan religion is indeed an allegory, a symbol of what men felt and knew about the universe; and all religions are symbols of that, altering always as that alters: but it seems to me a radical perversion and even *in*version, of the business, to put that forward as the origin and moving cause, when it was rather the result and termination. To get beautiful allegories, a perfect poetic symbol, was not the want of men; but to know what they were to believe about this universe, what course they were to steer in it; what, in this mysterious life of theirs, they had to hope and to fear, to do and to forbear doing. The "Pilgrim's Progress" is an allegory and a beautiful, just and serious one: but consider whether Bunyan's allegory could have *preceded* the faith it symbolizes! The faith had to be already there, standing believed by everybody— of which the allegory could *then* become a shadow; and, with all its seriousness, we may say a *sportful* shadow, a mere play of the fancy, in comparison with that awful fact and scientific certainty which it poetically strives to emblem. The allegory is the product of the certainty, not the producer of it; not in Bunyan's nor in any other case. For paganism, therefore, we have still to inquire, whence came that scientific certainty, the parent of such a bewildered heap of allegories, errors and confusions? How was it, what was it?

Surely it were a foolish attempt to pretend "explaining," in this place, or in any place, such a phenomenon as that far-distant distracted cloudy imbroglio of paganism—more like a cloudfield than a distant continent of firm land and facts! It is no longer a reality, yet it was one. We ought to understand that this seeming cloudfield was once a reality; that not poetic allegory, least of all that dupery and deception was the origin of it. Men, I say, never did believe idle songs, never risked their soul's life on allegories: men in all times, especially in early earnest times, have had an instinct for detecting quacks, for detesting quacks. Let us try if, leaving out both the quack theory and the allegory one and listening with affectionate attention to that far-off confused rumor of the pagan ages, we cannot ascertain so much as this at least: that there was a kind of fact at the heart of them; that they too were not mendacious and distracted, but in their own poor way true and sane!

You remember that fancy of Plato's, of a man who had grown to maturity in some dark distance and was brought on a sudden into the upper air to see the sun rise. What would his wonder be, his rapt astonishment at the sight we daily witness with indifference! With the free open sense of a child, yet with the ripe faculty of a man, his whole heart would be kindled by that sight, he would discern it well to be godlike, his soul would fall down in worship before it. Now, just such a childlike greatness was in the primitive nations. The first pagan thinker among rude men, the first man that began to think, was precisely this child-man of Plato's. Simple, open as a child, yet with the depth and strength of a man. Nature had as yet no name to him; he had not yet united under a name the infinite variety of sights, sounds, shapes and motions, which we now collectively name universe, nature, or the like—and so with a name dismiss it from us. To the wild deep-hearted man all was yet new, not veiled under names or formulas; it stood naked, flashing-in on him there, beautiful, awful, unspeakable. Nature was to this man, what to the thinker and prophet it forever is, *preter*natural. This green flowery rock-built earth, the trees, the mountains, rivers, many-sounding seas; that great deep sea of azure that swims overhead; the winds sweeping through it; the black cloud fashioning itself together, now pouring out fire, now hail and rain; what *is* it? Ay, what? At bottom we do not yet know; we can never know at all. It is not by our superior insight that we escape the difficulty; it is by our superior levity, our inattention, our *want* of insight. It is by *not* thinking that we cease to wonder at it. Hardened round us, encasing wholly every notion we form, is a wrappage of traditions, hearsays, mere *words*. We call that fire of the black thunder-cloud "electricity," and lecture learnedly about it and grind the like of it out of glass and silk: but *what* is it? What made it? Whence comes it? Whither goes it? Science has done much for us; but it is a poor science that would hide from us the great deep sacred infinitude of nescience, whither we can never penetrate, on which all science swims as a mere superficial film. This world, after all our science and sciences, is still a miracle; wonderful, inscrutable, *magical* and more, to whosoever will *think* of it.

That great mystery of time, were there no other; the illimitable, silent, never-resting thing called time, rolling, rushing on, swift, silent, like an all-embracing ocean-tide, on which we and all the universe swim like exhalations, like apparitions which *are* and then *are not*: this is forever very literally a miracle; a thing to strike us dumb—for we have no word to speak about it. This universe, ah me—what could the wild man know of it; what can we yet know? That it is a force and thousandfold complexity of forces; a force which is *not we*. That is all; it is not we, it is altogether different from *us*. Force, force, everywhere force; we ourselves a mysterious force in the center of that. "There is not a leaf rotting on the highway but has force in it: how else could it rot?" Nay surely, to the atheistic thinker, if such a one were possible, it must be a miracle too, this huge illimitable whirlwind of force, which envelopes us here; never-resting whirlwind, high as immensity, old as eternity. What is it? God's creation, the religious people answer; it is the Almighty God's! Atheistic science babbles poorly of it, with scientific nomenclatures, experiments and what not, as if it were a poor dead thing, to be bottled up in Leyden jars and sold over counters: but the natural sense of man, in all times, if he will honestly apply his sense, proclaims to be a living thing—ah, an unspeakable, godlike thing; toward which the best attitude for us, after never so much science, is awe, devout prostration and humility of soul; worship if not in words, then in silence.

But now I remark further: What in such a time as ours it requires a prophet or poet to teach us, namely, the stripping-off of those poor undevout wrappages, nomenclatures and scientific hearsays—this, the ancient earnest soul, as yet unencumbered with these things, did for itself. The world, which is now divine only to the gifted was then divine to whosoever would turn his eye upon it. He stood bare before it face to face. "All was godlike or god:" Jean Paul still finds it so; the giant Jean Paul, who has power to escape out of hearsays; but there then were no hearsays. Canopus shining-down over the desert, with its blue diamond brightness (that wild blue spirit-like brightness, far brighter than we ever witness here), would pierce into the heart of the wild Ishmaelitish man, whom it was guiding through the solitary waste there. To his wild heart, with all feelings in it, with no *speech* for any feeling, it might seem a little eye, that Canopus, glancing-out on him from the great deep eternity; revealing the inner splendor to him. Cannot we understand how these men *worshiped* Canopus; became what we call Sabeans, worshiping the stars? Such is to me the secret of all forms of paganism. Worship is transcendent wonder; wonder for which there is now no limit or measure; that is worship. To these primeval men, all things and everything they saw exist beside them were an emblem of the godlike, of some god.

And look what perennial fiber of truth was in that. To us also, through every star, through every blade of grass, is not a god made visible, if we will open our minds and eyes? We do not worship in that way now: but is it not reckoned still a merit, proof of what we call a "poetic nature," that we recognize how every object has a divine beauty in it; how every object still verily is "a window though which we may look into infinitude itself?" He that can discern the loveliness of things, we call him poet, painter, man of genius, gifted, lovable. These poor Sabeans did even what he does—in their own fashion. That they did it, in what fashion soever, was a merit: better than what the entirely stupid man did, what the horse and camel did—namely, nothing!

But now if all things whatsoever that we look upon are emblems to us of the highest god, I add that more so than any of them is man such an emblem. You have heard of St. Chrysostom's celebrated saying in reference to the shekinah, or ark of testimony, visible revelation of God, among the Hebrews: "The true shekinah is man!" Yes, it is even: so this is no vain phrase; it is veritably so. The essence of our being, the mystery in us that calls itself "I"—ah, what words have we for such things?—is a breath of heaven; the highest being reveals himself in man. This body, these faculties, this life of ours, is it not all as a vesture for that unnamed? "There is but one temple in the universe," says the devout Novalis, "and that is the body of man. Nothing is holier than that high form. Bending before men is a reverence done to this revelation in the flesh. We touch heaven when we lay our hand on a human body!" This sounds much like a mere flourish of rhetoric; but it is not so. If well meditated, it will turn out to be a scientific fact; the expression, in such words as can be had, of the actual truth of the thing. *We* are the miracle of miracles—the great inscrutable mystery of God. We cannot understand it, we know not how to speak of it; but we may feel and know, if we like, that it is verily so.

Well; these truths were once more readily felt than now. The young generations of the world, who had in them the freshness of young children, and yet the depth of earnest men, who did not think that they had finished-off all things in heaven and earth by merely giving them scientific names, but had to gaze direct at them there, with awe and wonder: they felt better what of divinity is in man and nature—they, without being mad, could *worship* nature and man more than anything else in nature. Worship, that is, as I said above, admire without limit: this, in the full use of their faculties, with all sincerity of heart, they could do. I consider hero-worship to be the grand modifying element in that ancient system of thought. What I called the perplexed jungle of paganism sprang, we may say, out of many roots: every admiration, adoration of a star or natural object, was a root or fiber of a root; but hero-worship is the deepest root of all; the tap-root, from which in a great degree all the rest were nourished and grown.

And now if worship even of a star had some meaning in it, how much more might that of a hero! Worship of a hero is transcendent admiration of a great man. I say great men are still admirable; I say there is, at bottom, nothing else admirable! No nobler feeling than this of admiration for one higher than himself dwells in the breast of man. It is to this hour, and at all hours, the vivifying influence in man's life. Religions I find stand upon it; not paganism only, but far higher and truer religions—all religion hitherto known. Hero-worship, heartfelt prostrate admiration, submission, burning, boundless, for a noblest godlike form of man—is not that the germ of Christianity itself? The greatest of all heroes is one—whom we do not name here! Let sacred silence meditate that sacred matter; you will find it the ultimate perfection of a principle extant throughout man's whole history on earth.

Or coming into lower, less *un*speakable provinces, is not all loyalty akin to religious faith also? Faith is loyalty to some inspired teacher, some spiritual hero. And what therefore is loyalty proper, the life-breath of all society, but an effluence of hero-worship, submissive admiration for the truly great? Society is founded on hero-worship. All dignities of rank, on which human association rests, are what we might call a *Hero*archy (government of heroes), or a hierarchy, for it is "sacred" enough withal! The duke means *dux*, leader; king is *kön-ning, kan-ning,* man that *knows* or *cans.* Society everywhere is some representation, not *in*supportably inaccurate, of a graduated worship of heroes—reverence and obedience done to men really great and wise. Not *in*supportably inaccurate, I say! They are all as bank-notes, these social dignitaries, all representing gold—and several of them, alas, always are *forged* notes. We can do with some forged false notes; with a good many even; but not with all, or the most of them forged! No: there have to come revolutions then; cries of democracy, liberty and equality and I know not what—the notes being all false and no gold to be had for *them,* people take to crying in their despair that there is no gold, that there never was any! "Gold," hero-worship, *is* nevertheless, as it was always and everywhere and cannot cease till man himself ceases.

I am well aware that in these days hero-worship, the thing I call hero-worship, professes to have gone out and finally ceased. This, for reasons which it will be worth while some time to inquire into, is an age that as it were denies the existence of great men; denies the desirableness of great men. Show our critics a great man, a Luther for example, they begin to what they call "account" for him; not to worship him, but take the dimen-sions of him—and bring him out to be a little kind of man! He was the "creature of the time," they say; the time called him forth, the time did everything, he nothing—but what we the little critic could have done too! This seems to me but melancholy work. The time call forth? Alas, we have known times *call* loudly enough for their great man; but not find him when they called! He was not there; providence had not sent him; the time, *calling* its loudest, had to go down to confusion and wreck because he would not come when called.

For if we will think of it, no time need have gone to ruin, could it have *found* a man great enough, a man wise and good enough: wisdom to discern truly what the time wanted, valor to lead it on the right road thither; these are the salvation of any time. But I liken common languid times, with their unbelief, distress, perplexity, with their languid doubting characters and embarrassed circumstances, impotently crumbling-down into ever worse distress toward final ruin—all this I liked to dry dead fuel, waiting for the lightning out of heaven that shall kindle it. The great man, with his free force direct out of God's own hand, is the lightning. His word is the wise healing word which all can believe in. All blazes round him now, when he has once struck on it, into fire like his own. The dry moldering sticks are thought to have called him forth. They did want him greatly; but as to call him forth—— Those are critics of small vision, I think, who cry: "See, is it not the sticks that made the fire?" No sadder proof can be given by a man of his own littleness than disbelief in great men. There is no sadder symptom of a generation than such general blindness to the spiritual lightning, with faith only in the heap of barren dead fuel. It is the last consummation of unbelief. In all epochs of the world's history, we shall find the great man to have been the indispensable savior of his epoch—the lightning, without which the fuel never would have burned. The history of the world, I said already, was the biography of great men.

Such small critics do what they can to promote unbelief and universal spiritual paralysis: but happily they cannot always completely succeed. In all times it is possible for a man to arise great enough to feel that they and their doctrines are chimeras and cobwebs. And what is notable, in no time whatever can they entirely eradicate out of living men's hearts a certain altogether peculiar reverence for great men; genuine admiration, loyalty, adoration, however dim and perverted it may be. Hero-worship endures forever while man endures. Boswell venerates his Johnson, right truly even in the eighteenth century. The unbelieving French believe in their Voltaire; and burst out round him into very curious hero-worship, in that last act of his life when they "stifle him under roses." It has always seemed to me extremely curious this of Voltaire. Truly, if Christianity be the highest instance of hero-worship, then we may find here in Voltaireism one of the lowest! He whose life was that of a kind of Antichrist, does again on this side exhibit a curious contrast. No people ever were so little prone to admire at all as those French of Voltaire. *Persiflage* was the character of their whole mind; adoration had nowhere a place in it. You see! The old man of Ferney comes up to Paris; an old, tottering, infirm man 84 years old. They feel that he too is a kind of hero; that he has spent his life in opposing error and injustice, delivering Calases, unmasking hypocrites in high places—in short that *he* too, though in a strange way, has fought like a valiant man. They feel withal that, if *persiflage* be the great thing, there never was such a *persifleur*. He is the realized ideal of every one of them; the thing they are all wanting to be; of all Frenchmen the most French. *He* is properly their god—such god as they are fit for. Accordingly all persons, from the Queen Antoinette to the Douanier at the Porte St. Denis, do they not worship him? People of quality disguise themselves as tavern-waiters. The Maître de Poste, with a broad oath, orders his postillion, "*Va bon train;* thou art driving M. de Voltaire." At Paris his carriage is "the nucleus of a comet, whose train fills whole streets." The ladies pluck a hair or two from his fur, to keep it as a sacred relic. There was nothing highest, beautifulest, noblest in all France, that did not feel this man to be higher, beautifuler, nobler.

Yes, from Norse Odin to English Samuel Johnson, from the divine founder of Christianity to the withered pontiff of encyclopedism, in all times and places, the hero has been worshiped. It will ever be so. We all love great men; love, venerate and bow down submissive before great men: nay, can we honestly bow down to anything else? Ah, does not every true man feel that he is himself made higher by doing reverence to what is really above him? No nobler or more blessed feeling dwells in man's heart. And to me it is very cheering to consider that no skeptical logic, or general triviality, insincerity and aridity of any time and its influences can destroy this noble inborn loyalty and worship that is in man. In times of unbelief, which soon have to become times of revolution, much down-rushing, sorrowful decay and ruin is visible to everybody. For myself in these days, I seem to see in this indestructibility of hero-worship the everlasting adamant lower than which the confused wreck of revolutionary things cannot fall. The confused wreck of things crumbling and even crashing and tumbling all round us in these revolutionary ages, will get down so far; *no* farther. It is an eternal corner-stone, from which they can begin to build themselves up again. That man, in some sense or other, worships heroes; that we all of us reverence and must ever reverence great men: this is, to me, the living rock amid all rushings-down whatsoever—the one fixed point in modern revolutionary history, otherwise as if bottomless and shoreless.

So much of truth, only under an ancient obsolete vesture, but the spirit of it still true, do I find in the paganism of old nations. Nature is still divine, the revelation of the workings of God; the hero is still worshipable: this, under poor cramped incipient forms, is what all pagan religions have struggled, as they could, to set forth. I think Scandinavian paganism, to us here, is more interesting than any other. It is, for one thing, the latest; it continued in these regions of Europe till the eleventh century: eight hundred years ago the Norwegians were still worshipers of Odin. It is interesting also as the creed of our fathers; the men whose blood still runs in our veins, whom doubtless we still resemble in so many ways strange: they did believe that, while we believe so differently. Let us look a little at this poor Norse creed, for many reasons. We have tolerable means to do it; for there is another point of interest in these Scandinavian mythologies: that they have been preserved so well.

In that strange island Iceland—burst-up, the geologists say, by fire from the bottom of the sea; a wild land of barrenness and lava; swallowed many months of every year in black tempests, yet with a wild gleaming beauty in summer-time; towering up there, stern and grim, in the North Ocean; with its snow jokuls, roaring geysers, sulphur-pools and horrid volcanic chasms, like the waste chaotic battle-field of frost and fire—where of all places we least looked for literature or written memorials, the record of these things was written down. On the seaboard of this wild land is a rim of grassy country where cattle can subsist, and men by means of them and of what the sea yields; and it seems they were poetic men these, men who had deep thoughts in them, and uttered musically their thoughts. Much would be lost, had Iceland not been burst-up from the sea, not been discovered by the Northmen! The old Norse poets were many of them natives of Iceland.

Sæmund, one of the early Christian priests there, who perhaps had a lingering fondness for paganism, collected certain of their old pagan songs, just about becoming obsolete then—poems or chants of a mythic, prophetic, mostly all of a religious character: that is what Norse critics call the *Elder* or poetic *Edda*. *Edda*, a word of uncertain etymology, is thought to signify *Ancestress*. Snorro Sturleson, an Iceland gentleman, an extremely notable personage, educated by this Sæmund's grandson, took in hand next, near a century afterward, to put together, among several books he wrote, a kind of prose synopsis of the whole mythology; elucidated by new fragments of traditionary verse. A work constructed really with great ingenuity, native talent, what one might call unconscious art; altogether a perspicuous clear work, pleasant reading still: This is the *Younger* or prose *Edda*. By these and the numerous other *Sagas*, mostly Icelandic, with the commentaries, Icelandic or not, which go on zealously in the north to this day, it is possible to gain some direct insight even yet; and see that old Norse system of belief, as it were, face to face. Let us forget that it is erroneous religion; let us look at it as old thought and try if we cannot sympathize with it somewhat.

The primary characteristic of his old Northland mythology I find to be impersonation of the visible workings of nature. Earnest simple recognition of the workings of physical nature, as a thing wholly miraculous, stupendous and divine. What we now lecture of as science, they wondered at and fell down in awe before, as religion. The dark hostile powers of nature they figure to themselves as "*Jötuns*," giants, huge shaggy beings of a demonic character. Frost, fire, sea-tempest; these are Jötuns. The friendly powers again, as summer-heat, the sun, are gods. The empire of this universe is divided between these two; they dwell apart, in perennial internecine feud. The gods dwell above in Asgard, the garden of the Asen, or divinities; Jötunheim, a distant dark chaotic land, is the home of the Jötuns.

Curious all this; and not idle or inane, if we will look at the foundation of it! The power of *fire*, or *flame*, for instance, which we designate by some trivial chemical name, thereby hiding from ourselves the essential character of wonder that dwells in it as in all things, is with these old Northmen, Loke, a most swift subtle *demon*, of the brood of the Jötuns. The savages of the Ladrones Islands too (say some Spanish voyagers) thought fire, which they never had seen before, was a devil or god, that bit you sharply when you touched it and that lived upon dry wood. From us too, no chemistry, if it had not stupidity to help it, would hide that flame is a wonder. What *is* flame? *Frost* the old Norse seer discerns to be a monstrous hoary Jötun, the giant *Thrym*, *Hrym*; or *Rime*, the old word now nearly obsolete here, but still used in Scotland to signify hoar frost. *Rime* was not then as now a dead chemical thing, but a living Jötun or devil; the monstrous Jötun *Rime* drove home his horses at night, sat "combing their manes"—which horses were *Hail-Clouds*, or fleet *Frost-Winds*. His cows—No, not his, but a kinsman's, the giant Hymir's cows are *Icebergs*: this Hymir "looks at the rocks" with his devil-eye and they *split* in the glance of it.

Thunder was not then mere electricity, vitreous or resinous; it was the god Donner (thunder) or Thor; god also of beneficent summer-heat. The thunder was his wrath; the gathering of the black clouds is the drawing-down of Thor's angry brows; the fire-bolt bursting out of heaven is the all-rending hammer flung from the hand of Thor; he urges his loud chariot over the mountain tops—that is the peal; wrathful he "blows· in his red beard"—that is the rustling storm-blast before the thunder begin. Balder again the white god, the beautiful, the just and benignant (whom the early Christian missionaries found to resemble Christ), is the sun; beautifulest of visible things; wondrous too, and divine still, after all our astronomies and almanacs? But perhaps the notablest god we hear tell of is one of whom Grimm the German etymologist finds trace; the god *Wünsch* or Wish. The god *Wish;* who could give us all that we *wished!* Is not this the sincerest and yet rudest voice of the spirit of man? The *rudest* ideal that man ever formed; which still shows itself in the latest forms of our spiritual culture. Higher considerations have to teach us that the god *Wish* is not the true god.

Of the other gods or Jötuns I will mention only for etymology's sake, that sea-tempest is the Jötun *Aegir*, a very dangerous Jötun; and now to this day, on our river Trent, as I learn the Nottingham bargemen, when the river is in a certain flooded state (a kind of backwater, or eddying swirl it has, very dangerous to them), call it *eager;* they cry out, "have a care, there is the *eager* coming!" Curious; that word surviving like the peak of a submerged world! The *oldest* Nottingham bargemen had believed in the god Aegir. Indeed our English blood too in a good part is Danish, Norse; or rather, at bottom, Danish and Norse and Saxon have no distinction, except a super-ficial one—as of heathen and Christian, or the like. But all over our island we are mingled largely with Danes proper—from the incessant invasions there were: and this of course in a greater proportion along the east coast; the greatest of all, as I find, in the north country. From the humbler upward, all over Scotland, the speech of the common people is still in a singular degree Icelandic; its Germanism has still a peculiar Norse tinge. They too are "Norman," Northmen, if that be any great beauty!

Of the chief god, Odin, we shall speak by and by. Mark at present so much; what the essence of Scandinavian and indeed of all paganism is: a recognition of the forces of nature as godlike, stupendous, personal agencies, as gods and demons. Not inconceivable to us. It is the infant thought of man opening itself, with awe and wonder, on this ever-stupendous universe. To me there is in the Norse system something very genuine, very great and man-like. A broad simplicity, rusticity, so very different from the light graceful-ness of the old Greek paganism, distinguishes this Scandinavian system. It is thought; the genuine thought of deep, rude, earnest minds, fairly opened to the things about them; a face-to-face and heart-to-heart inspection of the things—the first characteristic of all good thought in all times. Not graceful lightness, half-sport, as in the Greek paganism; a certain homely truthfulness and rustic strength, a great rude sincerity, discloses itself here. It is strange, after our beautiful Apollo statues and clear smiling mythuses, to come down upon the Norse gods "brewing ale" to hold their feast with Aegir, the Sea-Jötun; sending out Thor to get the caldron for them in the Jötun country; Thor, after many adventures, clapping the pot on his head, like a huge hat, and walking off with it—quite lost in it, the ears of the pot reaching down to his heels! A kind of vacant hugeness, large awkward gianthood, charac-terizes that Norse system; enormous force, as yet altogether untutored, stalking helpless with large uncertain strides. Consider only their primary mythus of the creation. The gods having got the giant Ymer slain, a giant made by "warm wind," and much confused work, out of the conflict of frost and fire—determined on constructing a world with him. His blood made the sea; his flesh was the land, the rocks his bones; of his eyebrows they formed Asgard their gods'-dwelling; his skull was the great blue vault of immensity, and the brains of it became the clouds. What a hyper-brobdignagian business! Untamed thought, great, giantlike, enormous; to be tamed in due time into the compact greatness, not giantlike, but godlike and stronger than gianthood, of the Shakespeare, the Goethes. Spiritually as well as bodily these men are our progenitors.

I like, too, that representation they have of the tree igdrasil. All life is figured by them as a tree. Igdrasil, the ash-tree of existence, has its roots deep-down in the kingdoms of hela or death; its trunk reaches up heaven high, spreads its boughs over the whole universe: it is the tree of existence. At the foot of it, in the death-kingdom, sit three *Nornas*, fates—the past, present, future; watering its roots from the sacred well. Its "boughs," with their buddings and disleafings—events, things suffered, things done, catastrophes—stretch through all lands and times. Is not every leaf of it a biography, every fiber there an act or word? Its boughs are histories of nations. The rustle of it is the noise of human existence, onward from of old. It grows there, the breath of human passion rustling through it—or storm-tossed, the storm-wind howling through it like the voice of all the gods. It is igdrasil, the tree of existence. It is the past, the present and the future; what was done, what is doing, what will be done; "the infinite conjugation of the verb *to do*." Considering how human things circulate, each inextricably in communion with all—how the word I speak to you to-day is borrowed, not from Ulfila the Mœsogoth only, but from all men since the first man began to speak—I find no similitude so true as this of a tree. Beautiful; altogether beautiful and great. The "*machine* of the universe"—alas, do but think of that in contrast!

Well, it is strange enough this old Norse view of nature; different enough from what we believe of nature. Whence it specially came, one would not like to be compelled to say very minutely! One thing we may say: It came from the thoughts of Norsemen—from the thought, above all, of the *first* Norseman who had an original power of thinking. The first Norse "man of genius," as we should call him! Innumerable men had passed by, across this universe, with a dumb vague wonder, such as the very animals may feel; or with a painful, fruitlessly inquiring wonder, such as men only feel—till the great thinker came, the *original* man, the seer; whose shaped spoken thought awakes the slumbering capability of all into thought. It is ever the way with the thinker, the spiritual hero. What he says, all men were not far from saying, were longing to say. The thoughts of all start up, as from painful enchanted sleep, round his thought; answering to it, Yes, even so! Joyful to men as the dawning of day from night—*is* it not, indeed, the awakening for them from no being into being, from death into life? We still honor such a man; call him poet, genius and so forth: but to these wild men he was a very magician, a worker of miraculous unexpected blessing for them; a prophet, a god! Thought once awakened does not again slumber; unfolds itself into a system of thought; grows, in man after man, generation after generation—till its full stature is reached and *such* system of thought can grow no further, but must give place to another.

For the Norse people, the man now named Odin and chief Norse god, we fancy, was such a man. A teacher and captain of soul and of body; a hero, of worth *im*measurable admiration for whom, transcending the known bounds, became adoration. Has he not the power of articulate thinking; and many other powers, as yet miraculous? So, with boundless gratitude, would the rude Norse heart feel. Has he not solved for them the sphinx-enigma of this universe; given assurance to them of their own destiny there? By him they know now what they have to do here, what to look for hereafter. Existence has become articulate, melodious by him; he first has made life alive! We may call this Odin, the origin of Norse mythology: Odin, or whatever name the first Norse thinker bore while he was a man among men. His view of the universe once promulgated, a like view starts into being in all minds; grows, keeps ever growing, while it continues credible there. In all minds it lay written, but invisibly, as in sympathetic ink; at his word it starts into visibility in all. Nay, in every epoch of the world, the great event, parent of all others, is it not the arrival of a thinker in the world!

One other thing we must not forget; it will explain a little the confusion of these Norse Eddas. They are not one coherent system of thought; but properly the *summation* of several successive systems. All this of the old Norse belief which is flung-out for us, in one level of distance in the Edda, like a picture painted on the same canvas, does not at all stand so in the reality. It stands rather at all manner of distances and depths, of successive generations since the belief first began. All Scandinavian thinkers, since the first of them, contributed to that Scandinavian system of thought; in ever-new elaboration and addition, it is the combined work of them all. What history it had, how it changed from shape to shape, by one thinker's contribution after another, till it got to the full final shape we see it under in the *Edda*, no man will now ever know; *its* councils of Trebisond, councils of Trent, Athanasiuses, Dantes, Luthers, are sunk without echo in the dark night! Only that it had such a history we can all know. Wheresoever a thinker appeared, there in the thing he thought-of was a contribution, accession, a change or revolution made. Alas, the grandest "revolution" of all, the one made by the man Odin himself, is not this too sunk for us like the rest! Of Odin what history? Strange rather to reflect that he *had* a history! That this Odin, in his wild Norse vesture, with his wild beard and eyes, his rude Norse speech and ways, was a man like us; with our sorrows, joys, with our limbs, features—intrinsically all one as we; and did such a work! But the work, much of it, has perished; the worker, all to the name. "*Wednes*day," men will say to-morrow; Odin's day! Of Odin there exists no history; no document of it; no guess about it worth repeating.

Snorro indeed, in the quietest manner, almost in a brief business style, writes down, in his *heimskringla*, how Odin was a heroic prince in the Black Sea region, with twelve peers, and a great people straitened for room. How he led these *Asen* (Asiatics) of his out of Asia; settled them in the north parts of Europe, by warlike conquest; invented letters, poetry and so forth—and came by and by to be worshiped as chief god by these Scandinavians, his twelve peers made into twelve sons of his own, gods like himself; Snorro has no doubt of this. Saxo Grammaticus, a very curious Northman of that same century, is still more unhesitating; scruples not to find out a historical fact in every individual mythus, and writes it down as a terrestrial event in Denmark or elsewhere. Torfæus, learned and cautious, some centuries later, assigns by calculation a *date* for it: Odin, he says, came into Europe about the year 70 before Christ. Of all which, as grounded on mere uncertainties, found to be untenable now, I need say nothing. Far, very far beyond the year 70! Odin's date, adventures, whole terrestrial history, figure and environment are sunk from us forever into unknown thousands of years.

Nay Grimm, the German antiquary, goes so far as to deny that any man Odin ever existed. He proves it by etymology. The word *Wuotan*, which is the original form of *Odin*, a word spread, as name of their chief divinity, over all the Teutonic nations everywhere; this word, which connects itself, according to Grimm, with the Latin *vadere*, with the English *wade* and suchlike—means primarily *movement*, source of movement, power; and is the fit name of the highest god, not of any man. The word signifies divinity, he says, among the old Saxon, German and all Teutonic nations; the adjectives formed from it all signify *divine, supreme,* or something pertaining to the chief god. Like enough! We must bow to Grimm in matters etymological. Let us consider it fixed that *Wuotan* means *wading,* force of *movement.* And now still, what hinders it from being the name of a heroic man and *mover,* as well as of a god? As for the adjectives, and words formed from it—did not the Spaniards in their universal admiration for lope, get into the habit of saying "a lope flower," "a lope *dama,*" if the flower or woman were of surpassing beauty? Had this lasted, *lope* would have grown, in Spain, to be an adjective signifying *godlike* also. Indeed, Adam Smith, in his "Essay on Language," surmises that all adjectives whatsoever were formed precisely in that way; some very green thing, chiefly notable for its greenness, got the appellative name *green,* and then the next thing remarkable for that quality, a tree for instance, was named the *green* tree—as we still say "the *steam* coach," "four-horse coach," or the like. All primary adjectives, according to Smith, were formed in this way; were at first substantives and things. We cannot annihilate a man for etymologies like that! Surely there was a first teacher and captain; surely there must have been an Odin, palpable to the sense at one time; no adjective, but a real hero of flesh and blood! The voice of all tradition, history or echo of history, agrees with all that thought will teach one about it, to assure us of this.

How the man Odin came to be considered a *god,* the chief god? That surely is a question which nobody would wish to dogmatize upon. I have said, his people knew no *limits* to their admiration of him; they had as yet no scale to measure admiration by. Fancy your own generous heart's love of some greatest man expanding till it *transcended* all bounds, till it filled and overflowed the whole field of your thought! Or what if this man Odin—since a great deep soul, with the afflatus and mysterious tide of vision and impulse rushing on him he knows not whence, is ever an enigma, a kind of terror and wonder to himself—should have felt that perhaps *he* was divine; that *he* was some effluence of the "Wuotan," "*movement*," supreme power and divinity, of whom to his rapt vision all nature was the awful flame-image; that some effluence of *Wuotan* dwelt here in him! He was not necessarily false; he was but mistaken, speaking the truest he knew. A great soul, any sincere soul, knows not *what* he is—alternates between the highest height and the lowest depth; can, of all things, the least measure—himself! What others take him for and what he guesses that he may be; these two items strangely act on one another, help to determine one another. With all men reverently admiring him; with his own wild soul full of noble ardors and affections, of whirlwind chaotic darkness and glorious new light; a divine universe bursting all into godlike beauty round him and no man to whom the like ever had befallen, what could he think himself to be? "Wuotan?" All men answered, "Wuotan!"

And then consider what mere time will do in such cases; how if a man was great while living, he becomes tenfold greater when dead. What an enormous *camera-obscura* magnifier is tradition! How a thing grows in the human memory, in the human imagination, when love, worship and all that lies in the human heart, is there to encourage it. And in the darkness, in the entire ignorance; without date or document, no book, no Arundel-marble; only here and there some dumb monumental cairn. Why, in thirty or forty years, were there no books, any great man would grow *mythic*, the contemporaries who had seen him, being once all dead. And in three hundred years and in three thousand years—— To attempt *theorizing* on such matters would profit little: they are matters which refuse to be *theoremed* and diagramed; which logic ought to know that she *cannot* speak of. Enough for us to discern, far in the uttermost distance, some gleam as of a small real light shining in the center of that enormous camera-obscura image; to discern that the center of it all was not a madness and nothing, but a sanity and something.

This light, kindled in the great dark vortex of the Norse mind, dark but living, waiting only for light; this is to me the center of the whole. How such light will then shine out and with wondrous thousandfold expansion spread itself, in forms and colors, depends not on *it*, so much as on the national mind recipient of it. The colors and forms of your light will be those of the *cutglass* it has to shine through. Curious to think how, for every man, any the truest fact is modeled by the nature of the man! I said, the earnest man, speaking to his brother men, must always have stated what seemed to him a *fact*, a real appearance of nature. But the way in which such appearance or fact shaped itself—what sort of *fact* it became for him—was and is modified by his own laws of thinking; deep, subtle, but universal, ever operating laws. The world of nature, for every man, is the phantasy of himself; this world is the multiplex "image of his own dream." Who knows to what unnameable subtleties of spiritual law all these pagan fables owe their shape! The number *twelve*, divisiblest of all, which could be halved, quartered, parted into three, into six, the most remarkable number—this was enough to determine the *signs of the Zodiac*, the number of Odin's *sons* and innumerable other twelves. Any vague rumor of number had a tendency to settle itself into twelve. So with regard to every other matter. And quite unconsciously too—with no notion of building up "allegories!" But the fresh clear glance of those first ages would be prompt in discerning the secret relations of things, and wholly open to obey these. Schiller finds in the "Cestus of Venus" an everlasting æsthetic truth as to the nature of all beauty; curious—but he is careful not to insinuate that the old Greek mythists had any notion of lecturing about the "philosophy of criticism!" On the whole, we must leave those boundless regions. Cannot we conceive that Odin was a reality? Error indeed, error enough: but sheer falsehood, idle fables, allegory aforethought—we will not believe that our fathers believed in these.

Odin's *runes* are a significant feature of him. Runes and the miracles of "magic" he worked by them, make a great feature in tradition. Runes are the Scandinavian alphabet; suppose Odin to have been the inventor of letters, as well as "magic," among that people! It is the greatest invention man has ever made, this of marking down the unseen thought that is in him by written characters. It is a kind of second speech, almost as miraculous as the first. You remember the astonishment and incredulity of Atahualpa the Peruvian king; how he made the Spanish soldier who was guarding him scratch *dios* on his thumb-nail, that he might try the next soldier with it, to ascertain whether such a miracle was possible. If Odin brought letters among his people, he might work magic enough!

Writing by runes has some air of being original among the Norsemen: not a Phœnician alphabet, but a native Scandinavian one. Snorro tells us further that Odin invented poetry; the music of human speech, as well as that miraculous runic marking of it. Transport yourselves into the early childhood of nations; the first beautiful morning-light of our Europe, when all yet lay in fresh young radiance as of a great sunrise, and our Europe was first beginning to think, to be! Wonder, hope; infinite radiance of hope and wonder, as of a young child's thoughts, in the hearts of these strong men! Strong sons of nature; and here was not only a wild captain and fighter; discerning with his wild flashing eyes what to do, with his wild lion-heart daring and doing it; but a poet too, all that we mean by a poet, prophet, great devout thinker and inventor—as the truly great man ever is. A hero is a hero at all points; in the soul and thought of him first of all. This Odin, in his rude semi-articulate way, had a word to speak. A great heart laid open to take in this great universe and man's life here, and utter a great word about it. A hero, as I say, in his rude manner; a wise, gifted, noble-hearted man. And now, if we still admire such a man beyond all others, what must these wild Norse souls, first awakened into thinking, have made of him! To them, as yet without names for it, he was noble and noblest; hero, prophet, god; *Wuotan*, the greatest of all. Thought is thought, however it speak or spell itself. Intrinsically, I conjecture, this Odin must have been of the same sort of stuff as the greatest kind of men. A great thought in the wild deep heart of him! The rough words he articulated, are they not the rudimental roots of those English words we still use! He worked so, in that obscure element. But he was as a *light* kindled in it; a light of intellect, rude nobleness of heart, the only kind of lights we have yet; a hero, as I say: and he had to shine there and make his obscure element a little lighter—as is still the task of us all.

We will fancy him to be the type Norseman; the finest Teuton whom that race has yet produced. The rude Norse heart burst up into *boundless* admiration round him; into adoration. He is as a root of so many great things; the fruit of him is found growing, from deep thousands of years, over the whole field of Teutonic life. Our own Wednesday, as I said, is it not still Odin's day? Wednesday, Wansborough, Wanstead, Wandsworth: Odin grew into England too, these are still leaves from that root! He was the chief god to all the Teutonic peoples; their pattern Norseman—in such way did *they* admire their pattern Norseman; that was the fortune he had in the world.

Thus if the man Odin himself have vanished utterly, there is this huge shadow of him which still projects itself over the whole history of his people. For this Odin once admitted to be god, we can understand well that the whole Scandinavian scheme of nature, or dim no-scheme, whatever it might before have been, would now begin to develop itself altogether differently and grow thenceforth in a new manner. What this Odin saw into, and taught with his runes and his rhymes, the whole Teutonic people laid to heart and carried forward. His way of thought became their way of thought—such, under new conditions, is the history of every great thinker still. In gigantic confused lineaments, like some enormous camera-obscura shadow thrown upward from the dead deeps of the past, and covering the whole northern heaven, is not that Scandinavian mythology in some sort the portraiture of this man Odin? The gigantic image of *his* natural face, legible or not legible there, expanded and confused in that manner! Ah, thought, I say, is always thought. No great man lives in vain. The history of the world is but the biography of great men.

To me there is something very touching in this primeval figure of hero-ism; in such artless, helpless, but hearty entire reception of a hero by his fellow men. Never so helpless in shape, it is the noblest of feelings, and a feeling in some shape or other perennial as man himself. If I could show in any measure, what I feel deeply for a long time now, that it is the vital element of manhood, the soul of man's history here in our world—it would be the chief use of this discoursing at present. We do not now call our great men gods, nor admire *without* limit; ah, no, *with* limit enough! But if we have no great men, or do not admire at all—that were a still worse case.

This poor Scandinavian hero-worship, that whole Norse way of looking at the universe and adjusting oneself there, has an indestructible merit for us. A rude childlike way of recognizing the divineness of nature, the divineness of man; most rude, yet heartfelt, robust, giantlike; betokening what a giant of a man this child would yet grow to! It was a truth and is none. Is it not as the half-dumb stifled voice of the long-buried generations of our own fathers, calling out of the depths of ages to us, in whose veins their blood still runs: "This then, this is what *we* made of the world: this is all the image and notion we could form to ourselves of this great mystery of a life and universe. Despise it not. You are raised high above it, to large free scope of vision; but you too are not yet at the top. No, your notion too, so much enlarged, is but a partial, imperfect one; that matter is a thing no man will ever, in time or out of time, comprehend; after thousands of years of ever-new expansion, man will find himself but struggling to comprehend again a part of it: the thing is larger than man, not to be comprehended by him; an infinite thing!"

The essence of the Scandinavian, as indeed of all pagan mythologies, we found to be recognition of the divineness of nature; sincere communion of man with the mysterious invisible powers visibly seen at work in the world round him. This, I should say, is more sincerely done in the Scandinavian than in any mythology I know. Sincerity is the great characteristic of it. Superior sincerity (far superior) consoles us for the total want of old Grecian grace. Sincerity, I think, is better than grace. I feel that these old Northmen were looking into nature with open eye and soul: most earnest, honest; childlike and yet manlike; with a great-hearted simplicity and depth and freshness, in a true, loving, admiring, unfearing way. A right valiant, true old race of men. Such recognition of nature one finds to be the chief element of paganism: recognition of man and his moral duty, though this too is not wanting, comes to be the chief element only in purer forms of religion. Here, indeed, is a great distinction and epoch in human beliefs; a great landmark in the religious development of mankind. Man first puts himself in relation with nature and her powers, wonders and worships over those; not till a later epoch does he discern that all power is moral, that the grand point is the distinction for him of good and evil, of *Thou shalt* and *Thou shalt not.*

With regard to all these fabulous delineations in the *Edda,* I will remark, moreover, as indeed was already hinted, that most probably they must have been of much newer date; most probably, even from the first, were comparatively idle for the old Norsemen and as it were a kind of poetic sport. Allegory and poetic delineation, as I said above, cannot be religious faith; the faith itself must first be there, then allegory enough will gather round it, as the fit body round its soul. The Norse faith, I can well suppose, like other faiths, was most active while it lay mainly in the silent state and had not yet much to say about itself, still less to sing.

Among those shadowy *Edda* matters, amid all that fantastic congeries of assertions and traditions, in their musical mythologies, the main practical belief a man could have was probably not much more than this: of the *Valkyrs* and the *Hall of Odin;* of an inflexible *destiny;* and that the one thing needful for a man was *to be brave.* The *Valkyrs* are choosers of the slain; a destiny inexorable, which it is useless trying to bend or soften, has appointed who is to be slain; this was a fundamental point for the Norse believer—

as indeed it is for all earnest men everywhere, for a Mahomet, a Luther, for a Napoleon too. It lies at the basis this for every such man; it is the woof out of which his whole system of thought is woven. The *Valkyrs;* and then that these *Choosers* lead the brave to a heavenly *Hall of Odin;* only the base and slavish being thrust elsewhither, into the realms of Hela the death-goddess: I take this to have been the soul of the whole Norse belief. They understood in their heart that it was indispensable to be brave; that Odin would have no favor for them, but despise and thrust them out, if they were not brave. Consider too whether there is not something in this! It is an ever-lasting duty, valid in our day as in that, the duty of being brave. *Valor* is still *value.* The first duty for a man is still that of subduing *fear.* We must get rid of fear; we cannot act at all till then. A man's acts are slavish, not true but specious; his very thoughts are false, he thinks too as a slave and coward, till he have got fear under his feet. Odin's creed, if we disentangle the real kernel of it, is true to this hour. A man shall and must be valiant; he must march forward and quit himself like a man—trusting imperturbably in the appointment and *choice* of the upper powers; and, on the whole, not fear at all. Now and always, the completeness of his victory over fear will determine how much of a man he is.

It is doubtless very savage that kind of valor of the old Northmen. Snorro tells us they thought it a shame and misery not to die in battle; and if natural death seemed to be coming on, they would cut wounds in their flesh, that Odin might receive them as warriors slain. Old kings, about to die, had their body laid into a ship; the ship sent forth, with sails set and slow fire burning it; that, once out at sea, it might blaze up in flame and in such manner bury worthily the old hero, at once in the sky and in the ocean! Wild bloody valor; yet valor of its kind; better, I say, than none. In the old sea-kings too, what an indomitable rugged energy! Silent, with closed lips, as I fancy them, unconscious that they were specially brave; defying the wild ocean with its monsters and all men and things—progenitors of our own Blakes and Nelsons! No Homer sung these Norse sea-kings; but Agamemnon's was a small audacity and of small fruit in the world, to some of them—to Hrolf's of Normandy, for instance! Hrolf, or Rollo Duke of Normandy, the wild sea-king, has a share in governing England at this hour.

Nor was it altogether nothing, even that wild sea-roving and battling, through so many generations. It needed to be ascertained which was the *strongest* kind of men; who were to be ruler over whom. Among the North-land sovereigns, too, I find some who got the title *wood-cutter;* forest-felling kings. Much lies in that. I suppose at bottom many of them were forest-fellers as well as fighters, though the Skalds talk mainly of the latter—misleading certain critics not a little; for no nation of men could ever live by fighting alone; there could not produce enough come out of that! I suppose the right good fighter was oftenest also the right good forest-feller—the right good improver, discerner, doer and worker in every kind; for true valor, different enough from ferocity, is the basis of all. A more legitimate kind of valor that; showing itself against the untamed forests and dark brute powers of nature, to conquer nature for us. In the same direction have not we their descendants since carried it far? May such valor last forever with us!

That the man Odin, speaking with a hero's voice and heart, as with an impressiveness out of heaven, told his people the infinite importance of valor, how man thereby became a god; and that his people, feeling a response to it in their own hearts, believed this message of his, and thought it a message out of heaven, and him a divinity for telling it them: this seems to me the primary seed-grain of the Norse religion, from which all manner of mythologies, symbolic practices, speculations, allegories, songs and sagas would naturally grow. Grow—how strangely! I called it a small light shining and shaping in the high vortex of Norse darkness. Yet the darkness itself was *alive;* consider that. It was the eager inarticulate uninstructed mind of the whole Norse people, longing only to become articulate, to go on articulating ever further! The living doctrine grows, grows—like a Banyan-tree; the first *seed* is the essential thing: any branch strikes itself down into the earth, becomes a new root; and so, in endless complexity, we have a whole wood, a whole jungle, one seed the parent of it all. Was not the whole Norse religion, accordingly, in some sense, what we called "the enormous shadow of this man's likeness?" Critics trace some affinity in some Norse mythuses, of the creation and suchlike, with those of the Hindoos. The cow Adumbla, "licking the rime from the rocks," has a kind of Hindoo look. A Hindoo cow, transported into frosty countries. Probable enough; indeed we may say undoubtedly, these things will have a kindred with the remotest lands, with the earliest times. Thought does not die, but only is changed. The first man that began to think in this planet of ours, he was the beginner of all. And then the second man and the third man—nay, every true thinker to this hour is a kind of Odin, teaches men *his* way of thought, spreads a shadow of his own likeness over sections of the history of the world.

Of the distinctive poetic character or merit of this Norse mythology I have not room to speak; nor does it concern us much. Some wild prophesies we have, as the *Völuspa* in the *Elder Edda;* of a rapt, earnest, sibylline sort. But they were comparatively an idle adjunct of the matter, men who as it were but toyed with the matter, these later Skalds; and it is *their* songs chiefly that survive. In later centuries, I suppose, they would go on singing, poetically symbolizing, as our modern painters paint, when it was no longer from the innermost heart, or not from the heart at all. This is everywhere to be well kept in mind.

Gray's fragments of Norse lore, at any rate, will give one no notion of it —any more than Pope will of Homer. It is no square-built gloomy palace of black ashlar marble, shrouded in awe and horror, as Gray gives it us: no; rough as the north rocks, as the Iceland deserts, it is; with a heartiness, homeliness, even a tint of good humor and robust mirth in the middle of these fearful things. The strong old Norse heart did not go upon theatrical sublimities; they had not time to tremble. I like much their robust simplicity; their veracity, directness of conception. Thor "draws down his brows" in veritable Norse rage: "grasps his hammer till the *knuckles grow white*." Beautiful traits of pity too, an honest pity. Balder "the white god" dies: the beautiful, benignant: he is the Sungod. They try all nature for a remedy: but he is dead. Frigga, his mother, sends Hermoder to seek or see him: nine days and nine nights he rides through gloomy deep valleys, a labyrinth of gloom; arrives at the bridge with its gold roof: the keeper says, "Yes, Balder did pass here; but the kingdom of the dead is down yonder, far toward the north." Hermoder rides on; leaps hell-gate, Hela's gate; does see Balder and speak with him: Balder cannot be delivered. Inexorable! Hela will not, for Odin or any god, give him up. The beautiful and gentle has to remain there. His wife had volunteered to go with him, to die with him. They shall forever remain there. He sends his ring to Odin; Nanna, his wife, sends her *thimble* to Frigga, as a remembrance—Ah me!

For indeed valor is the fountain of pity too—of truth and all that is great and good in man. The robust homely vigor of the Norse heart attaches one much, in these delineations. Is it not a trait of right honest strength, says Uhland, who has written a fine essay on Thor, that the old Norse heart finds its friend in the thunder-god? That it is not frightened away by his thunder; but finds that summer-heat, the beautiful noble summer, must and will have thunder withal! The Norse heart *loves* this Thor and his hammer-bolt; sports with him. Thor is summer-heat; the god of peaceable industry as well as thunder. He is the peasant's friend; his true henchman and attendant is Thialfi, *manual labor*. Thor himself engages in all manner of rough manual work, scorns no business for its plebeianism; is ever and anon traveling to the country of the Jötuns, harrying those chaotic frost-monsters, subduing them, at least straightening and damaging them. There is a great broad humor in some of these things.

Thor, as we saw above, goes to Jötun-land, to seek Hymir's caldron, that the gods may brew beer. Hymir the huge giant enters, his gray beard all full of hoar-frost; splits pillars with the very glance of his eye: Thor, after much rough tumult, snatches the pot, claps it on his head; the "handles of it reach down to his heels." The Norse Skald has a kind of loving sport with Thor. This is the Hymir whose cattle, the critics have discovered, are icebergs. Huge untutored brobdignag genius—needing only to be tamed down; into Shakespeares, Dantes, Goethes! It is all gone now, that old Norse work —Thor the thunder-god changed into Jack the Giant-killer: but the mind that made it is here yet. How strangely things grow and die, and do not die! There are twigs of that great world-tree of Norse belief still curiously traceable. This poor Jack of the nursery, with his miraculous shoes of swiftness, coat of darkness, sword of sharpness, he is one. *Hynde Etin* and still more decisively *Red Etin of Ireland*, in the Scottish ballads, these are both derived from Norseland; *Etin* is evidently a *Jötun*. Nay, Shakespeare's *Hamlet* is a twig too of this same world-tree; there seems no doubt of that. Hamlet *Amleth*; I find, is really a mythic personage; and his tragedy, of the poisoned father, poisoned asleep by drops in his ear and the rest, is a Norse mythus! Old Saxo, as his wont was, made it a Danish history; Shakespeare, out of Saxo, made it what we see. That is a twig of the world-tree that has *grown*, I think—by nature or accident that one has grown!

In fact, these old Norse songs have a *truth* in them, an inward perennial truth and greatness—as, indeed, all must have that can very long preserve itself by tradition alone. It is a greatness not of mere body and gigantic bulk, but a rude greatness of soul. There is a sublime uncomplaining melancholy traceable in these old hearts. A great free glance into the very deeps of thought. They seem to have seen, these brave old Northmen, what meditation has taught all men in all ages, that this world is after all but a show—a phenomenon or appearance, no real thing. All deep souls see into that—the Hindoo mythologist, the German philosopher—the Shakespeare, the earnest thinker, wherever he may be:

> *"We are such stuff as dreams are made of!"*

One of Thor's expeditions, to Utgard (the *outer* garden, central seat of Jötun-land), is remarkable in this respect. Thialfi was with him and Loke. After various adventures, they entered upon giant-land; wandered over plains, wild uncultivated places, among stones and trees. At nightfall they noticed a house; and as the door, which indeed formed one whole side of the house, was open, they entered. It was a simple habitation; one large hall, altogether empty. They stayed there. Suddenly in the dead of the night loud noises alarmed them. Thor grasped his hammer; stood in the door, prepared for fight. His companions within ran hither and thither in their terror, seeking some outlet in that rude hall; they found a little closet at last and took refuge there. Neither had Thor any battle: for, lo, in the morning it turned out that the noise had been only the *snoring* of a certain enormous but peaceable giant, the giant Skrymir, who lay peaceably sleeping near by; and this that they took for a house was merely his *glove*, thrown aside there; the door was the glove-wrist; the little closet they had fled into was the thumb! Such a glove—I remark too that it had not fingers as ours have, but only a thumb and the rest undivided: a most ancient, rustic glove!

Skrymir now carried their portmanteau all day; Thor, however, had his own suspicions, did not like the ways of Skrymir; determined at night to put an end to him as he slept. Raising his hammer, he struck down into the giant's face a right thunderbolt blow, of force to rend rocks. The giant merely awoke; rubbed his cheek and said: "Did a leaf fall?" Again Thor struck, so soon as Skrymir again slept; a better blow than before; but the giant only murmured: "Was that a grain of sand?" Thor's third stroke was with both his hands (the "knuckles white" I suppose) and seemed to dint deep into Skrymir's visage; but he merely checked his snore and remarked: "There must be sparrows roosting in this tree, I think; what is that they have dropped?" At the gate of Utgard, a place so high that you had to "strain your neck bending back to see the top of it," Skrymir went his ways. Thor and his companions were admitted; invited to take share in the games going on. To Thor, for his part, they handed a drinking-horn; it was a common feat, they told him, to drink this dry at one draught. Long and fiercely, three times over, Thor drank; but made hardly any impression. He was a weak child they told him: could he lift that cat he saw there? Small as the feat seemed, Thor with his whole godlike strength could not; he bent up the creature's back, could not raise its feet off the ground, could at the utmost raise one foot. "Why, you are no man," said the Utgard people; there is an old woman that will wrestle you! Thor, heartily ashamed, seized this haggard old woman; but could not throw her.

And now, on their quitting Utgard, the chief Jötun, escorting them politely a little way, said to Thor: "You are beaten then—yet be not so much ashamed; there was deception of appearance in it. That horn you tried to drink was the *sea;* you did make it ebb; but who could drink that, the bottomless! The cat you would have lifted—why, that is the *midgard-snake,* the great world-serpent, which, tail in mouth, girds and keeps up the whole created world; had you torn that up, the world must have rushed to ruin! As for the old woman, she was *time,* old age, duration: with her what can wrestle? No man nor no god with her; gods or men, she prevails over all! And then those three strokes you struck—look at these *three valleys;* your three strokes made these!" Thor looked at his attendant Jötun: it was Skrymir—it was, say Norse critics, the old chaotic rocky *earth* in person and that glove-*house* was some earth-cavern! But Skrymir had vanished; Utgard with its skyhigh gates, when Thor grasped his hammer to smite them, had gone to air; only the giant's voice was heard mocking: "Better come no more to Jötunheim!"

This is of the allegoric period, as we see, and, half play, not of the prophetic and entirely devout: but as a mythus is there not real antique Norse gold in it? More true metal, rough from the mimer-stithy, than in many a famed Greek mythus *shaped* far better! A great broad brobdignag grin of true humor is in this Skrymir; mirth resting on earnestness and sadness, as the rainbow on black tempest: only a right valiant heart is capable of that. It is the grim humor of our own Ben Jonson, rare old Ben; runs in the blood of us, I fancy; for one catches tones of it, under a still other shape, out of the American backwoods.

That is also a very striking conception that of the *ragnarök,* consummation, or *twilight of the gods.* It is in the *Völuspa* song; seemingly a very old, prophetic idea. The gods and Jötuns, the divine powers and the chaotic brute ones, after long contest and partial victory by the former, meet at last in universal world-embracing wrestle and duel; world-serpent against Thor, strength against strength; mutually extinctive; and ruin, "twilight" sinking into darkness, swallows the created universe. The old universe with its gods is sunk; but it is not final death: there is to be a new heaven and a new earth; a higher supreme god and justice to reign among men. Curious this law of mutation, which also is a law written in man's inmost thought, had been deciphered by these old earnest thinkers in their rude style; and how, though all dies, and even gods die, yet all death is but a phœnix fire-death and new-birth into the greater and the better! It is the fundamental law of being for a creature made of time, living in this place of hope. All earnest men have seen into it; may still see into it.

And now, connected with this, let us glance at the *last* mythus of the appearance of Thor; and end there. I fancy it to be the latest in date of all these fables; a sorrowing protest against the advance of Christianity—set forth reproachfully by some conservative pagan. King Olaf has been harshly blamed for his over-zeal in introducing Christianity; surely I should have blamed him far more for an under-zeal in that! He paid dear enough for it; he died by the revolt of his pagan people, in battle, in the year 1023, at Stickelstad, near that Drontheim, where the chief cathedral of the north has now stood for many centuries, dedicated gratefully to his memory as *Saint* Olaf. The mythus about Thor is to this effect. King Olaf, the Christian reform king, is sailing with fit escort along the shore of Norway, from haven to haven; dispensing justice, or doing other royal work: on leaving a certain haven, it is found that a stranger, of grave eyes and aspect, red beard, of stately robust figure, has stepped in. The courtiers address him: his answers surprise by their pertinency and depth: at length he is brought to the king. The stranger's conversation here is not less remarkable, as they sail along the beautiful shore; but after some time, he addresses King Olaf thus: "Yes, King Olaf, it is all beautiful, with the sun shining on it there; green, fruitful, a right fair home for you; and many a sore day had Thor, many a wild fight with the rock Jötuns, before he could make it so. And now you seem minded to put away Thor. King Olaf, have a care!" said the stranger, drawing down his brows—and when they looked again, he was nowhere to be found. This is the last appearance of Thor on the stage of this world!

Do we not see well enough how the fable might arise, without unveracity on the part of any one? It is the way most gods have come to appear among men: thus, if in Pindar's time "Neptune was seen once at the Nemean games," what was this Neptune too but a "stranger of noble grave aspect"—*fit* to be "seen!" There is something pathetic, tragic for me in this last voice of paganism. Thor is vanished, the whole Norse world has vanished; and will not return ever again. In like fashion to that pass away the highest things. All things that have been in this world, all things that are or will be in it, have to vanish: we have our sad farewell to give them.

That Norse religion, a rude but earnest, sternly impressive *consecration of valor* (so we may define it), sufficed for these old valiant Northmen. Consecration of valor is not a *bad* thing! We will take it for good, so far as it goes. Neither is there no use in *knowing* something about this old paganism of our fathers. Unconsciously and combined with higher things, it is in *us* yet, that old faith withal! To know it consciously, brings us into closer and clearer relation with the past—with our own possessions in the past. For the whole past, as I keep repeating, is the possession of the present; the past had always something *true* and is a precious possession. In a different time, in a different place, it is always some other *side* of our common human nature that has been developing itself. The actual true is the *sum* of all these; not any one of them by itself constitutes what of human nature is hitherto developed. Better to know them all than misknow them. "To which of these three religions do you specially adhere?" inquires Meister of his teacher. "To all the three!" answers the other: "To all the three; for they by their union first constitute the true religion."

LECTURE II.[1]

THE HERO AS PROPHET—MAHOMET—ISLAM.

FROM the first rude times of paganism among the Scandinavians in the north, we advance to a very different epoch of religion, among a very different people: Mahometanism among the Arabs. A great change; what a change and progress is indicated here, in the universal condition and thoughts of men!

The hero is now regarded as a god among his fellow-men; but as one god-inspired, as a prophet. It is the second phasis of hero-worship; the first or oldest, we may say, has passed away without return; in the history of the world there will not again be any man, never so great, whom his fellow-men will take for a god. Nay we might rationally ask, did any set of human beings ever really think the man they *saw* there standing beside them a god, the maker of this world? Perhaps not; it was usually some man they remembered, or *had* seen. But neither can this any more be. The great man is not recognized henceforth as a god any more.

It was a rude gross error, that of counting the great man a god. Yet let us say that it is at all times difficult to know *what* he is, or how to account of him and receive him! The most significant feature in the history of an epoch is the manner it has of welcoming a great man. Ever, to the true instincts of men, there is something godlike in him. Whether they shall take him to be a god, to be a prophet, or what they shall take him to be? that is ever a grand question; by their way of answering that, we shall see, as through a little window, into the very heart of these men's spiritual condition. For at bottom the great man, as he comes from the hand of nature, is ever the same kind of thing; Odin, Luther, Johnson, Burns; I hope to make it appear that these are all originally of one stuff; that only by the world's reception of them, and the shapes they assume, are they so immeasurably diverse. The worship of Odin astonishes us—to fall prostrate before the great man, into *deliquium* of love and wonder over him, and feel in their hearts that he was a denizen of the skies, a god! This was imperfect enough: but to welcome, for example, a Burns as we did, was that what we can call perfect? The most precious gift that heaven can give to the earth; a man of "genius" as we call it; the soul of a man actually sent down from the skies with a God's-message to us—this we waste away as an idle artificial firework, sent to amuse us a little, and sink it into ashes, wreck and ineffectuality: *such* reception of a great man I do not call very perfect either! Looking into the

[1]Delivered Friday, May 8, 1840.

heart of the thing, one may perhaps call that of Burns a still uglier phenomenon, betokening still sadder imperfections in mankind's ways, than the Scandinavian method itself! To fall into mere unreasoning *deliquium* of love and
admiration, was not good; but such unreasoning, nay irrational supercilious
no-love at all is perhaps still worse! It is a thing forever changing, this of
hero-worship: different in each age, difficult to do well in any age. Indeed,
the heart of the whole business of the age, one may say, is to do it well.

We have chosen Mahomet not as the most eminent prophet; but as the
one we are freest to speak of. He is by no means the truest of prophets; but
I do esteem him a true one. Farther, as there is no danger of our becoming,
any of us, Mahometans, I mean to say all the good of him I justly can. It is
the way to get at his secret: let us try to understand what *he* meant with
the world; what the world meant and means with him, will then be a more
answerable question. Our current hypothesis about Mahomet, that he was a
scheming impostor, a falsehood incarnate, that his religion is a mere mass of
quackery and fatuity, begins really to be now untenable to any one. The
lies, which well-meaning zeal has heaped round this man, are disgraceful to
ourselves only. When Pococke inquired of Grotius, where the proof was of
that story of the pigeon, trained to pick peas from Mahomet's ear and pass
for an angel dictating to him? Grotius answered that there was no proof!
It is really time to dismiss all that. The word this man spoke has been the
life-guidance now of a hundred and eighty millions of men these twelve hundred years. These hundred and eighty millions were made by God as well
as we. A greater number of God's creatures believe in Mahomet's word at
this hour than in any other word whatever. Are we to suppose that it was
a miserable piece of spiritual legerdemain, this which so many creatures of
the Almighty have lived by and died by? I, for my part, cannot form any
such supposition. I will believe most things sooner than that. One would be
entirely at a loss what to think of this world at all, if quackery so grew and
were sanctioned here.

Alas, such theories are very lamentable. If we would attain to knowledge
of anything in God's true creation, let us disbelieve them wholly! They are
the product of an age of skepticism; they indicate the saddest spiritual
paralysis and mere death-life of the souls of men: more godless theory, I
think, was never promulgated in this earth. A false man found a religion?
Why, a false man cannot build a brick house! If he do not know and follow
truly the properties of mortar, burned clay and what else he works in, it is
no house that he makes, but a rubbish heap. It will not stand for twelve
centuries, to lodge a hundred and eighty millions; it will fall straightway. A
man must conform himself to nature's laws, *be* verily in communion with
nature and the truth of things, or nature will answer him, No, not at all!
Speciosities are specious—ah me! A Cagliostro, many Cagliostros, prominent
world-leaders, do prosper by their quackery, for a day. It is like a forged
bank-note; they get it passed out of *their* worthless hands: others, not they,
have to smart for it. Nature bursts up in fire-flames, French revolutions and
suchlike, proclaiming with terrible veracity that forged notes are forged.

But of a great man especially, of him I will venture to assert that it is incredible he should have been other than true. It seems to me the primary foundation of him and of all that can lie in him, this. No Mirabeau, Napoleon, Burns, Cromwell, no man adequate to do anything, but is first of all in right earnest about it; what I call a sincere man. I should say *sincerity*, a deep, great, genuine sincerity, is the first characteristic of all men in any way heroic. Not the sincerity that calls itself sincere; ah no, that is a very poor matter indeed—a shallow braggart conscious sincerity; oftenest self-conceit mainly. The great man's sincerity is of the kind he cannot speak of, is not conscious of: nay, I suppose, he is conscious rather of *in*sincerity; for what man can walk accurately by the law of truth for one day? No, the great man does not boast himself sincere, far from that; perhaps does not ask himself if he is so: I would say rather, his sincerity does not depend on himself; he cannot help being sincere! The great fact of existence is great to him. Fly as he will, he cannot get out of the awful presence of this reality. His mind is so made; he is great by that, first of all. Fearful and wonderful, real as life, real as death, is this universe to him. Though all men should forget its truth and walk in a vain show, he cannot. At all moments the flame-image glares in upon him; undeniable, there, there! I wish you to take this as my primary definition of a great man. A little man may have this, it is competent to all men that God has made: but a great man cannot be without it.

Such a man is what we call an *original* man; he comes to us at first hand. A messenger he, sent from the infinite unknown with tidings to us. We may call him poet, prophet, god—in one way or other, we all feel that the words he utters are as no other man's words. Direct from the inner fact of things— he lives, and has to live, in daily communion with that. Hearsays cannot hide it from him; he is blind, homeless, miserable, following hearsays; *it* glares in upon him. Really his utterances, are they not a kind of "revelation"—what we must call such for want of some other name? It is from the heart of the world that he comes; he is portion of the primal reality of things. God has made many revelations: but this man too, has not God made him, the latest and newest of all? The "inspiration of the Almighty giveth *him* understand- ing:" we must listen before all to him.

This Mahomet, then, we will in no wise consider as an inanity and the- atricality, a poor conscious ambitious schemer; we cannot conceive him so. The rude message he delivered was a real one withal; an earnest confused voice from the unknown deep. The man's words were not false, nor his workings here below; no inanity and simulacrum; a fiery mass of life cast-up from the great bosom of nature herself. To *kindle* the world; the world's Maker had ordered it so. Neither can the faults, imperfections, insincerities even, or Mahomet, if such were never so well proved against him, shake this primary fact about him.

On the whole, we make too much of faults; the details of the business hide the real center of it. Faults? The greatest of faults, I should say, is to be con- scious of none. Readers of the Bible above all, one would think, might know better. Who is called there "the man according to God's own heart?" David, the Hebrew king, had fallen into sins enough; blackest crimes; there was no want of sins. And thereupon the unbelievers sneer and ask, "Is this your man according to God's heart?" The sneer I must say, seems to me but a shallow one. What are faults, what are the outward details of a life; if the inner secret of it, the remorse, temptations, true, often-baffled, never-ended struggle of it, be forgotten? "It is not in man that walketh to direct his steps." Of all acts, is not, for a man, *repentance* the most divine? The deadliest sin, I say, were that same supercilious consciousness of no sin—that is death; the heart so conscious is divorced from sincerity, humility and fact; is dead: it is "pure" as dead dry sand is pure. David's life and history, as written for us in those psalms of his, I consider to be the truest emblem ever given of a man's moral progress and warfare here below. All earnest souls will ever discern in it the faithful struggle of an earnest human soul toward what is good and best. Struggle often baffled, sore baffled, down as into entire wreck; yet a struggle never ended; ever, with tears, repentance, true unconquerable purpose, begun anew. Poor human nature! Is not a man's walking, in truth, always that: "a succession of falls?" Man can do no other. In this wild element of a life, he has to struggle onward; now fallen, deep-abased; and ever, with tears, repentance, with bleeding heart, he has to rise again, struggle again still onward. That his struggle *be* a faithful unconquerable one; that is the question of questions. We will put up with many sad details, if the soul of it were true. Details by themselves will never teach us what it is. I believe we misestimate Mahomet's faults even as faults; but the secret of him will never be got by dwelling there. We will leave all this behind us; and assuring ourselves that he did mean some true thing, ask candidly what it was or might be.

These Arabs Mahomet was born among are certainly a notable people. Their country itself is notable; the fit habitation for such a race. Savage inaccessible rock-mountains, great grim deserts, alternating with beautiful strips of verdure: wherever water is, there is greenness, beauty; odoriferous balm-shrubs, date-trees, frankincense-trees. Consider that wide waste horizon of sand, empty, silent, like a sand-sea, dividing habitable place from habitable. You are all alone there, left alone with the universe; by day a fierce sun blazing down on it with intolerable radiance; by night the great deep heaven with its stars. Such a country is fit for a swift-handed, deep-hearted race of men. There is something most agile, active, and yet most meditative, enthusiastic in the Arab character. The Persians are called the French of the East; we will call the Arabs Oriental Italians. A gifted noble people; a people of wild strong feelings, and of iron restraint over these: the characteristic of noblemindedness, of genius. The wild Bedouin welcomes the stranger to his tent, as one having right to all that is there; were it his worst enemy, he will slay his foal to treat him, will serve him with sacred hospitality for three days, will set him fairly on his way—and then, by another law as sacred, kill him if he can. In words too, as in action. They are not a loquacious people, taciturn rather; but eloquent, gifted when they do speak. An earnest, truthful kind of men. They are, as we know, of Jewish kindred; but with that deadly terrible earnestness of the Jews they seem to combine something graceful, brilliant, which is not Jewish. They had "poetic contests" among them before the time of Mahomet. Sale says, at Ocadh, in the south of Arabia, there were yearly fairs, and there, when the merchandising was done, poets sang for prizes—the wild people gathered to hear that.

One Jewish quality these Arabs manifest; the outcome of many or of all high qualities: what we may call religiosity. From of old they had been zealous worshipers, according to their light. They worshiped the stars, as Sabeans; worshiped many natural objects—recognized them as symbols, immediate manifestations, of the Maker of nature. It was wrong; and yet not wholly wrong. All God's works are still in a sense symbols of God. Do we not, as I urged, still account it a merit to recognize a certain inexhaustible significance, "poetic beauty" as we name it, in all natural objects whatsoever? A man is a poet and honored, for doing that and speaking or singing it—a kind of diluted worship. They had many prophets, these Arabs; teachers each to his tribe, each according to the light he had. But indeed, have we not from of old the noblest of proofs, still palpable to every one of us, of what devoutness and noblemindedness had dwelt in these rustic thoughtful peoples? Biblical critics seem agreed that our own "Book of Job" was written in that region of the world. I call that, apart from all theories about it, one of the grandest things ever written with pen. One feels, indeed, as if it were not Hebrew; such a noble universality, different from noble patriotism or sectarianism, reigns in it. A noble book; all men's book! It is our first, oldest statement of the never-ending problem—man's destiny and God's ways with him here in this earth. And all in such free flowing outlines; grand in its sincerity, in its simplicity; in its epic melody and repose of reconcilement. There is the seeing eye, the mildly understanding heart. So *true* every way; true eyesight and vision for all things; material things no less than spiritual: the horse—"hast thou clothed his neck with *thunder?*" He "*laughs* at the shaking of the spear!" Such living likenesses were never since drawn. Sublime sorrow, sublime reconciliation; oldest choral melody as of the heart of mankind—so soft and great; as the summer midnight, as the world with its seas and stars! There is nothing written, I think, in the Bible or out of it, of equal literary merit.

To the idolatrous Arabs one of the most ancient universal objects of worship was that black stone, still kept in the building called Caabah at Mecca. Diodorus Siculus mentions this Caabah in a way not to be mistaken, as the oldest, most honored temple in his time; that is, some half century before our era. Silvestre de Sacy says there is some likelihood that the black stone is an aerolite. In that case, some man might *see* it fall out of heaven! It stands now beside the well Zemzem; the Caabah is built over both. A well is in all places a beautiful affecting object, gushing out like life from the hard earth—still more so in those hot dry countries, where it is the first condition of being. The well Zemzem has its name from the bubling sound of the waters, *zem-zem;* they think it is the well which Hagar found with her little

Ishmael in the wilderness: the aerolite and it have been sacred now and had a Caabah over them, for thousands of years. A curious object, that Caabah! There it stands at this hour, in the black cloth-covering the Sultan sends it yearly; "twenty seven cubits high;" with circuit, with double circuit of pillars, with festoon-rows of lamps and quaint ornaments: the lamps will be lighted again *this* night—to glitter again under the stars. An authentic fragment of the oldest past. It is the *keblah* of all Moslem: from Delhi all onward to Morocco, the eyes of innumerable praying men are turned toward *it*, five times, this day and all days: one of the notablest centers in the habitation of men.

It had been from the sacredness attached to this Caabah stone and Hagar's well, from the pilgrimings of all tribes of Arabs thither, that Mecca took its rise as a town. A great town once, though much decayed now. It has no natural advantage for a town; stands in a sandy hollow amid bare barren hills, at a distance from the sea; its provisions, its very bread, have to be imported. But so many pilgrims needed lodgings: and then all places of pilgrimage do, from the first, become places of trade. The first day pilgrims meet, merchants have also met; where men see themselves assembled for one object, they find that they can accomplish other objects which depend on meeting together. Mecca became the fair of all Arabia. And thereby indeed the chief staple and warehouse of whatever commerce there was between the Indian and the western countries, Syria, Egypt, even Italy. It had at one time a population of 100,000; buyers, forwarders of those eastern and western products; importers for their own behoof of provisions and corn. The government was a kind of irregular aristocratic republic, not without a touch of theocracy. Ten men of a chief tribe, chosen in some rough way, were governors of Mecca, and keepers of the Caabah. The Koreish were the chief tribe in Mahomet's time; his own family was of that tribe. The rest of the nation, fractioned and cut-asunder by deserts, lived under similar rude patriarchal governments by one or several: herdsmen, carriers, traders, generally robbers too; being oftenest at war one with another, or with all: held together by no open bond, if it were not this meeting at the Caabah, where all forms of Arab idolatry assembled in common adoration—held mainly by the *inward* indissoluble bond of common blood and language. In this way had the Arabs lived for long ages, unnoticed by the world; a people of great qualities, unconsciously waiting for the day when they should become notable to all the world. Their idolatries appear to have been in a tottering state; much was getting into confusion and fermentation among them. Obscure tidings of the most important event ever transacted in this world, the life and death of the Divine Man in Judea, at once the symptom and cause of immeasurable change to all people in the world, had in the course of centuries reached into Arabia too; and could not but, of itself, have produced fermentation there.

It was among this Arab people, so circumstanced, in the year 570 of our era, that the man Mahomet was born. He was of the family of Hashem, of the Koreish tribe as we said; though poor, connected with the chief persons of his country. Almost at his birth he lost his father; at the age of six years his mother too, a woman noted for her beauty, her worth and sense: he fell to the charge of his grandfather, an old man, a hundred years old. A good old man: Mahomet's father, Abdallah, had been his youngest favorite son. He saw in Mahomet, with his old life-worn eyes, a century old, the lost Abdallah come back again, all that was left of Abdallah. He loved the little orphan boy greatly; used to say, "they must take care of that beautiful little boy, nothing in their kindred was more precious than he." At his death, while the boy was still but two years old, he left him in charge to Abu Thaleb the eldest of the uncles, as to him that now was head of the house. By this uncle, a just and rational man as everything betokens, Mahomet was brought up in the best Arab way.

Mahomet, as he grew up, accompanied his uncle on trading journeys and suchlike; in his eighteenth year one finds him a fighter following his uncle in war. But perhaps the most significant of all his journeys is one we find noted as of some years' earlier date; a journey to the fairs of Syria. The young man here first came in contact with a quite foreign world—with one foreign element of endless moment to him: the Christian religion. I know not what to make of that "Sergius, the Nestorian monk," whom Abu Thaleb and he are said to have lodged with; or how much any monk could have taught one still so young. Probably enough it is greatly exaggerated, this of the Nestorian monk. Mahomet was only fourteen; had no language but his own: much in Syria must have been a strange unintelligible whirlpool to him. But the eyes of the lad were open; glimpses of many things would doubtless be taken in, and lie very enigmatic as yet, which were to ripen in a strange way into views, into beliefs and insights one day. These journeys to Syria were probably the beginning of much to Mahomet.

One other circumstance we must not forget: that he had no school-learning; of the thing we call school-learning none at all. The art of writing was but just introduced into Arabia; it seems to be the true opinion that Mahomet never could write! Life in the desert, with its experiences, was all his education. What of this infinite universe he, from his dim place, with his own eyes and thoughts, could take in, so much and no more of it was he to know. Curious, if we will reflect on it, this of having no books. Except by what he could see for himself, or hear of by uncertain rumor of speech in the obscure Arabian desert, he could know nothing. The wisdom that had been before him or at a distance from him in the world, was in a manner as good as not there for him. Of the great brother souls, flame-beacons through so many lands and times, no one directly communicates with this great soul. He is alone there, deep down in the bosom of the wilderness; has to grow up so—alone with nature and his own thoughts.

But, from an early age, he had been remarked as a thoughtful man. His companions named him "*Al Amin*, the faithful." A man of truth and fidelity; true in what he did, in what he spoke and thought. They noted that *he* always meant something. A man rather taciturn in speech; silent when there was nothing to be said; but pertinent, wise, sincere, when he did speak; always throwing light on the matter. This is the only sort of speech *worth* speaking! Through life we find him to have been regarded as an altogether solid, brotherly, genuine man. A serious, sincere character; yet amiable, cordial, companionable, jocose even—a good laugh in him withal: there are men whose laugh is as untrue as anything about them; who cannot laugh. One hears of Mahomet's beauty: his fine sagacious honest face, brown florid complexion, beaming black eyes—I somehow like too that vein on the brow, which swelled up black when he was in anger: like the "*horse-shoe* vein" in Scott's *red gauntlet*. It was a kind of feature in the Hashem family, this black swelling vein in the brow; Mahomet had it prominent, as would appear. A spontaneous, passionate, yet just, true-meaning man! Full of wild faculty, fire and light; of wild worth, all uncultured; working out his life-task in the depths of the desert there.

How he was placed with Kadijah, a rich widow, as her steward and traveled in her business, again to the fairs of Syria; how he managed all, as one can well understand, with fidelity, adroitness; how her gratitude, her regard for him grew: the story of their marriage is altogether a graceful intelligible one, as told us by the Arab authors. He was twenty-five; she forty, though still beautiful. He seems to have lived in a most affectionate, peaceable, wholesome way with this wedded benefactress; loving her truly and her alone. It goes greatly against the impostor theory, the fact that he lived in this entirely unexceptional, entirely quiet and commonplace way, till the heat of his years was done. He was forty before he talked of any mission from heaven. All his irregularities, real and supposed date from after his fiftieth year, when the good Kadijah died. All his "ambition," seemingly, had been, hitherto, to live an honest life; his "fame," the mere good opinion of neighbors that knew him, had been sufficient hitherto. Not till he was already getting old, the prurient heat of his life all burned out and *peace* growing to be the chief thing this world could give him, did he start on the "career of ambition;" and, belying all his past character and existence, set up as a wretched empty charlatan to acquire what he could now no longer enjoy! For my share, I have no faith whatever in that.

Ah no: this deep-hearted son of the wilderness, with his beaming black eyes and open social deep soul, had other thoughts in him than ambition. A silent great soul; he was one of those who cannot *but* be in earnest; whom nature herself has appointed to be sincere. While others walk in formulas and hearsays, contented enough to dwell there, this man could not screen himself in formulas; he was alone with his own soul and the reality of things. The great mystery of existence, as I said, glared in upon him, with its terrors, with its splendors; no hearsays could hide that unspeakable fact, "Here am I!" Such *sincerity*, as we named it, has in very truth something of divine. The word of such a man is a voice direct from nature's own heart. Men do and must listen to that as to nothing else—all else is wind in comparison. From of old, a thousand thoughts, in his pilgrimings and wanderings, had been in this man: What am I? What *is* this unfathomable thing I live in, which men name universe? What is life; what is death? What am I to believe? What am I to do? The grim rocks of Mount Hara, of Mount Sinai, the stern sandy solitudes answered not. The great heaven rolling silent overhead, with its blue-glancing stars, answered not. There was no answer. The man's own soul and what of God's inspiration dwelled there, had to answer!

It is the thing which all men have to ask themselves; which we too have to ask and answer. This wild man felt it to be of *infinite* moment; all other things of no moment whatever in comparison. The jargon of argumentative Greek sects, vague traditions of Jews, the stupid routine of Arab idolatry: there was no answer in these. A hero, as I repeat, has this first distinction, which indeed we may call first and last, the alpha and omega of his whole heroism, that he looks through the shows of things into *things*. Use and wont, respectable hearsay, respectable formula: all these are good, or are not good. There is something behind and beyond all these, which all these must correspond with, be the image of, or they are—*idolatries;* "bits of black wood pretending to be God;" to the earnest soul a mockery and abomination. Idolatries never so gilded, waited on by heads of the Koreish, will do nothing for this man. Though all men walk by them, what good is it? The great reality stands glaring there upon *him*. He there has to answer it, or perish miserably. Now, even now, or else though all eternity never! Answer it; *thou* must find an answer—ambition? What could all Arabia do for this man; with the crown of Greek Heraclius, of Persian Chosroes, and all crowns in the earth—what could they all do for him? It was not of the earth he wanted to hear tell; it was of the heaven above and the hell beneath. All crowns and sovereignties whatsoever, where would *they* in a few brief years be? To be sheik of Mecca or Arabia, and have a bit of gilt wood put into your hand—will that be one's salvation? I decidedly think not. We will leave it altogether, this impostor hypothesis, as not credible; not very tolerable even, worthy chiefly of dismissal by us.

Mahomet had not been wont to retire yearly, during the month Ramadhan, into solitude and silence; as indeed was the Arab custom; a praiseworthy custom, which such a man, above all, would find natural and useful. Communing with his own heart, in the silence of the mountains; himself silent; open to the "small still voices:" it was a right natural custom! Mahomet was in his fortieth year, when having withdrawn to a cavern in Mount Hara, near Mecca, during this Ramadhan, to pass the month in prayer, and meditation on those great questions, he one day told his wife Kadijah, who with his household was with him or near him this year, That by the unspeakable special favor of heaven he had now found it all out; was in doubt and darkness no longer, but saw it all. That all these idols and formulas were nothing, miserable bits of wood; that there was one God in and over all; and we must leave all idols, and look to Him. That God is great; and that there is nothing else great! He is the reality. Wooden idols are not real; He is real. He made us at first, sustains us yet; we and all things are but the shadow of Him; a transitory garment veiling the eternal splendor. "*Allah akbar*, God is great"—and then also "*Islam*," that we must *submit* to God.

That our whole strength lies in resigned submission to Him, whatsoever He do to us. For this world, and for the other! The things he sends to us, were it death and worse than death, shall be good, shall be best; we resign ourselves to God. "If this be *Islam*," says Goethe, "do we not all live in *Islam?*" Yes, all of us that have any moral life; we all live so. It has ever been held the highest wisdom for a man not merely to submit to necessity—necessity will make him submit—but to know and believe well that the stern thing which necessity had ordered was the wisest, the best, the thing wanted there. To cease his frantic pretension of scanning this great God's-world in his small fraction of a brain; to know that it *had* verily, though deep beyond his soundings, a just law, that the soul of it was good—that his part in it was to conform to the law of the whole, and in devout silence follow that; not questioning it, obeying it as unquestionable.

I say, this is yet the only true morality known. A man is right and invincible, virtuous and on the road toward sure conquest, precisely while he joins himself to the great deep law of the world, in spite of all superficial laws, temporary appearances, profit-and-loss calculations; he is victorious while he co-operates with that great central law, not victorious otherwise—and surely his first chance of co-operating with it, or getting into the course of it, is to know with his whole soul that it *is;* that it is good, and alone good! This is the soul of Islam; it is properly the soul of Christianity—for Islam is definable as a confused form of Christianity; had Christianity not been, neither had it been. Christianity also commands us, before all, to be resigned to God. We are to take no counsel with flesh-and-blood; give ear to no vain cavils, vain sorrows and wishes: to know that we know nothing; that the worst and cruelest to our eyes is not what it seems; that we have to receive whatsoever befalls us as sent from God above, and say, it is good and wise, God is great! "Though He slay me, yet will I trust in Him," Islam means in its way denial of self, annihilation of self. This is yet the highest wisdom that heaven has revealed to our earth.

Such light has come, as it could, to illuminate the darkness of this wild Arab soul. A confused dazzling splendor as of life and heaven, in the great darkness which threatened to be death: he called it revelation and the angel Gabriel—who of us yet can know what to call it? It is the "inspiration of the Almighty that giveth us understanding." To *know;* to get into the truth of anything, is ever a mystic act—of which the best logics can but babble on the surface. "Is not belief the true god-announcing miracle?" says Novalis. That Mahomet's whole soul, set in flame with this grand truth vouchsafed him, should feel as if it were important and the only important thing, was very natural. That Providence had unspeakably honored *him* by revealing it, saving him from death and darkness; that he therefore was bound to make known the same to all creatures: this is what was meant by "Mahomet is the prophet of God;" this too is not without its true meaning.

The good Kadijah, we can fancy, listened to him with wonder, with doubt; at length she answered: "Yes, it was *true* this that he said." One can fancy too the boundless gratitude of Mahomet; and how of all the kindnesses she had done him, this of believing the earnest struggling word he now spoke was the greatest. "It is certain," says Novalis, "my conviction gains infinitely, the moment another soul will believe in it." It is boundless favor. He never forgot this good Kadijah. Long afterward, Ayesha his young favorite wife, a woman who indeed distinguished herself among the Moslem, by all manner of qualities, through her whole long life; this young brilliant Ayesha was, one day, questioning him: "Now am not I better than Kadijah? She was a widow; old and had lost her looks: you love me better than you did her?" "No, by Allah!" answered Mahomet: "No, by Allah! She believed in me when none else would believe. In the whole world I had but one friend and she was that!" Seid, his slave, also believed in him; these with his young cousin Ali, Abu Thaleb's son, were his first converts.

He spoke of his doctrine to this man and that; but the most treated it with ridicule, with indifference; in three years, I think, he had gained but thirteen followers. His progress was slow enough. His encouragement to go on, was altogether the usual encouragement that such a man in such a case meets. After some three years of small success, he invited forty of his chief kindred to an entertainment; and there stood up and told them what his pretension was: that he had this thing to promulgate abroad to all men; that it was the highest thing, the one thing: which of them would second him in that? Amid the doubt and silence of all, young Ali, as yet a lad of sixteen, impatient of the silence, started up and exclaimed in passionate fierce language, that he would! The assembly, among whom was Abu Thaleb, Ali's father, could not be unfriendly to Mahomet; yet the sight there, of one unlettered elderly man, with a lad of sixteen, deciding on such an enterprise against all mankind, appeared ridiculous to them; the assembly broke up in laughter. Nevertheless it proved not a laughable thing; it was a very serious thing! As for this young Ali, one cannot but like him. A noble-minded creature, as he shows himself, now and always afterward; full of affection, of fiery daring. Something chivalrous in him; brave as a lion; yet with a grace, a truth and affection worthy of Christian knighthood. He died by assassination in the mosque at Bagdad; a death occasioned by his own generous fairness, confidence in the fairness of others: he said, "If the wound proved not unto death, they must pardon the assassin; but if it did, then they must slay him straightway, that so they two in the same hour might appear before God and see which side of that quarrel was the just one!"

Mahomet naturally gave offense to the Koreish, keepers of the Caabah, superintendents of the idols. One or two men of influence had joined him: the thing spread slowly, but it was spreading. Naturally he gave offense to everybody: who is this that pretends to be wiser than we all; that rebukes us all, as mere fools and worshipers of wood! Abu Thaleb the good uncle spoke with him: "Could he not be silent about all that; believe it all for himself and not trouble others, anger the chief men, endanger himself and them all, talking of it?" Mahomet answered: "If the sun stood on his right hand and the moon on his left, ordering him to hold his peace, he could not obey! No: there was something in this truth he had got which was of nature herself; equal in rank to sun, or moon, or whatsoever thing nature had made. It would speak itself there, so long as the Almighty allowed it, in spite of sun and moon and all Koreish and all men and things. It must do that and could do no other." Mahomet answered so; and, they say, "burst into tears." Burst into tears: he felt that Abu Thaleb was good to him; that the task he had got was no soft, but a stern and great one.

He went on speaking to who would listen to him; publishing his doctrine among the pilgrims as they came to Mecca; gaining adherents in this place and that. Continual contradiction, hatred, open or secret danger attended him. His powerful relations protected Mahomet himself; but by and by, on his own advice, all his adherents had to quit Mecca, and seek refuge in Abyssinia over the sea. The Koreish grew ever angrier; laid plots and swore oaths among them, to put Mahomet to death with their own hands. Abu Thaleb was dead, the good Kadijah was dead. Mahomet is not solicitous of sympathy from us; but his outlook at this time was one of the dismalest. He had to hide in caverns, escape in disguise; fly hither and thither; homeless, in continual peril of his life. More than once it seemed all over with him; more than once it turned on a straw, some rider's horse taking fright or the like, whether Mahomet and his doctrine had not ended there and not been heard of at all. But it was not to end so.

In the thirteenth year of his mission, finding his enemies all banded against him, forty sworn men, one out of every tribe, waiting to take his life and no continuance possible at Mecca for him any longer, Mahomet fled to the place then called Yathreb, where he had gained some adherents: the place they now call Medina, or *"Medinat al Nabi,* the city of the prophet," from that circumstance. It lay some 200 miles off, through rocks and deserts; not without great difficulty, in such mood as we may fancy, he escaped thither and found welcome. The whole East dates its era from this flight, *Hegira* as they name it: the year 1 of this Hegira is 622 of our era, the fifty-third of Mahomet's life. He was now becoming an old man; his friends sinking round him one by one; his path desolate, encompassed with danger: unless he could find hope in his own heart, the outward face of things was but hopeless for him. It is so with all men in the like case. Hitherto Mahomet had professed to publish his religion by the way of preaching and persuasion alone. But now, driven foully out of his native country, since unjust men had not only given no ear to his earnest heaven's-message, the deep cry of his heart, but would not even let him live if he kept speaking it—the wild son of the desert resolved to defend himself, like a man and Arab. If the Koreish will have it so, they shall have it. Tidings, felt to be of infinite moment to them and all men, they would not listen to these; would trample them down by sheer violence, steel and murder: well, let steel try it then! Ten years more this Mahomet had; all of fighting, of breathless impetuous toil and struggle; with what result we know.

Much has been said of Mahomet's propagating his religion by the sword. It is no doubt far nobler what we have to boast of the Christian religion, that it propagated itself peaceably in the way of preaching and conviction. Yet withal, if we take this for an argument of the truth or falsehood of a religion, there is a radical mistake in it. The sword indeed: but where will you get your sword! Every new opinion, at its starting, is precisely in a *minority of one*. In one man's head alone, there it dwells as yet. One man alone of the whole world believes it; there is one man against all men. That *he* take a sword and try to propagate with that, will do little for him. You must first get your sword! On the whole, a thing will propagate itself as it can. We do not find, of the Christian religion either, that it always disdained the sword, when once it had got one. Charlemagne's conversion of the Saxons was not by preaching. I care little about the sword: I will allow a thing to struggle for itself in this world, with any sword or tongue or implement it has, or can lay hold of. We will let it preach, and pamphleteer, and fight and to the uttermost bestir itself and do, beak and claws, whatsoever is in it; very sure that it will, in the long run, conquer nothing which does not deserve to be conquered. What is better than itself, it cannot put away, but only what is worse. In this great duel, nature herself is umpire and can do no wrong: the thing which is deepest-rooted in nature, what we call *truest*, that thing and not the other will be found growing at last.

Here however, in reference to much that there is in Mahomet and his success, we are to remember what an umpire nature is: what a greatness, composure of depth and tolerance there is in her. You take wheat to cast into the earth's bosom: your wheat may be mixed with chaff, chopped straw, barn-sweepings, dust and all imaginable rubbish; no matter: you cast it into the kind just earth; she grows the wheat—the whole rubbish she silently absorbs shrouds *it* in, says nothing of the rubbish. The yellow wheat is growing there; the good earth is silent about all the rest—has silently turned all the rest to some benefit too, and makes no complaint about it! So everywhere in nature! She is true and not a lie; and yet so great, and just, and motherly in her truth. She requires of a thing only that it *be* genuine of heart; she will protect it if so; will not, if not so. There is a soul of truth in all the things she ever gave harbor to. Alas, is not this the history of all highest truth that comes or ever came into the world? The *body* of them all is imperfection, an element of light *in* darkness: to us they have to come embodied in mere logic, in some merely *scientific* theorem of the universe; which *cannot* be complete; which cannot but be found, one day, *in*complete, erroneous, and so die and disappear. The body of all truth dies; and yet in all, I say, there is a soul which never dies; which in new and ever-nobler embodiment lives immortal as man himself! It is the way with nature. The genuine essence of truth never dies. That it be genuine, a voice from the great deep of nature, there is the point at nature's judgment-seat. What *we* call pure or impure, is not with her the final question. Not how much chaff is in you; but whether you have any wheat. Pure? I might say to many a man: Yes, you are pure; pure enough; but you are chaff—insincere hypothesis, hearsay, formality; you never were in contact with the great heart of the universe at all; you are properly neither pure nor impure; you *are* nothing, nature has no business with you.

Mahomet's creed we called a kind of Christianity; and really, if we look at the wild rapt earnestness with which it was believed and laid to heart, I should say a better kind than that of those miserable Syrian sects, with their vain janglings about *homoiousion* and *homoousion,* the head full of worthless noise, the heart empty and dead! The truth of it is embedded in portentous error and falsehood; but the truth of it makes it be believed, not the falsehood; it succeeded by its truth. A bastard kind of Christianity, but a living kind; with a heart-life in it; not dead, chopping barren logic merely! Out of all that rubbish of Arab idolatries, argumentative theologies, traditions, subtleties, rumors and hypotheses of Greeks and Jews, with their idle wiredrawings, this wild man of the desert, with his wild sincere heart, earnest as death and life, with his great flashing natural eyesight, had seen into the kernel of the matter. Idolatry is nothing: these wooden idols of yours, "ye rub them with oil and wax, and the flies stick on them"—these are wood, I tell you! They can do nothing for you; they are an impotent blasphemous pretence; a horror and abomination, if ye knew them. God alone is; God alone has power: He made us, He can kill us and keep us alive: "*Allah akbar,* God is great." Understand that His will is the best for you; that howsoever sore to flesh-and-blood, you will find it the wisest, best: you are bound to take it so; in this world and in the next, you have no other thing that you can do!

And now if the wild idolatrous men did believe this, and with their fiery hearts lay hold of it to do it, in what form soever it came to them, I say it was well worthy of being believed. In one form or the other, I say it is still the one thing worthy of being believed by all men. Man does hereby become the high-priest of this temple of a world. He is in harmony with the decrees of the author of the world; co-operating with them, not vainly withstanding them: I know, to this day, no better definition of duty than that same. All that is *right* includes itself in this of co-operating with the real tendency of the world: you succeed by this (the world's tendency will succeed), you are good and in the right course there. *Homoiousion, Homoousion* vain logical jangle, then or before or at any time, may jangle itself out, and go whither and how it likes: this is the *thing* it all struggles to mean, if it would mean anything. If it do not succeed in meaning this, it means nothing. Not that abstractions, logical propositions, be correctly worded or incorrectly; but that living concrete sons of Adam do lay this to heart: that is the important point. Islam devoured all these vain jangling sects; and I think had right to do so. It was a reality, direct from the great heart of nature once more. Arab idolatries, Syrian formulas, whatsoever was not equally real, had to go up in flame—mere dead *fuel,* in various senses, for this which was *fire.*

It was during these wild warfarings and strugglings, especially after the flight to Mecca, that Mahomet dictated at intervals his sacred book, which they name Koran, or Reading, "thing to be read." This is the work he and his disciples made so much of, asking all the world, "Is not that a miracle?" The Mahometans regard their Koran with a reverence which few Christians

pay even to their Bible. It is admitted everywhere as the standard of all law
and all practice; the thing to be gone upon in speculation and life: the message sent direct out of heaven, which this earth has to conform to and walk
by; the thing to be read. Their judges decide by it; all Moslem are bound to
study it, seek in it for the light of their life. They have mosques where it
is all read daily; thirty relays of priests take it up in succession, get through
the whole each day. There, for twelve hundred years, has the voice of this
book, at all moments, kept sounding through the ears and the hearts of so
many men. We hear of Mahometan doctors that had read it seventy thousand times!

Very curious: if one sought for "discrepancies of national taste," here
surely were the most eminent instance of that! We also can read the Koran;
our translation of it, by Sale, is known to be a very fair one. I must say, it is
as toilsome reading as I ever undertook. A wearisome confused jumble,
crude, incondite; endless iterations, long-windedness, entanglement; most
crude, incondite—insupportable stupidity, in short! Nothing but a sense of
duty could carry any European through the Koran. We read in it, as we
might in the state paper office, unreadable masses of lumber, that perhaps
we may get some glimpses of a remarkable man. It is true we have it under
disadvantages: the Arabs see more method in it than we. Mahomet's followers found the Koran lying all in fractions, as it had been written down at
first promulgation; much of it, they say, on shoulder-blades of mutton, flung
pell-mell into a chest: and they published it, without any discoverable order
as to time or otherwise—merely trying, as would seem, and this not very
strictly, to put the longest chapters first. The real beginning of it, in that
way, lies almost at the end: for the earliest portions were the shortest. Read
in its historical sequence it perhaps would not be so bad. Much of it, too,
they say, is rhythmic; a kind of wild chanting song, in the original. This
may be a great point; much perhaps has been lost in the translation here.
Yet with every allowance, one feels it difficult to see how any mortal ever
could consider this Koran as a book written in heaven, too good for the
earth; as a well-written book, or indeed as a *book* at all; and not a bewildered
rhapsody; *written*, so far as writing goes, as badly as almost any book ever
was! So much for national discrepancies and the standard of taste.

Yet I should say, it was not unintelligible how the Arabs might so love it.
When once you get this confused coil of a Koran fairly off your hands and
have it behind you at a distance, the essential type of it begins to disclose
itself; and in this there is a merit quite other than the literary one. If a book
come from the heart, it will contrive to reach other hearts; all art and
authorcraft are of small amount to that. One would say the primary character of the Koran is this of its *genuineness*, of its being a *bona fide* book.
Prideaux, I know, and others have represented it as a mere bundle of jug-
gleries; chapter after chapter got up to excuse and varnish the author's
successive sins, forward his ambitions and quackeries: but really it is time
to dismiss all that. I do not assert Mahomet's continual sincerity: who is
continually sincere? But I confess I can make nothing of the critic, in these

times, who would accuse him of deceit *prepense;* of conscious deceit generally, or perhaps at all—still more, of living in a mere element of conscious deceit and writing this Koran as a forger and juggler would have done! Every candid eye, I think, will read the Koran far otherwise than so. It is the confused ferment of a great rude human soul; rude, untutored, that cannot even read, but fervent, earnest, struggling vehemently to utter itself in words. With a kind of breathless intensity he strives to utter himself; the thoughts crowd on him pell-mell: for very multitude of things to say, he can get nothing said. The meaning that is in him shapes itself into no form of composition, is stated in no sequence, method, or coherence—they are not *shaped* at all, these thoughts of his; flung out unshaped, as they struggle and tumble there, in their chaotic inarticulate state. We said "stupid:" yet natural stupidity is by no means the character of Mahomet's book; it is natural uncultivation rather. The man has not studied speaking; in the haste and pressure of continual fighting, has not time to mature himself into fit speech. The panting breathless haste and vehemence of a man struggling in the thick of battle for life and salvation; this is the mood he is in! A headlong haste; for very magnitude of meaning, he cannot get himself articulate into words. The successive utterances of a soul in that mood, colored by the various vicissitudes of twenty-three years; now well uttered, now worse: this is the Koran.

For we are to consider Mahomet, through these twenty-three years, as the center of a world wholly in conflict. Battles with the Kornish and Heathen, quarrels among his own people, backslidings of his own wild heart; all this kept him in a perpetual whirl, his soul knowing rest no more. In wakeful nights, as one may fancy, the wild soul of the man, tossing amid these vortices, would hail any light of a decision for them as a veritable light from heaven; *any* making up of his mind, so blessed, indispensable for him there, would seem the inspiration of a Gabriel. Forger and juggler? No, no! This great fiery heart, seething, simmering like a great furnace of thoughts, was not a juggler's. His life was a fact to him; this God's universe an awful fact and reality. He has faults enough. The man was an uncultured semi-barbarous son of nature, much of the Bedouin still clinging to him: we must take him for that. But for a wretched simulacrum, a hungry impostor without eyes or heart, practicing for a mess of pottage such blasphemous swindlery, forgery of celestial documents, continual high treason against his Maker and self, we will not and cannot take him.

Sincerity, in all senses, seems to me the merit of the Koran; what had rendered it precious to the wild Arab men. It is, after all, the first and last merit in a book; gives rise to merits of all kinds—nay, at bottom, it alone can give rise to merit of any kind. Curiously, through these incondite masses of tradition, vituperation, complaint, ejaculation in the Koran, a vein of true direct insight, of what we might almost call poetry, is found straggling. The body of the book is made up of mere tradition and as it were vehement enthusiastic extempore preaching. He returns forever to the old stories of the prophets as they went current in the Arab memory: how prophet after prophet, the prophet Abraham, the prophet Hud, the prophet Moses, Christian and other real and fabulous prophets, had come to this tribe and to that, warning men of their sin; and been received by them even as he Mahomet was—which is a great solace to him. These things he repeats ten, perhaps twenty times; again and ever again, with wearisome iteration; has never done repeating them. A brave Samuel Johnson, in his forlorn garret, might con-over the biographies of authors in that way! This is the great staple of the Koran. But curiously, through all this, comes ever and anon some glance as of the real thinker and seer. He has actually an eye for the world, this Mahomet: with a certain directness and rugged vigor, he brings home still, to our heart, the thing his own heart has been opened to. I make but little of his praises of Allah, which many praise; they are borrowed I suppose mainly from the Hebrew, at least they are far surpassed there. But the eye that flashes direct into the heart of things and *sees* the truth of them; this is to me a highly interesting object. Great nature's own gift; which she bestows on all; but which only one in the thousand does not cast sorrowfully away: it is what I call sincerity of vision; the test of a sincere heart.

Mahomet can work no miracles; he often answers impatiently: "I can work no miracles. I? I am public preacher; appointed to preach this doctrine to all creatures." Yet the world, as we can see, had really from of old been all one great miracle to him. Look over the world, says he; is it not wonderful, the work of Allah; wholly "a sign to you," if your eyes were open! This earth, God made it for you; "appointed paths in it;" you can live in it, go to and fro on it. The clouds in the dry country of Arabia, to Mahomet they are very wonderful: great clouds, he says, born in the deep bosom of the upper immensity, where do they come from! They hang there, the great black monsters; pour down their rain deluges "to revive a dead earth," and grass springs, and "tall leafy palm-trees with their date-clusters hanging round. Is not that a sign?" Your cattle too—Allah made them; serviceable dumb creatures; they change the grass into milk; you have your clothing from them, very strange creatures; they come ranking home at evening-time, "and," adds he, "and are a credit to you!" Ships also—he talks often about ships: huge moving mountains, they spread out their cloth wings, go bounding through the water there, heaven's wind driving them; anon they lie motionless, God has withdrawn the wind, they lie dead and cannot stir! Miracles? cries he: What miracle would you have? Are not you yourselves there? God made *you*, "shaped you out of a little clay." Ye were small once; a few years ago ye were not at all. Ye have beauty, strength, thoughts, "ye have compassion on one another." Old age comes on you and gray hairs; your strength fades into feebleness; ye sink down, and again are not. "Ye have compassion on one another:" this struck me much: Allah might have made you having no compassion on one another—how had it been then! This is a great direct thought, a glance at first-hand into the very fact of things. Rude vestiges of poetic genius, of whatsoever is best and truest, are visible in this man. A strong untutored intellect; eyesight, heart: a strong wild man—might have shaped himself into poet, king, priest, any kind of hero.

To his eyes it is forever clear that this world wholly is miraculous. He sees what, as we said once before, all great thinkers, the rude Scandinavians themselves, in one way or other, have contrived to see: that this so solid-looking material world is, at bottom, in very deed, nothing; is a visual and tactual manifestation of God's power and presence—a shadow hung out by Him on the bosom of the void infinite; nothing more. The mountains, he says, these great rock mountains, they shall dissipate themselves "like clouds;" melt into the blue as clouds do and not be! He figures the earth, in the Arab fashion, Sale tells us, as an immense plain on that plate of ground, the mountains are set on that to *steady* it. At the last day they shall disappear "like clouds;" the whole earth shall go spinning, whirl itself off into wreck and as dust and vapor vanish in the inane. Allah withdraws his hand from it and it ceases to be. The universal empire of Allah, presence everywhere of an unspeakable power, a splendor and a terror not to be named, as the true force, essence and reality, in all things whatsoever, was continually clear to this man. What a modern talks of by the name, forces of nature, laws of nature; and does not figure as a divine thing; not even as one thing at all, but as a set of things, undivine enough—saleable, curious, good for propelling steam-ships! With our sciences and cyclopædias, we are apt to forget the *divineness*, in those laboratories of ours. We ought not to forget it! That once well forgotten, I know not what else were worth remembering. Most sciences, I think, were then a very dead thing; withered, contentious, empty—a thistle in late autumn. The best science, without this, is but as the dead *timber;* it is not the growing tree and forest—which gives ever-new timber, among other things! Man cannot *know* either, unless he can *worship* in some way. His knowledge is a pedantry and dead thistle, otherwise.

Much has been said and written about the sensuality of Mahomet's religion; more than was just. The indulgences, criminal to us, which he permitted, were not of his appointment; he found them practiced, unquestioned from immemorial time in Arabia; what he did was to curtail them, restrict them, not on one but on many sides. His religion is not an easy one: with rigorous fasts, lavations, strict complex formulas, prayers five times a day, and ab-tinence from wine, it did not "succeed by being an easy religion." As if indeed any religion, or cause holding of religion, could succeed by that! It is a calumny on men to say that they are roused to heroic action by ease, hope of pleasure, recompense—sugar-plums of any kind, in this world or the next! In the meanest mortal there lies something nobler. The poor swearing soldier, hired to be shot, has his "honor of a soldier," different from drill-regulations and the shilling a day. It is not to taste sweet things, but to do noble and true things and vindicate himself under God's heaven as a god-made man, that the poorest son of Adam dimly longs. Show him the way of doing that, the dullest daydrudge kindles into a hero. They wrong man greatly who say he is to be seduced by ease. Difficulty, abnegation, martyr-dom, death are the *allurements* that act on the heart of man. Kindle the inner genial life of him, you have a flame that burns up all lower considerations. Not happiness, but something higher: one sees this even in the frivolous classes, with their "point of honor" and the like. Not by flattering our appetites; no, by awakening the heroic that slumbers in every heart, can any religion gain followers.

Mahomet himself, after all that can be said about him, was not a sensual man. We shall err widely if we consider this man as a common voluptuary intent mainly on base enjoyments—nay on enjoyments of any kind. His household was of the frugalest; his common diet barley-bread and water: sometimes for months there was not a fire once lighted on his hearth. They record with just pride that he would mend his own shoes, patch his own cloak. A poor, hard-toiling, ill-provided man; careless of what vulgar men toil for. Not a bad man, I should say; something better in him than *hunger* of any sort—or these wild Arab men, fighting and jostling twenty-three years at his hand, in close contact with him always, would not have reverenced him so! They were wild men, bursting ever and anon into quarrel, into all kinds of fierce sincerity; without right worth and manhood, no man could have commanded them. They called him prophet, you say? Why, he stood there face to face with them; bare, not enshrined in any mystery; visibly clouting his own cloak, cobbling his own shoes; fighting, counseling, ordering in the midst of them: they must have seen what kind of a man he *was,* let him be *called* what you like! No emperor with his tiaras was obeyed as this man in a cloak of his own clouting. During twenty-three years of rough actual trial. I find something of a veritable hero necessary for that, of itself

His last words are a prayer; broken ejaculations of a heart struggling up in trembling hope, toward its Maker. We cannot say that his religion made him *worse;* it made him better; good, not bad. Generous things are recorded of him: when he lost his daughter, the thing he answers is, in his own dialect, everyway sincere, and yet equivalent to that of Christians, "The Lord giveth, and the Lord taketh away; blessed be the name of the Lord." He answered in like manner of Seid, his emancipated well-beloved slave, the second of the believers. Seid had fallen in the war of Tabûc, the first of Mahomet's fightings with the Greeks. Mahomet said, it was well; Seid had done his Master's work, Seid had now gone to his Master: it was all well with Seid. Yet Seid's daughter found him weeping over the body—the old gray-haired man melting in tears! "What do you see?" said she. "You see a friend weeping over his friend." He went out for the last time into the mosque, two days before his death; asked, if he had injured any man? Let his own back bear the stripes. If he owed any man? A voice answered, "Yes, me three drachms," borrowed on such an occasion. Mahomet ordered them to be paid: "Better be in shame now," said he, "than at the day of judgment." You remember Kadijah, and the "no, by Allah!" Traits of that kind show us the genuine man, the brother of us all, brought visible through twelve centuries—the veritable son of our common mother.

Withal I like Mahomet for his total freedom from cant. He is a rough self-helping son of the wilderness; does not pretend to be what he is not. There is no ostentatious pride in him; but neither does he go much upon humility: he is there as he can be, in cloak and shoes of his own clouting.

speaks plainly to all manner of Persian kings, Greek emperors, what it is they are bound to do; knows well enough, about himself, "the respect due unto thee." In a life-and-death war with Bedouins, cruel things could not fail; but neither are acts of mercy, of noble natural pity and generosity wanting. Mahomet makes no apology for the one, no boast of the other. They were each the free dictate of his heart; each called for, there and then. Not a mealy-mouthed man! A candid ferocity, if the case call for it, is in him; he does not mince matters! The war of Tabûc is a thing he often speaks of: his men refused, many of them, to march on that occasion; pleaded the heat of the weather, the harvest, and so forth; he can never forget that. Your harvest? It lasts for a day. What will become of your harvest through all eternity? Hot weather? Yes, it was hot; "but hell will be hotter!" Sometimes a rough sarcasm turns up: he says to the unbelievers, ye shall have the just measure of your deeds at that great day. They will be weighed out to you; ye shall not have short weight! Everywhere he fixes the matter in his eye; he *sees* it: his heart, now and then, is as if struck dumb by the greatness of it. "Assuredly," he says: that word, in the Koran, is written down sometimes as a sentence by itself: "Assuredly."

No *dilettantism* in this Mahomet; it is a business of reprobation and salvation with him, of time and eternity: he is in deadly earnest about it! Dilettantism, hypothesis, speculation, a kind of amateur search for truth, toying and coquetting with truth: this is the sorest sin. The root of all other imaginable sins. It consists in the heart and soul of the man never having been *open* to truth—"living in a vain show." Such a man not only utters and produces falsehoods, but *is* himself a falsehood. The rational moral principle, sparks of the divinity, is sunk deep in him, in quiet paralysis of life-death. The very falsehoods of Mahomet are truer than the truths of such a man. He is the insincere man: smooth-polished, respectable in some times and places; inoffensive, says nothing harsh to anybody; most *cleanly*—just as carbonic acid is, which is death and poison.

We will not praise Mahomet's moral precepts as always of the superfinest sort; yet it can be said that there is always a tendency to good in them; that they are the true dictates of a heart aiming toward what is just and true. The sublime forgiveness of Christianity, turning of the other cheek when the one has been smitten, is not here: you *are* to revenge yourself, but it is to be in measure, not overmuch, or beyond justice. On the other hand, Islam, like any great faith, and insight into the essence of man, is a perfect equalizer of men: the soul of one believer outweighs all earthly kingships; all men, according to Islam too, are equal. Mahomet insists not on the propriety of giving alms, but on the necessity of it: he marks down by law how much you are to give, and it is at your peril if you neglect. The tenth part of a man's annual income, whatever that may be, is the *property* of the poor, of those that are afflicted and need help. Good all this: the natural voice of humanity, of pity and equity dwelling in the heart of this wild son of nature speaks *so*.

Mahomet's paradise is sensual, his hell sensual: true; in the one and the other there is enough that shocks all spiritual feeling in us. But we are to recollect that the Arabs already had it so; that Mahomet, in whatever he changed of it, softened and diminished all this. The worst sensualities, too, are the work of doctors, followers of his, not his work. In the Koran there is really very little said about the joys of paradise; they are intimated rather than insisted on. Nor is it forgotten that the highest joys even there shall be spiritual; the poor presence of the highest, this shall infinitely transcend all other joys. He says, "Your salutation shall be peace." *Salam*, have peace—the thing that all rational souls long for, and seek, vainly here below, as the one blessing. "Ye shall sit on seats, facing one another: all grudges shall be taken away out of your hearts." All grudges! Ye shall love one another freely; for each of you, in the eyes of his brothers, there will be heaven enough!

In reference to this of the sensual paradise and Mahomet's sensuality, the sorest chapter of all for us, there were many things to be said; which it is not convenient to enter upon here. Two remarks only I shall make, and therewith leave it to your candor. The first is furnished me by Goethe; it is a casual hint of his which seems well worth taking note of. In one of his delineations, in "Meister's Travels" it is, the hero comes upon a society of men with very strange ways, one of which was this: "We require," says the master, "that each of our people shall restrict himself in one direction," shall go right against his desire in one matter, and *make* himself do the thing he does not wish, "should we allow him the greater latitude on all other sides." There seems to me a great justness in this. Enjoying things which are pleasant; that is not the evil: it is the reducing of our moral self to slavery by them that is. Let a man assert withal that he is king over his habitudes; that he could and would shake them off, on cause shown: this is an excellent law. The month Ramadhan for the Moslem, much in Mahomet's religion, much in his own life, bears in that direction; if not by forethought, or clear purpose of moral improvement on his part, than by a certain healthy manful instinct, which is as good.

But there is another thing to be said about the Mahometan heaven and hell. This namely, that however gross and material they may be, they are an emblem of an everlasting truth, not always so well remembered elsewhere. That gross sensual paradise of his; that horrible flaming hell; the great enormous day of judgment he perpetually insists on: what is all this but a rude shadow, in the rude Bedouin imagination, of that grand spiritual fact and beginning of facts, which it is ill for us too if we do not all know and feel: the infinite nature of duty? That man's actions here are of *infinite* moment to him and never die or end at all; that man, with his little life, reaches upward high as heaven, downward low as hell and in his three-score years of time holds an eternity fearfully and wonderfully hidden: all this had burned itself, as in flame-characters into the wild Arab soul. As in flame and lightning, it stands written there; awful, unspeakable, ever present to him. With bursting earnestness, with a fierce savage sincerity, halt, articulating, not able to articulate, he strives to speak it, bodies it forth in that heaven and that hell. Bodied forth in what way you will, it is the first of all truths. It is venerable under all embodiments. What is the chief end of man here below? Mahomet has answered this question, in a way that might put some of *us* to shame! He does not, like a Bentham, a Paley, take right and wrong and calculate the profit and loss, ultimate pleasure of the one and of the other; and summing all up by addition and subtraction into a net result, ask you, whether on the whole the right does not preponderate considerably? No; it is not *better* to do the one than the other; the one is to the other as life is to death—as heaven is to hell. The one must in nowise be done, the other in nowise left undone. You shall not measure them; they are incommeasurable: the one is death eternal to a man, the other is life eternal. Benthamee utility, virtue by profit and loss; reducing this God's-world to a dead brute steam-engine, the infinite celestial soul of man to a kind of hay-balance for weighing hay and thistles on, pleasures and pains on: If you ask me which gives, Mahomet or they, the beggarlier and falser view of man and his destinies in this universe, I will answer it: It is not Mahomet!

On the whole, we will repeat that this religion of Mahomet's is a kind of Christianity; has a genuine element of what is spiritually highest looking through it, not to be hidden by all its imperfections. The Scandinavian god *Wish*, the god of all rude men—this has been enlarged into a heaven by Mahomet; but a heaven symbolical of sacred duty and to be earned by faith and well-doing, by valiant action and a divine patience which is still more valiant. It is Scandinavian paganism and a truly celestial element superadded to that. Call it not false; look not at the falsehood of it, look at the truth of it. For these twelve centuries, it has been the religion and life-guidance of the fifth part of the whole kindred of mankind. Above all things, it has been a religion heartily *believed*. These Arabs believe their religion and try to live by it! No Christians, since the early ages, or only perhaps the English Puritans in modern times, have ever stood by their faith as the Moslem do by theirs—believing it wholly, fronting time with it and eternity with it. This night the watchman on the streets of Cairo when he cries: "Who goes?" will hear from the messenger, along with his answer: "There is no God but God." *Allah akbar, Islam,* sounds through the souls and whole daily existence, of these dusky millions. Zealous missionaries preach it abroad among Malays, black Papuans, brutal idolaters—displacing what is worse, nothing that is better or good.

To the Arab nation it was as a birth from darkness into light; Arabia first became alive by means of it. A poor shepherd people, roaming unnoticed in its deserts since the creation of the world: a hero-prophet was sent down to them with a word they could believe: see, the unnoticed becomes world-notable, the small has grown world-great; within one century afterward, Arabia is at Grenada on this hand, at Delhi on that—glancing in valor and splendor and the light of genius, Arabia shines through long ages over a great section of the world. Belief is great, live-giving. The history of a nation becomes fruitful, soul-elevating, great, so soon as it believes. These Arabs, the man Mahomet and that one century—it is not as if a spark had fallen, one spark, on a world of what seemed black unnoticeable sand; but lo, the sand proves explosive powder, blazes heaven-high from Delhi to Grenada! I said, the great man was always as lightning out of heaven; the rest of men waited for him like fuel and then they too would flame.

LECTURE III.[1]

THE HERO AS POET—DANTE—SHAKESPEARE.

THE HERO as divinity, the hero as prophet, are productions of old ages; not to be repeated in the new. They presuppose a certain rudeness of conception, which the progress of mere scientific knowledge puts an end to. There needs to be, as it were, a world vacant, or almost vacant of scientific forms, if men in their loving wonder are to fancy their fellow-man either a god or one speaking with the voice of a god. Divinity and prophet are past. We are now to see our hero in the less ambitious, but also less questionable, character of poet; a character which does not pass. The poet is a heroic figure belonging to all ages; whom all ages possess, when once he is produced, whom the newest age as the oldest may produce—and will produce, always when nature pleases. Let nature send a hero-soul; in no age is it other than possible that he may be shaped into a poet.

Hero, prophet, poet—many different names, in different times and places, do we give to great men; according to varieties we note in them, according to the sphere in which they have displayed themselves! We might give many more names, on this same principle. I will remark again, however, as a fact not unimportant to be understood, that the different *sphere* constitutes the grand origin of such distinction; that the hero can be poet, prophet, king, priest or what you will, according to the kind of world he finds himself born into. I confess, I have no notion of a truly great man that could not be *all* sorts of men. The poet who could merely sit on a chair and compose stanzas, would never make a stanza worth much. He could not sing the heroic warrior, unless he himself were at least a heroic warrior too. I fancy there is in him the politician, the thinker, legislator, philosopher—in one or the other degree, he could have been, he is all these. So too I cannot understand how a Mirabeau, with that great glowing heart, with the fire that was in it, with the bursting tears that were in it, could not have written verses, tragedies, poems and touched all hearts in that way, had his course of life and education led him thitherward. The grand fundamental character is that of great man; that the man be great. Napoleon has words in him which are like Austerlitz battles. Louis XIV's marshals are a kind of poetical men withal; the things Turenne says are full of sagacity and geniality, like sayings of Samuel Johnson. The great heart, the clear deep-seeing eye: there it lies; no man whatever, in what province soever, can prosper at all without these. Petrarch and Boccaccio did diplomatic messages, it seems, quite well: one can easily believe it; they had done things a little harder than these! Burns, a

[1]Delivered Tuesday, May 12, 1840.

gifted song-writer might have made a still better Mirabeau. Shakespeare—
one knows not what *he* could not have made, in the supreme degree.

True, there are aptitudes of nature too. Nature does not make all great
men, more than all other men, in the self-same mold. Varieties of aptitude
doubtless; but infinitely more of circumstance; and far oftenest it is the
latter only that are looked to. But it is as with common men in the learning
of trades. You take any man, as yet a vague capability of a man, who could
be any kind of craftsman; and make him into a smith, a carpenter, a mason:
he is then and thenceforth that and nothing else. And if, as Addison complains, you sometimes see a street-porter staggering under his load on spindle-
shanks and near at hand a tailor with the frame of a Samson handling a bit
of cloth and small Whitechapel needle—it cannot be considered that aptitude
of nature alone has been consulted here either! The great man also, to what
shall he be bound apprentice? Given your hero, is he to become conqueror,
king, philosopher, poet? It is an inexplicable complex controversial calculation between the world and him! He will read the world and its laws: the
world with its laws will be there to be read. What the world, on *this* matter,
shall permit and bid is, as we said, the most important fact about the world.

Poet and prophet differ greatly in our loose modern notions of them. In
some old languages, again, the titles are synonymous; *vates* means both
prophet and poet; and indeed at all times, prophet and poet, well understood, have much kindred of meaning. Fundamentally indeed they are still
the same; in this most important respect especially, that they have penetrated
both of them into the sacred mystery of the universe; what Goethe calls
"the open secret." "Which is the great secret?" asks one. "The *open* secret"
—open to all, seen by almost none! That divine mystery, which lies everywhere in all beings, "the divine idea of the world," that which lies at "the
bottom of appearance," as Fichte styles it; of which all appearance, from the
starry sky to the grass of the field, but especially the appearance of man and
his work, is but the *vesture,* the embodiment that renders it visible. This
divine mystery *is* in all times and in all places; veritably is. In most times
and places it is greatly overlooked; and the universe definable always in one
or the other dialect, as the realized thought of God, is considered a trivial,
inert, commonplace matter—as if, says the satirist, it were a dead thing,
which some upholsterer had put together! It could do no good, at present,
to *speak* much about this; but it is a pity for every one of us if we do not
know it, live ever in the knowledge of it. Really a most mournful pity—a
failure to live at all, if we live otherwise!

But now, I say, whoever may forget this divine mystery, the *vates,*
whether prophet or poet, has penetrated into it; is a man sent hither to make
it more impressively known to us. That always is his message; he is to reveal
that to us—that sacred mystery which he more than others lives ever present
with. While others forget it, he knows it—I might say, he has been driven
to know it; without consent asked of *him,* he finds himself living in it, bound
to live in it. Once more, here is no hearsay, but a direct insight and belief;

this man too could not help being a sincere man! Whoever may live in the shows of things, it is for him a necessity of nature to live in the very fact of things. A man once more, in earnest with the universe, though all others were but toying with it. He is a *vates*, first of all, in virture of being sincere. So far poet and prophet, participators in the "open secret," are one.

With respect to their distinction again: the *vates* prophet, we might say, has seized that sacred mystery rather on the moral side, as good and evil, duty and prohibition; the *vates* poet on what the Germans call the æsthetic side, as beautiful, and the like. The one we may call a revealer of what we are to do, the other of what we are to love. But indeed these two provinces run into one another, and cannot be disjoined. The prophet too has his eye on what we are to love: how else shall he know what it is we are to do? The highest voice ever heard on this earth said withal: "Consider the lilies of the field; they toil not, neither do they spin: yet Solomon in all his glory was not arrayed like one of these." A glance, that, into the deepest deep of beauty. "The lilies of the field"—dressed finer than earthly princes, springing up there in the humble furrow-field; a beautiful *eye* looking out on you, from the great inner sea of beauty! How could the rude earth make these, if her essence, rugged as she looks and is, were not inwardly beauty? In this point of view, too, a saying of Goethe's, which has staggered several, may have meaning: "The beautiful," he intimates, "is higher than the good;" the beautiful includes in it "the good." The *true* beautiful; which however, I have said somewhere, "differs from the *false* as heaven does from Vauxhall!" So much for the distinction and identity of poet and prophet.

In ancient and also in modern periods we find a few poets who are accounted perfect; whom it were a kind of treason to find fault with. This is noteworthy; this is right: yet in strictness it is only an illusion. At bottom, clearly enough, there is no perfect poet! A vein of poetry exists in the hearts of all men; no man is made altogether of poetry. We are all poets when we *read* a poem well. The "imagination that shudders at the hell of Dante," is not that the same faculty, weaker in degree, as Dante's own? No one but Shakespeare can embody, out of *Saxo Grammaticus*, the story of "Hamlet" as Shakespeare did: but every one models some kind of story out of it; every one embodies it better or worse. We need not spend time in defining. Where there is no specific difference, as between round and square, all definition must be more or less arbitrary. A man that has *so* much more of the poetic element developed in him as to have become noticeable, will be called poet by his neighbors. World poets too, those whom we are to take for perfect poets, are settled by critics in the same way. One who rises *so* far above the general level of poets will, to such and such critics, seem a universal poet; as he ought to do. And yet it is and must be, an arbitrary distinction. All poets, all men, have some touches of the universal; no man is wholly made of that. Most poets are very soon forgotten: but not the noblest Shakespeare or Homer of them can be remembered *forever*—a day comes when he too is not!

Nevertheless, you will say, there must be a difference between true poetry and true speech not poetical: what is the difference? On this point many things have been written, especially by late German critics, some of which are not very intelligible at first. They say, for example, that the poet has an *infinitude* in him; communicates an *unendlichkeit*, a certain character of "infinitude," to whatsoever he delineates. This, though not very precise, yet on so vague a matter is worth remembering: if well meditated, some meaning will gradually be found in it. For my own part, I find considerable meaning in the old vulgar distinction of poetry being *metrical*, having music in it, being a song. Truly, if pressed to give a definition, one might say this as soon as anything else: If your delineation be authentically *musical*, musical not in word only, but in heart and substance, in all the thoughts and utterances of it, in the whole conception of it, then it will be poetical; if not, not. Musical: how much lies in that! A *musical* thought is one spoken by a mind that has penetrated into the inmost heart of the thing; detected the inmost mystery of it, namely the *melody* that lies hidden in it; the inward harmony of coherence which is its soul, whereby it exists and has a right to be, here in this world. All inmost things, we may say, are melodious; naturally utter themselves in song. The meaning of song goes deep. Who is there that, in logical words, can express the effect music has on us? A kind of inarticulate unfathomable speech, which leads us to the edge of the infinite and lets us for moments gaze into that!

Nay all speech, even the commonest speech, has something of song in it: not a parish in the world but has its parish accent—the rhythm or *tune* to which the people there *sing* what they have to say! Accent is a kind of chanting; all men have accent of their own—though they only *notice* that of others. Observe too how all passionate language does of itself become musical—with a finer music than the mere accent; the speech of a man even in zealous anger becomes a chant, a song. All deep things are song. It seems somehow the very central essence of us, song; as if all the rest were but wrappages and hulls! The primal element of us; of us and of all things. The Greeks fabled of sphere-harmonies: it was the feeling they had of the inner structure of nature; that the soul of all her voices and utterances was perfect music. Poetry, therefore, we will call *musical thought*. The poet is he who *thinks* in that manner. At bottom, it turns still on power of intellect; it is a man's sincerity and depth of vision that makes him a poet. See deep enough and you see musically; the heart of nature *being* everywhere music, if you can only reach it.

The *vates* poet, with his melodious apocalypse of nature, seems to hold a poor rank among us, in comparison with the *vates* prophet; his function and our esteem of him for his function, alike slight. The hero taken as divinity; the hero taken as prophet; then next the hero taken only as poet: does it not look as if our estimate of the great man, epoch after epoch, were continually diminishing? We take him first for a god, then for one god-inspired; and now in the next stage of it, his most miraculous word gains from us only the recognition that he is a poet, beautiful verse-maker, man of genius, or such-like! It looks so; but I persuade myself that intrinsically it is not so.

If we consider well, it will perhaps appear that in man still there is the *same* altogether peculiar admiration for the heroic gift, by what name soever called, that there at any time was.

I should say, if we do not now reckon a great man literally divine, it is that our notions of God, of the supreme unattainable fountain of splendor, wisdom and heroism, are ever rising *higher;* not altogether that our reverence for these qualities, as manifested in our like, is getting lower. This is worth taking thought of. Skeptical dilettantism, the curse of these ages, a curse which will last forever, does indeed in this the highest province of human things, as in all provinces, make sad work; and our reverence for great men, all crippled, blinded, paralytic as it is, comes out in poor plight, hardly recognizable. Men worship the shows of great men; the most disbelieve that there is any reality of great men to worship. The dreariest, fatalest faith; believing which, one would literally despair of human things. Nevertheless look, for example, at Napoleon! A Corsican lieutenant of artillery; that is the show of *him:* yet is he not obeyed, *worshiped* after his sort, as all the tiaraed and diademed of the world put together could not be? High duchesses, and ostlers of inns, gather round the Scottish rustic, Burns—a strange feeling dwelling in each that they never heard a man like this; that, on the whole, this is the man! In the secret heart of these people it still dimly reveals itself, though there is no accredited way of uttering it at present, that this rustic, with his black brows and flashing sun-eyes, and strange words moving laughter and tears, is of a dignity far beyond all others, incommensurable with all others. Do not we feel it so? But now, were dilettantism, skepticism, triviality, and all that sorrowful brood, cast out of us—as, by God's blessing, they shall one day be; were faith in the shows of things entirely swept out, replaced by clear faith in the *things* so that a man acted on the impulse of that only, and counted the other non-extant; what a new livelier feeling toward this Burns were it!

Nay here in these ages, such as they are, have we not two mere poets, if not deified, yet we may say beatified? Shakespeare and Dante are saints of poetry; really, if we will think of it, *canonized,* so that it is impiety to meddle with them. The unguided instinct of the world, working across all these perverse impediments, has arrived at such result. Dante and Shakespeare are a peculiar two. They dwell apart, in a kind of royal solitude; none equal, none second to them: in the general feeling of the world, a certain transcendentalism, a glory as of complete perfection, invests these two. They *are* canonized, though no pope or cardinals took hand in doing it! Such, in spite of every perverting influence, in the most unheroic times, is still our indestructible reverence for heroism. We will look a little at these two, the poet Dante and the poet Shakespeare: what little it is permitted us to say here of the hero as poet will most fitly arrange itself in that fashion.

Many volumes have been written by way of commentary on Dante and his book; yet, on the whole, with no great result. His biography is, as it were, irrecoverably lost for us. An unimportant, wandering, sorrow-stricken man, not much note was taken of him while he lived; and the most of that has vanished, in the long space that now intervenes. It is five centuries since he ceased writing and living here. After all commentaries, the book itself is mainly what we know of him. The book—and one might add that portrait commonly attributed to Giotto, which, looking on it, you cannot help inclining to think genuine, whoever did it. To me it is a most touching face; perhaps of all faces that I know, the most so. Lonely there, painted as on vacancy, with the simple laurel wound round it; the deathless sorrow and pain, the known victory which is also deathless—significant of the whole history of Dante! I think it is the mournfulest face that ever was painted from reality; an altogether tragic, heart-affecting face. There is in it, as foundation of it, the softness, tenderness, gentle affection as of a child; but all this is as if congealed into sharp contradiction, into abnegation, isolation, proud hopeless pain. A soft ethereal soul looking out so stern, implacable, grim-trenchant, as from imprisonment of thick ribbed ice! Withal it is a silent pain too, a silent scornful one: the lip is curled in a kind of godlike disdain of the thing that is eating out his heart—as if it were withal a mean insignificant thing, as if he whom it had power to torture and strangle were greater than it. The face of one wholly in protest, and life-long unsurrendering battle, against the world. Affection all converted into indignation: an implacable indignation: slow, equable, silent, like that of a god! The eye too, it looks out: in a kind of *surprise*, a kind of inquiry, why the world was of such a sort? This is Dante: so he looks, this "voice of ten silent centuries," and sings us "his mystic unfathomable song."

The little that we know of Dante's life corresponds well enough with this portrait and this book. He was born at Florence, in the upper class of society, in the year 1265. His education was the best then going; much school divinity, Aristotelean logic, some Latin classics—no inconsiderable insight into certain provinces of things: and Dante, with his earnest intelligent nature, we need not doubt, learned better than most all that was learnable. He has a clear cultivated understanding and of great subtlety; this best fruit of education he had contrived to realize from these scholastics. He knows accurately and well what lies close to him; but, in such a time, without printed books or free intercourse, he could not know well what was distant: the small clear light, most luminous for what is near, breaks itself into singular *chiaroscuro* striking on what is far off. This was Dante's learning from the schools. In life, he had gone through the usual destinies; been twice out campaigning as a soldier for the Florentine state, been on embassy; had in his thirty-fifth year, by natural gradation of talent and service, become one of the chief magistrates of Florence. He had met in boyhood a certain Beatrice Portinari, a beautiful little girl of his own age and rank and grown-up thenceforth in partial sight of her, in some distant intercourse with her. All readers know his graceful affecting account of this; and then of their being parted; of her being wedded to another and of her death soon after. She makes a great figure in Dante's poem; seems to have made a great figure in his life. Of all beings it might seem as if she, held apart from him, far apart at last in the dim eternity, were the only one he had ever with his whole strength of affection loved. She died: Dante himself was wedded; but it seems not happily, far from happily. I fancy, the rigorous earnest man, with his keen excitabilities, was not altogether easy to make happy.

We will not complain of Dante's miseries: had all gone right with him as he wished it, he might have been prior, podestà, or whatsoever they call it, of Florence, well accepted among neighbors—and the world had wanted one of the most notable words ever spoken or sung. Florence would have had another prosperous lord mayor; and the ten dumb centuries continued voiceless and the ten other listening centuries (for there will be ten of them and more) had no "Divina Commedia" to hear! We will complain of nothing. A nobler destiny was appointed for this Dante; and he, struggling like a man led toward death and crucifixion, could not help fulfilling it. Give *him* the choice of his happiness! He knew not, more than we do, what was really happy, what was really miserable.

In Dante's priorship, the Guelf-Ghibelline, Bianchi-Neri, or some other confused disturbances rose to such a height, that Dante, whose party had seemed the stronger, was with his friends cast unexpectedly forth into banishment; doomed thenceforth to a life of woe and wandering. His property was all confiscated and more; he had the fiercest feeling that it was entirely unjust, nefarious in the sight of God and man. He tried what was in him to get reinstated; tried even by warlike surprisal with arms in his hand: but it would not do; bad only had become worse. There is a record, I believe, still extant in the Florence archives, dooming this Dante, wheresoever caught, to be burned alive. Burned alive; so it stands, they say: a very curious civic document. Another curious document, some considerable number of years later, is a letter of Dante's to the Florentine magistrates, written in answer to a milder proposal of theirs, that he should return on condition of apologizing and paying a fine. He answers, with fixed stern pride: "If I cannot return without calling myself guilty, I will never return, *nunquam revertar.*"

For Dante there was now no home in this world. He wandered from patron to patron, from place to place; proving, in his own bitter words, "How hard is the path, *Come è duro calle.*" The wretched are not cheerful company. Dante, poor and banished, with his proud earnest nature, with his moody humors, was not a man to conciliate men. Petrarch reports of him that being at Can della Scala's court and blamed one day for his gloom and taciturnity, he answered in no courtier-like way. Della Scala stood among his courtiers, with mimes and buffoons (*nebulones ac histriones*) making him heartily merry; when turning to Dante, he said: "Is it not strange, now, that this poor fool should make himself so entertaining; while you, a wise man, sit there day after day, and have nothing to amuse us with at all?" Dante answered bitterly: "No, not strange; your highness is to recollect the proverb, *like to like*"—given the amuser, the amusee must also be given! Such a man, with his proud silent ways, with his sarcasms and sorrows, was not made to succeed at court. By degrees, it came to be evident to him that he had no longer any resting-place, or hope of benefit, in this earth. The earthly world had cast him forth, to wander, wander; no living heart to love him now; for his sore miseries there was no solace here.

The deeper naturally would the eternal world impress itself on him; that awful reality over which, after all, this time-world, with its Florences and banishments, only flutters as an unreal shadow. Florence thou shall never see: but hell and purgatory and heaven thou shall surely see! What is Florence, Can della Scala, and the world and life altogether? ETERNITY: thither, of a truth, not elsewhither, art thou and all things bound! The great soul of Dante, homeless on earth, made its home more and more in that awful other world. Naturally his thoughts brooded on that, as on the one fact important for him. Bodied or bodiless, it is the one fact important for all men—but to Dante, in that age, it was bodied in fixed certainty of scientific shape; he no more doubted of the *Malebolge* pool, that it all lay there with its gloomy circles, with its *alti guai*, and that he himself should see it, than we doubt that we should see Constantinople if we went thither. Dante's heart, long filled with this, brooding over it in speechless thought and awe, bursts forth at length into "mystic unfathomable song;" and this his "Divine Comedy," the most remarkable of all modern books, is the result.

It must have been a great solacement to Dante, and was, as we can see, a proud thought for him at times, that he, here in exile, could do this work; that no Florence, nor no man or men, could hinder him from doing it, or even much help him in doing it. He knew too, partly, that it was great; the greatest a man could do. "If thou follow thy star, *Se tu segui tua stella*"— so could the hero, in his forsakenness, in his extreme need, still say to himself: "Follow thou thy star, thou shalt not fail of a glorious heaven!" The labor of writing, we find, and indeed could know otherwise, was great and painful for him; he says, this book, "which has made me lean for many years." Ah yes, it was won, all of it, with pain and sore toil—not in sport, but in grim earnest. His book, as indeed most good books are, has been written, in many senses, with his heart's blood. It is his whole history, this book. He died after finishing it; not yet very old, at the age of fifty-six— broken-hearted rather, as is said. He lies buried in his death-city Ravenna: *Hic claudor Dantes patriis extorris ab oris.* The Florentines begged back his body, in a century after; the Ravenna people would not give it. "Here am I Dante laid, shut out from my native shores."

I said, Dante's poem was a song: it is Tieck who calls it "a mystic un- fathomable song;" and such is literally the character of it. Coleridge remarks very pertinently somewhere, that wherever you find a sentence musically worded, of true rhythm and melody in the words, there is some- thing deep and good in the meaning too. For body and soul, word and idea, go strangely together here as everywhere. Song: we said before, it was the heroic of speech! All *old* poems, Homer's and the rest, are authentically songs. I would say, in strictness, that all right poems are; that whatsoever is not *sung* is properly no poem, but a piece of prose cramped into jingling lines—to the great injury of the grammar, to the great grief of the reader, for most part! What we want to get at is the *thought* the man had, if he had any: why should he twist it into jingle, if he *could* speak it out plainly? It is only when the heart of him is rapt into true passion of melody, and the very tones of him, according to Coleridge's remark, become musical by the greatness, depth and music of his thoughts, that we can give him right to rhyme and sing; that we call him a poet, and listen to him as the heroic of speakers—whose speech *is* song. Pretenders to this are many; and to an earnest reader, I doubt, it is for the most part a very melancholy, not to say an insupportable business, that of reading rhyme! Rhyme that had no inward necessity to be rhymed—it ought to have told us plainly, without any jingle, what it was aiming at. I would advise all men who *can* speak their thought, not to sing it; to understand that, in a serious time, among serious men, there is no vocation in them for singing it. Precisely as we love the true song, and are charmed by it as by something divine, so shall we hate the false song, and account it a mere wooden noise, a thing hollow, superfluous, altogether an insincere and offensive thing.

I give Dante my highest praise when I say of his "Divine Comedy" that it is, in all senses, genuinely a song. In the very sound of it there is a *canto fermo;* it proceeds as by a chant. The language, his simple *terza rima,* doubtless helped him in this. One reads along naturally with a sort of *lilt.* But I add, that it could not be otherwise; for the essence and material of the work are themselves rhythmic. Its depth and rapt passion and sincerity, make it musical—go *deep* enough, there is music everywhere. A true inward symmetry, what one calls an architectural harmony, reigns in it, proportionates it all: architectural; which also partakes of the character of music. The three kingdoms, *inferno, purgatorio, paradiso,* look out on one another like compartments of a great edifice; a great supernatural world-cathedral, piled up there, stern, solemn, awful; Dante's world of souls! It is, at bottom, the *sincerest* of all poems; sincerity, here too, we find to be the measure of worth. It came deep out of the author's heart of hearts; and it goes deep and through long generations, into ours. The people of Verona, when they saw him on the streets, used to say, "*Eccovi l' uom ch' è stato all' inferno,* See, there is the man that was in hell!" Ah yes, he had been in hell—in hell enough, in long severe sorrow and struggle; as the like of him is pretty sure to have been. Commedias that come out *divine* are not accomplished otherwise. Thought, true labor of any kind, highest virtue itself, is it not the daughter of pain? Born as out of the black whirlwind—true *effort,* in fact, as of a captive struggling to free himself: that is thought. In all ways we are "to become perfect through *suffering.*" But as I say, no work known to me is so elaborated as this of Dante's. It has all been as if molten, in the hottest furnace of his soul. It had made him "lean" for many years. Not the general whole only; every compartment of it is worked out, with intense earnestness, into truth, into clear visuality. Each answers to the other; each fits in its place, like a marble stone accurately hewn and polished. It is the soul of Dante, and in this the soul of the middle ages, rendered forever rhythmically visible there. No light task; a right intense one: but a task which is *done*.

Perhaps one would say, *intensity*, with the much that depends on it, is the prevailing character of Dante's genius. Dante does not come before us as a large catholic mind; rather as a narrow and even sectarian mind: it is partly the fruit of his age and position, but partly too of his own nature. His greatness has, in all senses, concentrated itself into fiery emphasis and depth. He is world-great not because he is world-wide, but because he is world-deep. Through all objects he pierces as it were down into the heart of being. I know nothing so intense as Dante. Consider, for example, to begin with the outermost development of his intensity, consider how he paints. He has a great power of vision; seizes the very type of a thing; presents that and nothing more. You remember that first view he gets of the Hall of Dite: *red* pinnacle, red-hot cone of iron glowing through the dim immensity of gloom—so vivid, so distinct, visible at once and forever! It is as an emblem of the whole genius of Dante. There is a brevity, an abrupt precision in him: Tacitus is not briefer, more condensed; and then in Dante it seems a natural condensation, spontaneous to the man. One smiting word; and then there is silence, nothing more said. His silence is more eloquent than words. It is strange with what a sharp decisive grace he snatches the true likeness of a matter: cuts into the matter as with a pen of fire. Plutus, the blustering giant, collapses at Virgil's rebuke; it is "as the sails sink, the mast being suddenly broken." Or that poor Brunetto Latini, with the *cotto aspetto*, "face *baked*," parched brown and lean; and the "fiery snow" that falls on them there, a "fiery snow without wind," slow, deliberate, never-ending! Or the lids of those tombs; square sarcophaguses, in that silent dim-burning hall, each with its soul in torment; the lids laid open there; they are to be shut at the day of judgment, through eternity. And how Farinata rises; and how Cavalcante falls—at hearing of his son and the past tense *"fue!"* The very movements in Dante have something brief; swift, decisive, almost military. It is of the inmost essence of his genius, this sort of painting. The fiery, swift Italian nature of the man, so silent, passionate, with its quick abrupt movements, its silent "pale rages," speaks itself in these things.

For though this of painting is one of the outermost developments of a man, it comes like all else from the essential faculty of him; it is physiognomical of the whole man. Find a man whose words paint you a likeness, you have found a man worth something; mark his manner of doing it, as very characteristic of him. In the first place, he would not have discerned the object at all, or seen the vital type of it, unless he had, what we may call, *sympathized* with it—had sympathy in him to bestow on objects. He must have been *sincere* about it too; sincere and sympathetic: a man without worth cannot give you the likeness of any object; he dwells in vague outwardness, fallacy and trivial hearsay, about all objects. And indeed may we not say that intellect altogether expresses itself in this power of discerning what an object is? Whatsoever of faculty a man's mind may have will come out here. Is it even of business, a matter to be done? The gifted man is he who *sees* the essential point, and leaves all the rest aside as surplusage: it is his faculty too, the man of business' faculty, that he discern the true *likeness,* not the false superficial one, of the thing he has got to work in. And how much of *morality* is in the kind of insight we get of anything; "the eye seeing in all things what it brought with it the faculty of seeing!" To the mean eye all things are trivial, as certainly as to the jaundiced they are yellow. Raphael, the painters tell us, is the best of all portrait-painters withal. No most gifted eye can exhaust the significance of any object. In the commonest human face there lies more than Raphael will take away with him.

Dante's painting is not graphic only, brief, true, and of a vividness as of fire in dark night; taken on the wider scale, it is everywhere noble, and the outcome of a great soul. Francesca and her lover, what qualities in that! A thing woven as out of rainbows, on a ground of eternal black. A small flute-voice of infinite wail speaks there, into our very heart of hearts. A touch of womanhood in it too: *della bella persona che mi fu tolta;* and how, even in the pit of woe, it is a solace that *he* will never part from her! Saddest tragedy in these *alti guai.* And the racking winds, in that *aer bruno,* whirl them away again, to wail forever! Strange to think: Dante was the friend of this poor Francesca's father; Francesca herself may have sat upon the poet's knee, as a bright innocent little child. Infinite pity, yet also infinite rigor of law: it is so nature is made; it is so Dante discerned that she was made. What a paltry notion is that of his "Divine Comedy's" being a poor splenetic impotent terrestrial libel; putting those into hell whom he could not be avenged upon on earth! I suppose if ever pity, tender as a mother's, was in the heart of any man, it was in Dante's. But a man who does not know rigor cannot pity either. His very pity will be cowardly, egoistic—senti-mentality, or little better. I know not in the world an affection equal to that of Dante. It is a tenderness, a trembling, longing, pitying love: like the wail of Æolean harps, soft, soft; like a child's young heart—and then that stern, sore-saddened heart! These longings of his toward his Beatrice; their meeting together in the *paradiso;* his gazing in her pure transfigured eyes, her that had been purified by death so long, separated from him so far—one likens it to the song of angels; it is among the purest utterances of affec-tion, perhaps the very purest, that ever came out of a human soul.

For the *intense* Dante is intense in all things; he has got into the essence of all. His intellectual insight as painter, on occasion too as reasoner, is but the result of all other sorts of intensity. Morally great, above all, we must call him: it is the beginning of all. His scorn, his grief are as transcendent as his love—as indeed, what are they but the *inverse* or *converse* of his love! "*A dio spiacenti ed a' nemici sui,* hateful to God and to the enemies of God:" lofty scorn, unappeasable silent reprobation and aversion; "*Non ragionam di lor,* we will not speak of *them,* look only and pass." Or think of this: "They have not the *hope* to die, *non han speranza dimorte.*" One day, it had risen sternly benign on the scathed heart of Dante, that he, wretched, never resting, worn as he was, would full surely *die;* "that destiny itself could not doom him not to die." Such works are in this man. For rigor, earnestness and depth, he is not to be paralleled in the modern world; to seek his parallel we must go into the Hebrew Bible, and live with the antique prophets there.

I do not agree with much modern criticism, in greatly preferring the *inferno* to the two other parts of the "Divina Commedia." Such preference belongs, I imagine, to our general Byronism of taste and is like to be a transient feeling. The *purgatorio* and *paradiso,* especially the former, one would almost say, is even more excellent than it. It is a noble thing that *purgatorio,* "mountain of purification;" an emblem of the noblest conception of that age. If sin is so fatal and hell is and must be so rigorous, awful, yet in repentance too is man purified; repentance is the grand Christian act. It is beautiful how Dante works it out. The *tremolar dell' onde,* that "trembling" of the ocean-waves, under the first pure gleam of morning, dawning afar on the wandering two, is as the type of an altered mood. Hope has now dawned; never-dying hope, if in company still with heavy sorrow. The obscure sojourn of demons and reprobate is underfoot; a soft breathing of penitence mounts higher and higher, to the throne of mercy itself. "Pray for me," the denizens of that mount of pain all say to him. "Tell my Giovanna to pray for me," my daughter Giovanna; "I think her mother loves me no more!" They toil painfully up by that winding steep, "bent down like corbels of a building," some of them—crushed together so "for the sin of pride;" yet nevertheless in years, in ages and æons, they shall have reached the top, which is heaven's gate and by mercy shall have been admitted in. The joy too of all, when one has prevailed; the whole mountain shakes with joy and a psalm of praise rises, when one soul has perfected repentance and got its sin and misery left behind! I call all this a noble embodiment of a true noble thought.

But indeed the three compartments mutually support one another, are indispensable to one another. The *paradiso,* a kind of inarticulate music to me, is the redeeming side of the *inferno;* the *inferno* without it were untrue. All three make up the true unseen world, as figured in the Christianity of the middle ages; a thing forever memorable, forever true in the essence of it, to all men. It was perhaps delineated in no human soul with such depth of veracity as in this of Dante's; a man *sent* to sing it, to keep it long memorable. Very notable with what brief simplicity he passes out of the every-day reality, into the invisible one; and in the second or third stanza, we find ourselves in the world of spirits; and dwell there, as among things palpable, indubitable! To Dante they *were* so; the real world, as it is called, and its facts, was but the threshold to an infinitely higher fact of a world. At bottom, the one was as *preter*natural as the other. Has not each man a soul? He will not only be a spirit, but is one. To the earnest Dante it is all one visible fact; he believes it, sees it; is the poet of it in virtue of that. Sincerity, I say again, is the saving merit, now as always.

Dante's hell, purgatory, paradise, are a symbol withal, an emblematic representation of his belief about this universe—some critic in a future age, like those Scandinavian ones the other day, who had ceased altogether to think as Dante did, may find this too all an "allegory," perhaps an idle allegory! It is a sublime embodiment, or sublimest, of the soul of Christianity. It expresses, as in huge world-wide architectural emblems, how the Christian Dante felt good and evil to be the two polar elements of this creation, on which it all turns; that these two differ not by *preferability* of one to the other, but by incompatibility absolute and infinite; that the one is excellent and high as light and heaven, the other hideous, black as Gehenna and the pit of hell! Everlasting justice, yet with penitence, with everlasting pity—all Christianism, as Dante and the middle ages had it, is emblemed here. Emblemed: and yet, as I urged the other day, with what entire truth of purpose; how unconscious of any embleming! Hell, purgatory, paradise: these things were not fashioned as emblems; was there, in our modern European mind, any thought at all of their being emblems! Were they not indubitable awful facts; the whole heart of man taking them for practically true, all nature everywhere confirming them? So is it always in these things. Men do not believe an allegory. The future critic, whatever his new thought may be, who considers this of Dante to have been all got up as an allegory, will commit one sore mistake! Paganism we recognized as a veracious expression of the earnest awe-struck feeling of man toward the universe; veracious, true once, and still not without worth for us. But mark here the difference of paganism and Christianism; one great difference. Paganism emblemed chiefly the operations of nature; the destinies, efforts, combinations, vicissitudes of things and men in this world; Christianism emblemed the law of human duty, the moral law of man. One was the sensuous nature: a rude helpless utterance of the *first* thought of men—the chief recognized virtue, courage, superiority to fear. The other was not for the sensuous nature, but for the moral. What a progress is here, if in that one respect only!

And so in this Dante, as we said, had ten silent centuries, in a very strange way, found a voice. The "Divina Commedia" is of Dante's writing; yet in truth *it* belongs to ten Christian centuries, only the finishing of it is Dante's. So always. The craftsman there, the smith with that metal of his, with these tools, with these cunning methods—how little of all he does is properly *his* work! All past inventive men work there with him—as indeed with all of us, in all things. Dante is the spokesman of the middle ages; the thought they lived by stands here, in everlasting music. These sublime ideas of his, terrible and beautiful, are the fruit of the Christian meditation of all the good men who had gone before him. Precious they; but also is not he precious? Much, had not he spoken, would have been dumb; not dead, yet living voiceless.

On the whole, is it not an utterance, this mystic song, at once of one of the greatest human souls, and of the highest thing that Europe had hitherto realized for itself? Christianism, as Dante sings it, is another than paganism in the rude Norse mind; another than "bastard Christianism" half-articulately spoken in the Arab desert seven hundred years before! The noblest *idea* made *real* hitherto among men, is sung, and emblemed-forth abidingly, by one of the noblest men. In the one sense and in the other, are we not right glad to possess it? As I calculate, it may last yet for long thousands of years. For the thing that is uttered from the inmost parts of a man's soul, differs altogether from what is uttered by the outer part. The outer is of the day, under the empire of mode; the outer passes away, in swift endless changes; the inmost is the same yesterday, to-day and forever. True souls, in all generations of the world, who look on this Dante, will find a brother-hood in him; the deep sincerity of his thoughts, his woes and hopes, will speak likewise to their sincerity; they will feel that this Dante too was a brother. Napoleon in Saint Helena is charmed with the genial veracity of old Homer. The oldest Hebrew prophet, under a vesture the most diverse from ours, does yet, because he speaks from the heart of man, speak to all men's hearts. It is the one sole secret of continuing long memorable. Dante for depth of sincerity, is like an antique prophet too; his words, like theirs, come from his very heart. One need not wonder if it were predicted that his poem might be the most enduring thing our Europe has yet made; for nothing so endures as a truly spoken word. All cathedrals, pontificalities, brass and stone, and outer arrangement never so lasting, are brief in com-parison to an unfathomable heart-song like this: one feels as if it might survive, still of importance to men, when these had all sunk into new irrecognizable combinations, and had ceased individually to be. Europe has made much; great cities, great empires, encyclopædias, creeds, bodies of opinion and practice: but it has made little of the class of Dante's thought. Homer yet *is*, veritably present face to face with every open soul of us; and Greece, where is *it*? Desolate for thousands of years; away, vanished; a bewildered heap of stones and rubbish, the life and existence of it all gone. Like a dream; like the dust of King Agamemnon! Greece was; Greece, except in the *words* it spoke, is not.

The uses of this Dante? We will not say much about his "uses." A human soul who has once got into that primal element of *song*, and sung-forth fitly somewhat therefrom, has worked in the *depths* of our existence; feeding through long times the life-*roots* of all excellent human things whatsoever—in a way that "utilities" will not succeed well in calculating! We will not estimate the sun by the quantity of gas-light it saves us; Dante shall be invaluable, or of no value. One remark I may make: the contrast in this respect between the hero poet and the hero prophet. In a hundred years, Mahomet, as we saw, had his Arabians at Grenada and at Delhi; Dante's Italians seem to be yet very much where they were. Shall we say, then, Dante's effect on the world was small in comparison? Not so: his arena is far more restricted; but also it is far nobler, clearer—perhaps not less but more important. Mahomet speaks to great masses of men, in the coarse dialect adapted to such; a dialect filled with inconsistencies, crudities, follies: on the great masses alone can he act and there with good and with evil strangely blended. Dante speaks with the noble, the pure and great, in all times and places. Neither does he grow obsolete, as the other does. Dante burns as a pure star, fixed there in the firmament, at which the great and the high of all ages kindle themselves: he is the possession of all the chosen of the world for uncounted time. Dante, one calculates, may long survive Mahomet. In this way the balance may be made straight again.

But, at any rate, it is not by what is called their effect on the world by what *we* can judge of their effect there, that a man and his work are measured. Effect? Influence? Utility? Let a man *do* his work; the fruit of it is the care of another than he. It will grow its own fruit; and whether embodied in caliph thrones and Arabian conquests, so that it "fills all morning and evening newspapers," and all histories, which are a kind of distilled newspapers; or not embodied so at all—what matters that? That is not the real fruit of it! The Arabian caliph, in so far only as he did something, was something. If the great cause of man, and man's work in God's earth, got no furtherance from the Arabian caliph, then no matter how many scimiters he drew, how many gold piasters pocketed and what uproar and blaring he made in this world—*he* was but a loud sounding inanity and futility; at bottom, he *was* not at all. Let us honor the great empire of *silence*, once more! The boundless treasury which we do *not* jingle in our pockets, or count up and present before men! It is perhaps, of all things, the usefulest for each of us to do, in these loud times.

As Dante, the Italian man, was sent into our world to embody musically the religion of the middle ages, the religion of our modern Europe, its inner life; so Shakespeare, we may say, embodies for us the outer life of our Europe as developed then, its chivalries, courtesies, humors, ambitions, what practical way of thinking, acting, looking at the world, men then had. As in Homer we may still construe old Greece; so in Shakespeare and Dante, after thousands of years, what our modern Europe was, in faith and in practice, will still be legible. Dante has given us the faith or soul; Shakespeare, in a not less noble way, has given us the practice or body. This latter also we were to have; a man was sent for it, the man Shakespeare. Just when that chivalric way of life had reached its last finish and was on the point of breaking down into slow or swift dissolution, as we now see it everywhere, this other sovereign poet, with his seeing eye, with his perennial singing voice, was sent to take note of it, to give long-enduring record of it. Two fit men: Dante, deep, fierce as the central fire of the world; Shakespeare, wide, placid, far-seeing, as the sun, the upper light of the world. Italy produced the one world-voice; we English had the honor of producing the other.

Curious enough how, as it were by mere accident, this man came to us. I think always, so great, quiet, complete and self-sufficing is this Shakespeare, had the Warwickshire squire not prosecuted him for deer-stealing, we had perhaps never heard of him as a poet! The woods and skies, the rustic life of man in Stratford there, had been enough for this man! But indeed that strange outbudding of our whole English existence, which we call the Elizabethan era, did not it too come as of its own accord? The "tree igdrasil" buds and withers by its own laws—too deep for our scanning. Yet it does bud and wither and every bough and leaf of it is there, by fixed eternal laws; not a Sir Thomas Lucy but comes at the hour fit for him. Curious, I say, and not sufficiently considered: how everything does co-operate with all; not a leaf rotting on the highway but is indissoluble portion of solar and stellar systems; no thought, word or act of man but has sprung withal out of all men and works sooner or later, recognizably or irrecognizably, on all men! It is all a tree: circulation of sap and influences, mutual communication of every minutest leaf with the lowest talon of a root, with every other greatest and minutest portion of the whole. The tree igdrasil, that has its roots down in the kingdoms of Hela and death and whose boughs overspread the highest heaven!

In some sense it may be said that this glorious Elizabethan era with its Shakespeare, as the outcome and flowerage of all which had preceded it, is itself attributable to the Catholicism of the middle ages. The Christian faith, which was the theme of Dante's song, had produced this practical life which Shakespeare was to sing. For religion then, as it now and always is, was the soul of practice; the primary vital fact in men's life. And remark here, as rather curious, that middle age Catholicism was abolished, so far as acts of parliament could abolish it, before Shakespeare, the noblest product of it, made his appearance. He did make his appearance nevertheless. Nature at her own time, with Catholicism or what else might be necessary, sent him forth; taking small thought of acts of parliament. King Henrys, Queen Elizabeths go their way; and nature too goes hers. Acts of parliament, on the whole, are small, notwithstanding the noise they make. What act of parliament, debate at St. Stephen's, on the hustings or elsewhere, was it that brought this Shakespeare into being? No dining at Freemasons' tavern, opening subscription-lists, selling of shares, and infinite other jangling and true or false endeavoring! This Elizabethan era, and all its nobleness and blessedness, came without proclamation, preparation of ours. Priceless Shakespeare was the free gift of nature; given altogether silently—received altogether silently, as if it had been a thing of little account. And yet, very literally, it is a priceless thing. One should look at that side of matters too.

Of this Shakespeare of ours, perhaps the opinion one sometimes hears a little idolatrously expressed is, in fact, the right one; I think the best judgment not of this country only, but of Europe at large, is slowly pointing to the conclusion, that Shakespeare is the chief of all poets hitherto; the greatest intellect who, in our recorded world, has left record of himself in the way of literature. On the whole, I know not such a power of vision, such a faculty of thought, if we take all the characters of it, in any other man. Such a calmness of depth; placid joyous strength; all things imaged in that great soul of his so true and clear, as in a tranquil unfathomable sea! It has been said, that in the constructing of Shakespeare's dramas there is, apart from all other "faculties" as they are called, an understanding manifested, equal to that in Bacon's "Novum Organum." That is true; and it is not a truth that strikes every one. It would become more apparent if we tried, any of us for himself, how, out of Shakespeare's dramatic materials, *we* could fashion such a result! The built house seems all so fit—everyway as it should be, as if it came there by its own law and the nature of things—we forget the rude disorderly quarry it was shaped from. The very perfection of the house, as if nature herself had made it, hides the builder's merit. Perfect, more perfect than any other man, we may call Shakespeare in this: he discerns, knows as by instinct, what condition he works under, what his materials are, what his own force and its relation to them is. It is not a transitory glance of insight that will suffice; it is deliberate illumination of the whole matter; it is a calmly *seeing* eye; a great intellect, in short. How a man, of some wide thing that he has witnessed, will construct a narrative, what kind of picture and delineation he will give of it—is the best measure you could get of what intellect is in the man. Which circumstance is vital and shall stand prominent; which unessential, fit to be suppressed; where is the true *beginning*, the true sequence and ending? To find out this, you task the whole force of insight that is in the man. He must *understand* the thing; according to the depth of his understanding, will the fitness of his answer be. You will try him so. Does like join itself to like; does the spirit of method stir in that confusion, so that its embroilment becomes order? Can the man say, *fiat lux*, let there be light; and out of chaos make a world? Precisely as there is *light* in himself, will he accomplish this.

Or indeed we may say again, it is in what I called portrait-painting, delineating of men and things, especially of men, that Shakespeare is great. All the greatness of the man comes out decisively here. It is unexampled, I think, that calm creative perspicacity of Shakespeare. The thing he looks at reveals not this or that face of it, but its inmost heart and generic secret: it dissolves itself as in light before him, so that he discerns the perfect structure of it. Creative, we said: poetic creation, what is this too but *seeing* the thing sufficiently? The *word* that will describe the thing, follows of itself from such clear intense sight of the thing. And is not Shakespeare's *morality*, his valor, candor, tolerance, truthfulness; his whole victorious strength and greatness, which can triumph over such obstructions, visible there too? Great as the world! No *twisted*, poor convex-concave mirror, reflecting all objects with its own convexities and concavities; a perfectly *level* mirror— that is to say withal, if we will understand it, a man justly related to all things and men, a good man. It is truly a lordly spectacle how this great soul takes in all kinds of men and objects, a Falstaff, an Othello, a Juliet, a Coriolanus; sets them all forth to us in their round completeness; loving just, the equal brother of all. *Novum organum* and all the intellect you will find in Bacon, is of a quite secondary order; earthly, material, poor in comparison with this. Among modern men, one finds, in strictness, almost nothing of the same rank. Goethe, alone, since the days of Shakespeare, reminds me of it. Of him too you say that he *saw* the object; you may say what he himself says of Shakespeare: "His characters are like watches with dial plates of transparent crystal; they show you the hour like others and the inward mechanism also is all visible."

The seeing eye! It is this that discloses the inner harmony of things; what nature meant, what musical idea nature has wrapped up in these often rough embodiments. Something she did mean. To the seeing eye that something were discernible. Are they base, miserable things? You can laugh over them, you can weep over them; you can in some way or other genially relate yourself to them—you can, at lowest, hold your peace about them, turn away your own and others' face from them, till the hour come for practically exterminating and extinguishing them! At bottom, it is the poet's first gift, as it is all men's, that he have intellect enough. He will be a poet if he have: a poet in word; or failing that, perhaps still better a poet in act. Whether he write at all; and if so, whether in prose or in verse, will depend on accidents: who knows on what extremely trivial accidents—perhaps on his having had a singing-master, on his being taught to sing in his boyhood! But the faculty which enables him to discern the inner heart of things and the harmony that dwells there (for whatsoever exists has a harmony in the heart of it, or it would not hold together and exist), is not the result of habits or accidents, but the gift of nature herself; the primary outfit for a heroic man in what sort soever. To the poet, as to every other, we say first of all, *See*. If you cannot do that, it is of no use to keep stringing rhymes together, jingling sensibilities against each other and *name* yourself a poet; there is no hope for you. If you can, there is, in prose or verse, in action or speculation, all manner of hope. The crabbed old school-master used to ask, when they brought him a new pupil, "But are ye sure he's *not a dunce?*" Why, really one might ask the same thing, in regard to every man proposed for whatsoever function; and consider it as the one inquiry needful: Are ye sure he's not a dunce? There is, in this world, no other entirely fatal person.

For, in fact, I say the degree of vision that dwells in a man is a correct measure of the man. If called to define Shakespeare's faculty, I should say superiority of intellect and think I had included all under that. What indeed are faculties? We talk of faculties as if they were distinct, things separable; as if a man had intellect, imagination, fancy, etc., as he has hands, feet and arms. That is a capital error. Then again, we hear of a man's "intellectual nature," and of his "moral nature," as if these again were divisible and existed apart. Necessities of language do perhaps prescribe such forms of utterance; we must speak, I am aware in that way, if we are to speak at all. But words ought not to harden into things for us. It seems to me, our apprehension of this matter is, for most part, radically falsified thereby. We ought to know withal and to keep forever in mind, that these divisions are at bottom but *names;* that man's spiritual nature, the vital force which dwells in him, is essentially one and indivisible; that what we call imagination, fancy, understanding and so forth, are but different figures of the same power of insight, all indissolubly connected with each other, physiognomically related; that if we knew one of them, we might know all of them. Morality itself, what we call the moral quality of a man, what is this but another *side* of the one vital force whereby he is and works? All that a man does is physiognomical of him. You may see how a man would fight, by the way in which he sings; his courage, or want of courage, is visible in the word he utters, in the opinion he has formed, no less than in the stroke he strikes. He is *one;* and preaches the same self abroad in all these ways.

Without hands a man might have feet, and could still walk: but, consider it—without morality intellect were impossible for him; a thoroughly immoral *man* could not know anything at all! To know a thing, what we can call knowing, a man must first *love* the thing, sympathize with it; that is, be *virtuously* related to it. If he have not the justice to put down his own selfishness at every turn, the courage to stand by the dangerous-true at every turn, how shall he know? His virtues, all of them, will lie recorded in his knowledge. Nature, with her truth, remains to the bad, to the selfish and the pusillanimous forever a sealed book: what such can know of nature is mean, superficial, small; for uses of the day merely. But does not the very fox know something of nature? Exactly so: it knows where the geese lodge! The human reynard, very frequent everywhere in the world, what more does he know but this and the like of this? Nay, it should be considered too, that if the fox had not a certain vulpine *morality*, he could not even know where the geese were, or get at the geese! If he spent his time in splenetic atrabiliar reflections on his own misery, his ill usage by nature, fortune and other foxes and so forth; and had not courage, promptitude, practicality, and other suitable vulpine gifts and graces, he would catch no geese. We may say of the fox too, that his morality and insight are of the same dimensions; different faces of the same internal unity of vulpine life! These things are worth stating; for the contrary of them acts with manifold very baleful perversion, in this time: what limitations, modifications they require, your own candor will supply.

If I say, therefore, that Shakespeare is the greatest of intellects, I have said all concerning him. But there is more in Shakespeare's intellect than we have yet seen. It is what I call an unconscious intellect; there is more virtue in it than he himself is aware of. Novalis beautifully remarks of him, that those dramas of his are products of nature too, deep as nature herself. I find a great truth in this saying. Shakespeare's art is not artifice; the noblest worth of it is not there by plan or precontrivance. It grows up from the deeps of nature, through this noble sincere soul, who is a voice of nature. The latest generations of men will find new meanings "new harmonies with the infinite structure of the universe; concurrences with later ideas, affinities with the higher powers and senses of man." This well deserves meditating. It is nature's highest reward to a true simple great soul, that he get thus to be *a part of herself*. Such a man's works, whatsoever he with utmost conscious exertion and forethought shall accomplish, grow up withal *un*consciously, from the unknown deeps in him—as the oak tree grows from the earth's bosom, as the mountains and waters shape themselves; with a symmetry grounded on nature's own laws, conformable to all truth whatsoever. How much in Shakespeare lies hid; his sorrows, his silent struggles known to himself; much that was not known at all, not speakable at all; like *roots*, like sap and forces working underground! Speech is great; but silence is greater.

Withal the joyful tranquility of this man is notable. I will not blame Dante for his misery: it is as battle without victory; but true battle—the first indispensable thing. Yet I call Shakespeare greater than Dante, in that he fought truly, and did conquer. Doubt it not, he had his own sorrows: those *sonnets* of his will even testify expressly in what deep waters he had waded, and swum struggling for his life—as what man like him ever failed to have to do? It seems to me a heedless notion, our common one that he sat like a bird on the bough; and sang forth, free and off-hand; never knowing the troubles of other men. Not so; with no man is it so. How could a man travel forward from rustic deer-poaching to such tragedy-writing, and not fall in with sorrows by the way? Or, still better, how could a man delineate a Hamlet, a Coriolanus, a Macbeth, so many suffering heroic hearts, if his own heroic heart had never suffered? And now, in contrast with all this, observe his mirthfulness, his genuine overflowing love of laughter! You would say, in no point does he *exaggerate* but only in laughter. Fiery objurgations, words that pierce and burn, are to be found in Shakespeare; yet he is always in measure here; never what Johnson would remark as a specially "good hater." But his laughter seems to pour from him in floods; he heaps all manner of ridiculous nicknames on the butt he is bantering, tumbles and tosses him in all sorts of horse-play; would you say, with his whole heart laughs. And then, if not always the finest, it is always a genial laughter. Not at mere weakness, at misery or poverty; never. No man who *can* laugh, what we call laughing, will laugh at these things. It is some poor character only *desiring* to laugh, and have the credit of wit, that does so. Laughter means sympathy; good laughter is not "the crackling of thorns under the pot." Even at stupidity and pretension this Shakespeare does not laugh otherwise than genially. Dogberry and Verges tickle our very hearts; and we dismiss them covered with explosions of laughter: but we like the poor fellows only the better for our laughing: and hope they will get on well there, and continue presidents of the city-watch. Such laughter, like sunshine on the deep sea, is very beautiful to me.

We have no room to speak of Shakespeare's individual works; though perhaps there is much still waiting to be said on that head. Had we, for instance, all his plays reviewed as *Hamlet* in "Wilhelm Meister," is! A thing which might, one day, be done. August Wilhelm Schlegel has a remark on his historical plays, "Henry V," and others, which is worth remembering. He calls them a kind of national epic. Marlborough, you recollect, said he knew no English history but what he had learned from Shakespeare. There are really, if we look to it, few as memorable histories. The great salient points are admirably seized; all rounds itself off, into a kind of rhythmic coherence; it is, as Schlegel says, *epic;* as indeed all delineation by a great thinker will be. There are right beautiful things in those pieces, which indeed together form one beautiful thing. That battle of Agincourt strikes me as one of the most perfect things, in its sort, we anywhere have of Shakespeare's. The description of the hosts: the worn-out, jaded English; the dread hour, big with destiny, when the battle shall begin; and then that deathless valor: "Ye good yeomen whose limbs were made in England!" There is a noble patriotism in it—far other than the "indifference" you sometimes hear ascribed to Shakespeare. A true English heart breathes, calm and strong, through the whole business; not boisterous, protrusive; all the better for that. There is a sound in it like the ring of steel. This man too had a right stroke in him, had it come to that!

But I will say, of Shakespeare's works generally, that we have no full impress of him there; even as full as we have of many men. His works are so many windows, through which we see a glimpse of the world that was in him. All his works seem, comparatively speaking, cursory, imperfect, written under cramping circumstances; giving only here and there a note of the full utterance of the man. Passages there are that come upon you like splendor out of heaven; bursts of radiance, illuminating the very heart of the thing: you say, "There is *true*, spoken once and forever; wheresoever and whensoever there is an open human soul, that will be recognized as true!" Such bursts, however, make us feel that the surrounding matter is not radiant; that it is, in part, temporary, conventional. Alas, Shakespeare had to write for the Globe playhouse: his great soul had to crush itself, as it could, into that and no other mould. It was with him, then, as it is with us all. No man works save under conditions. The sculptor cannot set his own free thought before us; but his thought as he could translate it into the stone that was given, with the tools that were given. *Disjecta membra* are all that we find of any poet, or of any man.

Whoever looks intelligently at this Shakespeare may recognize that he too was a *Prophet* in his way; of an insight analogous to the prophet, though he took it up in another strain. Nature seemed to this man also divine; *un*speakable, deep as tophet, high as heaven: "We are such stuff as dreams are made of!" That scroll in Westminster Abbey, which few read with understanding, is of the depth of any seen. But the man sang; did not preach, except musically. We called Dante the melodious priest of middle-age Catholicism. May we not call Shakespeare the still more melodious priest of a *true* Catholicism, the "universal church" of the future and of all times? No narrow superstition, harsh asceticism, intolerance, fanatical fierceness or perversion: a revelation so far as it goes, that such a thousandfold hidden beauty and divineness dwells in all nature; which let all men worship as they can! We may say without offense, that there rises a kind of universal psalm out of this Shakespeare too; not unfit to make itself heard among the still more sacred psalms. Not in disharmony with these, if we understood them, but in harmony! I cannot call this Shakespeare a "skeptic," as some do; his indifference to creeds and theological quarrels of his time misleading them. No: neither unpatriotic, though he says little about his patriotism; nor skeptic, though he says little about his faith. Such "indifference" was the fruit of his greatness withal: his whole heart was in his own grand sphere of worship (we may call it such); these other controversies, vitally important to other men, were not vital to him.

But call it worship, call it what you will, is it not a right glorious thing, and set of things, this that Shakespeare has brought us? For myself, I feel that there is actually a kind of sacredness in the fact of such a man sent into this earth. Is he not an eye to us all; a blessed heaven-sent bringer of light? And at bottom, was it not perhaps far better that this Shakespeare, everyway an unconscious man, was *conscious* of no heavenly message? He did not feel, like Mahomet, because he saw into those internal splendors, that he specially was the "prophet of God:" and was he not greater than Mahomet in that? Greater; and also, if we compute strictly, as we did in Dante's case more successful. It was intrinsically an error that notion of Mahomet's of his supreme prophethood; and has come down to us inextricably involved in error to this day; dragging along with it such a coil of fables, impurities, intolerances, as make it a questionable step for me here and now to say, as I have done, that Mahomet was a true speaker at all, and not rather, an ambitious charlatan, perversity and simulacrum; no speaker, but a babbler! Even in Arabia, as I compute, Mahomet will have exhausted himself and become obsolete, while this Shakespeare, this Dante may still be young—while this Shakespeare may still pretend to be a priest of mankind, of Arabia as of other places, for unlimited periods to come!

Compared with any speaker or singer one knows, even with Æschylus or Homer, why should he not, for veracity and universality, last like them? He is *sincere* as they; reaches deep down like them, to the universal and perennial. But as for Mahomet, I think it had been better for him *not* to be so conscious! Alas, poor Mahomet; all that he was *conscious* of was a mere error; a futility and triviality—as indeed such ever is. The truly great in him too was the unconscious: that he was a wild Arab lion of the desert, and did speak out with that great thunder-voice of his, not by words which he *thought* to be great, but by action, by feelings, by a history which *were* great! His Koran has become a stupid piece of prolix absurdity; we do not believe, like him, that God wrote that! The great man here too, as always, is a force of nature: whatsoever is truly great in him springs up from the *in*articulate deeps.

Well: this is our poor Warwickshire peasant, who rose to be manager of a playhouse, so that he could live without begging; whom the Earl of Southampton cast some kind glances on; whom Sir Thomas Lucy, many thanks to him, was for sending to the treadmill! We did not account him a god, like Odin, while he dwelt with us—on which point there were much to be said. But I will say rather, or repeat: in spite of the sad state hero worship now lies in, consider what this Shakespeare has actually become among us. Which Englishman we ever made, in this land of ours, which million of Englishmen, would we not give up rather than the Stratford peasant? There is no regiment of highest dignitaries that we would sell him for. He is the grandest thing we have yet done. For our honor among foreign nations, as an ornament to our English household, what item is there that we would not surrender rather than him? Consider now, if they asked us, Will you give up your Indian empire or your Shakespeare, you English; never have had any Indian empire, or never have had any Shakespeare? Really it were a grave question. Official persons would answer doubtless in official language; but we, for our part too, should not we be forced to answer: Indian empire, or no Indian empire; we cannot do without Shakespeare! Indian empire will go, at any rate, some day; but this Shakespeare does not go, he lasts forever with us; we cannot give up our Shakespeare!

Nay, apart from spiritualities; and considering him merely as a real, marketable, tangibly-useful possession. England, before long, this island of ours, will hold but a small fraction of the English: in America, in New Holland, east and west to the very antipodes, there will be a Saxondom covering great spaces of the globe. And now, what is it that can keep all these together into virtually one nation, so that they do not fall out and fight, but live at peace, in brotherlike intercourse, helping one another? This is justly regarded as the greatest practical problem, the thing all manner of sovereignties and governments are to accomplish: what is it that will accomplish this? Acts of parliament, administrative prime-ministers cannot. America is parted from us, so far as parliament could part it. Call it not fantastic, for there is much reality in it; Here, I say, is an English king, whom no time or chance, parliament or combination of parliaments, can dethrone! This King Shakespeare does he not shine, in crowded sovereignty, over us all, as the noblest, gentlest, yet strongest of rallying signs; indestructible; really more valuable in that point of view than any other means or appliance whatsoever? We can fancy him as radiant aloft over the nations of Englishmen, a thousand years hence. From Paramatta, from New York, wheresoever, under what sort of parish constable soever, English men and women are, they will say to one another: "Yes, this Shakespeare is ours; we produced him, we speak and think by him; we are of one blood and kind with him." The most common sense politician, too, if he pleases, may think of that.

Yes, truly, it is a great thing for a nation that it get an articulate voice; that it produce a man who will speak forth melodiously what the heart of it means! Italy, for example, poor Italy lies dismembered, scattered asunder, not appearing in any protocol or treaty as a unity at all; yet the noble Italy is actually *one*: Italy produced its Dante; Italy can speak! The czar of all the Russias, he is strong, with so many bayonets, Cossacks and cannons; and does a great feat in keeping such a tract of earth politically together; but he cannot yet speak. Something great in him, but he is a dumb greatness. He has no voice of genius, to be heard of all men and times. He must learn to speak. He is a great dumb monster hitherto. His cannons and Cossacks will have rusted into nonentity, while that Dante's voice is still audible. The nation that has a Dante is bound together as no dumb Russia can be. We must here end what we had to say of the hero poet.

LECTURE IV.[1]

THE HERO AS PRIEST—LUTHER—REFORMATION—KNOX—PURITANISM.

OUR PRESENT DISCOURSE is to be of the great man as priest. We have repeatedly endeavored to explain that all sorts of heroes are intrinsically of the same material; that given a great soul, open to the divine significance of life, then there is given a man fit to speak of this, to sing of this, to fight and work for this, in a great, victorious, enduring manner; there is given a hero—the outward shape of whom will depend on the time and the environment he finds himself in. The priest too, as I understand it, is a kind of prophet; in him too there is required to be a light of inspiration, as we must name it. He presides over the worship of the people; is the uniter of them with the unseen holy. He is the spiritual captain of the people; as the prophet is their spiritual king with many captains: he guides them heavenward, by wise guidance through this earth and its work. The ideal of him is, that he too be what we can call a voice from the unseen heaven; interpreting, even as the prophet did and in a more familiar manner unfolding the same to men. The unseen heaven—the "open secret of the universe"—which so few have an eye for! He is the prophet shorn of his more awful splendor; burning with mild equable radiance, as the enlightener of daily life. This, I say, is the ideal of a priest. So in old times; so in these and in all times. One knows very well that, in reducing ideals to practice, great latitude of tolerance is needful; very great. But a priest who is not this at all, who does not any longer aim or try to be this, is a character—of whom we had rather not speak in this place.

Luther and Knox were by express vocation priests, and did faithfully perform that function in its common sense. Yet it will suit us better here to consider them chiefly in their historical character, rather as reformers than priests. There have been other priests perhaps equally notable, in calmer times, for doing faithfully the office of a leader of worship; bringing down, by faithful heroism in that kind, a light from heaven into the daily life of their people; leading them forward, as under God's guidance, in the way wherein they were to go. But when this same *way* was a rough one, of battle, confusion and danger, the spiritual captain, who led through that, becomes, especially to us who live under the fruit of his leading, more notable than any other. He is the warfaring and battling priest; who led his people, not to quiet faithful labor as in smooth times, but to faithful valorous conflict, in times all violent, dismembered: a more perilous service and a more memorable one, be it higher or not. These two men we will account our best priests, inasmuch as they were our best reformers. Nay, I may ask, Is not every true reformer, by the nature of him, a *priest* first of all? He appeals to heaven's invisible justice against earth's visible force; knows that

[1]Delivered Friday, May 15, 1840.

it, the invisible, is strong and alone strong. He is a believer in the divine truth of things; a *seer*, seeing through the shows of things; a worshiper, in one way or the other, of the divine truth of things; a priest, that is. If he be not first a priest, he will never be good for much as a reformer.

Thus then, as we have seen great men, in various situations, building up religions, heroic forms of human existence in this world, theories of life worthy to be sung by a Dante, practices of life by a Shakespeare—we are now to see the reverse process; which also is necessary, which also may be carried on in the heroic manner. Curious how this should be necessary: yet necessary it is. The mild shining of the poet's light has to give place to the fierce lightning of the reformer: unfortunately the reformer too is a personage that cannot fail in history! The poet indeed, with his mildness, what is he but the product and ultimate adjustment of reform, or prophecy, with its fierceness? No wild Saint Dominics and Thebaïd Eremites, there had been no melodious Dante; rough practical endeavor, Scandinavian and other, from Odin to Walter Raleigh, from Ulfila to Cranmer, enabled Shakespeare to speak. Nay the finished poet, I remark sometimes, is a symptom that his epoch itself has reached perfection and is finished; that before long there will be a new epoch, new reformers needed.

Doubtless it were finer, could we go along always in the way of *music*; be tamed and taught by our poets, as the rude creatures were by their Orpheus of old. Or failing this rhythmic *musical* way, how good were it could we get so much as into the *equable* way; I mean, if *peaceable* priests, reforming from day to day, would always suffice us! But it is not so; even this latter has not yet been realized. Alas, the battling reformer too is, from time to time, a needful and inevitable phenomenon. Obstructions are never wanting: the very things that were once indispensable furtherances become obstructions; and need to be shaken off, and left behind us—a business often of enormous difficulty. It is notable enough, surely, how a theorem or spiritual representation, so we may call it, which once took in the whole universe, and was completely satisfactory in all parts of it to the highly-discursive acute intellect of Dante, one of the greatest in the world—had in the course of another century become dubitable to common intellects; become deniable; and is now, to every one of us, flatly incredible, obsolete as Odin's theorem! To Dante, human existence, and God's ways with men, were all well represented by those *malebolges, purgatorios;* to Luther not well. How was this? Why could not Dante's Catholicism continue; but Luther's Protestantism must needs follow? Alas, nothing will *continue.*

I do not make much of "progress of the species," as handled in these times of ours; nor do I think you would care to hear much about it. The talk on that subject is too often of the most extravagant, confused sort. Yet I may say, that fact itself seems certain enough; nay we can trace-out the inevitable necessity of it in the nature of things. Every man, as I have stated somewhere, is not only a learner but a doer: he learns with the mind given him what has been; but with the same mind he discovers farther, he invents and devises somewhat of his own. Absolutely without originality there is no man. No man whatever believes, or can believe, exactly what his grand-father believed; he enlarges somewhat, by fresh discovery, his view of the universe, and consequently his theorem of the universe—which is an *infinite* universe, and can never be embraced wholly or finally by any view or theorem, in any conceivable enlargement: he enlarges somewhat, I say, finds somewhat that was credible to his grandfather incredible to him, false to him, inconsistent with some new thing he has discovered or observed. It is the history of every man; and in the history of mankind we see it summed up into great historical amounts—revolutions, new epochs. Dante's mountain of purgatory does *not* stand "in the ocean of the other hemisphere," when Columbus has once sailed thither! Men find no such thing extant in the other hemisphere. It is not there. It must cease to be believed to be there. So with all beliefs whatsoever in this world—all systems of belief, and systems of practice that spring from these.

If we add now the melancholy fact, that when belief waxes uncertain, practice too becomes unsound, and errors, injustices and miseries every-where more and more prevail, we shall see material enough for revolution. At all turns, a man who will *do* faithfully, needs to believe firmly. If he have to ask at every turn the world's suffrage; if he cannot dispense with the world's suffrage, and make his own suffrage serve, he is a poor eye-servant; the work committed to him will be *mis*done. Every such man is a daily contributor to the inevitable downfall. Whatsoever work he does, dishon-estly, with an eye to the outward look of it, is a new offense, parent of new miseries to somebody or other. Offenses accumulate till they become insupportable; and are then violently burst through, cleared off as by explosion. Dante's sublime Catholicism, incredible now in theory, and defaced still worse by faithless, doubting and dishonest practice, has to be torn asunder by a Luther; Shakespeare's noble feudalism, as beautiful as it once looked and was, has to end in a French revolution. The accumu-lation of offenses is, as we say, too literally *exploded*, blasted asunder vol-canically; and there are long troublous periods before matters come to a settlement again.

Surely it were mournful enough to look only at this face of the matter and find in all human opinions and arrangements merely the fact that they were uncertain, temporary, subject to the law of death! At bottom, it is not so: all death, here too we find, is but of the body, not of the essence or soul; all destruction, by violent revolution or howsoever it be, is but new creation on a wider scale. Odinism was *valor*; Christianism was *humility*, a nobler kind of valor. No thought that ever dwelt honestly as true in the heart of man but *was* an honest insight into God's truth on man's part and *has* an essential truth in it which endures through all changes, an everlasting possession for us all. And, on the other hand, what a melancholy notion is that, which has to represent all men, in all countries and times except our own, as having spent their life in blind condemnable error, mere lost pagans, Scandinavians, Mahometans, only that we might have the true ultimate knowledge! All generations of men were lost and wrong, only that this present little section of a generation might be saved and right. They all marched forward there, all generations since the beginning of the world, like the Russian soldiers into the ditch of Schweidnitz Fort, only to fill up the ditch with their dead bodies, that we might march over and take the place! It is an incredible hypothesis.

Such incredible hypothesis we have seen maintained with fierce emphasis; and this or the other poor individual man, with his sect of individual men, marching as over the dead bodies of all men, toward sure victory: but when he too, with his hypothesis and ultimate infallible credo, sank into the ditch and became a dead body, what was to be said? Withal, it is an important fact in the nature of man, that he tends to reckon his own insight as final and goes upon it as such. He will always do it, I suppose, in one or the other way; but it must be in some wider, wiser way than this. Are not all true men that live, or that ever lived, soldiers of the same army, enlisted, under heaven's captaincy, to do battle against the same enemy, the empire of darkness and wrong? Why should we misknow one another, fight not against the enemy but against ourselves, from mere difference of uniform? All uniforms shall be good, so they hold in them true valiant men. All fashions of arms, the Arab turban and swift scimiter, Thor's strong hammer smiting down *Jötuns*, shall be welcome. Luther's battle-voice, Dante's march-melody, all genuine things are with us, not against us. We are all under one captain, soldiers of the same host. Let us now look a little at this Luther's fighting; what kind of battle it was and how he comported himself in it. Luther too was of our spiritual heroes; a prophet to his country and time.

As introductory to the whole, a remark about idolatry will perhaps be in place here. One of Mahomet's characteristics, which indeed belongs to all prophets, is unlimited implacable zeal against idolatry. It is the grand theme of prophets: idolatry, the worshiping of dead idols as the divinity, is a thing they cannot away with, but have to denounce continually and brand with inexpiable reprobation; it is the chief of all the sins they see done under the sun. This is worth noting. We will not enter here into the theological question about idolatry. Idol is *Ediolon,* a thing seen, a symbol. It is not God, but a symbol of God; and perhaps one may question whether any of the most benighted mortal ever took it for more than a symbol. I fancy, he did not think that the poor image his own hands had made *was* God; but that God was emblemed by it, that God was in it some way or other. And now in this sense, one may ask, "Is not all worship whatsoever a worship by symbols, by *eidola,* or things seen?" Whether *seen,* rendered visible as an image or picture to the bodily eye; or visible only to the inward eye, to the imagination, to the intellect: this makes a superficial, but no substantial difference. It is still a thing seen, significant of godhead; an idol. The most rigorous puritan has his confession of faith and intellectual representation of divine things and worships thereby; thereby is worship first made possible for him. All creeds, liturgies, religious forms, conceptions that fitly invest religious feelings, are in this sense *eidola*, things seen. All worship whatsoever must proceed by symbols, by idols—we may say, all idolatry is comparative and the worst idolatry is only *more* idolatrous.

Where, then, lies the evil of it? Some fatal evil must lie in it, or earnest prophetic men would not on all hands so reprobate it. Why is idolatry so hateful to prophets? It seems to me as if, in the worship of those poor wooden symbols, the thing that had chiefly provoked the prophet and filled his inmost soul with indignation and aversion, was not exactly what suggested itself to his own thought and came out of him in words to others, as the thing. The rudest heathen that worshiped Canopus, or the Caabah black stone, he, as we saw, was superior to the horse that worshiped nothing at all! Nay there was a kind of lasting merit in that poor act of his; analogous to what is still meritorious in poets: recognition of a certain endless *divine* beauty and significance in stars and all natural objects whatsoever. Why should the prophet so mercilessly condemn him? The poorest mortal worshiping his fetich, while his heart is full of it, may be an object of pity, of contempt and avoidance, if you will; but cannot surely be an object of hatred. Let his heart *be* honestly full of it, the whole space of his dark narrow mind illuminated thereby; in one word, let him entirely *believe* in his fetich—it will then be, I should say, if not well with him, yet as well as it can readily be made to be and you will leave him alone, unmolested there.

But here enters the fatal circumstance of idolatry, that, in the era of the prophets, no man's mind *is* any longer honestly filled with his idol or symbol. Before the prophet can arise who, seeing through it, knows it to be mere wood, many men must have begun dimly to doubt that it was little more. Condemnable idolatry is *insincere* idolatry. Doubt has eaten out the heart of it: a human soul is seen clinging spasmodically to an ark of the covenant, which it half feels now to have become a phantasm. This is one of the balefulest sights. Souls are no longer *filled* with their fetich; but only pretend to be filled and would fain make themselves feel that they are filled. "You do not believe," said Coleridge; "you only believe that you believe." It is the final scene in all kinds of worship and symbolism; the sure symptom that death is now nigh. It is equivalent to what we call formulism and worship of formulas, in these days of ours. No more immoral act can be done by a human creature; for it is the beginning of all immorality, or rather it is the impossibility henceforth of any morality whatsoever: the innermost moral soul is paralyzed thereby, cast into fatal magnetic sleep! Men are no longer *sincere* men. I do not wonder that the earnest man denounces this, brands it, prosecutes it with inextinguishable aversion. He and it, all good and it, are at death-feud. Blamable idolatry is *cant* and even what one may call sincere cant. Sincere cant: that is worth thinking of! Every sort of worship ends with this phasis.

I find Luther to have been a breaker of idols, no less than any other prophet. The wooden gods of the koreish, made of timber and bees-wax, were not more hateful to Mahomet than Tetzel's pardons of sin, made of sheepskin and ink, were to Luther. It is the property of every hero, in every time, in every place and situation, that he come back to reality; that he stand upon things and not shows of things. According as he loves and venerates, articulately or with deep speechless thought, the awful realities of things, so will the hollow shows of things, however regular, decorous, accredited by koreishes or conclaves, be intolerable and destestable to him. Protestantism too is the work of a prophet: the prophet-work of that sixteenth century. The first stroke of honest demolition to an ancient thing grown false and idolatrous; preparatory afar off to a new thing, which shall be true and authentically divine!

At first view it might seem as if Protestantism were entirely destructive to this that we call hero worship and represent as the basis of all possible good, religious or social, for mankind. One often hears it said that Protestantism introduced a new era, radically different from any the world had ever seen before: the era of "private judgment," as they call it. By this revolt against the pope, every man became his own pope; and learned, among other things, that he must never trust any pope, or spiritual hero-captain, any more! Whereby, is not spiritual union, all hierarchy and subordination among men, henceforth an impossibility? So we hear it said. Now I need not deny that Protestantism was a revolt against spiritual sovereignties, popes and much else. Nay I will grant that English Puritanism, revolt against earthly sovereignties, was the second act of it; that the enormous French revolution itself was the third act, whereby all sovereignties earthly and spiritual were, as might seem, abolished or made sure of abolition. Protestantism is the grand root from which our whole subsequent European history branches out. For the spiritual will always body itself forth in the temporal history of men; the spiritual is the beginning of the temporal. And now, sure enough, the cry is everywhere for liberty and equality, independence and so forth; instead of kings, ballot-boxes and electoral suffrages: it seems made out that any hero sovereign, or loyal obedience of men to a man, in things temporal or things spiritual, has passed away forever from the world. I should despair of the world altogether, if so. One of my deepest convictions is, that it is not so. Without sovereigns, true sovereigns, temporal and spiritual, I see nothing possible but an anarchy; the hatefulest of things. But I find Protestantism, whatever anarchic democracy it have produced, to be the beginning of new genuine sovereignty and order. I find it to be a revolt against false sovereigns; the painful but indispensable first preparative for true sovereigns getting place among us! This is worth explaining a little.

Let us remark, therefore, in the first place, that this of "private judgment" is, at bottom, not a new thing in the world, but only new at that epoch of the world. There is nothing generically new or peculiar in the reformation; it was a return to truth and reality in opposition to falsehood and semblance, as all kinds of improvement and genuine teaching are and have been. Liberty of private judgment, if we will consider it, must at all times have existed in the world. Dante had not put out his eyes, or tied shackles on himself; he was at home in that Catholicism of his, a free-seeing soul in it—if many a poor Hogstraten, Tetzel and Dr. Eck had now become slaves in it. Liberty of judgment? No iron chain, or outward force of any kind, could ever compel the soul of a man to believe or to disbelieve: it is his own indefeasible light, that judgment of his; he will reign and believe there, by the grace of God alone! The sorriest sophistical Bellarmine, preaching sightless faith and passive obedience, must first, by some kind of *conviction,* have abdicated his right to be convinced. His "private judgment" indicated that, as the advisablest step *he* could take. The right of private judgment will subsist, in full force, wherever true men subsist. A true man *believes* with his whole judgment, with all the illumination and discernment that is in him and has always so believed. A false man, only struggling to "believe that he believes," will naturally manage it in some other way. Protestantism said to this latter, "Woe!" and to the former, "Well done!" At bottom, it was no new saying; it was a return to all old sayings that ever had been said. Be genuine, be sincere: that was, once more, the meaning of it. Mahomet believed with his whole mind; Odin with his whole mind—he and all *true* followers of Odinism. They, by their private judgment, had "judged"—*so.*

And now I venture to assert, that the exercise of private judgment, faithfully gone about, does by no means necessarily end in selfish independence, isolation; but rather ends necessarily in the opposite of that. It is not honest inquiry that makes anarchy; but it is error, insincerity, half-belief and untruth that make it. A man protesting against error is on the way toward uniting himself with all men that believe in truth. There is no communion possible among men who believe only in hearsays. The heart of each is lying dead; has no power of sympathy even with *things*—or he would believe *them* and not hearsays. No sympathy even with things; how much less with his fellow-men! He cannot unite with men; he is an anarchic man. Only in a world of sincere men is unity possible—and there, in the long run, it is as good as *certain.*

For observe one thing, a thing too often left out of view, or rather altogether lost sight of, in this controversy: That it is not necessary a man should himself have *discovered* the truth he is to believe in and never so *sincerely* to believe in. A great man, we said, was always sincere, as the first condition of him. But a man need not be great in order to be sincere; that is not the necessity of nature and all time, but only of certain corrupt unfortunate epochs of time. A man can believe and make his own, in the most genuine way, what he has received from another—and with boundless gratitude to that other! The merit of *originality* is not novelty; it is sincerity. The believing man is the original man; whatsoever he believes, he believes it for himself, not for another. Every son of Adam can become a sincere man, an original man, in this sense; no mortal is doomed to be an insincere man. Whole ages, what we call ages of faith, are original; all men in them, or the most of men in them, sincere. These are the great and fruitful ages: every worker, in all spheres, is a worker not on semblance but on substance; every work issues in a result: the general sum of such work is great; for all of it, as genuine, tends toward one goal; all of it is *additive,* none of it subtractive. There is true union, true kingship, loyalty, all true and blessed things, so far as the poor earth can produce blessedness for men.

Hero worship? Ah me, that a man be self-subsistent, original, true, or what we call it, is surely the farthest in the world from indisposing him to reverence and believe other men's truth! It only disposes, necessitates and invincibly compels him to *dis*believe other men's dead formulas, hearsays and untruths. A man embraces truth with his eyes open and because his eyes are open: does he need to shut them before he can love his teacher of truth? He alone can love, with a right gratitude and genuine loyalty of soul, the hero teacher who has delivered him out of darkness into light. Is not such a one a true hero and serpent-queller; worthy of all reverence! The black monster, falsehood, our one enemy in this world, lies prostrate by his valor; it was he that conquered the world for us! See, accordingly, was not Luther himself reverenced as a true pope, or spiritual father, *being* verily such? Napoleon, from amid boundless revolt of sansculottism, became a king. Hero worship never dies, nor can die. Loyalty and sovereignty are everlasting in the world—and there is this in them, that they are grounded not on garnitures and semblances, but on realities and sincerities. Not by shutting your eyes, your "private judgment;" no, but by opening them and by having something to see! Luther's message was deposition and abolition to all false popes and potentates, but life and strength, though afar off to new genuine ones.

All this of liberty and equality, electoral suffrages, independence and so forth, we will take, therefore, to be a temporary phenomenon, by no means a final one. Though likely to last a long time, with sad enough embroilments for us all, we must welcome it, as the penalty of sins that are past, the pledge of inestimable benefits that are coming. In all ways, it behoved men to quit simulacra and return to fact; cost what it might, that did behove to be done. With spurious popes, and believers having no private judgment— quacks pretending to command over dupes—what can you do? Misery and mischief only. You cannot make an association out of insincere men; you cannot build an edifice except by plummet and level—at *right*-angles to one another! In all this wild revolutionary work, from Protestantism downward, I see the blessedest result preparing itself: not abolition of hero worship, but rather what I would call a whole world of heroes. If hero mean *sincere man*, why may not every one of us be a hero? A world all sincere, a believing world: the like has been; the like will again be—cannot help being. That were the right sort of worshipers for heroes: never could the truly better be so reverenced as where all were true and good! But we must hasten to Luther and his life.

Luther's birthplace was Eisleben in Saxony; he came into the world there on November 10, 1483. It was an accident that gave this honor to Eisleben. His parents, poor mine-laborers in a village of that region, named Mohra, had gone to the Eisleben winter-fair: in the tumult of this scene the Frau Luther was taken with travail, found refuge in some poor house there and the boy she bore was named Martin Luther. Strange enough to reflect upon it. This poor Frau Luther, she had gone with her husband to make her small merchandisings; perhaps to sell the lock of yarn she had been spinning, to buy the small winter-necessaries for her narrow hut or household; in the whole world, that day, there was not a more entirely unimportant-looking pair of people than this miner and his wife. And yet what were all emperors, popes and potentates, in comparison? There was born here, once more, a mighty man; whose light was to flame as the beacon over long centuries and epochs of the world; the whole world and its history was waiting for this man. It is strange, it is great. It leads us back to another birth-hour, in a still meaner environment, eighteen hundred years ago—of which it is fit that we *say* nothing, that we think only in silence; for what words are there! The age of miracles past? The age of miracles is forever here!

I find it altogether suitable to Luther's function in this earth, and doubtless wisely ordered to that end by the providence presiding over him and us and all things, that he was born poor, and brought up poor, one of the poorest of men. He had to beg, as the school-children in those times did; singing for alms and bread, from door to door. Hardship, rigorous necessity was the poor boy's companion; no man nor no thing would put on a false face to flatter Martin Luther. Among things, not among the shows of things, had he to grow. A boy of rude figure, yet with weak health, with his large greedy soul, full of all faculty and sensibility, he suffered greatly. But it was his task to get acquainted with *realities,* and keep acquainted with them, at whatever cost: his task was to bring the whole world back to reality, for it had dwelt too long with semblance! A youth nursed up in wintry whirlwinds, in desolate darkness and difficulty, that he may step forth at last from his stormy Scandinavia, strong as a true man, as a god: a Christian Odin—a right Thor once more, with his thunder-hammer, to smite asunder ugly enough *Jötuns* and giant monsters!

Perhaps the turning incident of his life, we may fancy, was that death of his friend Alexis, by lightning, at the gate of Erfurt. Luther had struggled up through boyhood, better and worse; displaying, in spite of all hindrances, the largest intellect, eager to learn: his father judging doubtless that he might promote himself in the world, set him upon the study of law. This was the path to rise; Luther, with little will in it either way, had consented: he was now nineteen years of age. Alexis and he had been to see the old Luther people at Mansfeldt; were got back again near Erfurt, when a thunderstorm came on; the bolt struck Alexis, he fell dead at Luther's feet. What is this life of ours—gone in a moment, burned up like a scroll, into the blank eternity! What are all earthly preferments, chancellorships, kingships? They lie shrunk together—there! The earth has opened on them; in a moment they are not, and eternity is. Luther, struck to the heart, determined to devote himself to God and God's service alone. In spite of all dissuasions from his father and others, he became a monk in the Augustine convent at Erfurt.

This was probably the first light-point in the history of Luther, his purer will now first decisively uttering itself; but, for the present, it was still as one light-point in an element all of darkness. He says he was a pious monk, *ich bin ein frommer Mönch gewesen;* faithfully, painfully struggling to work out the truth of this high act of his; but it was to little purpose. His misery had not lessened; had rather, as it were, increased into infinitude. The drudgeries he had to do, as novice in his convent, all sorts of slave-work, were not his grievance: the deep earnest soul of the man had fallen into all manner of black scruples, dubitations; he believed himself likely to die soon, and far worse than die. One hears with new interest for poor Luther that, at this time, he lived in terror of the unspeakable misery; fancied that he was doomed to eternal reprobation. Was it not the humble sincere nature of the man? What was he, that he should be raised to heaven! He that had known only misery, and mean slavery: the news was too blessed to be credible. It could not become clear to him how, by fasts, vigils, formalities and mass-work, a man's soul could be saved. He fell into the blackest wretchedness; had to wander staggering as on the verge of bottomless despair.

It must have been a most blessed discovery, that of an old Latin Bible which he found in the Erfurt library about this time. He had never seen the book before. It taught him another lesson than that of fasts and vigils. A brother monk too, of pious experience, was helpful. Luther learned now that a man was saved not by singing masses, but by the infinite grace of God: a more credible hypothesis. He gradually got himself founded, as on the rock. No wonder he should venerate the Bible, which had brought this blessed help to him. He prized it as the word of the Highest must be prized by such a man. He determined to hold by that; as through life and to death he firmly did.

This, then, is his deliverance from darkness, his final triumph over darkness, what we call his conversion; for himself the most important of all epochs. That he should now grow daily in peace and clearness; that, unfolding now the great talents and virtues implanted in him, he should rise to importance in his convent, in his country, and be found more and more useful in all honest business of life, is a natural result. He was sent on missions by his Augustine order, as a man of talent and fidelity fit to do their business well: the elector of Saxony, Friedrich, named the Wise, a truly wise and just prince, had cast his eye on him as a valuable person; made him professor in his new university of Wittenberg, preacher too at Wittenberg; in both which capacities, as in all duties he did, this Luther, in the peaceable sphere of common life, was gaining more and more esteem with all good men.

It was in his twenty-seventh year that he first saw Rome; being sent hither, as I said, on mission from his convent. Pope Julius II and what was going on at Rome, must have filled the mind of Luther with amazement. He had come as to the sacred city, throne of God's highpriest on earth; and he found it—what we know! Many thoughts it must have given the man; many which we have no record of, which perhaps he did not himself know how to utter. This Rome, this scene of false priests, clothed not in the beauty of holiness, but in far other vesture, is *false:* but what is it to Luther? A mean man he, how shall he reform a world? That was far from his thoughts. A humble, solitary man, why should he at all meddle with the world? It was the task of quite higher men than he. His business was to guide his own footsteps wisely through the world. Let him do his own obscure duty in it well; the rest, horrible and dismal as it looks, is in God's hand, not in his.

It is curious to reflect what might have been the issue, had Roman popery happened to pass this Luther by; to go on in its great wasteful orbit and not come athwart his little path and force him to assault it! Conceivable enough that, in this case, he might have held his peace about the abuses of Rome; left providence and God on high, to deal with them! A modest quiet man; not prompt he to attack irreverently persons in authority. His clear task, as I say, was to do his own duty; to walk wisely in this world of confused wickedness and save his own soul alive. But the Roman highpriesthood did come athwart him: afar off at Wittenberg he, Luther, could not get lived in honesty for it; he remonstrated, resisted, came to extremity; was struck at, struck again and so it came to wager a battle between them! This is worth attending to in Luther's history. Perhaps no man of so humble, peaceable a disposition ever filled the world with contention. We cannot but see that he would have loved privacy, quiet diligence in the shade; that it was against his will he ever became a notoriety. Notoriety: what would that do for him? The goal of his march through this world was the infinite heaven; an indubitable goal for him: in a few years, he should either have attained that, or lost it forever! We will say nothing at all, I think, of that sorrowfulest of theories, of its being some mean shopkeeper grudge, of the Augustine monk against the Dominican, that first kindled the wrath of Luther and produced the Protestant reformation. We will say to the people who maintain it, if indeed any such exist now: Get first into the sphere of thought by which it is so much as possible to judge of Luther, or of any man like Luther, otherwise than distractedly; we may then begin arguing with you.

The Monk Tetzel, sent out carelessly in the way of trade, by Leo X—who merely wanted to raise a little money and for the rest seems to have been a pagan rather than a Christian, so far as he was anything—arrived at Wittenberg and drove his scandalous trade there. Luther's flock bought indulgencies; in the confessional of his church, people pleaded to him that they had already got their sins pardoned. Luther, if he would not be found wanting at his own post, a false sluggard and coward at the very center of the little space of ground that was his own and no other man's, had to step forth against indulgencies and declare aloud that *they* were a futility and sorrowful mockery, that no man's sins could be pardoned by *them*. It was the beginning of the whole reformation. We know how it went; forward from this first public challenge of Tetzel, on the last day of October 1517, through remonstrance and argument—spreading ever wider, rising ever higher; till it became unquenchable and enveloped all the world. Luther's heart's-desire was to have this grief and other griefs amended; his thought was still far other than that of introducing separation in the church, or revolting against the pope, father of Christendom. The elegant pagan pope cared little about this monk and his doctrines; wished, however, to have done with the noise of him: in a space of some three years, having tried various softer methods, he thought good to end it by *fire*. He dooms the monk's writings to be burned by the hangman and his body to be sent bound to Rome—probably for a similar purpose. It was the way they had ended with Huss, with Jerome, the century before. A short argument, fire. Poor Huss: he came to that Constance council, with all imaginable promises and safe-conducts; an earnest, not rebellious kind of man: they laid him instantly in a stone dungeon "three feet wide, six feet high, seven feet long;" *burned* the true voice of him out of this world; choked it in smoke and fire. That was *not* well done!

I, for one, pardon Luther for now altogether revolting against the pope. The elegant pagan, by this fire-decree of his, had kindled into noble just wrath the bravest heart then living in this world. The bravest, if also one of the humblest, peaceablest; it was now kindled. These words of mine, words of truth and soberness, aiming faithfully, as human inability would allow, to promote God's truth on earth, and save men's souls, you, God's vicegerent on earth, answer them by the hangman and fire? You will burn me and them, for answer to the God's-message they strove to bring you? *You* are not God's vicegerent; you are another's than His, I think! I take your bull, as an emparchmented lie, and burn *it*. You will do what you see good next: this is what I do. It was on December 10, 1520, three years after the beginning of the business, that Luther, "with a great concourse of people," took this indignant step of burning the pope's fire-decree "at the Elster gate of Wittenberg." Wittenberg looked on "with shoutings;" the whole world was looking on. The pope should not have provoked that "shout!" It was the shout of the awakening of nations. The quiet German heart, modest, patient of much, had at length got more than it could bear. Formulism, pagan popeism, and other falsehood and corrupt semblance had ruled long enough: and here once more was a man found who durst tell all men that God's-world stood not on semblances but on realities; that life was a truth, and not a lie!

At bottom, as was said above, we are to consider Luther as a prophet idol-breaker; a bringer-back of men to reality. It is the function of great men and teachers. Mahomet said, These idols of yours are wood; you put wax and oil on them, the flies stick on them: they are not God, I tell you, they are black wood! Luther said to the pope, This thing of yours that you call a pardon of sins, it is a bit of rag-paper with ink. It *is* nothing else; it, and so much like it, is nothing else. God alone can pardon sins. Popeship, spiritual fatherhood of God's church, is that a vain semblance, of cloth and parchment? It is an awful fact. God's church is not a semblance, heaven and hell are not semblances. I stand on this, since you drive me to it. Standing on this, I a poor German monk am stronger than you all. I stand solitary, friendless, but on God's truth; you with your tiaras, triple-hats, with your treasuries and armories, thunders spiritual and temporal, stand on the devil's lie, and are not so strong!

The Diet of Worms, Luther's appearance there on April 17, 1521, may be considered as the greatest scene in modern European history; the point, indeed, from which the whole subsequent history of civilization takes its rise. After multiplied negotiations, disputations, it had come to this. The young Emperor Charles V, with all the princes of Germany, papal nuncios, dignitaries spiritual and temporal, are assembled there: Luther is to appear and answer for himself, whether he will recant or not. The world's pomp and power sits there on this hand: on that, stands up for God's truth, one man, the poor miner Hans Luther's son. Friends had reminded him of Huss, advised him not to go; he would not be advised. A large company of friends rode out to meet him, with still more earnest warnings; he answered: "Were there as many devils in Worms as there are roof-tiles, I would on." The people, on the morrow, as he went to the hall of the diet, crowded the windows and house-tops, some of them calling out to him, in solemn words, not to recant: "Whosoever denieth me before men!" they cried to him—as in a kind of solemn petition and adjuration. Was it not in reality our petition too, the petition of the whole world, lying in dark bondage of soul, paralyzed under a black spectral nightmare and triple-hatted chimera, calling itself father of God, and what not: "Free us; it rests with thee; desert us not!"

Luther did not desert us. His speech, of two hours, distinguished itself by its respectful, wise and honest tone; submissive to whatsoever could lawfully claim submission, not submissive to any more than that. His writings, he said, were partly his own, partly derived from the word of God. As to what was his own, human infirmity entered upon it; unguarded anger, blindness, many things doubtless which it were a blessing for him could he abolish altogether. But as to what stood on sound truth and the word of God, he could not recant it. How could he? "Confute me," he concluded, "by proofs of scripture, or else by plain just arguments: I cannot recant otherwise. For it is neither safe nor prudent to do aught against conscience. Here stand I; I can do no other: God assist me!" It is, as we say, the greatest moment in the modern history of men. English puritanism, England and its parliaments, Americas, and vast work these two centuries; French revolution, Europe and its work everywhere at present: the germ of it all lay there: had Luther in that moment done other, it had all been otherwise! The European world was asking him: Am I to sink ever lower into falsehood, stagnant putrescence, loathsome accursed death; or, with whatever paroxysm, to cast the falsehoods out of me, and be cured and live?

Great wars, contentions and disunion followed out of this reformation; which last down to our day, and are yet far from ended. Great talk and crimination has been made about these. They are lamentable, undeniable; but after all, what has Luther or his cause to do with them? It seems strange reasoning to charge the reformer with all this. When Hercules turned the purifying river into King Augeas' stables, I have no doubt the confusion that resulted was considerable all around: but I think it was not Hercules' blame; it was some other's blame! The reformation might bring what results it liked when it came, but the reformation simply could not help coming. To all popes and popes' advocates, expostulating, lamenting and accusing, the answer of the world is: Once for all, your popehood has become untrue. No matter how good it was, how good you say it is, we cannot believe it; the light of our whole mind, given us to walk by from heaven above, finds it henceforth a thing unbelievable. We will not believe it, we will not try to believe it—we dare not! The thing is *untrue;* we were traitors against the Giver of all truth, if we durst pretend to think it true. Away with it; let whatsoever likes come in the place of it: with *it* we can have no farther trade! Luther and his Protestantism is not responsible for wars; the false simulacra that forced him to protest, they are responsible. Luther did what every man that God has made has not only the right, but lies under the sacred duty, to do: answered a falsehood when it questioned him, Dost thou believe me? No! At what cost soever, without counting of costs, this thing behoved to be done. Union, organization spiritual and material, a far nobler than any popedom or feudalism in their truest days, I never doubt, is coming for the world; sure to come. But on fact alone, not on semblance and simulacrum, will it be able either to come, or to stand when come. With union grounded on falsehood, and ordering us to speak and act lies, we will not have anything to do. Peace? A brutal lethargy is peaceable, the noisome grave is peaceable. We hope for a living peace, not a dead one!

And yet, in prizing justly the indispensable blessings of the new, let us not be unjust to the old. The old *was* true, if it no longer is. In Dante's days it needed no sophistry, self-binding or other dishonesty, to get itself reckoned true. It was good then; nay there is in the soul of it a deathless good. The cry of "No popery" is foolish enough in these days. The speculation that popery is on the increase, building new chapels and so forth, may pass for one of the idlest ever started. Very curious: to count up a few popish chapels, listen to a few Protestant logic-choppings—to much dull-droning drowsy inanity that still calls itself Protestant, and say: See, Protestantism is *dead;* popeism is more alive than it, will be alive after it! Drowsy inanities, not a few, that call themselves Protestant are dead; but *Protestantism* has not died yet, that I hear of! Protestantism, if we will look, has in these days produced its Goethe, its Napoleon; German literature and the French revolution; rather considerable signs of life! Nay, at bottom, what else is alive *but* Protestantism? The life of most else that one meets is a galvanic one merely—not a pleasant, not a lasting sort of life!

Popery can build new chapels; welcome to do so, to all lengths. Popery cannot come back, any more than paganism can; *which* also still lingers in some countries. But, indeed, it is with these things, as with the ebbing of the sea: you look at the waves oscillating hither, thither on the beach; for *minutes* you cannot tell, how it is going; look in half an hour where it is; look in half a century where your popehood is! Alas, would there were no greater danger to our Europe than the poor old pope's revival! Thor may as soon try to revive. And withal this oscillation has a meaning. The poor old popehood will not die away entirely, as Thor has done, for some time yet; nor ought it. We may say, the old never dies till this happen, till all the soul of good that was in it have got itself transfused into the practical new. While a good work remains capable of being done by the Romish form; or, what is inclusive of all, while a *pious life* remains capable of being led by it, just so long, if we consider, will this or the other human soul adopt it, go about as a living witness of it. So long it will obtrude itself on the eye of us who reject it, till we in our practice too have appropriated whatsoever of truth was in it. Then, but also not till then, it will have no charm more for any man. It lasts here for a purpose. Let it last as long as it can.

Of Luther I will add now, in reference to all these wars and bloodshed, the noticeable fact that none of them began so long as he continued living. The controversy did not get to fighting so long as he was there. To me is the proof of his greatness in all senses, this fact. How seldom do we find a man that has stirred up some vast commotion, who does not himself perish, swept away in it! Such is the usual course of revolutionists. Luther continued, in a good degree, sovereign of this greatest revolution: all Protestants, of what rank or function soever, looking much to him for guidance: and he held it peaceable, continued firm at center of it. A man to do this must have a kingly faculty: he must have the gift to discern at all turns where the true heart of the matter lies, and to plant himself courageously on that, as a strong true man, that other true men may rally round him there. He will not continue leader of men otherwise. Luther's clear deep force of judgment, his force of all sorts, of *silence*, of tolerance and moderation, among others, are very notable in these circumstances.

Tolerance, I say; a very genuine kind of tolerance: he distinguishes what is essential, and what is not; the unessential may go very much as it will. A complaint comes to him that such and such a reformed preacher "will not preach without a cassock." "Well," answers Luther, "what harm will a cassock do the man? Let him have a cassock to preach in; let him have three cassocks if he find benefit in them!" His conduct in the matter of Karlstadt's wild image-breaking; of the Anabaptists; of the peasants' war, shows a noble strength, very different from spasmodic violence. With sure prompt insight he discriminates what is what: a strong just man, he speaks forth what is the wise course, and all men follow him in that. Luther's written works give similar testimony of him. The dialect of these speculations is now grown obsolete for us; but one still reads them with a singular attraction. And indeed the mere grammatical diction is still legible enough; Luther's merit in literary history is of the greatest; his dialect became the language of all writing. They are not well written, these four-and-twenty quartos of his; written hastily, with quite other than literary objects. But in no books have I found a more robust, genuine, I will say noble faculty of a man than in these. A rugged honesty, homeliness, simplicity: a rugged sterling sense and strength. He flashes out illumination from him; his smiting idiomatic phrases seem to cleave into the very secret of the matter. Good humor too, nay tender affection, nobleness, and depth: this man could have been a poet too! He had to *work* an epic poem, not write one. I call him a great thinker; as indeed his greatness of heart already betokens that.

Richter says of Luther's words, "his words are half-battles." They may be called so. The essential quality of him was, that he could fight and conquer; that he was a right piece of human valor. No more valiant man, no mortal heart to be called *braver*, that one has record of, ever lived in that Teutonic kindred, whose character is valor. His defiance of the "devils" in Worms was not a mere boast, as the like might be if now spoken. It was a faith of Luther's that there were devils, spiritual denizens of the pit, continually besetting men. Many times, in his writings, this turns up; and a most small sneer has been grounded on it by some. In the room of the Wartburg where he sat translating the Bible, they still show you a black spot on the wall; the strange memorial of one of these conflicts. Luther sat translating one of the psalms; he was worn down with long labor, with sickness, abstinence from food: there rose before him some hideous indefinable image, which he took for the evil one, to forbid his work: Luther started up, with fiend-defiance; flung his inkstand at the specter and it disappeared! The spot still remains there; a curious monument of several things. Any apothecary's apprentice can now tell us what we are to think of this apparition, in a scientific sense: but the man's heart that dare rise defiant, face to face, against hell itself, can give no higher proof of fearlessness. The thing he will quail before exists not on this earth or under it. Fearless enough! "The devil is aware," writes he on one occasion, "that this does not proceed out of fear in me. I have seen and defied innumerable devils. Duke George, of Leipzig," a great enemy of his, "Duke George is not equal to one devil"—far short of a devil! "If I had business at Leipzig, I would ride into Leipzig, though it rained Duke Georges for nine days running." What a reservoir of Dukes to ride into!

At the same time, they err greatly who imagine that this man's courage was ferocity, mere coarse disobedient obstinacy and savagery, as many do. Far from that. There may be an absence of fear which arises from the absence of thought or affection, from the presence of hatred and stupid fury. We do not value the courage of the tiger highly! With Luther it was far otherwise; no accusation could be more unjust than this of mere ferocious violence brought against him. A most gentle heart withal, full of pity and love, as indeed the truly valiant heart ever is. The tiger before a *stronger* foe—flies: the tiger is not what we call valiant, only fierce and cruel. I know few things more touching than those soft breathings of affection, soft as a child's or a mother's, in this great wild heart of Luther. So honest, unadulterated with any cant; homely, rude in their utterance;

pure as water welling from the rock. What, in fact, was all that down-pressed mood of despair and reprobation, which we saw in his youth, but the outcome of pre-eminent thoughtful gentleness, affections too keen and fine? It is the course such men as the poor poet Cowper fall into. Luther to a slight observer might have seemed a timid, weak man; modesty, affectionate shrinking tenderness the chief distinction of him. It is a noble valor which is roused in a heart like this, once stirred up into defiance, all kindled into a heavenly blaze.

In Luther's "Table-Talk," a posthumous book of anecdotes and sayings collected by his friends, the most interesting now of all the books proceeding from him, we have many beautiful unconscious displays of the man and what sort of nature he had. His behavior at the death-bed of his little daughter, so still, so great and loving, is among the most affecting things. He is resigned that his little Magdalene should die, yet longs inexpressibly that she might live—follows, in awestruck thought, the flight of her little soul through those unknown realms. Awestruck; most heartfelt, we can see; and sincere—for after all dogmatic creeds and articles, he feels what nothing it is that we know, or can know: His little Magdalene shall be with God, as God wills; for Luther too that is all; *Islam* is all.

Once, he looks out from his solitary Patmos, the castle of Coburg, in the middle of the night: The great vault of immensity, long flights of clouds sailing through it—dumb, gaunt, huge—who supports all that? "None ever saw the pillars of it; yet it is supported." God supports it. We must know that God is great, that God is good; and trust, where we cannot see. Returning home from Leipzig once, he is struck by the beauty of the harvest-fields: How it stands, that golden yellow corn, on its fair taper stem, its golden head bent, all rich and waving there—the meek earth, at God's kind bidding, has produced it once again; the bread of man! In the garden at Wittenberg one evening at sunset, a little bird has perched for the night: That little bird, says Luther, above it are the stars and deep heaven of worlds; yet it has folded its little wings; gone trustfully to rest there as in its home: the Maker of it has given it too a home! Neither are mirthful turns wanting: there is a great free human heart in this man. The common speech of him has a rugged nobleness, idiomatic, expressive, genuine; gleams here and there with beautiful poetic tints. One feels him to be a great brother man. His love of music, indeed, is not this, as it were, the summary of all these affections in him? Many a wild unutterability he spoke forth from him in the tones of his flute. The devils fled from his flute, he says. Death-defiance on the one hand and such love of music on the other; I could call these the two opposite poles of a great soul; between these two all great things had room.

Luther's face is to me expressive of him; in Kranach's best portraits I find the true Luther. A true plebeian face; with its huge crag-like brows and bones, the emblem of rugged energy; at first, almost a repulsive face. Yet in the eyes especially there is a wild silent sorrow; an unnamable melancholy, the element of all gentle and fine affections; giving to the rest the true stamp of nobleness. Laughter was in this Luther, as we said; but tears also were there. Tears also were appointed him; tears and hard toil. The basis of his life was sadness, earnestness. In his latter days, after all triumphs and victories, he expresses himself heartily weary of living; he considers that God alone can and will regulate the course things are taking and that perhaps the day of judgment is not far. As for him, he longs for one thing: that God would release him from his labor and let him depart and be at rest. They understand little of the man who cite this in *dis*credit of him! I will call this Luther a true great man; great in intellect, in courage, affection and integrity; one of our most lovable and precious men. Great, not as a hewn obelisk; but as an Alpine mountain—so simple, honest, spontaneous, not setting up to be great at all; there for quite another purpose than being great! Ah yes, unsubduable granite, piercing far and wide into the heavens; yet in the clefts of it fountains, green beautiful valleys with flowers! A right spiritual hero and prophet; once more, a true son of nature and fact, for whom these centuries and many that are to come yet, will be thankful to heaven.

The most interesting phasis which the reformation anywhere assumes, especially for us English, is that of Puritanism. In Luther's own country Protestantism soon dwindled into a rather barren affair: not a religion or faith, but rather now a theological jangling of argument, the proper seat of it not the heart; the essence of it skeptical contention: which indeed has jangled more and more, down to Voltaireism itself—through Gustavus-Adolphus contentions onward to French revolution ones! But in our island there arose a Puritanism, which even got itself established as a Presbyterian-ism and national church among the Scotch; which came forth as a real business of the heart; and has produced in the world very notable fruit. In some senses, one may say it is the only phasis of Protestantism that ever got to the rank of being a faith, a true heart-communication with heaven and of exhibiting itself in history as such. We must spare a few words for Knox; himself a brave and remarkable man; but still more important as chief priest and founder, which one may consider him to be, of the faith that became Scotland's, New England's, Oliver Cromwell's. History will have something to say about this, for some time to come!

We may censure Puritanism as we please; and no one of us, I suppose, but would find it a very rough defective thing. But we and all men, may under-stand that it was a genuine thing; for nature has adopted it and it has grown and grows. I say sometimes, that all goes by wager-of-battle in this world; that *strength*, well understood, is the measure of all worth. Give a thing time; if it can succeed, it is a right thing. Look now at American Saxondom; and at that little fact of the sailing of the Mayflower, two hundred years ago, from Delft haven in Holland! Were we of open sense as the Greeks were, we had found a poem here; one of nature's own poems, such as she writes in broad facts over great continents. For it was properly the begin-ning of America: there were straggling settlers in America before, some material as of a body was there; but the soul of it was first this. These poor men, driven out of their own country, not able well to live in Holland, determine on settling in the New World. Black untamed forests are there and wild savage creatures; but not so cruel as star-chamber hangmen. They thought the earth would yield them food, if they tilled honestly; the ever-lasting heaven would stretch, there too, overhead; they should be left in peace, to prepare for eternity by living well in this world of time; worship-ing in what they thought the true, not the idolatrous way. They clubbed their small means together; hired a ship, the little ship Mayflower and made ready to set sail.

In Neal's "History of the Puritans"[2] is an account of the ceremony of their departure: solemnity, we might call it rather, for it was a real act of worship. Their minister went down with them to the beach, and their brethren whom they were to leave behind; all joined in solemn prayer, That God would have pity on His poor children, and go with them into that waste wilderness, for He also had made that, He was there also as well as here. Hah! These men, I think, had a work! The weak thing, weaker than a child, becomes strong one day, if it be a true thing. Puritanism was only despicable, laughable then; but nobody can manage to laugh at it now. Puritanism has got weapons and sinews; it has fire-arms, war-navies; it has cunning in its ten fingers, strength in its right arm; it can steer ships, fell forests, remove mountains—it is one of the strongest things under the sun at present!

In the history of Scotland, too, I can find properly but one epoch: we may say, it contains nothing of world-interest at all but this reformation by Knox. A poor barren country, full of continual broils, dissensions, massa-crings; a people in the last state of rudeness and destitution, little better perhaps than Ireland at this day. Hungry fierce barons, not so much as able to form any arrangement with each other *how to divide* what they fleeced from these poor drudges; but obliged, as the Columbian republics are at this day, to make of every alteration a revolution; no way of changing a min-istry but by hanging the old ministers on gibbets: this is a historical spec-tacle of no very singular significance! "Bravery" enough, I doubt not; fierce fighting in abundance: but not braver or fiercer than that of their old Scandinavian sea-king ancestors; *whose* exploits we have not found worth dwelling on! It is a country as yet without a soul: nothing developed in it but what is rude, external, semi-animal. And now at the reformation, the internal life is kindled, as it were, under the ribs of this outward material death. A cause, the noblest of causes kindles itself, like a beacon set on high; high as heaven, yet attainable from earth—whereby the meanest man be-comes not a citizen only, but a member of Christ's visible church; a verita-ble hero, if he prove a true man!

Well; this is what I mean by a whole "nation of heroes;" a *believing* nation. There needs not a great soul to make a hero; there needs a god-creatured soul which will be true to its origin; that will be a great soul!

[2]Neal (London, 1755), i. 490.

The like has been seen, we find. The like will be again seen, under wider forms than the Presbyterian: there can be no lasting good done till then. Impossible! say some. Possible? Has it not *been*, in this world, as a practiced fact? Did hero-worship fail in Knox's case? Or are we made of other clay now? Did the Westminster confession of faith add some new property to the soul of man? God made the soul of man. He did not doom any soul of man to live as a hypothesis and hearsay, in a world filled with such, and with the fatal work and fruit of such!

But to return: this that Knox did for his nation, I say, we may really call a resurrection as from death. It was not a smooth business; but it was welcome surely, and cheap at that price, had it been far rougher. On the whole, cheap at any price—as life is. The people began to *live:* they needed first of all to do that, at what cost and costs soever. Scotch literature and thought, Scotch industry; James Watt, David Hume, Walter Scott, Robert Burns: I find Knox and the reformation acting in the heart's core of every one of these persons and phenomena; I find that without the reformation they would not have been. Or what of Scotland? The Puritanism of Scotland became that of England, of New England. A tumult in the high church of Edinburgh spread into a universal battle and struggle over all these realms—there came out, after fifty years struggling, what we call the "*glorious* revolution," a *habeas corpus* act, free parliaments, and much else! Alas, is it not too true what we said, That many men in the van do always, like Russian soldiers march into the ditch of Schweidnitz, and fill it up with their dead bodies, that the rear may pass over them dry-shod, and gain the honor? How many earnest rugged Cromwells, Knoxes, poor peasant covenanters, wrestling, battling for very life, in rough miry places, have to struggle, and suffer, and fall, greatly censured, *bemired*—before a beautiful revolution of eighty-eight can step over them in official pumps and silk stockings, with universal three-times-three!

It seems to me hard measure that this Scottish man, now after three hundred years, should have to plead like a culprit before the world; intrinsically for having been, in such way as it was then possible to be, the bravest of all Scotchmen! Had he been a poor half-and-half, he could have crouched into the corner, like so many others; Scotland had not been delivered; and Knox had been without blame. He is the one Scotchman to whom, of all others, his country and the world owe a debt. He has to plead that Scotland would forgive him for having been worth to it any million "unblamable" Scotchmen that need no forgiveness! He bared his breast to the battle; had to row in French galleys, wander forlorn in exile, in clouds and storms; was censured, shot at through his windows; had a right sore fighting life: if this world were his place of recompense, he had made but a bad venture of it. I cannot apologize for Knox. To him it is very indifferent, there two hundred and fifty years or more, what men say of him. But we, having got above all those details of his battle, and living now in clearness on the fruits of his victory, we for our own sake, ought to look through the rumors and controversies enveloping the man, into the man himself.

For one thing, I will remark that this post of prophet to his nation was not of his seeking; Knox had lived forty years quietly obscure, before he became conspicuous. He was the son of poor parents; had got a college education; become a priest; adopted the reformation, and seemed well content to guide his own steps by the light of it, nowise unduly intruding it on others. He had lived as tutor in gentlemen's families; preaching when any body of persons wished to hear his doctrine: resolute he to walk by the truth, and speak the truth when called to do it; not ambitious of more; not fancying himself capable of more. In this entirely obscure way he had reached the age of forty; was with the small body of reformers who were standing siege in St. Andrew's castle—when one day in their chapel, the preacher after finishing his exhortation to these fighters in the forlorn hope, said suddenly: That there ought to be other speakers, that all men who had a priest's heart and gift in them ought now to speak—which gifts and heart one of their number, John Knox the name of him, had: Had he not? said the preacher, appealing to all the audience: what then is *his* duty? The people answered affirmatively; it was a criminal forsaking of his post, if such a man held the word that was in him silent. Poor Knox was obliged to stand up; he attempted to reply; he could say no word—burst into a flood of tears and ran out. It is worth remembering, that scene. He was in grievous trouble for some days. He felt what a small faculty was his for this great work. He felt what a baptism he was called to be baptised withal. He "burst into tears."

Our primary characteristic of a hero, that he is sincere, applies emphatically to Knox. It is not denied anywhere that this, whatever might be his other qualities or faults, is among the truest of men. With a singular instinct he holds to the truth and fact; the truth alone is there for him, the rest a mere shadow and deceptive nonentity. However feeble, forlorn the reality may seem, on that and that only *can* he take his stand. In the galleys of the River Loire, whither Knox and the others, after their castle of St. Andrew's was taken, had been sent as galley-slaves—some officer or priest, one day presented them an image of the Virgin Mother, requiring that they, the blasphemous heretics, should do it reverence. Mother? Mother of God? said Knox, when the turn came to him: This is no mother of God: this is "a *pented bredd*"—a piece of wood, I tell you, with paint on it! She is fitter for swimming, I think, than for being worshiped, added Knox; and flung the thing into the river. It was not very cheap jesting there: but come of it what might, this thing to Knox was and must continue nothing other than the real truth; it was a *pented bredd:* worship it he would not.

He told his fellow-prisoners, in this darkest time, to be of courage; the cause they had was the true one and must and would prosper; the whole world could not put it down. Reality is of God's making; it is alone strong. How many *pented bredds*, pretending to be real, are fitter to swim than to be worshiped! This Knox cannot live but by fact: he clings to reality as the shipwrecked sailor to the cliff. He is an instance to us how a man, by sincerity itself, becomes heroic: it is the grand gift he has. We find in Knox a good honest intellectual talent, no transcendent one—a narrow, inconsiderable man, as compared with Luther: but in heartfelt instinctive adherence to truth, in *sincerity*, as we say, he has no superior; nay, one might ask, "What equal he has?" The heart of him is of the true prophet cast. "He lies there," said the Earl of Morton at his grave, "who never feared the face of man." He resembles, more than any of the moderns, an old Hebrew prophet. The same inflexibility, intolerance, rigid narrow-looking adherence to God's truth, stern rebuke in the name of God to all that forsake truth: an old Hebrew prophet in the guise of an Edinburgh minister of the sixteenth century. We are to take him for that; not require him to be other.

Knox's conduct to Queen Mary, the harsh visits he used to make in her own palace, to reprove her there, have been much commented upon. Such cruelty, such coarseness fills us with indignation. On reading the actual narrative of the business, what Knox said and what Knox meant, I must say one's tragic feeling is rather disappointed. They are not so coarse, these speeches; they seem to me about as fine as the circumstances would permit! Knox was not there to do the courtier; he came on another errand. Whoever, reading these colloquies of his with the queen, thinks they are vulgar insolences of a plebeian priest to a delicate high lady, mistakes the purport and essence of them altogether. It was unfortunately not possible to be polite with the Queen of Scotland, unless one proved untrue to the nation and cause of Scotland. A man who did not wish to see the land of his birth made a hunting-field for intriguing ambitious guises and the cause of God trampled underfoot of falsehoods, formulas and the devil's cause, had no method of making himself agreeable! "Better that women weep," said Morton, "than that bearded men be forced to weep." Knox was the constitutional opposition-party in Scotland: the nobles of the country, called by their station to take that post, were not found in it; Knox had to go, or no one. The hapless queen—but the still more hapless country, if *she* were made happy! Mary herself was not without sharpness enough, among her other qualities: "Who are you," said she once, "that presume to school the nobles and sovereign of this realm?" "Madam, a subject born within the same," answered he. Reasonably answered! If the "subject" have truth to speak, it is not the "subject's" footing that will fail him here.

We blame Knox for his intolerance. Well, surely it is good that each of us be as tolerant as possible. Yet, at bottom, after all the talk there is and has been about it, what is tolerance? Tolerance has to tolerate the *un*essential; and to see well what that is. Tolerance has to be noble, measured, just in its very wrath, when it can tolerate no longer. But, on the whole, we are not altogether here to tolerate! We are here to resist, to control and vanquish withal. We do not "tolerate" falsehoods, thieveries, iniquities, when they fasten on us; we say to them, Thou art false, thou art not tolerable! We are here to extinguish falsehoods and put an end to them, in some wise way! I will not quarrel so much with the way; the doing of the thing is our great concern. In this sense Knox was, full surely, intolerant.

A man sent to row in French galleys and such-like, for teaching the truth in his own land, cannot always be in the mildest humor! I am not prepared to say that Knox had a soft temper; nor do I know that he had what we call an ill-temper. An ill-nature he decidedly had not. Kind honest affections dwelt in the much-enduring, hard-worn, ever-battling man. That he *could* rebuke queens and had such weight among those proud turbulent nobles, proud enough whatever else they were; and could maintain to the end a kind of virtual presidency and sovereignty in that wild realm, he who was only "a subject born within the same:" this of itself will prove to us that he was found, close at hand, to be no mean acrid man; but at heart a healthful, strong, sagacious man. Such alone can bear rule in that kind. They blame him for pulling down cathedrals and so forth, as if he were a seditious rioting demagogue: precisely the reverse is seen to be the fact, in regard to cathedrals and the rest of it, if we examine! Knox wanted no pulling down of stone edifices; he wanted leprosy and darkness to be thrown out of the lives of men. Tumult was not his element; it was the tragic feature of his life that he was forced to dwell so much in that. Every such man is the born enemy of disorder; hates to be in it: but what then? Smooth falsehood is not order; it is the general sum total of *dis*order. Order is *truth*—each thing standing on the basis that belongs to it: order and falsehood cannot subsist together.

Withal, unexpectedly enough, this Knox has a vein of drollery in him; which I like much, in combination with his other qualities. He has a true eye for the ridiculous. His *history*, with its rough earnestness, is curiously enlivened with this. When the two prelates, entering Glasgow cathedral, quarrel about precedence; march rapidly up, take to hustling one another, twitching one another's rochets and at last flourishing their crosiers like quarter-staves, it is a great sight for him everyway! Not mockery, scorn, bitterness alone; though there is enough of that too. But a true, loving, illuminating laugh mounts up over the earnest visage; not a loud laugh; you would say, a laugh in the *eyes* most of all. An honest-hearted, brotherly man; brother to the high, brother also to the low; sincere in his sympathy with both. He had his pipe of Bordeaux too, we find, in that old Edinburgh house of his; a cheery social man, with faces that loved him! They go far wrong who think this Knox was a gloomy, spasmodic, shrieking fanatic. Not at all: he is one of the solidest of men. Practical, cautious-hopeful, patient; a most shrewd, observing, quietly discerning man. In fact, he has very much the type of character we assign to the Scotch at present; a certain sardonic taciturnity is in him; insight enough; and a stouter heart than he himself knows of. He has the power of holding his peace over many things which do not vitally concern him—"They? what are they?" But the thing which does vitally concern him, that thing he will speak of; and in a tone the whole world shall be made to hear: all the more emphatic for his long silence.

This prophet of the Scotch is to me no hateful man! He had a sore fight of an existence: wrestling with popes and principalities; in defeat, contention, life-long struggle; rowing as a galley-slave, wandering as an exile. A sore fight: but he won it. "Have you hope?" they asked him in his last moment, when he could no longer speak. He lifted his finger, "pointed upward with his finger," and so died. Honor to him! His works have not died. The letter of his work dies, as of all men's; but the spirit of it never.

One word more as to the letter of Knox's work. The unforgivable offense in him is, that he wished to set up priests over the head of kings. In other words, he strove to make the government of Scotland a *theocracy*. This indeed is properly the sum of his offenses, the essential sin; for which what pardon can there be? It is most true, he did, at bottom, consciously or unconsciously, mean a theocracy, or government of God. He did mean that kings and prime ministers, and all manner of persons, in public or private, diplomatizing or whatever else they might be doing, should walk according to the gospel of Christ, and understand that this was their law, supreme over all laws. He hoped once to see such a thing realized; and the petition, *thy kingdom come*, no longer an empty word. He was sore grieved when he saw greedy worldly barons clutch hold of the church's property; when he expostulated that it was not secular property, that it was spiritual property, and should be turned to *true* churchly uses, education, schools, worship;— and the Regent Murray had to answer, with a shrug of the shoulders: "It is a devout imagination!" This was Knox's scheme of right and truth; this he zealously endeavored after, to realize it. If we think his scheme of truth was too narrow, was not true, we may rejoice that he could not realize it; that it remained after two centuries of effort, unrealizable, and is a "devout imagination" still. But how shall we blame *him* for struggling to realize it? Theocracy government of God, is precisely the thing to be struggled for! All prophets, zealous priests, are there for that purpose. Hildebrand wished a theocracy; Cromwell wished it, fought for it; Mahomet attained it. Nay, is it not what all zealous men, whether prophets, whatsoever else called, do essentially wish and must wish? That right and truth or God's law, reign supreme among men, this is the heavenly ideal (well named in Knox's time, and namable in all times, a revealed "will of God") toward which the reformer will insist that all be more and more approximated. All true reformers, as I said, are by the nature of them priests, and strive for a theocracy. How far such ideals can ever be introduced into practice, and at what point our impatience with their non-introduction ought to begin, is always a question I think we may say safely, Let them introduce themselves as far as they can contrive to do it! If they are the true faith of men, all men ought to be more or less impatient always where they are not found introduced. There will never be wanting Regent Murrays enough to shrug their shoulders, and say, "A devout imagination!" We will praise the hero priest rather, who does what is in *him* to bring them in; and wears out, in toil, calumny, contradiction, a noble life, to make God's kingdom of this earth. The earth will not become too godlike!

LECTURE V.[1]

The Hero as Man of Letters—Johnson, Rousseau, Burns.

Hero gods, prophets, poets, priests are forms of heroism that belong to the old ages, make their appearance in the remotest times; some of them have ceased to be possible long since, and cannot any more show themselves in this world. The hero as *man of letters*, again, of which class we are to speak to-day, is altogether a product of these new ages; and so long as the wondrous art of *writing*, or of ready-writing which we call *printing*, subsists, he may be expected to continue, as one of the main forms of heroism for all future ages. He is, in various respects, a very singular phenomenon.

He is new, I say; he has hardly lasted above a century in the world yet. Never, till about a hundred years ago, was there seen any figure of a great soul living apart in that anomalous manner; endeavoring to speak-forth the inspiration that was in him by printed books, and find place and subsistence by what the world would please to give him for doing that. Much had been sold and bought, and left to make its own bargain in the market-place; but the inspired wisdom of a heroic soul never till then, in that naked manner. He, with his copy-rights and copy-wrongs, in his squalid garret, in his rusty coat; ruling (for this is what he does), from his grave, after death, whole nations and generations who would, or would not give him bread while living—is a rather curious spectacle! Few shapes of heroism can be more unexpected.

Alas, the hero from of old has had to cramp himself into strange shapes: the world knows not well at any time what to do with him, so foreign is his aspect in the world! It seemed absurd to us, that men, in their rude admiration, should take some wise great Odin for a god, and worship him as such; some wise great Mahomet for one god-inspired, and religiously follow his law for twelve centuries: but that a wise great Johnson, a Burns, a Rousseau, should be taken for some idle nondescript, extant in the world to amuse idleness, and have a few coins and applauses thrown in him, that he might live thereby; *this* perhaps, as before hinted, will one day seem a still absurder phasis of things! Meanwhile, since it is the spiritual always that determines the material, this same man-of-letters hero must be regarded as our most important modern person. He, such as he may be, is the soul of all. What he teaches, the whole world will do and make. The world's manner of dealing with him is the most significant feature of the world's general position. Looking well at his life, we may get a glance, as deep as is readily possible for us, into the life of those singular centuries which have produced him, in which we ourselves live and work.

There are genuine men of letters, and not genuine; as in every kind there

[1]Delivered Tuesday, May 19, 1840.

in a genuine and a spurious. If *hero* be taken to mean genuine, then I say the hero as man of letters will be found discharging a function for us which is ever honorable, ever the highest; and was once well known to be the highest. He is uttering forth in such way as he has, the inspired soul of him; all that a man in any case, can do. I say *inspired;* for what we call "originality," "sincerity," "genius," the heroic quality we have no good name for, signifies that. The hero is he who lives in the inward sphere of things, in the true, divine and eternal, which exists always, unseen to most, under the temporary, trivial: his being is in that; he declares that abroad, by act or speech as it may be, in declaring himself abroad. His life, as we said before, is a piece of the everlasting heart of nature herself: all men's life is—but the weak many know not the fact, and are untrue to it, in most times; the strong few are strong, heroic, perennial, because it cannot be hidden from them. The man of letters, like every hero, is there to proclaim this in such sort as he can. Intrinsically it is the same function which the old generations named a man prophet, priest, divinity for doing: which all manner of heroes, by speech or by act, are sent into the world to do.

Fichte the German philosopher delivered, some forty years ago at Erlangen, a highly remarkable course of lectures on this subject: *"Ueber das wesen des Gelehrten,* On the nature of the literary man." Fichte, in conformity with the transcendental philosophy, of which he was a distinguished teacher, declares first: That all things which we see or work with in this earth, especially we ourselves and all persons, are as a kind of vesture or sensuous appearance: that under all there lies, as the essence of them, what he calls the "divine idea of the world;" this is the reality which "lies at the bottom of all appearance." To the mass of men no such divine idea is recognizable in the world; they live merely, says Fichte, among the superficialities, practicalities and shows of the world, not dreaming that there is anything divine under them. But the man of letters is sent hither specially that he may discern for himself, and make manifest to us, this same divine idea: in every new generation it will manifest itself in a new dialect; and he is there for the purpose of doing that. Such is Fichte's phraseology; with which we need not quarrel. It is his way of naming what I here, by other words, am striving imperfectly to name; what there is at present no name for: The unspeakable divine significance, full of splendor, of wonder and terror, that lies in the being of every man, of every thing—the presence of the God who made every man and thing. Mahomet taught this in his dialect; Odin in his: it is the thing which all thinking hearts in one dialect or another, are here to teach.

Fichte calls the man of letters, therefore, a prophet, or as he prefers to phrase it, a priest, continually unfolding the godlike to men: men of letters are a perpetual priesthood, from age to age, teaching all men that a God is still present in their life; that all "appearance," whatsoever we see in the world, is but as a vesture for the "divine idea of the world," for "that which lies at the bottom of appearance." In the true literary man there is thus ever, acknowleged or not by the world, a sacredness: he is the light of the world; the world's priest: guiding it, like a sacred pillar of fire, in its dark pilgrimage through the waste of time. Fichte discriminates with sharp zeal the *true* literary man, what we here call the *hero* as man of letters, from multitudes of false unheroic. Whoever lives not wholly in this divine idea, or living partially in it, struggles not, as for the one good, to live wholly in it—he is, let him live where else he like, in what pomps and prosperities he like, no literary man; he is, says Fichte, a "bungler, *stümper.*" Or at best, if he belong to the prosaic provinces, he may be a "Hodman;" Fichte even calls him elsewhere a "nonentity," and has in short no mercy for him, no wish that *he* should continue happy among us! This is Fichte's notion of the man of letters. It means, in its own form, precisely what we here mean.

In this point of view, I consider that for the last hundred years, by far the notablest of all literary men is Fichte's countryman, Goethe. To that man too, in a strange way, there was given what we may call a life in the divine idea of the world; vision of the inward divine mystery: and strangely, out of his books, the world rises imaged once more as godlike, the workmanship and temple of a God. Illuminated all, not in fierce impure fire-splendor as of Mahomet, but in mild celestial radiance; really a prophecy in these most unprophetic times; to my mind, far the greatest though one of the quietest, among all the great things that have come to pass in them. Our chosen specimen of the hero as literary man would be this Goethe. And it were a very pleasant plan for me here to discourse of his heroism: for I consider him to be a true hero; heroic in what he said and did, and perhaps still more in what he did not say and did not do; to me a noble spectacle: a great heroic ancient man, speaking and keeping silence as an ancient hero, in the guise of a most modern, high-bred, high-cultivated man of letters! We have had no such spectacle; no man capable of affording such, for the last hundred and fifty years.

But at present, such is the general state of knowledge about Goethe, it were worse than useless to attempt speaking of him in this case. Speak as I might, Goethe, to the great majority of you, would remain problematic, vague; no impression but a false one could be realized. Him we must leave to future times. Johnson, Burns, Rousseau, three great figures from a prior time, from a far inferior state of circumstances, will suit us better here. Three men of the eighteenth century; the conditions of their life far more resemble what those of ours still are in England, than what Goethe's in Germany were. Alas, these men did not conquer like him; they fought bravely, and fell. They were not heroic bringers of the light, but heroic seekers of it. They lived under galling conditions; struggling as under mountains of impediment, and could not unfold themselves into clearness, or victorious interpretation on that "divine idea." It is rather the *tombs* of three literary heroes that I have to show you. There are the monumental heaps, under which three spiritual giants lie buried. Very mournful, but also great and full of interest for us. We will linger by them for a while.

Complaint is often made, in these times, of what we call the disorganized condition of society: how ill many arranged forces of society fulfill their work; how many powerful forces are seen working in a wasteful, chaotic, altogether unarranged manner. It is too just a complaint, as we all know. But perhaps if we look at books and the writers of books, we shall find here, as it were, the summary of all other disorganization; a sort of *heart*, from which, and to which, all other confusion circulates in the world! Considering what book-writers do in the world, and what the world does with book-writers, I should say, It is the most anomalous thing the world at present has to show. We should get into a sea far beyond sounding, did we attempt to give account of this: but we must glance at it for the sake of our subject. The worst element in the life of these three literary heroes was, that they found their business and position such a chaos. On the beaten road there is tolerable traveling; but it is sore work, and many have to perish, fashioning a path though the impassable!

Our pious fathers, feeling well what importance lay in the speaking of man to men, founded churches, made endowments, regulations; everywhere in the civilized world there is a pulpit, environed with all manner of complex dignified appurtenances and furtherances, that therefrom a man with the tongue may, to best advantage, address his fellow-men. They felt that this was the most important thing; that without this there was no good thing. It is a right pious work, that of theirs; beautiful to behold! But now with the art of writing, with the art of printing, a total change has come over that business. The writer of a book, is not he a preacher preaching not to this parish or that, on this day or that, but to all men in all times and places? Surely it is of the last importance that *he* do his work right, whoever do it wrong; that the *eye* report not falsely, for then all the other members are astray! Well; how he may do his work, whether he do it right or wrong, or do it at all, is a point which no man in the world has taken the pains to think of. To a certain shopkeeper, trying to get some money for his books, if lucky, he is of some importance; to no other man of any. Whence he came, whither he is bound, by what ways he arrived, by what he might be furthered on his course, no one asks. He is an accident in society. He wanders like a wild Ishmaelite, in a world of which he is as the spiritual light either the guidance or the misguidance!

Certainly the art of writing is the most miraculous of all things man has devised. Odin's *runes* were the first form of the work of a hero; *books*, written words, are still miraculous *runes*, the latest form! In books lies the *soul* of the whole past time; the articulate audible voice of the past, when the body and material substance of it has altogether vanished like a dream. Mighty fleets and armies, harbors and arsenals, vast cities, high-domed, many-engined—they are precious, great: but what do they become? Agamemnon, the many Agamemnons, Pericleses, and their Greece; all is gone now to some ruined fragments, dumb mournful wrecks and blocks: but the books of Greece? There Greece, to every thinker, still very literally lives; can be called up again into life. No magic *rune* is stranger than a book. All that mankind has done, thought, gained or been: it is lying as in magic preservation in the pages of books. They are the chosen possession of men.

Do not books still accomplish *miracles* as *runes* were fabled to do? They persuade men. Not the wretchedest circulating-library novel, which foolish girls thumb and con in remote villages, but will help to regulate the actual practical weddings and households of those foolish girls. So "Celia" felt, so "Clifford" acted: the foolish theorem of life, stamped into those young brains, comes out as a solid practice one day. Consider whether any *rune* in the wildest imagination of mythologist ever did such wonders as, on the actual firm earth, some books have done! What built St. Paul's cathedral? Look at the heart of the matter, it was that divine Hebrew book—the word partly of the man Moses, an outlaw tending his Midianitish herds, four thousand years ago, in the wildernesses of Sinai! It is the strangest of things, yet nothing is truer. With the art of writing, of which printing is a simple, an inevitable and comparatively insignificant corollary, the true reign of miracles for mankind commenced. It related, with a wondrous new contiguity and perpetual closeness, the past and distant with the present in time and place; all times and all places with this our actual here and now. All things were altered for men; all modes of important work of men: teaching, preaching, governing and all else.

To look at teaching, for instance. Universities are a notable, respectable product of the modern ages. Their existence too is modified, to the very basis of it, by the existence of books. Universities arose while there were yet no books procurable; while a man, for a single book, had to give an estate of land. That, in those circumstances, when a man had some knowledge to communicate, he should do it by gathering the learners round him, face to face, was a necessity for him. If you wanted to know what Abelard knew, you must go and listen to Abelard. Thousands, as many as thirty thousand, went to hear Abelard and that metaphysical theology of his. And now for any other teacher who had also something of his own to teach, there was a great convenience opened: so many thousands eager to learn were already assembled yonder; of all places the best place for him was that. For any third teacher it was better still; and grew ever the better, the more teachers there came. It only needed now that the king took notice of this new phenomenon; combined or agglomerated the various schools into one school; gave it edifices, privileges, encouragements and named it *universitas*, or school of all sciences: the university of Paris, in its essential characters, was there. The model of all subsequent universities; which down even to these days, for six centuries now, have gone on to found themselves. Such, I conceive, was the origin of universities.

It is clear, however, that with this simple circumstance, facility of getting books, the whole conditions of the business from top to bottom were changed. Once invent printing, you metamorphosed all universities, or superseded them! The teacher needed not now to gather men personally round him, that he might *speak* to them what he knew: print it in a book, and all learners far and wide, for a trifle, had it each at his own fireside, much more effectually to learn it! Doubtless there is still peculiar virtue in speech; even writers of books may still, in some circumstances, find it convenient to speak also—witness our present meeting here! There is, one would say, and must ever remain while man has a tongue, a distinct province for speech as well as for writing and printing. In regard to all things this must remain; to universities among others. But the limits of the two have nowhere yet been pointed out, ascertained; much less put in practice: the university which would completely take in that great new fact, of the existence of printed books and stand on a clear footing for the nineteenth century as the Paris one did for the thirteenth, has not yet come into existence. If we think of it, all that a university, or final highest school can do for us, is still but what the first school began doing—teach us to *read*. We learn to *read*, in various languages, in various sciences; we learn the alphabet and letters of all manner of books. But the place where we are to get knowledge, even theoretic knowledge, is the books themselves! It depends on what we read, after all manner of professors have done their best for us. The true university of these days is a collection of books.

But to the church itself, as I hinted already, all is changed, in its preaching, in its working, by the introduction of books. The church is the working recognized union of our priests or prophets, of those who by wise teaching guide the souls of men. While there was no writing, even while there was no easy-writing or *printing*, the preaching of the voice was the natural sole method of performing this. But now with books! He that can write a true book, to persuade England, is not he the bishop and archbishop, the primate of England and of all England? I many a time say, the writers of newspapers, pamphlets, poems, books, these *are* the real working effective church of a modern country. Nay not only our preaching, but even our worship, is not it too accomplished by means of printed books? The noble sentiment which a gifted soul has clothed for us in melodious words, which brings melody into our hearts—is not this essentially, if we will understand it, of the nature of worship? There are many, in all countries, who, in this confused time, have no other method of worship. He who, in any way, shows us better than we knew before that a lily of the fields is beautiful, does he not show it us as an effluence of the fountain of all beauty; as the *handwriting*, made visible there of the great Maker of the universe? He has sung for us, made us sing with him, a little verse of a sacred psalm. Essentially so. How much more he who sings, who says, or in any way brings home to our heart the noble doings, feelings, darings and endurances of a brother man! He has verily touched our hearts as with a live coal *from the altar*. Perhaps there is no worship more authentic.

Literature, so far as it is literature, is an "apocalypse of nature," a revealing of the "open secret." It may well enough be named, in Fichte's style, a "continuous revelation" of the godlike in the terrestrial and common. The godlike does ever, in very truth, endure there; is brought out, now in this dialect, now in that, with various degrees of clearness: all true gifted singers and speakers are, consciously or unconsciously, doing so. The dark stormful indignation of a Byron, so wayward and perverse, may have touches of it; nay the withered mockery of a French skeptic—his mockery of the false, a love and worship of the true. How much more the sphere-harmony of a Shakespeare, of a Goethe; the cathedral-music of a Milton! They are something too, those humble genuine lark-notes of a Burns—sky-lark, starting from the humble furrow, far overhead into the blue depths and singing to us so genuinely there! For all true singing is of the nature of worship; as indeed all true *working* may be said to be—whereof such *singing* is but the record, and fit melodious representation, to us. Fragments of a real "church liturgy" and "body of homilies," strangely disguised from the common eye, are to be found weltering in that huge froth-ocean of printed speech we loosely call literature! Books are our church too. .

Or turning now to the government of men. Witenagemote, old parliament was a great thing. The affairs of the nation were there deliberated and decided; what we were to *do* as a nation. But does not, though the name parliament subsists, the parliamentary debate go on now, everywhere and at all times, in a far more comprehensive way, *out* of parliament altogether? Burke said there were three estates in parliament; but, in the reporters' gallery yonder, there sat a *fourth estate* more important far than they all. It is not a figure of speech, or a witty saying; it is a literal fact—very momentous to us in these times. Literature is our parliament too. Printing, which comes necessarily out of writing, I say often, is equivalent to democracy: invent writing, democracy is inevitable. Writing brings printing; brings universal every-day extempore printing, as we see at present. Whoever can speak, speaking now to the whole nation, becomes a power, a branch of government, with inalienable weight in law-making, in all acts of authority. It matters not what rank he has, what revenues or garnitures: the requisite thing is, that he have a tongue which others will listen to; this and nothing more is requisite. The nation is governed by all that has tongue in the nation: democracy is virtually *there*. Add only, that whatsoever power exists will have itself, by and by, organized; working secretly under bandages, obscurations, obstructions, it will never rest till it get to work free, unencumbered, visible to all. Democracy virtually extant will insist on becoming palpably extant.

On all sides, are we not driven to the conclusion that, of the things which man can do or make here below, by far the most momentous, wonderful and worthy are the things we call books! Those poor bits of rag-paper with black ink on them—from the daily newspaper to the sacred Hebrew book, what have they not done, what are they not doing! For indeed, whatever be the outward form of the thing (bits of paper, as we say, and black ink), is it not verily, at bottom, the highest act of man's faculty that produces a book? It is the *thought* of man; the true thaumaturgic virtue; by which man works all things whatsoever. All that he does and brings to pass, is the vesture of a thought. This London city, with all its houses, palaces, steam-engines, cathedrals and huge immeasurable traffic and tumult, what is it but a thought, but millions of thoughts made into one—a huge immeasurable spirit of a thought, embodied in brick, in iron, smoke, dust, palaces, parlia-

ments, hackney coaches, Katherine docks and the rest of it! Not a brick
was made but some man had to *think* of the making of that brick. The
thing we called "bits of paper with traces of black ink," is the *purest*
embodiment a thought of man can have. No wonder it is, in all ways, the
activest and noblest.

All this, of the importance and supreme importance of the man of letters
in modern society and how the press is to such a degree superseding the
pulpit, the senate, the *senatus academicus* and much else, has been admitted
for a good while; and recognized often enough, in late times, with a sort of
sentimental triumph and wonderment. It seems to me, the sentimental by
and by will have to give place to the practical. If men of letters *are* so
incalculably influential, actually performing such work for us from age to
age and even from day to day, then I think we may conclude that men
of letters will not always wander like unrecognized unregulated Ishmaelites
among us! Whatsoever thing, as I said above, has virtual unnoticed power
will cast off its wrappages, bandages and step forth one day with palpably
articulated, universally visible power. That one man wear the clothes and
take the wages, of a function which is done by quite another: there can be
no profit in this; this is not right, it is wrong. And yet, alas, the *making* of
it right—what a business, for long times to come! Sure enough, this what
we call organization of the literary guild is still a great way off, encumbered with all manner of complexities. If you asked me what were the best
possible organization for the men of letters in modern society; the arrangement of furtherance and regulation, grounded the most accurately on the
actual facts of their position and of the world's position—I should beg to
say that the problem far exceeded my faculty! It is not one man's faculty;
it is that of many successive men turned earnestly upon it, that will bring
out even an approximate solution. What the best arrangement were, none of
us could say. But if you ask: "Which is the worst?" I answer: "This which
we now have, that chaos should sit umpire in it; this is the worst." To the
best, or any good one, there is yet a long way.

One remark I must not omit, That royal or parliamentary grants of
money are by no means the chief thing wanted! To give our men of letters
stipends, endowments and all furtherance of cash, will do little toward the
business. On the whole, one is weary of hearing about the omnipotence
of money. I will say rather that, for a genuine man, it is no evil to
be poor; that there ought to be literary men poor—to show whether
they are genuine or not! Mendicant orders, bodies of good men doomed
to *beg*, were instituted in the Christian church; a most natural and
even necessary development of the spirit of Christianity. It was itself
founded on poverty, on sorrow, contradiction, crucifixion, every species of worldly distress and degradation. We may say, that he who has
not known those things, and learned from them the priceless lessons
they have to teach, has missed a good opportunity of schooling. To
beg and go barefoot, in coarse woollen cloak with a rope round your loins
and be despised of all the world, was no beautiful business—nor an honor-

able one in any eye, till the nobleness of those who did so had made it honored of some!

Begging is not in our course at the present time: but for the rest of it, who will say that a Johnson is not perhaps the better for being poor? It is needful for him, at all rates, to know that outward profit, that success of any kind is *not* the goal he has to aim at. Pride, vanity, ill-conditioned egoism of all sorts, are bred in his heart, as in every heart; need, above all, to be cast out of his heart—to be, with whatever pangs, torn out of it, cast forth from it, as a thing worthless. Byron, born rich and noble, made out even less than Burns, poor and plebeian. Who knows but, in that same "best possible organization" as yet far off, poverty may still enter as an important element? What if our men of letters, men setting up to be spiritual heroes, were still *then*, as they now are, a kind of "involuntary monastic order;" bound still to this same ugly poverty—till they had tried what was in it too, till they had learned to make it to do for them! Money, in truth, can do much, but it cannot do all. We must know the province of it and confine it there; and even spurn it back, when it wishes to get farther.

Besides, were the money-furtherances, the proper season for them, the fit assigner of them, all settled—how is the Burns to be recognized that merits these? He must pass through the ordeal and prove himself. *This* ordeal; this wild welter of a chaos which is called literary life: this too is a kind of ordeal! There is clear truth in the idea that a struggle from the lower classes of society, toward the upper regions and rewards of society, must ever continue. Strong men are born there, who ought to stand elsewhere than there. The manifold, inextricably complex, universal struggle of these constitutes and must constitute, what is called the progress of society. For men of letters, as for all other sorts of men. How to regulate that struggle? There is the whole question. To leave it as it is, at the mercy of blind chance; a whirl of distracted atoms, one cancelling the other; one of the thousand arriving saved, nine hundred and ninety-nine lost by the way; your royal Johnson languishing inactive in garrets, or harnessed to the yoke of printer cave; your Burns dying broken-hearted as a gauger; your Rousseau driven into mad exasperation, kindling French revolutions by his paradoxes: this, as we said, is clearly enough the *worst* regulation. The *best*, alas, is far from us!

And yet there can be no doubt but it is coming; advancing on us, as yet hidden in the bosom of centuries: this is a prophesy one can risk. For so soon as men get to discern the importance of a thing, they do infallibly set about arranging it, facilitating, forwarding it; and rest not till, in some approximate degree, they have accomplished that. I say, of all priesthoods, aristocracies, governing classes at present extant in the world, there is no class comparable for importance to that priesthood of the writers of books. This is a fact which he who runs may read—and draw inferences from. "Literature will take care of itself," answered Mr. Pitt, when applied to for some help for Burns. "Yes," adds Mr. Southey, "it will take care of itself; *and of you too*, if you do not look to it!"

The result to individual men of letters is not the momentous one; they are but individuals, an infinitesimal fraction of the great body; they can struggle on and live or else die, as they have been wont. But it deeply concerns the whole society, whether it will set its *light* on high places, to walk thereby; or trample it under foot and scatter it in all ways of wild waste (not without conflagration), as heretofore! Light is the one thing wanted for the world. Put wisdom in the head of the world, the world will fight its battle victoriously and be the best world man can make it. I call this anomaly of a disorganic literary class the heart of all other anomalies, at once product and parent; some good arrangement for that would be as the *punctum saliens* of a new vitality and just arrangement for all. Already, in some European countries, in France, in Prussia, one traces some beginnings of an arrangement for the literary class; indicating the gradual possibility of such. I believe that it is possible; that it will have to be possible.

By far the most interesting fact I hear about the Chinese is one on which we cannot arrive at clearness, but which excites endless curiosity even in the dim state: this namely, that they do attempt to make their men of letters their governors! It would be rash to say, one understood how this was done, or with what degree of success it was done. All such things must be very *un*successful; yet a small degree of success is precious; the very attempt how precious! There does seem to be, all over China, a more or less active search everywhere to discover the men of talent that grow up in the young generation. Schools there are for every one: a foolish sort of training, yet still a sort. The youths who distinguish themselves in the lower school are promoted into favorable stations in the higher, that they may still more distinguish themselves—forward and forward: it appears to be out of these that the official persons and incipient governors, are taken. These are they whom they *try* first, whether they can govern or not. And surely with the best hope: for they are the men that have already shown intellect. Try them: they have not governed or administered as yet; perhaps they cannot; but there is no doubt they *have* some understanding—without which no man can! Neither is understanding a *tool*, as we are too apt to figure; "it is a *hand* which can handle any tool." Try these men: they are of all others the best worth trying. Surely there is no kind of government, constitution, revolution, social apparatus or arrangement, that I know of in this world, so promising to one's scientific curiosity as this. The man of intellect at the top of affairs: this is the aim of all constitutions and revolutions, if they have any aim. For the man of true intellect, as I assert and believe always, is the noble-hearted man withal, the true, just, humane and valiant man. Get *him* for governor, all is got; fail to get him, though you had constitutions plentiful as blackberries and a parliament in every village, there is nothing yet got!

These things look strange, truly; and are not such as we commonly speculate upon. But we are fallen into strange times; these things will require to be speculated upon; to be rendered practicable, to be in some way put in practice. These and many others. On all hands of us, there is the announcement, audible enough, that the old empire of routine has ended; that to say a thing has long been, is no reason for its continuing to be. The things which have been are fallen into decay, are fallen into incompetence; large masses of mankind, in every society of our Europe, are no longer capable of living at all by the things which have been. When millions of men can no longer by their utmost exertion gain food for themselves, and "the third man for thirty-six weeks each year is short of third-rate potatoes," the things which have been must decidedly prepare to alter themselves! I will now quit this of the organization of men of letters.

Alas, the evil that pressed heaviest on those literary heroes of ours was not the want of organization for men of letters, but a far deeper one; out of which, indeed, this and so many other evils for the literary man and for all men, had, as from their fountain, taken rise. That our hero as man of letters had to travel without highway, companionless, through an inorganic chaos—and leave his own life and faculty lying there, as a partial contribution toward *pushing* some highway through it: this, had not his faculty itself been so perverted and paralyzed, he might have put up with, might have considered to be but the common lot of heroes. His fatal misery was the *spiritual paralysis*, so we may name it, of the age in which his life lay; whereby his life too, do what he might, was half-paralyzed! The eighteenth was a *skeptical* century; in which little word there is a whole Pandora's box of miseries. Skepticism means not intellectual doubt alone, but moral doubt; all sorts of *in*fidelity, insincerity, spiritual paralysis. Perhaps, in few centuries that one could specify since the world began, was a life of heroism more difficult for a man. That was not an age of faith—an age of heroes! The very possibility of heroism had been, as it were, formerly abnegated in the minds of all. Heroism was gone forever; triviality, formulism and commonplace were come forever. The "age of miracles" had been, or perhaps had not been; but it was not any longer. An effete world; wherein wonder, greatness, godhood could not now dwell—in one word, a godless world!

How mean, dwarfish are their ways of thinking, in this time—compared not with the Christian Shakespeares and Miltons, but with the old pagan Skalds, with any species of believing men! The living tree igdrasil, with the melodious prophetic waving of its world-wide boughs, deep-rooted as Hela, has died out into the clanking of a world-machine. "Tree" and "machine:" contrast these two things. I, for my share, declare the world to be no machine! I say that it does *not* go by wheel-and-pinion "motives," self-interests, checks, balances; that there is something far other in it than the clank of spinning-jennies and parliamentary majorities; and, on the whole, that it is not a machine at all! The old Norse heathen had a truer notion of God's-world than these poor machine-skeptics: the old heathen Norse were *sincere* men. But for these poor skeptics there was no sincerity, no truth. Half-truth and hearsay were called truth. Truth, for most men, meant plausibility; to be measured by the number of votes you could get. They had lost any notion that sincerity was possible, or of what sincerity was. How many plausibilities asking, with unaffected surprise and the air of offended virtue, What! am not I sincere? Spiritual paralysis, I say, nothing left but a mechanical life, was the characteristic of that century. For the common man, unless happily he stood *below* his century and belonged to another prior one, it was impossible to be a believer, a hero; he lay buried, unconscious, under these baleful influences. To the strongest man, only with infinite struggle and confusion was it possible to work himself half-loose; and lead as it were, in an enchanted, most tragical way, a spiritual death-in-life and be a half-hero!

Skepticism is the name we give to all this; as the chief symptom, as the chief origin of all this. Concerning which so much were to be said! It would take many discourses, not a small fraction of one discourse, to state what one feels about that eighteenth century and its ways. As indeed this and the like of this, which we now call skepticism, is precisely the black malady and like-foe, against which all teaching and discoursing since man's life began has directed itself: the battle of belief against unbelief the never-ending battle! Neither is it in the way of crimination that one would wish to speak. Skepticism, for that century, we must consider as the decay of old ways of believing, the preparation afar off for new, better and wider ways— an inevitable thing. We will not blame men for it; we will lament their hard fate. We will understand that destruction of old *forms* is not destruction of everlasting *substances;* that skepticism, as sorrowful and hateful as we see it, is not an end but a beginning.

The other day speaking, without prior purpose that way, of Bentham's theory of man and man's life, I chanced to call it a more beggarly one than Mahomet's. I am bound to say, now when it is once uttered, that such is my deliberate opinion. Not that one would mean offense against the man Jeremy Bentham, or those who respect and believe him. Bentham himself, and even the creed of Bentham, seems to me comparatively worthy of praise. It is a determinate *being* what all the world, in a cowardly half-and-half manner, was tending to be. Let us have the crisis; we shall either have death or the cure. I call this gross, steam-engine utilitarianism an approach toward new faith. It was a laying-down of cant; a saying to oneself: "Well then, this world is a dead iron machine, the god of it gravitation and selfish hunger; let us see what, by checking and balancing and good adjustment of tooth and pinion, can be made of it!" Benthamism has something complete, manful, in such fearless committal of itself to what it finds true; you may call it heroic, though a heroism with its *eyes* put out! It is the culminating point and fearless ultimatum, of what lay in the half-and-half state, pervading man's whole existence in that eighteenth century. It seems to me, all deniers of godhood and all lip-believers of it, are bound to be Benthamites, if they have courage and honesty. Benthamism is an *eyeless* heroism: the human species, like a hapless blinded Samson grinding in the Philistine mill, clasps convulsively the pillars of its mill; brings huge ruin down, but ultimately deliverance withal. Of Bentham I meant to say no harm.

But this I do say and would wish all men to know and lay to heart, that he who discerns nothing but mechanism in the universe has in the fatalest way missed the secret of the universe altogether. That all godhood should vanish out of men's conception of this universe seems to me precisely the most brutal error—I will not disparage heathenism by calling it a heathen error—that men could fall into. It is not true; it is false at the very heart of it. A man who thinks so will think *wrong* about all things in the world; this original sin will vitiate all other conclusions he can form. One might call it the most lamentable of delusions—not forgetting witchcraft itself! Witch-craft worshiped at least a living devil; but this worships a dead iron devil; no God, not even a devil! Whatsoever is noble, divine, inspired, drops thereby out of life. There remains everywhere in life a despicable *caput-mortuum;* the mechanical hull, all soul fled out of it. How can a man act heroically? The "doctrine of motives" will teach him that it is, under more or less disguise, nothing but a wretched love of pleasure, fear of pain; that hunger, of applause, of cash, of whatsoever victual it may be, is the ultimate fact of man's life. Atheism, in brief—which does indeed frightfully punish itself. The man, I say, is become spiritually a paralytic man; this godlike universe a dead mechanical steam-engine, all working by motives, checks, balances and I know not what; wherein, as in the detestable belly of some Phalaris'-bull of his own contriving, he the poor Phalaris sits miserably dying!

Belief I define to be the healthy act of man's mind. It is a mysterious indescribable process, that of getting to believe—indescribable, as all vital acts are. We have our mind given us, not that it may cavil and argue, but that it may see into something, give us clear belief and understanding about something, whereon we are then to proceed to act. Doubt, truly, is not itself a crime. Certainly we do not rush out, clutch up the first thing we find and straightway believe that! All manner of doubts, inquiry, σηέψις as it is named, about all manner of objects, dwells in every reasonable mind. It is the mystic working of the mind, on the object it is *getting* to know and believe. Belief comes out of all this, above ground, like the tree from its hidden *roots.* But now if, even on common things, we require that a man keep his doubts *silent* and not babble of them till they in some measure become affirmations or denials; how much more in regard to the highest things, impossible to speak of in words at all! That a man parade his doubt and get to imagine that debating and logic (which means at best only the manner of *telling* us your thought, your belief or disbelief, about a thing) is the triumph and true work of what intellect he has: alas, this is as if you should *overturn* the tree and instead of green boughs, leaves and fruits, show us ugly taloned roots turned up into the air—and no growth, only death and misery going on!

For the skepticism, as I said, is not intellectual only; it is moral also; a chronic atrophy and disease of the whole soul. A man lives by believing something; not by debating and arguing about many things. A sad case for him when all that he can manage to believe is something he can button in his pocket and with one or the other organ eat and digest! Lower than that he will not get. We call those ages in which he gets so low the mournfulest, sickest and meanest of all ages. The world's heart is palsied, sick: how can any limb of it be whole? Genuine acting ceases in all departments of the world's work; dextrous similitude of acting begins. The world's wages are pocketed, the world's work is not done. Heroes have gone out; quacks have come in. Accordingly, what century, since the end of the Roman world, which also was a time of skepticism, simulacra and universal decadence, so abounds with quacks as the eighteenth? Consider them, with their tumid sentimental vaporing about virtue, benevolence—the wretched quack-squadron, Cagliostro at the head of them! Few men were without quackery; they had got to consider it a necessary ingredient and amalgam for truth. Chatham, our brave Chatham himself, comes down to the house, all wrapped and bandaged; he "has crawled out in great bodily suffering," and so on—*forgets*, says Walpole, that he is acting the sick man; in the fire of debate, snatches his arm from the sling and oratorically swings and brandishes it! Chatham himself lives the strangest mimetic life, half-hero, half-quack, all along. For indeed the world is full of dupes; and you will have to gain the *world's* suffrage! How the duties of the world will be done in that case, what quantities of error, which means failure, which means sorrow and misery, to some and to many, will gradually accumulate in all provinces of the world's business, we need not compute.

It seems to me, you lay your finger here on the heart of the world's maladies, when you call it a skeptical world. An insincere world; a godless untruth of a world! It is out of this, as I consider, that the whole tribe of social pestilences, French revolutions, chartisms and what not, have derived their being—their chief necessity to be. This must alter. Till this alter, nothing can beneficially alter. My one hope of the world, my inexpugnable consolation in looking at the miseries of the world, is that this is altering. Here and there one does now find a man who knows, as of old, that this world is a truth and no plausibility and falsity; that he himself is alive, not dead or paralytic; and that the world is alive, instinct with godhood, beautiful and awful, even as in the beginning of days! One man once knowing this, many men, all men, must by and by come to know it. It lies there clear, for whosoever will take the *spectacles* off his eyes and honestly look, to know! For such a man the unbelieving century, with its unblessed products, is already past: a new century is already come. The old unblessed products and performances, as solid as they look, are phantasms, preparing speedily to vanish. To this and the other noisy, very great-looking simulacrum with the whole world huzzahing at its heels, he can say, composedly stepping aside: "Thou art not *true;* thou art not extant, only semblant; go thy way!" Yes, hollow formulism, gross Benthamism and other unheroic atheistic insincerity is visibly and even rapidly declining. An unbelieving eighteenth century is but an exception—such as now and then occurs. I prophesy that the world will once more become *sincere;* a believing world; with *many* heroes in it, a heroic world! It will then be a victorious world; never till then.

Or indeed what of the world and its victories? Men speak too much about the world. Each one of us here, let the world go how it will, and be victorious or not victorious, has he not a life of his own to lead? One life; a little gleam of time between two eternities; no second chance to us forevermore! It were well for *us* to live not as fools and simulacra, but as wise and realities. The world's being saved will not save us; nor the world's being lost destroy us. We should look to ourselves: there is great merit here in the "duty of staying at home!" And, on the whole, to say truth, I never heard of "worlds" being "saved" in any other way. That mania of saving worlds is itself a piece of the eighteenth century with its windy sentimentalism. Let us not follow it too far. For the saving of the *world* I will trust confidently to the Maker of the world; and look a little to my own saving, which I am more competent to! In brief, for the world's sake and for our own, we will rejoice greatly that skepticism, insincerity, mechanical atheism, with all their poison-dews, are going and as good as gone.

Now it was under such conditions, in those times of Johnson, that our men of letters had to live. Times in which there was properly no truth in life. Old truths had fallen nigh dumb; the new lay yet hidden, not trying to speak. That man's life here below was a sincerity and fact and would forever continue such, no new intimation, in that dusk of the world, had yet dawned. No intimation; not even any French revolution—which we define to be a truth once more, though a truth clad in hellfire! How different was the Luther's pilgrimage, with its assured goal, from the Johnson's, girt with mere traditions, suppositions, grown now incredible, unintelligible! Mahomet's formulas were of "wood waxed and oiled," and could be *burned* out of one's way: poor Johnson's were far more difficult to burn. The Strong man will ever find *work*, which means difficulty, pain, to the full measure of his strength. But to make out a victory, in those circumstances of our poor hero as man of letters, was perhaps more difficult than in any. Not obstruction, disorganization, Bookseller Osborne and four-pence-halfpenny a day; not this alone; but the light of his own soul was taken from him. No landmark on the earth; and, alas, what is that to having no loadstar in the heaven! We need not wonder that none of those three men rose to victory. That they fought truly is the highest praise. With a mournful sympathy we will contemplate, if not three living victorious heroes, as I said, the tombs of three fallen heroes! They fell for us too; making a way for us. There are the mountains which they hurled abroad in their confused war of the giants; under which, their strength and life spent, they now lie buried.

I have already written of these three literary heroes, expressly or incidentally; what I suppose is known to most of you; what need not be spoken or written a second time. They concern us here as the singular *prophets* of that singular age; for such they virtually were; and the aspect they and their world exhibit, under this point of view, might lead us into reflections enough! I call them, all three, genuine men more or less; faithfully, for most part unconsciously, struggling, to be genuine and plant themselves on the everlasting truth of things. This to a degree that eminently distinguishes them from the poor artificial mass of their contemporaries; and renders them worthy to be considered as speakers, in some measure, of the everlasting truth, as prophets in that age of theirs. By nature herself a noble necessity was laid on them to be so. They were men of such magnitude that they could not live on unrealities—clouds, froth and all inanity gave way under them: there was no footing for them but on firm earth; no rest or regular motion for them, if they got not footing there. To a certain extent, they were sons of nature once more in an age of artifice; once more, original men.

As for Johnson, I have always considered him to be, by nature, one of our great English souls. A strong and noble man; so much left undeveloped in him to the last: in a kindlier element what might he not have been—poet, priest, sovereign ruler! On the whole, a man must not complain of his "element," of his "time," or the like; it is thriftless work doing so. His time is bad: well then, he is there to make it better! Johnson's youth was poor, isolated, hopeless, very miserable. Indeed, it does not seem possible that, in even the favorablest outward circumstances, Johnson's life could have been other than a painful one. The world might have had more of profitable *work* out of him, or less; but his *effort* against the world's work could never have been a light one. Nature, in return for his nobleness, had said to him, "Live in an element of diseased sorrow." Nay, perhaps the sorrow and the nobleness were intimately and even inseparably connected with each other. At all events, poor Johnson had to go about girt with continual hypochondria, physical and spiritual pain. Like a Hercules with the burning Nessus'-shirt on him, which shoots in on him dull incurable misery: the Nessus'-shirt not to be stripped off, which is his own natural skin! In this manner *he* had to live. Figure him there, with his scrofulous diseases, with his great greedy heart and unspeakable chaos of thoughts; stalking mournful as a stranger in this earth; eagerly devouring what spiritual thing he could come at: school-languages and other merely grammatical stuff, if there were nothing better! The largest soul that was in all England; and provision made for it of "fourpence-halfpenny a day." Yet a giant invincible soul; a true man's. One remembers always that story of the shoes at Oxford: the rough, seamy-faced, rawboned college servitor stalking about, in winter-season, with his shoes worn out; how the charitable gentleman commoner secretly places a new pair at his door; and the rawboned servitor, lifting them, looking at them near, with his dim eyes, with what thoughts—pitches them out of the window! Wet feet, mud, frost, hunger or what you will; but not beggary: we cannot stand beggary! Rude stubborn self-help here; a whole world of squalor, rudeness, confused misery and want, yet of nobleness and manfulness withal. It is a type of the man's life, this pitching away of the shoes. An original man—not a second-hand, borrowing or begging man. Let us stand on our own basis, at any rate! On such shoes as we ourselves can get. On frost and mud, if you will, but honestly on that—on the reality and substance which nature gives *us,* not on the semblance, on the thing she has given another than us!

And yet with all this rugged pride of manhood and self-help, was there ever soul more tenderly affectionate, loyally submissive to what was really higher than he? Great souls are always loyally submissive, reverent to what is over them; only small mean souls are otherwise. I could not find a better proof of what I said the other day, "That the sincere man was by nature the obedient man; that only in a world of heroes was there loyal obedience to the heroic." The essence of *originality* is not that it be *new:* Johnson believed altogether in the old; he found the old opinions credible for him, fit for him; and a right heroic manner lived under them. He is well worth study in regard to that. For we are to say that Johnson was far other than a mere man of words and formulas; he was a man of truths and facts. He stood by the old formulas; the happier was it for him that he could so stand: but in all formulas that *he* could stand by, there needed to be a most genuine substance. Very curious how, in that poor paper-age, so barren, artificial, thick-quilted with pedantries, hearsays, the great fact of this universe glared in, forever wonderful, indubitable, unspeakable, divine-infernal, upon this man too! How he harmonized his formulas with it, how he managed at all under such circumstances: that is a thing worth seeing. A thing "to be looked at with reverence, with pity, with awe." That church of St. Clement Danes, where Johnson still *worshiped* in the era of Voltaire, is to me a venerable place.

It was in virtue of his *sincerity,* of his speaking still in some sort from the heart of nature, though in the current artificial dialect, that Johnson was a prophet. Are not all dialects "artificial"? Artificial things are not all false—nay every true product of nature will infallibly *shape* itself; we may say all artificial things are, at the starting of them, *true.* What we call "formulas" are not in their origin bad; they are indispensably good. Formula is *method,* habitude; found wherever man is found. Formulas fashion themselves as paths do, as beaten highways, leading toward some sacred or high object, whither many men are bent. Consider it. One man, full of heartfelt earnest impulse, finds out a way of doing somewhat—were it of uttering his soul's reverence for the highest, were it but of fitly saluting his fellow-man. An inventor was needed to do that, a *poet;* he has articulated the dim-struggling thought that dwelled in his own and many hearts. This is his way of doing that; these are his footsteps, the beginning of a "path." And now see: the second man travels naturally in the footsteps of his foregoer, it is the *easiest* method. In the footsteps of his foregoer; yet with improvements, with changes where such seem good; at all events with enlargements, the path ever *widening* itself as more travel it—till at last there is a broad highway whereon the whole world may travel and drive. While there remains a city or shrine, or any reality to drive to, at the farther end, the highway shall be right welcome! When the city is gone, we will forsake the highway. In this manner all institutions, practices, regulated things in the world have come into existence and gone out of existence. Formulas all begin by being *full* of substance; you may call them the *skin*, the articulation into shape, into limbs and skin, of a substance that is already there: *they* had not been there otherwise. Idols, as we said, are not idolatrous till they become doubtful, empty for the worshiper's heart. Much as we talk against formulas, I hope no one of us is ignorant withal of the significance of *true* formulas; that they were and will ever be, the indispensablest furniture of our habitation in this world.

Mark, too, how little Johnson boasts of his "sincerity." He has no suspicion of his being particularly anything! A hard-struggling, weary-hearted man, or "scholar" as he calls himself, trying hard to get some honest livelihood in the world, not to starve, but to live—without stealing! A noble unconsciousness is in him. He does not "engrave *truth* on his watch-seal;" no, but he stands by truth, speaks by it, works and lives by it. Thus it ever is. Think of it once more. The man whom nature has appointed to do great things is, first of all, furnished with that openness to nature which renders him incapable of being *in*sincere! To his large, open, deep-feeling heart nature is a fact: all hearsay is hearsay; the unspeakable greatness of this mystery of life, let him acknowledge it or not, nay even though he seem to forget it or deny it, is ever present to *him*—fearful and wonderful, on this hand and on that. He has a basis of sincerity; unrecognized, because never questioned or capable of question. Mirabeau, Mahomet, Cromwell, Napoleon: all the great men I ever heard of have this as the primary material of them. Innumerable commonplace men are debating, are talking everywhere their commonplace doctrines, which they have learned by logic, by rote, at second-hand: to that kind of man all this is still nothing. He must have truth; truth which *he* feels to be true. How shall he stand otherwise? His whole soul, at all moments, in all ways, tells him that there is no standing. He is under the noble necessity of being true. Johnson's way of thinking about this world is not mine, any more than Mahomet's was: but I recognize the everlasting element of heart-*sincerity* in both; and see with pleasure how neither of them remains ineffectual. Neither of them is as *chaff* sown; in both of them is something which the seed-field will *grow*.

Johnson was a prophet to his people; preached a gospel to them—as all like him always do. The highest gospel he preached we may describe as a kind of moral prudence: "in a world where much is to be done and little is to be known," see how you will *do* it! A thing well worth preaching. "A world where much is to be done and little is to be known:" do not sink yourselves in boundless bottomless abysses of doubt, of wretched god-forgetting unbelief—you were miserable then, powerless, mad: how could you *do* or work at all? Such gospel Johnson preached and taught—coupled, theoretically and practically, with this other great gospel, "Clear your mind of cant!" Have no trade with cant: stand on the cold mud in the frosty weather, but let it be in your own *real* torn shoes: "that will be better for you," as Mahomet says! I call this, I call these two things *joined together*, a great gospel, the greatest perhaps that was possible at that time.

Johnson's writings, which once had such currency and celebrity, are now, as it were, disowned by the young generation. It is not wonderful; Johnson's opinions are fast becoming obsolete: but his style of thinking and of living, we may hope, will never become obsolete. I find in Johnson's book the indisputablest traces of a great intellect and great heart—ever welcome, under what obstructions and perversions soever. They are *sincere* words, those of his; he means things by them. A wondrous buckram style—the best he could get to then; a measured grandiloquence, stepping or rather stalking along in a very solemn way, grown obsolete now; sometimes a tumid *size* of phraseology not in proportion to the contents of it: all this you will put up with. For the phraseology, tumid or not, has always *something within it*. So many beautiful styles and books, with *nothing* in them—a man is a *male*factor to the world who writes such! *They* are the avoidable kind! Had Johnson left nothing but his "Dictionary," one might have traced there a great intellect, a genuine man. Looking to its clearness of definition, its general solidity, honesty, insight and successful method, it may be called the best of all dictionaries. There is in it a kind of architectural nobleness; it stands there like a great solid square-built edifice, finished, symmetrically complete: you judge that a true builder did it.

One word, in spite of our haste, must be granted to poor Bozzy. He passes for a mean, inflated, gluttonous creature; and was so in many senses. Yet the fact of his reverence for Johnson will ever remain noteworthy. The foolish conceited Scotch Laird, the most conceited man of his time, approaching in such awe-struck attitude the great dusty irascible pedagogue in his mean garret there: it is a genuine reverence for excellence; a *worship* for heroes, at a time when neither heroes nor worship were surmised to exist. Heroes, it would seem, exist always, and a certain worship of them! We will also take the liberty to deny altogether that of the witty Frenchman, that no man is a hero to his valet-de-chambre. Or if so, it is not the hero's blame, but the valet's: that his soul, namely, is a mean *valet*-soul! He expects his hero to advance in royal stage-trappings, with measured steps, trains borne behind him, trumpets sounding before him. It should stand rather, no man can be a *grand-monarque* to his valet-de-chambre. Strip your Louis Quatorze of his king-gear, and there *is* left nothing but a poor forked raddish with a head fantastically carved—admirable to no valet. The valet does not know a hero when he sees him! Alas, no: it requires a kind of *hero* to do that—and one of the world's wants, in *this* as in other senses, is for most part want of such.

On the whole, shall we not say, that Boswell's admiration was well bestowed; that he could have found no soul in all England so worthy of bending down before? Shall we not say, of this great mournful Johnson too, that he guided his difficult confused existence wisely; led it *well*, like a right valiant man! That waste chaos of authorship by trade; that waste chaos of skepticism in religion and politics, in life-theory and life-practice; in his poverty, in his dust and dimness, with the sick body and the rusty coat: he made it do for him, like a brave man. Not wholly without a loadstar in the eternal; he had still a loadstar, as the brave all need to have: with his eye set on that, he would change his course for nothing in these confused vortices of the lower sea of time. "To the spirit of lies, bearing death and hunger, he would in no wise strike his flag." Brave old Samuel: *ultimus Romanorum!*

Of Rousseau and his heroism I cannot say so much. He is not what I call a strong man. A morbid, excitable, spasmodic man; at best, intense rather than strong. He had not "the talent of silence," an invaluable talent; which few Frenchmen, or indeed men of any sort in these times, excel in! The suffering man ought really "to consume his own smoke;" there is no good in emitting *smoke* till you have made it into *fire*—which, in the metaphorical sense too, all smoke is capable of becoming! Rousseau has not depth or width, not calm force for difficulty; the first characteristic of true greatness. A fundamental mistake to call vehemence and rigidity strength! A man is not strong who takes convulsion-fits; though six men cannot hold him then. He that can walk under the heaviest weight without staggering, he is the strong man. We need forever, especially in these loud shrieking days to remind ourselves of that. A man who cannot *hold his peace*, till the time comes for speaking and acting, is no right man.

Poor Rousseau's face is to me expressive of him. A high but narrow contracted intensity in its bony brows; deep, straight set eyes, in which there is something bewildered-looking—bewildered, peering with lynx-eagerness. A face full of misery, even ignoble misery and also of the antagonism against that; something mean, plebeian there, redeemed only by *intensity:* the face of what is called a fanatic—a sadly *contracted* hero! We name him here because, with all his drawbacks, and they are many, he has the first and chief characteristic of a hero: he is heartily *in earnest*. In earnest, if ever man was; as none of these French philosophers were. Nay, one would say, of an earnestness too great for his otherwise sensitive, rather feeble nature; and which indeed in the end drove him into the strangest incoherences, almost delirations. There had come, at last, to be a kind of madness in him: his ideas *possessed* him like demons; hurried him so about, drove him over steep places!

The fault and misery of Rousseau was what we easily name by a single word, *egoism;* which is indeed the source and summary of all faults and miseries whatsoever. He had not perfected himself into victory over mere desire; a mean hunger, in many sorts, was still the motive principle of him. I am afraid he was a very vain man; hungry for the praises of men. You remember Genlis' experience of him. She took Jean Jacques to the theater; he bargaining for a strict incognito—"*He* would not be seen there for the world!" The curtain did happen nevertheless to be drawn aside: the pit recognized Jean Jacques, but took no great notice of him! He expressed the bitterest indignation; gloomed all evening, spoke no other than surly words. The glib countess remained entirely convinced that his anger was **not** at being seen, but at not being applauded when seen. How the whole nature of the man is poisoned; nothing but suspicion, self-isolation, fierce moody ways! He could not live with anybody. A man of some rank from the country, who visited him often and used to sit with him, expressing all reverence and affection for him, comes one day, finds Jean Jacques full of the sourest unintelligible humor. "Monsieur," said Jean Jacques, with flaming eyes, "I know why you come here. You come to see what a poor life I lead; how little is in my poor pot that is boiling there. Well, look into the pot! There is half a pound of meat, one carrot and three onions; that is all; go and tell the whole world that, if you like, monsieur!" A man of this sort was far gone. The whole world got itself supplied with anecdotes, for light laughter, for a certain theatrical interest, from these perversions and contortions of poor Jean Jacques. Alas, to him they were not laughing or theatrical; too real to him! The contortions of a dying gladiator: the crowded amphitheater looks on with entertainment: but the gladiator is in agonies and dying.

And yet this Rousseau, as we say, with his passionate appeals to mothers, with his *contrat-social*, with his celebrations of nature, even of savage life in nature, did once more touch upon reality, struggle toward reality; was doing the function of a prophet to his time. As *he* could and as the time could! Strangely through all that defacement, degradation and almost madness, there is in the inmost heart of poor Rousseau a spark of real heavenly fire. Once more, out of the element of that withered mocking philosophism, skepticism and persiflage, there has arisen in this man the ineradicable feeling and knowledge that this life of ours is *true;* not a skepticism, theorem, or persiflage, but a fact, an awful reality. Nature has made that revelation to him; had ordered him to speak it out. He got it spoken out; if not well and clearly, then ill and dimly—as clearly as he could. Nay what are all errors and perversities of his, even those stealings of ribbons, aimless confused miseries and vagabondisms, if we will interpret them kindly, but the blinkard dazzlement and staggerings to and fro of a man sent on an errand he is too weak for, by a path he cannot yet find? Men are led by strange ways. One should have tolerance for a man, hope of him; leave him to try yet what he will do. While life lasts, hope lasts for every man.

Of Rousseau's literary talents, greatly celebrated still among his countrymen, I do not say much. His books, like himself, are what I call unhealthy; not the good sort of books. There is a sensuality in Rousseau. Combined with such an intellectual gift as his, it makes pictures of a certain gorgeous attractiveness: but they are not genuinely poetical. Not white sunlight; something *operatic;* a kind of rosepink, artificial bedizenment. It is frequent, or rather it is universal, among the French since his time. Madame de Staël has something of it; St. Pierre; and down onward to the present astonishing convulsionary "literature of desperation," it is everywhere abundant. That same *rosepink* is not the right hue. Look at Shakespeare, at a Goethe, even at a Walter Scott! He who has once seen into this, has seen the difference of the true and the sham-true, and will discriminate them ever afterward.

We had to observe in Johnson how much good a prophet, under all disadvantages and disorganizations, can accomplish for the world. In Rousseau we are called to look rather at the fearful amount of evil which, under such disorganization, may accompany the good. Historically it is a most pregnant spectacle, that of Rousseau. Banished into Paris garrets, in the gloomy company of his own thoughts and necessities there, driven from post to pillar; fretted, exasperated till the heart of him went mad, he had grown to feel deeply that the world was not his friend nor the world's law. It was expedient, if anyway possible, that such a man should *not* have been set in flat hostility with the world. He could be cooped into garrets, laughed at as a maniac, left to starve like a wild-beast in his cage—but he could not be hindered from setting the world on fire. The French revolution found its evangelists in Rousseau. His semi-delirious speculations on the miseries of civilized life, the preferability of the savage to the civilized, and suchlike, helped well to produce a whole delirium in France generally. True you may well ask, what could the world, the governors of the world, do with such a man? Difficult to say what the governors of the world could do with him! What he could do with them is unhappily clear enough—*guillotine* a great many of them! Enough now of Rousseau.

It was a curious phenomenon, in the withered, unbelieving, second-hand eighteenth century, that of a hero starting up, among the artificial pasteboard figures and productions, in the guise of Robert Burns. Like a little well in the rocky desert places—like a sudden splendor of heaven in the artificial Vauxhall! People knew not what to make of it. They took it for a piece of the Vauxhall fire-work; alas, it *let* itself be so taken, though struggling half-blindly, as in bitterness of death, against that! Perhaps no man had such a false reception from his fellow-men. Once more a very wasteful life-drama was enacted under the sun.

The tragedy of Burns' life is known to all of you. Surely we may say, if discrepancy between place held and place merited constitute perverseness of lot for a man, no lot could be more perverse than Burns'. Among those second-hand acting-figures, *mimes* for most part, of the eighteenth century, once more a giant original man; one of those men who reach down to the perennial deeps, who take rank with the heroic among men: and he was born in a poor Ayrshire hut. The largest soul of all the British lands came among us in the shape of a hard-handed Scottish peasant.

His father, a poor toiling man, tried various things; did not succeed in any; was involved in continual difficulties. The steward, factor as the Scotch call him, used to send letters and threatenings, Burns says: "which threw us all into tears." The brave, hard-toiling, hard-suffering father, his brave heroine of a wife; and those children, of whom Robert was one! In this earth, so wide otherwise, no shelter for *them*. The letters "threw us all into tears:" figure it. The brave father, I say always—a *silent* hero and poet; without whom the son had never been a speaking one! Burns' school-

master came afterward to London, learned what good soc.
declares that in no meeting of men did he ever enjoy better di
at the hearth of this peasant. And this poor "seven acres of nurse.
—not that, nor the miserable patch of clay-farm, nor anything h
get a living by, would prosper with him; he had a sore unequal l
his days. But he stood to it valiantly; a wise, faithful, unconquerable
swallowing-down how many sore sufferings daily into silence; fightin
an unseen hero—nobody publishing newspaper paragraphs about his nc
ness; voting pieces of plate to him! However, he was not lost: nothing
lost. Robert is there; the outcome of him—and indeed of many generation
of such as him.

This Burns appeared under every disadvantage: uninstructed, poor, born
only to hard manual toil; and writing, when it came to that, in a rustic
special dialect, known only to a small province of the country he lived
in. Had he written, even what he did write, in the general language of
England, I doubt not he had already become universally recognized as
being, or capable to be, one of our greatest men. That he should have
tempted so many to penetrate through the rough husk of that dialect of
his, is proof that there lay something far from common within it. He
has gained a certain recognition, and is continuing to do so over all quarters of our wide Saxon world: wheresoever a Saxon dialect is spoken, it
begins to be understood, by personal inspection of this and the other, that
one of the most considerable Saxon men of the eighteenth century was an
Ayrshire peasant named Robert Burns. Yes, I will say, here too was a piece
of the right Saxon stuff: strong as the Harz-rock, rooted in the depths
of the world—rock, yet with wells of living softness in it! A wild impetuous
whirlwind of passion and faculty slumbered quiet there; such heavenly
melody dwelling in the heart of it. A noble rough genuineness; homely,
rustic, honest; true simplicity of strength; with its lightning-fire, with its
soft dewy pity—like the old Norse Thor, the peasant-god!

Burns' brother Gilbert, a man of much sense and worth, has told me
that Robert, in his young days, in spite of their hardship, was usually the
gayest of speech; a fellow of infinite frolic, laughter, sense and heart; far
pleasanter to hear there, stripped cutting peats in the bog, or suchlike, than
he ever afterward knew him. I can well believe it. This basis of mirth
("*fond gaillard*," as old Marquis Mirabeau calls it), a primal-element of
sunshine and joyfulness, coupled with his other deep and earnest qualities,
is one of the most attractive characteristics of Burns. A large fund of hope
dwells in him; spite of his tragical history, he is not a mourning man. He
shakes his sorrows gallantly aside; bounds forth victorious over them.
It is as the lion shaking "dew-drops from his mane; as the swift-bounding
horse, that *laughs* at the shaking of the spear. But indeed, hope, mirth, of
the sort like Burns', are they not the outcome properly of warm generous
affection—such as is the beginning of all to every man!

You would think it strange if I called Burns the most gifted British soul

WORKS OF THOMAS CARLYLE

e had in all that century of his: and yet I believe the day is coming when here will be little danger in saying so. His writings, all that he *did* under such obstructions, are only a poor fragment of him. Professor Stewart remarked very justly, what indeed is true of all poets good for much, that his poetry was not any particular faculty; but the general result of a naturally vigorous original mind expressing itself in that way. Burns' gifts, expressed in conversation, are the theme of all that ever heard him. All kinds of gifts: from the gracefulest utterances of courtesy, to the highest fire of passionate speech; loud floods of mirth, soft wailings of affection, laconic emphasis, clear piercing insight; all was in him. Witty duchesses celebrate him as a man whose speech "led them off their feet." This is beautiful: but still more beautiful that which Mr. Lockhart has recorded, which I have more than once alluded to, How the waiters and ostlers at inns would get out of bed and come crowding to hear this man speak! Waiters and ostlers—they too were men and here was a man! I have heard much about his speech; but one of the best things I ever heard of it was, last year, from a venerable gentleman long familiar with him. That it was speech distinguished by always *having something in it.* "He spoke rather little than much," this old man told me; "sat rather silent in those early days, as in the company of persons above him; and always when he did speak, it was to throw new light on the matter." I know not why any one should ever speak otherwise! But if we look at his general force of soul, his healthy *robustness* everyway, the rugged downrightness, penetration, generous valor and manfulness that was in him—where shall we readily find a better-gifted man?

Among the great men of the eighteenth century, I sometimes feel as if Burns might be found to resemble Mirabeau more than any other. They differ widely in vesture; yet look at them intrinsically. There is the same burly thick-necked strength of body as of soul—built in both cases, on what the old marquis calls a *fond gaillard.* By nature, by course of breeding, indeed by nation, Mirabeau has much more of bluster; a noisy, forward, unresting man. But the characteristic of Mirabeau too is veracity and sense, power of true *insight,* superiority of vision. The thing that he says is worth remembering. It is a flash of insight into some object or other: so do both these men speak. The same raging passions; capable too in both of manifesting themselves as the tenderest noble affections. Wit, wild laughter, energy, directness, sincerity: these were in both. The types of the two men are not dissimilar. Burns too could have governed, debated in national assemblies; politicized, as few could. Alas, the courage which had to exhibit itself in capture of smuggling schooners in the Solway Frith; in keeping *silence* over so much, where no good speech, but only inarticulate rage was possible: this might have bellowed forth Ushers de Brézé and the like; and made itself visible to all men, in managing of kingdoms, in ruling of great ever-memorable epochs! But they said to him reprovingly, his official superiors said, and wrote: "You are to work, not think." Of your *thinking*-faculty, the greatest in this land, we have no need; you are to gauge beer there; for that only are *you* wanted. Very notable—and worth mentioning, though we know what is to be said and answered! As if thought, power of thinking, were not at all times, in all places and situations of the world, precisely the thing that *was* wanted. The fatal man, is he not always the *un*thinking man, the man who cannot think and *see;* but only grope, and hallucinate, and *mis*see the nature of the thing he works with? He missees it, mis*takes* it as we say; takes it for one thing, and it *is* another thing—and leaves him standing like a futility there! He is the fatal man; unutterably fatal, put in the high places of men. "Why complain of this?" say some: "Strength is mournfully denied its arena; that was true from the old." Doubtless; and the worse for the *arena,* answer I! *Complaining* profits little; stating of the truth may profit. That a Europe, with its French revolution just breaking out, finds no need of a Burns except for gauging beer—is a thing I, for one, cannot *rejoice* at!

Once more we have to say here, that the chief quality of Burns is the *sincerity* of him. So in his poetry, so in his life. The song he sings is not of fantasticalities; it is of a thing felt, really there; the prime merit of this, as of all in him, and of his life generally, is truth. The life of Burns is what we may call a great tragic sincerity—not cruel, far from that; but wild, wrestling naked with the truth of things. In that sense, there is something of the savage in all great men.

Hero worship—Odin, Burns? Well; these men of letters too were not without a kind of hero worship: but what a strange condition has that got into now! The waiters and ostlers of Scotch inns, prying about the door, eager to catch any word that fell from Burns, were doing unconscious reverence to the heroic. Johnson had his Boswell for worshiper. Rousseau had worshipers enough: princes calling on him in his mean garret; the great, the beautiful doing reverence to the poor moonstruck man. For himself a most portentous contradiction; the two ends of his life not to be brought into harmony. He sits at the tables of grandees; and has to copy music for his own living. He cannot even get his music copied. "By dint of dining out," says he, "I run the risk of dying by starvation at home." For his worshipers too a most questionable thing! If doing hero worship well or badly be the test of vital well-being or ill-being to a generation, can we say that *these* generations are very first-rate? And yet our heroic men of letters do teach, govern, are kings, priests, or what you like to call them; intrinsically there is no preventing it by any means whatever. The world *has* to obey him who thinks and sees in the world. The world can alter the manner of that; can either have it as blessed continuous summer sunshine, or unblessed black thunder and tornado—with unspeakable differ- ence of profit for the world! The manner of it is very alterable; the matter and fact of it is not alterable by any power under the sky. Light; or, failing that, lightning: the world can take its choice. Not whether we call an Odin god, prophet, priest, or what we call him; but whether we believe the word he tells us: there it all lies. If it be a true word, we shall have to believe it; believing it, we shall have to do it. What *name* or welcome we give him or it, is a point that concerns ourselves mainly. *It*, the new truth, new deeper revealing of the secret of this universe, is verily of the nature of a message from on high; and must and will have itself obeyed.

My last remark is on that notablest phasis of Burns' history—his visit to Edinburgh. Often it seems to me as if his demeanor there were the highest proof he gave of what a fund of worth and genuine manhood was in him. If we think of it, few heavier burdens could be laid on the strength of a man. So sudden; all common *lionism*, which ruins innumerable men, was as nothing to this. It is as if Napoleon had been made a king of, not gradually, but at once from the artillery lieutenancy in the regiment La Fère. Burns, still only in his twenty-seventh year, is no longer even a plowman; he is flying to the West Indies to escape disgrace and a jail. This month he is a ruined peasant, his wages £7 a year and these gone from him: next month he is in the blaze of rank and beauty, handing down jewelled duchesses to dinner; the cynosure of all eyes! Adversary is sometimes hard upon a man; but for one man who can stand prosperity, there are a hundred that will stand adversity. I admire much the way in which Burns met all this. Perhaps no man one could point out, was ever so sorely tried and so little forgot himself. Tranquil, unastonished; not abashed, not inflated, neither awkwardness nor affectation: he feels that *he* there is the man Robert Burns; that the "rank is but the guinea-stamp;" that the celebrity is but the candle-light, which will show *what* man, not in the least make him a better or other man! Alas, it may readily, unless he look to it, make him a *worse* man; a wretched inflated wind bag—inflated till he *burst* and become a *dead* lion; for whom, as some one has said, "there is no resurrection of the body;" worse than a living dog! Burns is admirable here.

And yet, alas, as I have observed elsewhere, these lion-hunters were the ruin and death of Burns. It was they that rendered it impossible for him to live! They gathered round him in his farm: hindered his industry; no place was remote enough from them. He could not get his lionism forgotten, honestly as he was disposed to do so. He falls into discontents, into miseries, faults; the world getting ever more desolate for him; health, character, peace of mind all gone—solitary enough now. It is tragical to think of! These men came but to *see* him; it was out of no sympathy with him, nor no hatred to him. They came to get a little amusement: they got their amusement—and the hero's life went for it!

Richter says, in the land of Sumatra there is a kind of "light-chafers," large fire-flies, which people stick upon spits and illuminate the ways with at night. Persons of condition can thus travel with a pleasant radiance, which they much admire. Great honor to the fire-flies. But——

LECTURE VI.[1]

THE HERO AS KING. CROMWELL, NAPOLEON—MODERN REVOLUTIONISM.

WE COME NOW to the last form of heroism; that which we call kingship. The commander over men; he to whose will our wills are to be subordinated, and loyally surrender themselves, and find there welfare in doing so, may be reckoned the most important of great men. He is practically the summary for us of *all* the various figures of heroism; priest, teacher, whatsoever of earthly or of spiritual dignity we can fancy to reside in a man, embodies itself here, to *command* over us, to furnish us with constant practical teaching, to tell us for the day and hour what we are to *do*. He is called *rex*, regulator, *roi*: our own name is still better; king, *könning*, which means *can*-ning, able-man.

Numerous considerations, pointing toward deep, questionable, and indeed unfathomable regions, present themselves here: on the most of which we must resolutely for the present forbear to speak at all. As Burke said that perhaps fair *trial by jury* was the soul of government, and that all legislation, administration, parliamentary debating, and the rest of it, went on, in "order to bring twelve impartial men into a jury-box"—so, by much stronger reason, may I say here, that the finding of your *ableman* and getting him invested with the *symbols of ability*, with dignity, worship (*worthship*), royalty, kinghood, or whatever we call it, so that *he* may actually have room to guide according to his faculty of doing it—is the business, well or ill accomplished, of all social procedure whatsoever in this world! Hustings speeches, parliamentary motions, reform bills, French revolutions, all mean at heart this; or else nothing. Find in any country the ablest man that exists there; raise *him* to the supreme place, and loyally reverence him: you have a perfect government for that country; no ballot-box, parliamentary eloquence, voting, constitution-building, or other machinery whatsoever can improve it a whit. It is in the perfect state; an ideal country. The ablest man; he means also the truest-hearted, justest, the noblest man; what he *tells us to do* must be precisely the wisest, fittest, that we could anywhere or anyhow learn—the thing which it will in all ways behove us, with right royal thankfulness, and nothing doubting, to do! Our *doing* and life were then, so far as government could regulate it, well regulated; that were the ideal of constitutions.

Alas, we know very well that ideals can never be completely embodied in practice. Ideals must ever lie a very great way off; and we will right thankfully content ourselves with any not intolerable approximation thereto! Let no man, as Schiller says, too querulously "measure by a scale of perfection the meager product of reality" in this poor world of ours. We will esteem him no wise man; we will esteem him a sickly, discontented, foolish

[1]Delivered Friday, May 22, 1840.

man. And yet, on the other hand, it is never to be forgotten that ideals do exist; that if they be not approximated to at all, the whole matter goes to wreck! Infallibly. No bricklayer builds a wall *perfectly* perpendicular, mathematically this is not possible; a certain degree of perpendicularity suffices him; and he, like a good bricklayer, who must have done with his job, leaves it so. And yet if he sways *too much* from the perpendicular; above all, if he throw plummet and level quite away from him, and pile brick on brick heedless, just as it comes to hand—— Such bricklayer, I think, is in a bad way. *He* has forgotten himself: but the law of gravitation does not forget to act on him; he and his wall rush down into confused welter of ruin!

This is the history of all rebellions, French revolutions, social explosions in ancient or modern times. You have put the too *un*able man at the head of affairs! The too ignoble, unvaliant, fatuous man. You have forgotten that there is any rule, or natural necessity whatever, of putting the able man there. Brick must lie on brick as it may and can. Unable simulacrum of ability, *quack*, in a word, must adjust himself with quack, in all manner of administration of human things—which accordingly lie unadministered, fermenting into unmeasured masses of failure, of indigent misery: in the outward, and in the inward or spiritual, miserable millions stretch out the hand for their due supply and it is not there. The "law of gravitation" acts; nature's laws do none of them forget to act. The miserable millions burst forth into sansculottism, or some other sort of madness: bricks and brick-layer lie as a fatal chaos!

Much sorry stuff, written some hundred years ago or more, about the "divine right of kings," molders unread now in the public libraries of this country. Far be it from us to disturb the calm process by which it is disappearing harmlessly from the earth, in those repositories! At the same time, not to let the immense rubbish go without leaving us, as it ought, some soul of it behind—I will say that it did mean something; something true, which it is important for us and all men to keep in mind. To assert that in whatever man you chose to lay hold of (by this or the other plan of clutching at him); and clapped a round piece of metal on the head of and called king—there straightway came to reside a divine virtue, so that *he* became a kind of god and a divinity inspired him with faculty and right to rule over you to all lengths; this—what can we do with this but leave it to rot silently in the public libraries? But I will say withal and that is what these divine-right men meant, That in kings and in all human authorities and relations that men god-created can form among each other, there is verily either a divine right or else a diabolic wrong; one or the other of these two! For it is false altogether, what the last skeptical century taught us, that this world is a steam-engine. There is a God in this world; and a God's sanction, or else the violation of such, does look out from all ruling and obedience, from all moral acts of men. There is no act more moral between men than that of rule and obedience. Woe to him that claims obedience when it is not due; woe to him that refuses it when it is! God's law is in that, I say, however the parchment-laws may run: there is a divine right or else a diabolic wrong at the heart of every claim that one man makes upon another.

It can do none of us harm to reflect on this: in all the relations of life it will concern us; in loyalty and royalty, the highest of these. I esteem the modern error, That all goes by self-interest and the cheeking and balancing of greedy knaveries and that, in short, there is nothing divine whatever in the association of men, a still more despicable error, natural as it is to an unbelieving century, than that of a "divine right" in people *called* kings. I say, find me the true *könning*, king, or able man and he *has* a divine right over me. That we knew in some tolerable measure how to find him and that all men were ready to acknowledge his divine right when found: this is precisely the healing which a sick world is everywhere, in these ages, seeking after! The true king, as guide of the practical, has ever something of the pontiff in him—guide of the spiritual, from which all practice has its rise. This too is a true saying, That the *king* is head of the *church*. But we will leave the polemic stuff of a dead century to lie quiet on its bookshelves.

Certainly it is a fearful business, that of having your able man to *seek* and not knowing in what manner to proceed about it! That is the world's sad predicament in these times of ours. They are times of revolution and have long been. The bricklayer with his bricks, no longer heedful of plummet or the law of gravitation, have toppled, tumbled and it all welters as we see! But the beginning of it was not the French revolution; that is rather the *end*, we can hope. It were truer to say, the *beginning* was three centuries farther back: in the reformation of Luther. That the thing which still called itself Christian church had become a falsehood and brazenly went about pretending to pardon men's sins for metallic coined money and to do much else which in the everlasting truth of nature it did *not* now do: here lay the vital malady. The inward being wrong, all outward went ever more and more wrong. Belief died away; all was doubt, disbelief. The builder *cast away* his plummet; said to himself, "What is gravitation? Brick lies on brick there!" Alas, does it not still sound strange to many of us, the assertion that there *is* a God's-truth in the business of God-created men; and all is not a kind of grimace, an "expediency," diplomacy, one knows not what!

From that first necessary assertion of Luther's, "You, self-styled *papa*, you are no father in God at all; you are—a chimera, who I know not how to name in polite language!" From that onward to the shout which rose round Camille Desmoulins in the Palais-Royal, "*aux armes!*" when the people had burst up against *all* manner of chimeras—I find a natural historical sequence. That shout too, so frightful, half infernal, was a great matter. Once more the voice of awakened nations—starting confusedly, as out of nightmare, as out of death-sleep, into some dim feeling that life was real; that God's world was not an expediency and diplomacy! Infernal—yes, since they would not have it otherwise. Infernal, since not celestial or terrestrial! Hollowness, insincerity *has* to cease; sincerity of some sort has to begin. Cost what it may, reigns of terror, horrors of French revolution or what else, we have to return to truth. Here is a truth, as I said: a truth clad in hell-fire, since they would not but have it so!

A common theory among considerable parties of men in England and elsewhere used to be, that the French nation had, in those days, as it were gone *mad;* that the French revolution was a general act of insanity, a temporary conversion of France and large sections of the world into a kind of bedlam. The event had risen and raged; but was a madness and nonentity—gone now happily into the region of dreams and the picturesque! To such comfortable philosophers, the three days of July 1830 must have been a surprising phenomenon. Here is the French nation risen again, in musketry and death struggle, out shooting and being shot, to make that same mad French revolution good! The sons and grandsons of those men, it would seem, persist in the enterprise: they do not disown it; they will have it made good; will have themselves shot, if it be not made good! To philosophers who had made up their life-system on that "madness" quietus, no phenomenon could be more alarming. Poor Niebuhr, they say, the Prussian professor and historian, fell broken-hearted in consequence; sickened if we can believe it, and died of the three days! It was surely not a very heroic death—little better than Racine's, dying because Louis XIV looked sternly on him once. The world had stood some considerable shocks, in its time; might have been expected to survive the three days too, and be found turning on its axes after even them! The three days told all mortals that the old French revolution, mad as it might look, was not a transitory ebullition of bedlam, but a genuine product of this earth where we all live; that it was verily a fact, and that the world in general would do well everywhere to regard it as such.

Truly, without the French revolution, one would not know what to make of an age like this at all. We will hail the French revolution, as shipwrecked mariners might the sternest rock, in a world otherwise all of baseless sea and waves. A true apocalypse, though a terrible one, to this false withered artificial time; testifying once more that nature is *preter*natural; if not divine, then diabolic; that semblance is not reality; that it has to become reality, or the world will take fire under it—burn *it* into what it is, namely nothing! Plausibility has ended; empty routine has ended; much has ended. This, as with a trump of doom, has been proclaimed to all men. They are the wisest who will learn it soonest. Long confused generations before it be learned; peace impossible till it be! The earnest man, surrounded as ever, with a world of inconsistencies, can await patiently, patiently strive to do *his* work, in the midst of that. Sentence of death is written down in heaven against all that; sentence of death is now proclaimed on the earth against it: this he with his eyes may see. And surely, I should say, considering the other side of the matter, what enormous difficulties lie there, and how fast, fearful fast, in all countries, the inexorable demand for solution of them is pressing on—

he may easily find other work to do than laboring in the sansculottic province at this time of day!

To me, in these circumstances, that of "hero worship" becomes a fact inexpressibly precious; the most solacing fact one sees in the world at present. There is an everlasting hope in it for the management of the world. Had all traditions, arrangements, creeds, societies that men ever instituted, sunk away, this would remain. The certainty of heroes being sent us; our faculty, our necessity, to reverence heroes when sent: it shines like a pole-star through smoke-clouds, dust-clouds, and all manner of down-rushing and conflagration.

Hero worship would have sounded very strange to those workers and fighters in the French revolution. Not reverence for great men; not any hope or belief, or even wish, that great men could again appear in the world! Nature, turned into a "machine," was as if effete now; could not any longer produce great men: I can tell her, she may give up the trade altogether, then; we cannot do without great men! But neither have I any quarrel with that of "liberty and equality;" with the faith that, wise great men being impossible, a level immensity of foolish small men would suffice. It was a natural faith then and there. "Liberty and equality; no authority needed any longer. Hero worship, reverence for *such* authorities, has proved false, is itself a falsehood; no more of it! We have had such *forgeries*, we will now trust nothing. So many base plated coins parring in the market, the belief has now become common that no gold any longer exists—and even that we can do very well without gold!" I find this, among other things, in that universal cry of liberty and equality; and find it very natural, as matters then stood.

And yet surely it is but the *transition* from false to true. Considered as the whole truth, it is false altogether—the product of entire skeptical blindness, as yet only *struggling* to see. Hero worship exists forever and everywhere: not loyalty alone; it extends from divine adoration down to the lowest practical regions of life. "Bending before men," if it is not to be a mere empty grimace, better dispensed with than practiced, is hero worship —a recognition that there does dwell in that presence of our brother something divine; that every created man, as Novalis said, is a "revelation in the flesh." They were poets too, that devised all those graceful courtesies which make life noble! Courtesy is not a falsehood or grimace; it need not be such. And loyalty, religious worship itself, are still possible; nay still inevitable.

May we not say, moreover, while so many of our late heroes have worked rather as revolutionary men, that nevertheless every great man, every genuine man, is by the nature of him a son of order, not of disorder? It is a tragical position for a true man to work in revolutions. He seems an anarchist; and indeed a painful element of anarchy does encumber him at every step—him to whose whole soul anarchy is hostile, hateful. His mission is order; every man's is. He is here to make what was disorderly, chaotic, into a thing ruled, regular. He is the missionary of order. Is not all work of man

in this world a *making of order?* The carpenter finds rough trees; shapes
them, constrains them into square fitness, into purpose and use. We are all
born enemies of disorder: it is tragical for us all to be concerned in image-
breaking and down-pulling; for the great man, *more* a man than we, it is
doubly tragical.

Thus too all human things, maddest French sansculottisms, do and must
work toward order. I say, there is not a *man* in them, raging in the thickest
of the madness, but is impelled withal, at all moments, toward order. His
very life means that; disorder is dissolution, death. No chaos but it seeks a
center to revolve round. While man is man, some Cromwell or Napoleon is
the necessary finish of a sansculottism. Curious: in those days when hero
worship was the most incredible thing to every one, how it does come out
nevertheless and assert itself practically, in a way which all have to credit.
Divine *right*, take it on the great scale, is found to mean divine *might* withal!
While old false formulas are getting trampled everywhere into destruction,
new, genuine substances unexpectedly unfold themselves indestructible. In
rebellious ages, when kingship itself seems dead and abolished, Cromwell,
Napoleon step forth again as kings. The history of these men is what we
have now to look at, as our last phasis of heroism. The old ages are brought
back to us; the manner in which kings were made and kingship itself first
took rise, is again exhibited in the history of these two.

We have had many civil wars in England; wars of Red and White Roses,
wars of Simon de Montfort; wars enough, which are not very memorable.
But that war of the Puritans has a significance which belongs to no one of
the others. Trusting to your candor, which will suggest on the other side
what I have not room to say, I will call it a section once more of that great
universal war which alone makes up the true history of the world—the war
of belief against unbelief! The struggle of men intent on the real essence
of things against men intent on the semblances and forms of things. The
Puritans, to many, seem mere savage Iconoclasts, fierce destroyers of forms;
but it were more just to call them hearers of *untrue* forms. I hope we know
how to respect Laud and his king as well as them. Poor Laud seems to me
to have been weak and ill-starred, not dishonest; an unfortunate pedant
rather than anything worse. His "dreams" and superstitions, at which they
laugh so, have an affectionate, lovable kind of character. He is like a college
tutor, whose whole world is forms, college rules; whose notion is that these
are the life and safety of the world. He is placed suddenly, with that unalterable luckless notion of his, at the head not of a college but of a nation,
to regulate the most complex deep-reaching interests of men. He thinks
they ought to go by the old descent regulations; nay that their salvation
will lie in extending and improving these. Like a weak man, he drives with
spasmodic vehemence toward his purpose; cramps himself to it, heeding no
voice of prudence, no cry of pity: he will have his college rules obeyed by
his collegians; that first; and till that, nothing. He is an ill-starred pedant
as I said. He would have it the world was a college of that kind, and the

world *was not* that. Alas, was not his doom stern enough? Whatever wrongs he did, were they not all frightfully avenged on him?

It is meritorious to insist on forms; religion and all else naturally clothes itself in forms. Everywhere the *formed* world is the only habitable one. The naked formlessness of Puritanism is not the thing I praise in the Puritans; it is the thing I pity—praising only the spirit which had rendered that inevitable! All substances clothe themselves in forms: but there are suitable true forms, and then there are untrue unsuitable. As the briefest definition, one might say, forms which *grow* round in substance, if we rightly understand that, will correspond to the real nature and purport of it, will be true, good; forms which are consciously *put* round a substance, bad. I invite you to reflect on this. It distinguishes true from false in ceremonial form, earnest solemnity from empty pageant, in all human things.

There must be a veracity, a natural spontaneity in forms. In the commonest meeting of men, a person making, what we call, "set speeches," is not he in offense? In the mere drawing-room, whatsoever courtesies you see to be grimaces, prompted by no spontaneous reality within, are a thing you wish to get away from. But suppose now it were some matter of vital concernment, some transcendent matter (as divine worship is), about which your whole soul, struck dumb with its excess of feeling, knew not how to *form* itself into utterance at all, and preferred formless silence to any utterance there possible—what should we say of a man coming forward to represent or utter it for you in the way of upholsterer-mummery? Such a man —let him depart swiftly, if he love himself! You have lost your only son; are mute, struck down, without even tears: an importunate man importunately offers to celebrate funeral games for him in the manner of the Greeks! Such mummery is not only to be accepted—it is hateful, unendurable. It is what the old prophets called "idolatry," worshiping of hollow *shows;* what all earnest men do and will reject. We can partly understand what those poor Puritans meant. Laud dedicating that St. Catherine Creed's church, in the manner we have it described; with his multiplied ceremonial bowings, gesticulations, exclamations: surely it is rather the rigorous formal *pedant,* intent on his "college rules," than the earnest prophet, intent on the essence of the matter!

Puritanism found *such* forms insupportable; trampled on such forms—we have to excuse it for saying, No forms at all rather than such! It stood preaching in its bare pulpit, with nothing but the Bible in its hand. Nay, a man preaching from his earnest *soul* into the earnest *souls* of men: is not this virtually the essence of all churches whatsoever? The nakedest, savagest reality, I say, is preferable to any semblance, however dignified. Besides, it will clothe itself with *due* semblance by and by, if it be real. No fear of that; actually no fear at all. Given the living *man,* there will be found *clothes* for him; he will find himself clothes. But the suit of clothes pretending that *it* is both clothes and man! We "cannot fight the French" by three hundred thousand red uniforms; there must be *men* in the inside of them! Semblance, I assert, must actually *not* divorce itself from reality. If semblance do—why then there must be men found to rebel against semblance, for it has become a lie! These two antagonisms at war here, in the case of Laud and the Puritans, are as old nearly as the world. They went to fierce battle over England in that age; and fought out their confused controversy to a certain length, with many results for all of us.

In the age which directly followed that of the Puritans, their cause or themselves were little likely to have justice done them. Charles II and his Rochesters were not the kind of men you would set to judge what the worth or meaning of such men might have been. That there could be any faith or truth in the life of a man, was what these poor Rochesters and the age they ushered in, had forgotten. Puritanism was hung on gibbets—like the bones of the leading Puritans. Its work nevertheless went on accomplishing itself. All true work of a man, hang the author of it on what gibbet you like, must and will accomplish itself. We have our *habeas corpus*, our free representation of the people; acknowledgment, wide as the world, that all men are, or else must, shall and will become, what we call *free* men—men with their life grounded on reality and justice, not on tradition, which has become unjust and a chimera! This in part, and much besides this, was the work of the Puritans.

And indeed, as these things became gradually manifest, the character of the Puritans began to clear itself. Their memories were, one after another, taken *down* from the gibbet; nay a certain portion of them are now, in these days, as good as canonized. Eliot, Hampden, Pym, nay Ludlow, Hutchinson, Vane himself, are admitted to be a kind of heroes; political conscript fathers, to whom in no small degree we owe what makes us a free England: it would not be safe for anybody to designate these men as wicked now. Few Puritans of note but find their apologists somewhere and have a certain reverence paid them by earnest men. One Puritan, I think, and almost he alone, our poor Cromwell, seems to hang yet on the gibbet and find no hearty apologist anywhere. Him neither saint nor sinner will acquit of great wickedness. A man of ability, infinite talent, courage and so forth: but he betrayed the cause. Selfish ambition, dishonesty, duplicity; a fierce, coarse, hypocritical *tartufe;* turning all that noble struggle for constitutional liberty into a sorry farce played for his own benefit: this and worse is the character they give to Cromwell. And then there come contrasts with Washington and others; above all, with these noble Pyms and Hampdens, whose noble work he stole for himself and ruined into a futility and deformity.

This view of Cromwell seems to me the not unnatural product of a century like the eighteenth. As we said of the valet, so of the skeptic: he does not know a hero when he sees him! The valet expected purple mantles, gilt scepters, body-guards and flourishes of trumpets: the skeptic of the eighteenth century looks for regulated respectable formulas, "principles," or what else he may call them; a style of speech and conduct which has got to seem "respectable," which can plead for itself in a handsome articulate manner and gain the suffrages of an enlightened skeptical eighteenth century! It is, at bottom, the same thing that both the valet and he expect; the garnitures of some *acknowledged* royalty, which *then* they will acknowledge! The king coming to them in the rugged *un*formulistic state shall be no king.

For my own share, far be it from me to say or insinuate a word of disparagement against such characters as Hampden, Eliot, Pym; whom I believe to have been right worthy and useful men. I have read diligently what books and documents about them I could come at—with the honestest wish to admire, to love and worship them like heroes; but I am sorry to say, if the real truth must be told, with very indifferent success! At bottom, I found that it would not do. They are very noble men, these; step along in their stately way, with their measured euphemisms, philosophies, parliamentary eloquences, ship-moneys, *monarchies of man;* a most constitutional, unblamable, dignified set of men. But the heart remains cold before them; the fancy alone endeavors to get up some worship of them. What man's heart does, in reality, break forth into any fire of brotherly love for these men? They are become dreadfully dull men! One breaks down often enough in the constitutional eloquence of the admirable Pym, with his "seventhly and lastly." You find that it may be the admirablest thing in the world, but that it is heavy—heavy as lead, barren as brick-clay: that, in a word, for you there is little or nothing now surviving there! One leaves all these nobilities standing in their nitches of honor: the rugged outcast Cromwell, he is the man of them all in whom one still finds human stuff. The great savage *Baresark:* he could write no euphemistic "Monarchy of Man;" did not speak, did not work with glib regularity; had no straight story to tell for himself anywhere. But he stood bare, not cased in euphemistic coat of mail; he grappled like a giant, face to face, heart to heart, with the naked truth of things! That, after all, is the sort of man for one. I plead guilty to valuing such a man beyond all other sorts of men. Smooth-shaven respectabilities not a few one finds, that are not good for much. Small thanks to a man for keeping his hands clean, who would not touch the work but with gloves on!

Neither, on the whole, does this constitutional tolerance of the eighteenth century for the other happier Puritans seem to be a very great matter. One might say, it is but a piece of formulism and skepticism, like the rest. They tell us, It was a sorrowful thing to consider that the foundation of our English liberties should have been laid by "superstition." These Puritans came forward with Calvinistic incredible creeds, anti-Laudisms, Westminster confessions; demanding, chiefly of all, that they should have liberty to *worship* in their own way. Liberty to *tax* themselves: that was the thing they should have demanded! It was superstition, fanaticism, disgraceful ignorance of constitutional philosophy to insist on the other thing! Liberty to *tax* oneself? Not to pay out money from your pocket except on reason shown? No century, I think, but a rather barren one would have fixed on that as the first right of man! I should say, on the contrary, a just man will generally have better cause than *money* in what shape soever, before deciding to revolt against his government. Ours is a most confused world; in which a good man will be thankful to see any kind of government maintain itself in a not insupportable manner: and here in England, to this hour, if he is not ready to pay a great many taxes which *he* can see very small reason in, it will not go well with him, I think! He must try some other climate than this. Taxgatherer? Money? He will say: "Take my money, since you *can*, and it is so desirable to you; take it—and take yourself away with it; and leave me alone to my work here. *I* am still here; can still work, after all the money you have taken from me!" But if they come to him and say, "Acknowledge a lie; pretend to say you are worshiping God, when you are not doing it: believe not the thing that *you* find true, but the thing that I find, or pretend to find true!" He will answer: "No; by God's help, no! You may take my purse; but I cannot have my moral self annihilated. The purse is any highwayman's who might meet me with a loaded pistol: but the self is mine and God my maker's; it is not yours; and I will resist you to the death, and revolt against you, and on the whole, front all manner of extremities, accusations and confusions, in defense of that!"

Really, it seems to me the one reason which could justify revolting, this of the Puritans. It has been the soul of all just revolts among men. Not *hunger* alone produced even the French revolution; no, but the feeling of the insupportable all-pervading *falsehood* which had now embodied itself in hunger, in universal material scarcity and nonentity, and thereby become *indisputably* false in the eyes of all! We will leave the eighteenth century with its "liberty to tax itself." We will not astonish ourselves that the meaning of such men as the Puritans remained dim to it. To men who believe in no reality at all, how shall a *real* human soul, the intensest of all realities, as it were the voice of this world's Maker still speaking to *us*—be intelligible! What it cannot reduce into constitutional doctrines relative to "taxing," or other the like material interest, gross, palpable to the sense, such a century will needs reject as an amorphous heap of rubbish. Hampdens, Pyms and shipmoney will be the theme of much constitutional eloquence, striving to be fervid—which will glitter, if not as fire does, then as *ice* does: and the irreducible Cromwell will remain a chaotic mass of "madness," "hypocrisy," and much else.

From of old, I will confess, this theory of Cromwell's falsity has been incredible to me. Nay I cannot believe the like, of any great man whatever. Multitudes of great men figure in history as false, selfish men; but if we will consider it, they are but *figures* for us, unintelligible shadows we do not see into them as men that could have existed at all. A superficial unbelieving generation only, with no eye but for the surfaces and semblances of things, could form such notions of great men. Can a great soul be possible without a *conscience* in it, the essence of all *real* souls, great or small? No, we cannot figure Cromwell as a falsity and fatuity; the longer I study him and his career, I believe this the less. Why should we? There is no evidence of it. Is it not strange that, after all the mountains of calumny this man has been subject to, after being represented as the very prince of liars, who never, or hardly ever, spoke truth, but always some cunning counterfeit of truth, there should not yet have been one falsehood brought clearly home to him? A prince of liars and no lie spoken by him. Not one that I could yet get sight of. It is like Pococke asking Grotius: "Where is your *proof* of Mahomet's pigeon?" No proof! Let us leave all these calumnious chimeras, as chimeras ought to be left. They are not portraits of the man; they are distracted phantasms of him, the joint product of hatred and darkness.

Looking at the man's life with our own eyes, it seems to me, a very different hypothesis suggests itself. What little we know of his earlier obscure years, distorted as it has come down to us, does it not all betoken an earnest, affectionate, sincere kind of man? His nervous melancholic temperament indicates rather a seriousness *too* deep for him. Of those stories of "specters;" of the white specter in broad daylight, predicting that he should be king of England, we are not bound to believe much—probably no more than of the other black specter, or devil in person, to whom the officer *saw* him sell himself before Worcester fight! But the mournful, over-sensitive, hypochondriac humor of Oliver, in his young years, is otherwise indisputably known. The Huntingdon physician told Sir Philip Warwick himself, he had often been sent for at midnight; Mr. Cromwell was full of hypochondria, thought himself near dying and "had fancies about the town-cross." These things are significant. Such an excitable deep-feeling nature, in that rugged stubborn strength of his, is not the symptom of falsehood; it is the symptom and promise of quite other than falsehood!

The young Oliver is sent to study law; falls, or is said to have fallen, for a little period, into some of the dissipations of youth; but if so, speedily repents, abandons all this: not much above twenty, he is married, settled as an altogether grave and quiet man. "He pays back what money he had won at gambling," says the story—he does not think any gain of that kind could be really *his*. It is very interesting, very natural, this "conversion," as they well name it; this awakening of a great true soul from the worldly slough, to see into the awful *truth* of things—to see that time and its shows all rested on eternity and this poor earth of ours was the threshold either of heaven or of hell! Oliver's life at St. Ives and Ely, as a sober industrious farmer, is it not altogether as that of a true and devout man? He has renounced the world and its ways; *its* prizes are not the thing that can enrich him. He tills the earth; he reads his Bible; daily assembles his servants round him to worship God. He comforts persecuted ministers, is fond of preachers; nay can himself preach—exhorts his neighbors to be wise, to redeem the time. In all this what "hypocrisy," "ambition," "cant," or other falsity? The man's hopes, I do believe, were fixed on the other higher world; his aim to get well *thither*, by walking well through his humble course in *this* world. He courts no notice: what could notice here do for him? "Ever in his great task-master's eye."

It is striking, too, how he comes out once into public view; he, since no other is willing to come: in resistance to a public grievance. I mean, in that matter of the Bedford Fens. No one else will go to law with authority;

therefore he will. That matter once settled, he returns back into obscurity, to his Bible and his plow. "Gain influence?" His influence is the most legitimate; derived from personal knowledge of him, as a just, religious, reasonable and determined man. In this way he has lived till past forty; old age is now in view of him and the earnest portal of death and eternity; it was at this point that he suddenly became "ambitious!" I do not interpret his parliamentary mission in that way!

His successes in parliament, his successes through the war, are honest successes of a brave man; who has more resolution in the heart of him, more light in the head of him than other men. His prayers to God; his spoken thanks to the god of victory, who had preserved him safe, and carried him forward so far, through the furious clash of a world all set in conflict, through desperate-looking envelopments at Dunbar; through the death-hail of so many battles; mercy after mercy; to the "crowning mercy" of Worcester fight: all this is good and genuine for a deep-hearted Calvinistic Cromwell. Only to vain unbelieving cavaliers, worshiping not God but their own "love locks," frivolities and formalities, living quite apart from contemplations of God, living *without* God in the world, need it seem hypocritical.

Nor will his participation in the king's death involve him in condemnation with us. It is a stern business killing of a king! But if you once go to war with him, it lies *there;* this and all else lies there. Once at war, you have made wager of battle with him: it is he to die, or else you. Reconciliation is problematic; may be possible, or, far more likely, is impossible. It is now pretty generally admitted that the parliament, having vanquished Charles I, had no way of making any tenable arrangement with him. The large Presbyterian party, apprehensive now of the independents, were most anxious to do so; anxious indeed as for their own existence; but it could not be. The unhappy Charles, in those final Hampden court negotiations, shows himself as a man fatally incapable of being dealt with. A man who, once for all, could not and would not *understand*—whose thought did not in any measure represent to him the real fact of the matter; nay worse, whose *word* did not at all represent his thought. We may say this of him without cruelty, with deep pity rather: but it is true and undeniable. Forsaken there of all but the *name* of kingship, he still, finding himself treated with outward respect as a king, fancied that he might play off party against party, and smuggle himself into his old power by deceiving both. Alas, they both *discovered* that he was deceiving them. A man whose *word* will not inform you at all what he means or will do, is not a man you can bargain with. You must get out of that man's way, or put him out of yours! The Presbyterians, in their despair, were still for believing Charles, though found false, unbelievable again and again. Not so Cromwell: "For all our fighting," says he, "we are to have a little bit of paper?" No!

In fact, everywhere we have to note the decisive practical *eye* of this man; how he drives toward the practical and practicable: has a genuine insight into what *is* fact. Such an intellect, I maintain, does not belong to a false man: the false man sees false shows, plausibilities, expediences: the true man is needed to discern even practical truth. Cromwell's advice about the parliament's army, early in the contest, how they were to dismiss their city tapsters, flimsy riotous persons, and choose substantial yeomen, whose heart was in the work, to be soldiers for them: this is advice by a man who *saw*. Fact answers, if you see into fact! Cromwell's *ironsides* were the embodiment of this insight of his; men fearing God; and without any other fear. No more conclusively genuine set of fighters ever trod the soil of England, or of any other land.

Neither will we blame greatly that word of Cromwell's to them; which was so blamed: "If the king should meet me in battle, I would kill the king." Why not? These words were spoken to men who stood as before a Higher than kings. They had set more than their own lives on the cast. The parliament may call it, in official language, a fighting "*for* the king;" but we, for our share, cannot understand that. To us it is no dilettante work, no sleek officiality: it is sheer rough death and earnest. They have brought it to the calling forth of *war;* horrid internecine fight, man grappling with man in fire-eyed rage—the *infernal* element in man called forth, to try it by that! *Do* that therefore; since that is the thing to be done. The successes of Cromwell seem to me a very natural thing! Since he was not shot in battle, they were an inevitable thing. That such a man, with the eye to see, with the heart to dare, should advance, from post to post, from victory to victory, till the Huntingdon farmer became, by whatever name you might call him, the acknowledged strongest man in England, virtually the king of England, requires no magic to explain it!

Truly it is a sad thing for a people, as for a man, to fall into skepticism, into dilettantism, insincerity; not to know a sincerity when they see it. For this world and for all worlds, what curse is so fatal? The heart lying dead, the eye cannot see. What intellect remains is merely the *vulpine* intellect. That a true *king* be sent them is of small use; they do not know him when sent. They say scornfully, "Is this your king?" The hero wastes his heroic faculty in bootless contradiction from the unworthy; and can accomplish little. For himself he does accomplish a heroic life, which is much, which is all; but for the world he accomplishes comparatively nothing. The wild rude sincerity, direct from nature, is not glib in answering from the witness-box: in your small-debt *pie-powder* court, he is scouted as a counterfeit. The vulpine intellect "detects" him. For being a man worth any thousand men, the response your Knox, your Cromwell gets, is an argument for two centuries whether he was a man at all. God's greatest gift to this earth is sneeringly flung away. The miraculous talisman is a paltry plated coin, not fit to pass in the shops as a common guinea.

Lamentable this! I say, this must be remedied. Till this be remedied in some measure, there is nothing remedied. "Detect quacks?" Yes do, for heaven's sake; but know withal the men that are to be trusted! Till we know that, what is all our knowledge; how shall we even so much as "detect?" For the vulpine sharpness, which considers itself to be knowledge and "detects" in that fashion, is far mistaken. Dupes indeed are many: but, of all *dupes*, there is none so fatally situated as he who lives in undue terror of being duped. The world does exist; the world has truth in it, or it would not exist! First recognize what is true, we shall *then* discern what is false; and properly never till then.

"Know the men that are to be trusted:" alas, this is yet, in these days, very far from us. The sincere alone can recognize sincerity. Not a hero only is needed, but a world fit for him; a world not of *valets*—the hero comes almost in vain to it otherwise! Yes, it is far from us: but it must come; thank God, it is visibly coming. Till it do come, what have we? Ballot-boxes, suffrages, French revolutions—if we are as valets and do not know the hero when we see him, what good are all these? A heroic Cromwell comes and for a hundred and fifty years he cannot have a vote from us. Why, the insincere, unbelieving world is the *natural property* of the quack and of the father of quacks and quackeries! Misery, confusion, unveracity are alone possible there. By ballot-boxes we alter the *figure* of our quack; but the substance of him continues. The valet-world *has* to be governed by the sham-hero, by the king merely *dressed* in king-gear. It is his; he is its! In brief, one of two things: We shall either learn to know a hero, a true governor and captain, somewhat better, when we see him; or else go on to be forever governed by the unheroic—had we ballot-boxes clattering at every street-corner, there were no remedy in these.

Poor Cromwell—great Cromwell! The inarticulate prophet; prophet who could not *speak*. Rude, confused, struggling to utter himself, with his savage depth, with his wild sincerity; and he looked so strange, among the elegant euphemisms, dainty little Falklands, didactic Chillingworths, diplomatic Clarendons! Consider him. An outer hull of chaotic confusion, visions of the devil, nervous dreams, almost semi-madness; and yet such a clear determinate man's energy working in the heart of that. A kind of chaotic man. The ray as of pure starlight and fire, working in such an element of boundless hypochondria, *unformed* black of darkness! And yet withal this hypochondria, what was it but the very greatness of the man? The depth and tenderness of his wild affections: the quantity of *sympathy* he had with things—the quantity of insight he would yet get into the heart of things, the mastery he would yet get over things: this was his hypochondria. The man's misery, as man's misery always does, came of his greatness. Samuel Johnson too is that kind of man. Sorrow-stricken, half-distracted; the wide element of mournful *black* enveloping him—wide as the world. It is the character of a prophetic man; a man with his whole soul *seeing* and struggling to see.

On this ground, too, I explain to myself Cromwell's reputed confusion of speech. To himself the internal meaning was sun-clear; but the material with which he was to clothe it in utterance was not there. He had *lived* silent; a great unnamed sea of thought round him all his days; and in his way of life little call to attempt *naming* or uttering that. With his sharp power of vision, resolute power of action, I doubt not he could have learned to write books withal, and speak fluently enough—he did harder things than writing of books. This kind of man is precisely he who is fit for doing manfully all things you will set him on doing. Intellect is not speaking and logicising; it is seeming and ascertaining. Virtue, *vir-tus*, manhood, *hero*hood, is not fair spoken immaculate regularity; it is first of all, what the Germans well name it, *tugend* (*taugend*, *dow*-ing or *dough* tiness), courage and the faculty to *do*. This basis of the matter Cromwell had in him.

One understands moreover how, though he could not speak in parliament, he might *preach*, rhapsodic preaching; above all, how he might be great in extempore prayer. These are the free outpouring utterances of what was in the heart: method is not required in them; warmth, depth, sincerity are all that is required. Cromwell's habit of prayer is a notable feature of him. All his great enterprises were commenced with prayer. In dark inextricable-looking difficulties, his officers and he used to assemble, and pray alternately, for hours, for days, till some definite resolution rose among them, some "door of hope," as they would name it, disclosed itself. Consider that. In tears, in fervent prayers, and cries to the great God, to have pity on them, to make His light shine before them. They, armed soldiers of Christ, as they felt themselves to be; a little band of Christian brothers, who had drawn the sword against a great black devouring world not Christian, but mammonish, devilish—they cry to God in their straits, in their extreme need, not to forsake the cause that was His. The light which now rose upon them —how could a human soul, by any means at all, get better light? Was not the purpose so formed like to be precisely the best, wisest, the one to be followed without hesitation any more? To them it was as the shining of heaven's own splendor in the waste-howling darkness; the pillar of fire by night, that was to guide them on their desolate perilous way. *Was* it not such? Can a man's soul, to this hour, get guidance by any other method than intrinsically by that same—devout prostration of the earnest struggling soul before the Highest, the Giver of all light; be such *prayer* a spoken, articulate, or be it a voiceless, inarticulate one? There is no other method. "Hypocrisy?" One begins to be weary of all that. They who call it so, have no right to speak on such matters. They never formed a purpose, what one can call a purpose. They went about balancing expediences, plausibilities; gathering votes, advices; they never were alone with the *truth* of a thing at all. Cromwell's prayers were likely to be "eloquent," and much more than that. His was the heart of a man who *could* pray.

But indeed his actual speeches, I apprehend, were not nearly so ineloquent, incondite, as they look. We find he was, what all speakers aim to be, an impressive speaker, even in parliament; one who, from the first, had weight. With that rude passionate voice of his, he was always understood to *mean* something, and men wished to know what. He disregarded eloquence, nay despised and disliked it; spoke always without premeditation of the words he was to use. The reporters, too, in those days seem to have been singularly candid; and to have given the printer precisely what they found on their own note-paper. And withal, what a strange proof is it of

Cromwell's being the premeditative ever-calculating hypocrite, acting a play before the world, that to the last he took no more charge of his speeches! How came he not to study his words a little, before flinging them out to the public? If the words were true words, they could be left to shift for themselves.

But with regard to Cromwell's "lying," we will make one remark. This, I suppose, or something like this, to have been the nature of it. All parties found themselves deceived in him; each party understood him to be meaning *this*, heard him even say so, and behold he turns out to have been meaning *that*! He was, cry they, the chief of liars. But now, intrinsically, is not all this the inevitable fortune, not of a false man in such times, but simply of a superior man? Such a man must have *reticences* in him. If he walks wearing his heart upon his sleeve for daws to pick at, his journey will not extend far! There is no use for any man's taking up his abode in a house built of glass. A man always is to be himself the judge how much of his mind he will show to other men; even to those he would have work along with him. There are impertinent inquiries made: your rule is, to leave the inquirer *un*informed on that matter; not, if you can help it, *mis*informed, but precisely as dark as he was! This, could one hit the right phrase of response, is what the wise and faithful man would aim to answer in such a case.

Cromwell, no doubt of it, spoke often in the dialect of small subaltern parties; uttered to them a *part* of his mind. Each little party thought him all its own. Hence their rage, one and all, to find him not of their party, but of his own party! Was it his blame? At all seasons of his history he must have felt, among such people, how, if he explained to them the deeper insight he had, they must either have shuddered aghast at it, or believing it, their own little compact hypothesis must have gone wholly to wreck. They could not have worked in his province any more; nay perhaps they could not now have worked in their own province. It is the inevitable position of a great man among small men. Small men, most active, useful, are to be seen everywhere, whose whole activity depends on some conviction which to you is palpably a limited one; imperfect, what we call an *error*. But would it be a kindness always, is it a duty always or often, to disturb them in that? Many a man, doing loud work in the world, stands only on some thin traditionality, conventionality; to him indubitable, to you incredible: break that beneath him, he sinks to endless depths! "I might have my hand full of truth," said Fontenelle, "and open only my little finger."

And if this be the fact even in matters of doctrine, how much more in all departments of practice! He that cannot withal *keep his mind to himself* cannot practice any considerable thing whatever. And we call it "dissimulation," all this? What would you think of calling the general of an army a dissembler because he did not tell every corporal and private soldier, who pleased to put the question, what his thoughts were about everything? Cromwell, I should rather say, managed all this in a manner we must admire for its perfection. An endless vortex of such questioning "corporals" rolled confusedly round him through his whole course; whom he did answer. It must have been as a great true-seeing man that he managed this too. Not one proved falsehood, as I said; not one! Of what man that ever wound himself through such a coil of things will you say so much?

But in fact there are two errors, widely prevalent, which pervert to the very basis our judgments formed about such men as Cromwell; about their "ambition," "falsity," and suchlike. The first is what I might call substituting the *goal* of their career for the course and starting-point of it. The vulgar historian of a Cromwell fancies that he had determined on being protector of England, at the time when he was plowing the marsh lands of Cambridge-shire. His career lay all mapped out: a programme of the whole drama; which he then step by step dramatically unfolded, with all manner of cunning, deceptive dramaturgy, as he went on—the hollow, scheming Ὑποκριτής, or play-actor, that he was? This is a radical perversion; all but universal in such cases. And think for an instant how different the fact is! How much does one of *us* foresee of his own life? Short way ahead of us it is all dim; an *un*wound skein of possibilities, of apprehensions, attemptabilities, vague looming hopes. This Cromwell had *not* his life lying all in that fashion of programme, which he needed then, with that unfathomable cunning of his, only to enact dramatically, scene after scene! Not so. We see it so; but to him it was in no measure so. What absurdities would fall away of themselves, were this one undeniable fact kept honestly in view by history! Historians indeed will tell you that they do keep it in view—but look whether such is practically the fact! Vulgar history, as in this Cromwell's case, omits it altogether; even the best kinds of history only remember it now and then. To remember it duly with rigorous perfection, as in the fact it *stood* requires indeed a rare faculty; rare, nay impossible. A very Shakespeare for faculty; or more than Shakespeare; who could *enact* a brother man's biography, see with the brother man's eyes at all points of his course what things *he* saw; in short, *know* his course and him, as few "historians" are like to do. Half or more of all the thick-plied per-versions which distort our image of Cromwell, will disappear, if we honestly so much as try to represent them so; in sequence, as they *were;* not in the lump, as they are thrown down before us.

But a second error, which I think the generality commit, refers to this same "ambition" itself. We exaggerate the ambition of great men; we mis-take what the nature of it is. Great men are not ambitious in that sense; he is a small poor man that is ambitious so. Examine the man who lives in misery because he does not shine above other men; who goes about pro-ducing himself, pruriently anxious about his gifts and claims; struggling to force everybody, as it were begging everybody for God's sake, to ac-knowledge him a great man, and set him over the heads of men! Such a creature is among the wretchedest sights seen under this sun. A *great* man? A poor morbid prurient empty man; fitter for the ward of a hospital, than for a throne among men. I advise you to keep out of his way. He cannot walk on quiet paths; unless you will look at him, wonder at him, write paragraphs about him, he cannot live. It is the *emptiness* of the man, not his greatness. Because there is nothing in himself, he hungers and thirsts that you would find something in him. In good truth, I believe no great man, not so much as a genuine man who had health and real substance in him of whatever magnitude, was ever much tormented in this way.

Your Cromwell, what good could it do him to be "noticed" by noisy crowds of people? God his Maker already noticed him. He, Cromwell, was already there; no notice would make *him* other than he already was. Till his hair was grown gray; and life from the downhill slope was all seen to be limited, not infinite but finite, and all a measurable matter *how* it went—he had been content to plow the ground, and read his Bible. He in his old days could not support it any longer, without selling himself to falsehood, that he might ride in gilt carriages to Whitehall, and have clerks with bundles of papers haunting him, "Decide this, decide that," which in utmost sorrow of heart no man can perfectly decide! What could gilt carriages do for this man? From of old, was there not in his life a weight of meaning, a terror and a splendor as of heaven itself? His existence there as man set him beyond the need of gilding. Death, judgment and eternity: these already lay as the background of whatsoever he thought or did. All his life lay begirt as in a sea of nameless thoughts, which no speech of a mortal could name. God's word, as the Puritan prophets of that time had read it: this was great, and all else was little to him. To call such a man "ambitious," to figure him as the prurient wind-bag described above, seems to me the poorest solecism. Such a man will say: "Keep your gilt carriages and huzzahing mobs, keep your red-tape clerks, your influentialities, your important businesses. Leave me alone, leave me alone; there is *too much of life* in me already!" Old Samuel Johnson, the greatest soul in England in his day, was not ambitious. "Corsica Boswell" flaunted at public shows with printed ribbons round his hat; but the great old Samuel stayed at home. The world-wide soul wrapped up in its thoughts, in its sorrows—what could paradings and ribbons in the hat do for it?

Ah yes, I will say again: the great *silent* men! Looking round on the noisy inanity of the world, words with little meaning, actions with little worth, one loves to reflect on the great empire of *silence*. The noble silent men, scattered here and there, each in his department; silently thinking, silently working; whom no morning newspaper makes mention of! They are the salt of the earth. A country that has none or few of these is in a bad way. Like a forest which had no *roots;* which had all turned into leaves and boughs—which must soon wither and be no forest. Woe for us if we had nothing but what we can *show*, or speak. Silence, the great empire of silence: higher than the stars; deeper than the kingdoms of death! It alone is great; all else is small. I hope we English will long maintain our *grand talent pour le silence*. Let others that cannot do without standing on barrelheads, to spout, and be seen of all the market-place, cultivate speech exclusively—become a most green forest without roots! Solomon says, There is a time to speak; but also a time to keep silence. Of some great silent Samuel, not urged to writing, as old Samuel Johnson says he was, by *want of money*, and nothing other, one might ask, "Why do not you too get up and speak; promulgate your system, found your sect?" "Truly," he will answer, "I am *continent* of my thought hitherto; happily I have yet had the ability to keep it in me, no compulsion strong enough to speak it. My 'system' is not for promulgation first of all; it is for serving myself to live by. That is the great purpose of it to me. And then the 'honor'? Alas, yes—but as Cato said of the statue: so many statues in that forum of yours, may it not be better if they ask, Where is Cato's statue?"

But now, by the way of counterpoise to this of silence, let me say that there are two kinds of ambition; one wholly blamable, the other laudable and inevitable. Nature has provided that the great silent Samuel shall not be silent too long. The selfish wish to shine over others, let it be accounted altogether poor and miserable. "Seekest thou great things, seek them not:" this is most true. And yet, I say, there is an irrepressible tendency in every man to develop himself according to the magnitude which nature has made him of; to speak out, to act out, what nature has laid in him. This is proper, fit, inevitable; nay it is a duty and even the summary of duties for a man. The meaning of life here on earth might be defined as consisting in this: To unfold your *self*, to work what thing you have the faculty for. It is a necessity for the human being, the first law of our existence. Coleridge beautifully remarks that the infant learns to *speak* by this necessity it feels. We will say therefore: "To decide about ambition, whether it is bad or not, you have two things to take into view. Not the coveting of the place alone, but the fitness of the man for the place withal:" that is the question. Perhaps the place was *his;* perhaps he had a natural right and even obligation, to seek the place! Mirabeau's ambition to be prime minister, how shall we blame it, if he were "the only man in France that could have done any good there?" Hopefuler perhaps had he not so clearly *felt* how much good he could do! But a poor Necker, who could do no good and had even felt that he could do none, yet sitting brokenhearted because they had flung him out and he was now quit of it, well might Gibbon mourn over him. Nature, I say, has provided amply that the silent great man shall strive to speak withal; *too* amply, rather!

Fancy, for example, you had revealed to the brave old Samuel Johnson, in his shrouded-up existence, that it was possible for him to do priceless divine work for his country and the whole world. That the perfect heavenly law might be made law on this earth; that the prayer he prayed daily, "Thy kingdom come," was at length to be fulfilled! If you had convinced his judgment of this; that it was possible, practicable; that he the mournful silent Samuel was called to take a part in it! Would not the whole soul of the man have flamed up into a divine clearness, into noble utterance and determination to act; casting all sorrows and misgivings under his feet, counting all affliction and contradiction small—the whole dark element of his existence blazing into articulate radiance of light and lightning? It were a true ambition this! And think now how it actually was with Cromwell. From of old, the sufferings of God's church, true zealous preachers of the truth flung into dungeons, whipped, set on pillories, their ears cropped off, God's gospel cause trodden under foot of the unworthy: all this had lain heavy on his soul. Long years he had looked upon it, in silence, in prayer; seeing no remedy on earth; trusting well that a remedy in heaven's goodness would come—that such a course was false, unjust and could not last forever. And now behold the dawn of it; after twelve years silent waiting, all England stirs itself; there is to be once more a parliament, the right will get a voice for itself: inexpressible well-grounded hope has come again into the earth. Was not such a parliament worth being a member of? Cromwell threw down his plows and hastened thither.

He spoke there—rugged bursts of earnestness, of a self-seen truth, where we get a glimpse of them. He worked there; he fought and strove, like a strong true giant of a man, through cannon-tumult and all else—on and on, till the cause *triumphed*, its once so formidable enemies all swept from before it and the dawn of hope had become clear light of victory and certainty. That *he* stood there as the strongest soul of England, the undisputed hero of all England—what of this? It was possible that the law of Christ's gospel could now establish itself in the world! The theocracy which John Knox in his pulpit might dream of as a "devout imagination," this practical man, experienced in the whole chaos of most rough practice, dared to consider as capable of being *realized*. Those that were highest in Christ's church, the devoutest wisest men, were to rule the land: in some considerable degree, it might be so and should be so. Was it not *true*, God's truth? And if *true*, was it not then the very thing to do? The strongest practical intellect in England dared to answer, Yes! This I call a noble true purpose; is it not, in its own dialect, the noblest that could enter into the heart of statesman or man? For a Knox to take it up was something; but for a Cromwell, with his great sound sense and experience of what our world *was*—history, I think, shows it only this once in such a degree. I account it the culminating point of Protestantism; the most heroic phasis that "faith in the Bible" was appointed to exhibit here below. Fancy it: that it were made manifest to one of us, how we could make the right supremely victorious over wrong and all that we had longed and prayed for, as the highest good to England and all lands, an attainable fact!

Well, I must say, the *vulpine* intellect, with its knowingness, its alertness and expertness in "detecting hypocrites," seems to me a rather sorry business. We have had but one such statesman in England; one man, that I can get sight of, who ever had in the heart of him any such purpose at all. One man, in the course of fifteen hundred years; and this was his welcome. He had adherents by the hundred or the ten; opponents by the million. Had England rallied all round him—why, then, England might have been a *Christian* land! As it is, vulpine knowingness sits yet at its hopeless problem, "Given a world of knaves, to educe an honesty from their united action;" how cumbrous a problem, you may see in chancery law-courts and some other places! Till at length, by heaven's just anger, but also by heaven's great grace, the matter begins to stagnate; and this problem is becoming to all men a *palpably* hopeless one.

But with regard to Cromwell and his purposes: Hume and a multitude following him, come upon me here with an admission that Cromwell *was* sincere at first; a sincere "fanatic" at first, but gradually became a "hypocrite" as things opened round him. This of the fanatic hypocrite is Hume's theory of it; extensively applied since—to Mahomet and many others. Think of it seriously, you will find something in it; not much, not all, very far from all. Sincere hero hearts do not sink in this miserable manner. The sun flings forth impurities, gets balefully incrusted with spots; but it does not quench itself and become no sun at all, but a mass of darkness! I will venture to say that such never befell a great deep Cromwell; I think, never. Nature's own lion-hearted son; Antæus-like, his strength is got by *touching the earth*, his mother; lift him up from the earth, lift him up into hypocrisy, inanity, his strength is gone. We will not assert that Cromwell was an immaculate man; that he fell into no faults, no insincerities among the rest. He was no dilettante professor of "perfections," "immaculate conducts." He was a rugged Orson, rending his rough way through actual true *work*—doubtless with many a *fall* therein. Insincerities, faults, very many faults daily and hourly: it was too well known to him; known to God and him! The sun was dimmed many a time; but the sun had not himself grown a dimness. Cromwell's last words, as he lay waiting for death, are those of a Christian heroic man. Broken prayers to God, that He would judge him and this cause, He since man could not, in justice yet in pity. They are most touching words. He breathed out his wild great soul, its toils and sins all ended now, into the presence of his Maker, in this manner.

I, for one, will not call the man a hypocrite! Hypocrite, mummer, the life of him a mere theatricality; empty barren quack, hungry for the shouts of mobs? The man had made obscurity do very well for him till his head was gray; and now he *was*, there as he stood recognized unblamed, the virtual king of England. Cannot a man do without king's coaches and cloaks? Is it such a blessedness to have clerks forever pestering you with bundles of papers in red tape? A simple Diocletian prefers planting of cabbages; a George Washington, no very immeasurable man, does the like. One would say, it is what any genuine man could do; and would do. The instant his real work were out in the matter of kingship—away with it!

Let us remark; meanwhile, how indispensable everywhere a *king* is, in all movements of men. It is strikingly shown, in this very war, what becomes of men when they cannot find a chief man and their enemies can. The Scotch nation was all but unanimous in Puritanism; zealous and of one mind about it, as in this English end of the island was always far from being the case. But there was no great Cromwell among them; poor tremulous, hesitating, diplomatic Argyles and suchlike; none of them had a heart true enough for the truth, or durst commit himself to the truth. They had no leader; and the scattered cavalier party in that country had one: Montrose, the noblest of all the cavaliers; an accomplished, gallant-hearted, splendid man; what one may call the hero cavalier. Well, look at it; on the one hand subjects without a king; on the other a king without subjects! The subjects without king can do nothing; the subjectless king can do something. This Montrose, with a handful of Irish or Highland savages, few of them so much as guns in their hands, dashes at the drilled Puritan armies like a wild whirlwind; sweeps them, time after time, some five times over, from the field before him. He was at one period, for a short while, master of all Scotland. One man; but he was a man: a million zealous men, but *without* the one; they against him were powerless! Perhaps of all the persons in that Puritan struggle, from first to last, the single indispensable one was verily Cromwell. To see and dare, and decide; to be a fixed pillar in the welter of uncertainty—a king among them, whether they call him so or not.

Precisely here, however, lies the rub for Cromwell. His other proceedings have all found advocates, and stand generally justified; but this dismissal of the rump parliament and the assumption of the protectorship, is what no one can pardon him. He had fairly grown to be king in England; chief man of the victorious party in England; but it seems he could not do without the king's cloak, and sold himself to perdition in order to get it. Let us see a little how this was.

England, Scotland, Ireland, all lying now subdued at the feet of the Puritan parliament, the practical question arose, what was to be done with it? How will you govern these nations, which providence in a wondrous way has given up to your disposal? Clearly those hundred surviving members of the long parliament, who sit there as supreme authority, cannot continue forever to sit. What *is* to be done? It was a question which theoretical constitution-builders may find easy to answer; but to Cromwell, looking there into the real practical facts of it, there could be none more complicated. He asked of the parliament, what it was they would decide upon? It was for the parliament to say. Yet the soldiers too, however contrary to formula, they who had purchased this victory with their blood, it seemed to them that they also should have something to say in it! We will not "for all our fighting have nothing but a little piece of paper." We understand that the law of God's gospel, to which He through us has given the victory, shall establish itself, or try to establish itself, in this land!

For three years, Cromwell says, this question had been sounded in the ears of the parliament. They could make no answer; nothing but talk, talk. Perhaps it lies in the nature of parliamentary bodies; perhaps no parliament could in such case make any answer but even that of talk, talk! Nevertheless the question must and shall be answered. You sixty men there, becoming fast odious, even despicable, to the whole nation, whom the nation already calls rump parliament, *you* cannot continue to sit there: who or what then is to follow? "Free parliament," right of election, constitutional formulas of one sort or the other—the thing is a hungry fact coming on us, which we must answer or be devoured by it! And who are you that prate of constitutional formulas, rights of parliament? You have had to kill your king, to make pride's purges, to expel and banish by the law of the stronger whosoever would not let your cause prosper: there are but fifty or three-score of you left there, debating in these days. Tell us what we shall do; not in the way of formula, but of practicable fact!

How they did finally answer, remains obscure to this day. The diligent Godwin himself admits that he cannot make it out. The likeliest is, that this poor parliament still would not, and indeed could not dissolve and disperse; that when it came to the point of actually dispersing, they again for the tenth or twentieth time, adjourned it—and Cromwell's patience failed him. But we will take the favorablest hypothesis ever started for the parliament; the favorablest, though I believe it is not the true one, but too favorable.

According to this version: at the uttermost crisis, when Cromwell and his officers were met on the one hand, and the fifty or sixty rump members on the other, it was suddenly told Cromwell that the rump in its despair *was* answering in a very singular way; that in their splenetic envious despair, to keep out the army at least, these men were hurrying through the house a kind of reform bill—parliament to be chosen by the whole of England; equable electoral division into districts; free suffrage and the rest of it! A very questionable, or indeed for *them* an unquestionable thing. Reform bill, free suffrage of Englishmen? Why, the royalists themselves, silenced indeed but not exterminated, perhaps out*number* us; the great numerical majority of England was always indifferent to our cause, merely looked at it and submitted to it. It is in weight and force, not by counting of heads, that we are the majority! And now with your formulas and reform bills, the whole matter, sorely won by our swords, shall again launch itself to sea; become a mere hope and likelihood, *small* even as a likelihood? And it is not a likelihood; it is a certainty, which we have won, by God's strength and our own right hands and do now hold *here*. Cromwell walked down to these refractory members; interrupted them in that rapid speed of their reform bill—ordered them to begone and talk there no more. Can we not forgive him? Can we not understand him? John Milton, who looked on it all near at hand, could applaud him. The reality had swept the formulas away before it. I fancy, most men who were realities in England might see into the necessity of that.

The strong daring man, therefore, has set all manner of formulas and logical superficialities against him; has dared appeal to the genuine fact of this England, whether it will support him or not. It is curious to see how he struggles to govern in some constitutional way; find some parliament to support him; but cannot. His first parliament, the one they call Barebones' parliament, is, so to speak, a *convocation of the notables*. From all quarters of England the leading ministers and chief Puritan officials nominate the man most distinguished by religious reputation, influence and attachment to the true cause: these are assembled to shape out a plan. They sanctioned what was past; shaped as they could what was to come. They were scornfully *Barebones' parliament;* the man's name, it seems, was not *Barebones,* but Barbone—a good enough man. Nor was it a jest, their work; it was a most serious reality—a trial on the part of these Puritan notables how far the law of Christ could become the law of this England. There were men of sense among them, men of some quality; men of deep piety I suppose the most of them were. They failed, it seems, and broke down, endeavoring to reform the court of chancery! They dissolved themselves, as incompetent; delivered up their power again into the hands of the Lord General Cromwell, to do with it what he liked and could.

What *will* he do with it? The Lord General Cromwell, "commander-in-chief of all the forces raised and to be raised;" he hereby sees himself, at this unexampled juncture, as it were the one available authority left in England, nothing between England and utter anarchy but him alone. Such is the undeniable fact of his position and England's, there and then. What will he do with it? After deliberation, he decides that he will *accept* it; will formally, with public solemnity, say and vow before God and man, "Yes, the fact is so and I will do the best I can with it!" Protectorship, instrument of government—these are the external forms of the thing; worked out and sanctioned as they could in the circumstances be, by the judges, by the leading official people, "council of officers and persons of interest in the nation:" and as for the thing itself, undeniably enough, at the pass matters had now come to, there *was* no alternative but anarchy or that. Puritan England might accept it or not; but Puritan England was, in real truth, saved from suicide thereby! I believe the Puritan people did, in an inarticulate, grumbling, yet on the whole grateful and real way, accept this anomalous act of Oliver's; at least, he and they together made it good and always better to the last. But in their parliamentary *articulate* way, they had their difficulties and never knew fully what to say to it!

Oliver's second parliament, properly his *first* regular parliament, chosen by the rule laid down in the instrument of government, did assemble and worked—but got, before long, into bottomless questions as to the protector's *right,* as to "usurpation," and so forth; and had at the earliest legal day to be dismissed. Cromwell's concluding speech to these men is a remarkable one. So likewise to his third parliament, in similar rebuke for their pedantries and obstinacies. Most rude, chaotic, all these speeches are; but most earnest-looking. You would say, it was a sincere helpless man; not used to *speak* the great inorganic thought of him, but to act it rather! A helplessness of utterance, in such bursting fullness of meaning. He talks much about "births of providence:" all these changes, so many victories and events, were not forethought, and theatrical contrivances of men, of *me* or of men; it is blind blasphemers that will persist in calling them so! He insists with a heavy sulphurous wrathful emphasis on this. As he well might. As if a Cromwell in that dark huge game he had been playing, the world wholly thrown into chaos round him, had *foreseen* it all, and played it all off like a precontrived puppet show by wood and wire! These things were foreseen by no man, he says; no man could tell what a day would bring forth; they were "births of providence," God's finger guided us on, and we came at last to clear height of victory, God's cause triumphant in these nations; and you as a parliament could assemble together, and say in what manner all this could be *organized*, reduced into rational feasibility among the affairs of men. "You have had such an opportunity as no parliament in England ever had." Christ's law, the right and true, was to be in some measure made the law of this land. In place of that, you have got into your idle pedantries, constitutionalities, bottomless cavilings and questionings about written laws for *my* coming here—and would send the whole matter in chaos again, because I have no notary's parchment, but only God's voice from the battle-whirlwind, for being president among you! That opportunity is gone; and we know not when it will return. You have had your constitutional logic; and Mammon's law, not Christ's law, rules yet in this land. "God be judge between you and me!" These are his final words to them: Take you your constitution formulas in your hand; and I my *in*formal struggles, purposes, realities and acts; and "God be judge between you and me!"

We said above what shapeless, involved chaotic things the printed speeches of Cromwell are. *Willfully* ambiguous, unintelligible, say the most: a hypocrite shrouding himself in confused Jesuitic jargon! To me they do not seem so. I will say rather, they afforded the first glimpses I could ever get into the reality of this Cromwell, nay into the possibility of him. Try to believe that he means something, search lovingly what that may be: you will find a real *speech* lying imprisoned in the broken rude tortuous utterances; a meaning in that great heart of this inarticulate man! You will, for the first time, begin to see that he was a man; not an enigmatic chimera, unintelligible to you, incredible to you. The histories and biographies written of this Cromwell, written in shallow skeptical generations that could not know or conceive of a deep believing man, are far more *obscure* than Cromwell's speeches. You look through them only into the infinite vague of black and the inane. "Heats and jealousies," says Lord Clarendon himself: "heats and jealousies," mere crabbed whims, theories and crotchets; these induced slow sober quiet Englishmen to lay down their plows and work; and fly into red fury of confused war against the best conditioned of kings! *Try* if you can find that true. Skepticism written about belief may have great gifts; but it is really *ultra vires* there. It is blindness laying down the laws of optics.

Cromwell's third parliament split on the same rock as his second. Ever the constitutional formula: how came *you* there? Show us some notary parchment! Blind pedants: "Why, surely the same power which makes you a parliament, that, and something more, made me a protector!" If my protectorship is nothing, what in the name of wonder is your parliamenteership, a reflex and creation of that?

Parliaments having failed, there remained nothing but the way of despotism. Military dictators each with his district, to *coerce* the royalist and other gainsayers, to govern them, if not by act of parliament, then by the sword.

Formula shall *not* carry it, while the reality is here! I will go on, protecting oppressed Protestants abroad, appointing just judges, wise managers, at home, cherishing true gospel ministers; doing the best I can to make England a Christian England, greater than old Rome, the queen of Protestant Christianity; I, since you will not help me; I while God leaves me life! Why did he not give it up; retire into obscurity again, since the law would not acknowledge him, cry several. That is where they mistake. For him there was no giving of it up! Prime Ministers have governed countries, Pitt, Pombal, Choiseul; and their word was a law while it held: but this prime minister was one that *could not get resigned*. Let him once resign, Charles Stuart and the cavaliers waited to kill him; to kill the cause *and* him. Once embarked, there is no retreat, no return. This prime minister could *retire* no whither except into his tomb.

One is sorry for Cromwell in his old days. His complaint is incessant of the heavy burden Providence has laid on him. Heavy; which he must bear till death. Old Colonel Hutchinson, as his wife relates it, Hutchinson, his old battle-mate, coming to see him on some indispensable business, much against his will—Cromwell "follows him to the door," in a most fraternal, domestic, conciliatory style; begs that he would be reconciled to him, his old brother in arms; says how much it grieves him to be misunderstood, deserted by true fellow-soldiers, dear to him from of old: the rigorous Hutchinson, cased in his republican formula, sullenly goes his way. And the man's head now white; his strong arm growing weary with its long work! I think always too of his poor mother, now very old, living in that palace of his; a right brave woman; as indeed they lived all an honest God-fearing household there: if she heard a shot go off, she thought it was her son killed. He had to come to her at least once a day, that she might see with her own eyes that he was yet living. The poor old mother! What had this man gained; what had he gained? He had a life of sore strife and toil, to his last day. Fame, ambition, place in history? His dead body was hung in chains; his "place in history"—place in history forsooth! has been a place of ignominy, accusation, blackness and disgrace; and here, this day, who knows if it is not rash in me to be among the first that ever ventured to pronounce him not a knave and liar, but a genuinely honest man! Peace to him. Did he not, in spite of all, accomplish much for us? *We* walk smoothly over his great rough heroic life; step over his body sunk in the ditch there. We need not *spurn* it, as we step on it! Let the hero rest. It was not to *men's* judgment that he appealed: nor have men judged him very well.

Precisely a century and a year after this of Puritanism had got itself hushed up into decent composure, and its results made smooth, in 1688, there broke out a far deeper explosion, much more difficult to hush up, known to all mortals, and like to be long known, by the name of French revolution. It is properly the third and final act of Protestantism; the explosive confused return of mankind to reality and fact, now that they were perishing of semblance and sham. We call our English Puritanism the second act: "Well then, the Bible is true; let us go by the Bible!" "In church," said Luther; "In church and state," said Cromwell, "let us go by what actually *is* God's truth." Men have to return to reality; they cannot live on semblance. The French revolution, or third act, we may well call the final one; for lower than that savage *sansculottism* men cannot go. They stand there on the nakedest haggard fact, undeniable in all seasons and circumstances; and may and must begin again confidently to build up from that. The French explosion, like the English one, got its king—who had no notary parchment to show for himself. We have still to glance for a moment at Napoleon, our second modern king.

Napoleon does by no means seem to me so great a man as Cromwell. His enormous victories which reached over all Europe, while Cromwell abode mainly in our little England, are but as the high *stilts* on which the man is seen standing; the stature of the man is not altered thereby. I find in him no such *sincerity* as in Cromwell; only a far inferior sort. No silent walking, through long years, with the awful unnamable of this universe; "walking with God," as he called it: and faith and strength in that alone: *latent* thought and valor, content to lie latent, then burst out as in blaze of heaven's lightning! Napoleon lived in an age when God was no longer believed; the meaning of all silence, latency, was thought to be nonentity: he had to begin not out of the Puritan Bible, but out of poor skeptical *encyclopédies*. This was the length the man carried it. Meritorious to get so far. His compact, prompt, everyway articulate character is in itself perhaps small, compared with our great chaotic *in*articulate Cromwell's. Instead of "*dumb* prophet struggling to speak," we have a portentous mixture of the quack withal! Hume's notion of the fanatic hypocrite, with such as it has, will apply much better to Napoleon than it did to Cromwell, to Mahomet or the like—where indeed taken strictly it has hardly any truth at all. An element of blamable ambition shows itself, from the first, in this man; gets the victory over him at last, and involves him and his work in ruin.

"False as a bulletin" became a proverb in Napoleon's time. He makes what excuse he could for it: that it was necessary to mislead the enemy, to keep-up his own men's courage, and so forth. On the whole, there are no excuses. A man in no case has liberty to tell lies. It had been, in the long run, *better* for Napoleon too if he had not told any. In fact, if a man have any purpose reaching beyond the hour and day, meant to be found extant *next* day, what good can it ever be to promulgate lies? The lies are found out; ruinous penalty is exacted for them. No man will believe the liar next time even when he speaks truth, when it is of the last importance that he be believed. The old cry of wolf! A lie is *no*-thing; you cannot of nothing make something; you make *nothing* at last, and lose your labor into the bargain.

Yes, Napoleon *had* a sincerity: we are to distinguish between what is superficial and what is fundamental in insincerity. Across these outer manœuvrings and quackeries of his, which were many and most blamable, let us discern withal that the man had a certain instinctive ineradicable feeling for reality; and did base himself upon fact, so long as he had any basis. He has an instinct of nature better than his culture was. His *savans*, Bourrienne tells us, in that voyage to Egypt were one evening busily occupied arguing that there could be no God. They had proved it, to their satisfaction, by all manner of logic. Napoleon looking up into the stars, answers: "Very ingenious, messieurs; but *who made* all that!" The atheistic logic runs off from him like water; the great fact stares him in the face: "Who made all that?" So too in practice: he, as every man that can be great, or have victory in this world, sees through all entanglements, the practical heart of the matter; drives straight toward that. When the steward of his Tuileries palace was exhibiting the new upholstery, with praises, and demonstrating how glorious it was, and how cheap withal, Napoleon, making little answer, asked for a pair of scissors, clipped one of the gold tassels from a window-curtain, put it in his pocket, and walked on. Some days afterward, he produced it at the right moment, to the horror of his upholstery functionary; it was not gold but tinsel! In St. Helena, it is notable how he still, to his last days, insists on the practical, and real. "Why talk and complain; above all, why quarrel with one another? There is no *result* in it; it comes to nothing that one can *do*. Say nothing, if one can do nothing!" He speaks often so, to his poor discontented followers; he is like a piece of silent strength in the middle of their morbid querulousness there.

And accordingly was there not what we can call a *faith* in him, genuine so far as it went? That this new enormous democracy asserting itself here in the French revolution is an insuppressible fact, which the whole world with its old forces and institutions cannot put down; this was a true insight of his, and took his conscience and enthusiasm along with it—a *faith*. And did he not interpret the dim purport of it well? "*La carrière ouverte aux talens*, The implements to him who can handle them:" this actually is the truth, and even the whole truth; it includes whatever the French revolution, or any revolution, could mean. Napoleon, in his first period, was a true democrat. And yet by the nature of him, fostered too by his military trade, he knew that democracy, if it were a true thing at all, could not be an anarchy: the man had a heart-hatred for anarchy. On that twentieth of June (1792), Bourrienne and he sat in a coffee-house, as the mob rolled by; Napoleon expresses the deepest contempt for persons in authority that they do not restrain this rabble. On the tenth of August he wonders why there is no man to command these poor Swiss; they would conquer if there were. Such a faith in democracy, yet hatred of anarchy, it is that carries Napoleon through all his great work. Through his brilliant Italian campaigns, onward to the peace of Leoben, one would say, his inspiration is: "Triumph to the French revolution; assertion of it against these Austrian simulacra that pretend to call it a simulacrum!" Withal, however he feels, and has a right to feel, how necessary a strong authority is; how the revolution cannot prosper or last without such. To bridle in that great devouring, self-devouring French revolution; to *tame* it, so that its intrinsic purpose can be made good, that it may become *organic*, and be able to live among other organisms and *formed* thing, not as a wasting destruction alone: is not this still what he partly aimed at, as the true purport of his life; nay what he actually managed to do? Through Wagrams, Austerlitzes; triumph after triumph—he triumphed so far. There was an eye to see in this man, a soul to dare and do. He rose naturally to be the king. All men saw that he *was* such. The common soldiers used to say on the march: "These babbling *avocats*, up at Paris; all talk and no work! What wonder it runs all wrong? We shall have to go and put our *petit caporal* there?" They went, and put him there; they and France at large. Chief-consulship, emperorship, victory over Europe; till the poor lieutenant of *La Fère*, not unnaturally, might seem to himself the greatest of all men that had been in the world for some ages.

But at this point, I think, the fatal charlatan element got the upper hand. He apostatized from his old faith in facts, took to believing in semblances; strove to connect himself with Austrian dynasties, popedoms, with the old false feudalities which he once saw clearly to be false; considered that *he* would found "his dynasty" and so forth; that the enormous French revolution meant only that! The man was "given-up to strong delusion, that he should believe a lie;" a fearful but most sure thing. He did not know true from false now when he looked at them—the fearfulest penalty a man pays for yielding to untruth of heart. *Self* and false ambition had now become his god: *self*-deception once yielded to, *all* other deceptions follow naturally more and more. What a paltry patchwork of theatrical paper-mantles, tinsel and mummery, had this man wrapped his own great reality in, thinking to make it more real thereby! His hollow pope's-*concordat* pretending to be a re-establishment of Catholicism, felt by himself to be the method of extirpating it, "*la vaccine de la religion:*" his ceremonial coronations, consecrations by the old Italian chimera in Notre Dame, "wanting nothing to complete the pomp of it," as Augereau said, "nothing but the half-million of men who had died to put an end to all that!" Cromwell's inauguration was by the sword and Bible: what we must call a genuinely *true* one. Sword and Bible were borne before him, without any chimera: were not these the *real* emblems of Puritanism; its true decoration and insignia! It had used them both in a very real manner, and pretended to stand by them now! But this poor Napoleon mistook: he believed too much in the *dupeability* of men; saw no fact deeper in man than hunger and this! He was mistaken. Like a man that should build upon cloud; his house and he fall down in confused wreck, and depart out of the world.

Alas, in all of us this charlatan element exists; and *might* be developed, were the temptation strong enough. "Lead us not into temptation!" But it is fatal, I say, that it *be* developed. The thing into which it enters as a cognizable ingredient is doomed to be altogether transitory; and however huge it may *look*, is in itself small. Napoleon's working, accordingly, what was it with all the noise it made? A flash as of gunpowder wide-spread; a blazing-up as of dry heath. For an hour the whole universe seems wrapped in smoke and flame; but only for an hour. It goes out: the universe with its old mountains and streams, its stars above and kind soil beneath, is still there.

The Duke of Weimar told his friends always, To be of courage; this

Napoleonism was *unjust*, a falsehood, and could not last. It is true doctrine. The heavier this Napoleon trampled on the world holding it tyrannously down, the fiercer would the world's recoil against him be, one day. Injustice pays itself with frightful compound interest. I am not sure but he had better have lost his best park of artillery, or had his best regiment drowned in the sea, than shot that poor German bookseller, Palm! It was a palpable tyrannous murderous injustice, which no man, let him paint an inch thick, could make out to be other. It burned deep into the hearts of men, it and the like of it; suppressed fire flashed in the eyes of men, as they thought of it —waiting their day: Which day *came:* Germany rose round him. What Napoleon *did* will in the long run amount to what he did *justly;* what nature with her laws will sanction. To what of reality was in him; to that and nothing more. The rest was all smoke and waste. *La carrière ouvert aux talens:* that great true message, which has yet to articulate and fulfill itself everywhere, he left in a most inarticulate state. He was a great *ébauche,* a rude draught never completed; as indeed what great man is other? Left in *too* rude a state, alas!

His notions of the world, as he expresses them there at St. Helena, are almost tragical to consider. He seems to feel the most unaffected surprise that it has all gone so; that he is flung out on the rock here, and the world is still moving on its axis. France is great, and all great; and at bottom, he is France. England itself, he says, is by nature only an appendage of France; "another Isle of Oleron to France." So it was *by nature*, by Napoleon-nature; and yet look how in fact—HERE AM I! He cannot understand it: inconceivable that the reality has not corresponded to his programme of it; that France was not all great, that he was not France. "Strong delusion," that he should believe the thing to be which *is* not! The compact, clear-seeing, decisive Italian nature of him, strong, genuine, which he once had, has enveloped itself, half-dissolved itself, in a turbid atmosphere of France fanfaronade. The world was not disposed to be trodden-down under foot; to be bound into masses and built together, as *he* liked, for a pedestal to France and him: the world had quite other purposes in view! Napoleon's astonishment is extreme. But alas, what help now? He had gone that way of his; and nature also had gone her way. Having once parted with reality, he tumbles helpless in vacuity; no rescue for him. He had to sink there, mournfully as man seldom did; and break his great heart, and die—this poor Napoleon: a great implement too soon wasted, till it was useless: our last great man!

Our last, in a double sense. For here finally these wide roamings of ours through so many times and places, in search and study of heroes, are to terminate. I am sorry for it: there was pleasure for me in this business, if also much pain. It is a great subject, and a most grave and wide one, this which, not to be too grave about it, I have named *hero-worship*. It enters deeply, as I think, into the secret of mankind's ways and vitalest interests in this world, and is well worth explaining at present. With six months, instead of six days, we might have done better. I promised to break ground on it; I know not whether I have even managed to do that. I have had to tear it up in the rudest manner in order to get into it at all. Often enough, with these abrupt utterances thrown out isolated, unexplained has your tolerance been put to the trial. Tolerance, patient candor, all hoping favor and kindness, which I will not speak of at present. The accomplished and distinguished, the beautiful, the wise, something of what is best in England, have listened patiently to my rude words. With many feelings, I heartily thank you all; and say, good be with you all!

CHARACTERISTICS

CHARACTERISTICS[1]

[1831.]

THE HEALTHY know not of their health, but only the sick: this is the Physician's Aphorism; and applicable in a far wider sense than he gives it. We may say, it holds no less in moral, intellectual, political, poetical, than in merely corporeal therapeutics; that wherever, or in what shape soever, powers of the sort which can be named *vital* are at work, herein lies the test of their working right or working wrong.

In the Body, for example, as all doctors are agreed, the first condition of complete health is, that each organ perform its function unconsciously, unheeded; let but any organ announce its separate existence, were it even boastfully, and for pleasure, not for pain, then already has one of those unfortunate 'false centres of sensibility' established itself, already is derangement there. The perfection of bodily well-being is, that the collective bodily activities seem one; and be manifested, moreover, not in themselves, but in the action they accomplish. If a Dr. Kitchiner boast that his system is in high order, Dietetic Philosophy may indeed take credit; but the true Peptician was that Countryman who answered that, "for his part, he had no system." In fact, unity, agreement is always silent, or soft-voiced; it is only discord that loudly proclaims itself. So long as the several elements of Life, all fitly adjusted, can pour forth their movement like harmonious tuned strings, it is a melody and unison; Life, from its mysterious fountains, flows out as in celestial music and diapason,—which also, like that other music of the spheres, even because it is perennial and complete, without interruption and without imperfection, might be fabled to escape the ear. Thus too, in some languages, is the state of health well denoted by a term expressing unity; when we feel ourselves as we wish to be, we say that we are *whole*.

Few mortals, it is to be feared, are permanently blessed with that felicity of 'having no system;' nevertheless, most of us looking back on young years, may remember seasons of a light, aërial translucency and elasticity and perfect freedom; the body had not yet become the prison-house of the soul, but was its vehicle and implement, like a creature of the thought, and altogether pliant to its bidding. We knew not that we had limbs, we only lifted, hurled and leapt; through eye and ear, and all avenues of sense, came clear unimpeded tidings from without, and from within issued clear victori-

[1]EDINBURGH REVIEW, No. 108.—1. An Essay on the Origin and Prospects of Man. By Thomas Hope. 3 vols. 8vo. London, 1831.

2. *Philosophische Vorlesungen, insbesondere über Philosophieder Sprache und des Wortes. Geschrieben und vorgetragen zu Dresden im December 1828, und in den ersten Tagen des Januars 1829* (Philosophical Lectures, especially on the Philosophy of Language and the Gift of Speech. Written and delivered at Dresden in December 1828, and the early days of January 1829). By Friedrich von Schlegel. 8vo. Vienna, 1830.

ous force; we stood as in the centre of Nature, giving and receiving, in harmony with it all; unlike Virgil's Husbandmen, 'too happy *because* we did not know our blessedness.' In those days, health and sickness were foreign traditions that did not concern us; our whole being was as yet One, the whole man like an incorporated Will. Such, were Rest or ever-successful Labour the human lot, might our life continue to be: a pure, perpetual, unregarded music; a beam of perfect white light, rendering all things visible, but itself unseen, even because it was of that perfect whiteness and no irregular obstruction had yet broken it into colours. The beginning of Inquiry is Disease: all Science, if we consider well, as it must have originated in the feeling of something being wrong, so it is and continues to be but Division, Dismemberment, and partial healing of the wrong. Thus, as was of old written, the Tree of Knowledge springs from a root of evil, and bears fruits of good and evil. Had Adam remained in Paradise, there had been no Anatomy and no Metaphysics.

But, alas, as the Philosopher declares, 'Life itself is a disease; a working incited by suffering;' action from passion! The memory of that first state of Freedom and paradisiac Unconsciousness has faded away into an ideal poetic dream. We stand here too conscious of many things: with Knowledge, the symptom of Derangement, we must even do our best to restore a little Order. Life is, in few instances, and at rare intervals, the diapason of a heavenly melody; oftenest the fierce jar of disruptions and convulsions, which, do what we will, there is no disregarding. Nevertheless, such is still the wish of Nature on our behalf; in all vital action, her manifest purpose and effort is, that we should be unconscious of it, and, like the peptic Countryman, never know that we 'have a system.' For indeed vital action everywhere is emphatically a means, not an end; Life is not given us for the mere sake of Living, but always with an ulterior external Aim: neither is it on the process, on the means, but rather on the result, that Nature, in any of her doings, is wont to entrust us with insight and volition. Boundless as is the domain of man, it is but a small fractional proportion of it that he rules with Consciousness and by Forethought: what he can contrive, nay what he can altogether know and comprehend, is essentially the mechanical, small; the great is ever, in one sense or other, the vital; it is essentially the mysterious, and only the surface of it can be understood. But Nature, it might seem, strives, like a kind mother, to hide from us even this, that she is a mystery: she will have us rest on her beautiful and awful bosom as if it were our secure home; on the bottomless boundless Deep, whereon all human things fearfully and wonderfully swim, she will have us walk and build, as if the film which supported us there (which any scratch of a bare bodkin will rend asunder, any sputter of a pistol-shot instantaneously burn up) were no film, but a solid rock-foundation. Forever in the neighbourhood of an inevitable Death, man can forget that he is born to die; of his Life, which, strictly meditated, contains in it an Immensity and an Eternity, he can conceive lightly, as of a simple implement wherewith to do day-labour and earn wages. So cunningly does Nature, the mother of all highest Art, which only apes her from afar, 'body forth the Finite from the Infinite;' and guide man safe on his wondrous path, not more by endowing him with vision, than, at the right place, with blindness! Under all her works, chiefly under her noblest work, Life, lies a basis of Darkness, which she benignantly conceals; in Life too, the roots and inward circulations which stretch down fearfully to the regions of Death and Night, shall not hint of their existence, and only the fair stem with its leaves and flowers, shone on by the fair sun, shall disclose itself, and joyfully grow.

However, without venturing into the abstruse, or too eagerly asking Why and How, in things where our answer must needs prove, in great part, an echo of the question, let us be content to remark farther, in the merely historical way, how that Aphorism of the bodily Physician holds good in quite other departments. Of the Soul, with her activities, we shall find it no less true than of the Body: nay, cry the Spiritualists, is not that very division of the unity, Man, into a dualism of Soul and Body, itself the symptom of disease; as perhaps, your frightful theory of Materialism, of his being but a Body, and therefore, at least, once more a unity, may be the paroxysm which was critical, and the beginning of cure! But omitting this, we observe, with confidence enough, that the truly strong mind, view it as Intellect, as Morality, or under any other aspect, is nowise the mind acquainted with its strength; that here as before the sign of health is Unconsciousness. In our inward, as in our outward world, what is mechanical lies open to us: not what is dynamical and has vitality. Of our Thinking, we might say, it is but the mere upper surface that we shape into articulate Thoughts;—underneath the region of argument and conscious discourse, lies the region of meditation; here, in its quiet mysterious depths, dwells what vital force is in us; here, if aught is to be created, and not merely manufactured and communicated, must the work go on. Manufacture is intelligible, but trivial; Creation is great, and cannot be understood. Thus if the Debater and Demonstrator, whom we may rank as the lowest of true thinkers, knows what he has done, and how he did it, the Artist, whom we rank as the highest, knows not; must speak of Inspiration, and in one or the other dialect, call his work the gift of a divinity.

But on the whole, 'genius is ever a secret to itself;' of this old truth we have, on all sides, daily evidence. The Shakespeare takes no airs for writing *Hamlet* and the *Tempest,* understands not that it is anything surprising; Milton, again, is more conscious of his faculty, which accordingly is an inferior one. On the other hand, what cackling and strutting must we not often hear and see, when, in some shape of academical prolusion, maiden speech, review article, this or the other well-fledged goose has produced its goose-egg, of quite measurable value, were it the pink of its whole kind; and wonders why all mortals do not wonder!

Foolish enough, too, was the College Tutor's surprise at Walter Shandy; how, though unread in Aristotle, he could nevertheless argue; and not knowing the name of any dialectic tool, handled them all to perfection. Is it the skilfullest anatomist that cuts the best figure at Sadler's Wells? Or does the boxer hit better for knowing that he has a *flexor longus* and a *flexor brevis?* But indeed, as in the higher case of the Poet, so here in that of the Speaker and Inquirer the true force is an unconscious one. The healthy Understanding, we should say, is not the Logical, argumentative, but the Intuitive; for the end of the Understanding is not to prove and find reasons, but to know and believe. Of logic, and its limits, and uses and abuses, there were much to be said and examined; one fact, however, which chiefly concerns us here, has long been familiar: that the man of logic and the man of insight; the Reasoner and the Discoverer, or even Knower, are quite separable,—indeed, for most part, quite separate characters. In practical matters, for example, has it not become almost proverbial that the man of logic cannot prosper? This is he whom business-people call Systematic and Theoriser and Wordmonger; his *vital* intellectual force lies dormant or extinct, his whole force is mechanical, conscious: of such a one it is foreseen that, when once confronted with the infinite complexities of the real world, his little compact theorem of the world will be found wanting; that unless he can throw it overboard, and become a new creature, he will necessarily founder. Nay, in mere Speculation itself, the most ineffectual of all characters, generally speaking, is your dialectic man-at-arms; were he armed cap-a-pie in syllogistic mail of proof, and perfect master of logic-fence, how little does it avail him! Consider the old Schoolmen, and their pilgrimage towards Truth: the faithfullest endeavour, incessant unwearied motion, often great natural vigour; only no progress: nothing but antic feats of one limb poised against the other; there they balanced, somersetted and made postures; at best gyrated swiftly, with some pleasure, like Spinning Dervishes, and ended where they began. So is it, so will it always be, with all System-makers and builders of logical card-castles; of which class a certain remnant must, in every age, as they do in our own, survive and build. Logic is good, but it is not the best. The Irrefragable Doctor, with his chains of induction, his corollaries, dilemmas, and other cunning logical diagrams and apparatus, will cast you a beautiful horoscope, and speak reasonable things; nevertheless your stolen jewel, which you wanted him to find you, is not forthcoming. Often by some winged word, winged as the thunderbolt is, of a Luther, a Napoleon, a Goethe, shall we see the difficulty split asunder, and its secret laid bare; while the Irrefragable, with all his logical tools, hews at it, and hovers round it, and finds it on all hands too hard for him.

Again, in the difference between Oratory and Rhetoric, as indeed everywhere in that superiority of what is called the Natural over the Artificial, we find a similar illustration. The Orator persuades and carries all with him, he knows not how; the Rhetorician can prove that he ought to have persuaded and carried all with him: the one is in a state of healthy unconsciousness, as if he 'had no system;' the other, in virtue of regimen and dietetic punctuality, feels at best that 'his system is in high order.' So stands it, in short, with all the forms of Intellect, whether as directed to the finding of truth, or to the fit imparting thereof; to Poetry, to Eloquence, to depth of insight, which is the basis of both these; always the characteristic of right performance is a certain spontaneity, an unconsciousness; 'the healthy know not of their health, but only the sick.' So that the old precept of the critic, as crabbed as it looked to his ambitious disciple, might contain in it a most fundamental truth, applicable to us all, and in much else than Literature: "Whenever you have written any sentence that looks particularly excellent, be sure to blot it out." In like manner, under milder phraseology, and with a meaning purposely much wider, a living Thinker has taught us: 'Of the Wrong we are always conscious, of the Right never.'

But if such is the law with regard to Speculation and the Intellectual power of man, much more is it with regard to Conduct, and the power, manifested chiefly therein, which we name moral. 'Let not thy left hand know what thy right hand doeth:' whisper not to thy own heart, How worthy is this action; for then it is already becoming worthless. The good man is he who *works* continually in well-doing; to whom well-doing is as his natural existence, awakening no astonishment, requiring no commentary; but there, like a thing of course, and as if it could not but be so. Self-contemplation, on the other hand, is infallibly the symptom of disease, be it or be it not the sign of cure. An unhealthy Virtue is one that consumes itself to leanness in repenting and anxiety; or, still worse, that inflates itself into dropsical boastfulness and vainglory: either way, there is a self-seeking; an unprofitable looking behind us to measure the way we have made: whereas the sole concern is to walk continually forward, and make more way. If in any sphere of man's life, then in the Moral sphere, as the inmost and most vital of all, it is good that there be wholeness; that there be unconsciousness, which is the evidence of this. Let the free, reasonable Will, which dwells in us, as in our Holy of Holies, be indeed free, and obeyed like a Divinity, as is its right and its effort: the perfect obedience will be the silent one. Such perhaps were the sense of that maxim, enunciating, as is usual, but the half of a truth: To say that we have a clear conscience, is to utter a solecism; had we never sinned, we should have had no conscience. Were defeat unknown, neither would victory be celebrated by songs of triumph.

This, true enough, is an ideal, impossible state of being; yet ever the goal towards which our actual state of being strives; which it is the more perfect the nearer it can approach. Nor, in our actual world, where Labour must often prove *in*effectual, and thus in all senses Light alternate with Darkness, and the nature of an ideal Morality be much modified, is the case, thus far, materially different. It is a fact which escapes no one, that, generally speaking, whoso is acquainted with his worth has but a little stock to cultivate acquaintance with. Above all, the public acknowledgment of such acquaintance, indicating that it has reached quite an intimate footing, bodes ill. Already, to the popular judgment, he who talks much about Virtue in the abstract begins to be suspect; it is shrewdly guessed that where there is great preaching, there will be little almsgiving. Or again, on a wider scale, we can remark that ages of Heroism are not ages of Moral Philosophy; Virtue, when it can be philosophised of, has become aware of itself, is sickly and beginning to decline. A spontaneous habitual all-pervading spirit of

Chivalrous Valour shrinks together and perks itself up into shrivelled Points of Honour: humane Courtesy and Nobleness of mind dwindle into punctilious Politeness, 'avoiding meats;' 'paying tithe of mint and anise, neglecting the weightier matters of the law.' Goodness, which was a rule to itself, must now appeal to Precept, and seek strength from Sanctions; the Freewill no longer reigns unquestioned and by divine right, but like a mere earthly sovereign, by expediency, by Rewards and Punishments: or rather, let us say, the Freewill, so far as may be, has abdicated and withdrawn into the dark, and a spectral nightmare of a Necessity usurps its throne; for now that mysterious Self-impulse of the whole man, heaven-inspired, and in all senses partaking of the Infinite, being captiously questioned in a finite dialect, and answering, as it needs must, by silence,—is conceived as non-extant, and only the outward Mechanism of it remains acknowledged: of Volition, except as the synonym of Desire, we hear nothing; of 'Motives,' without any Mover, more than enough.

So too, when the generous Affections have become well-nigh paralytic, we have the reign of Sentimentality. The greatness, the profitableness, at any rate the extremely ornamental nature of high feeling, and the luxury of doing good; charity, love, self-forgetfulness, devotedness and all manner of godlike magnanimity,—are everywhere insisted on, and pressingly inculcated in speech and writing, in prose and verse; Socinian Preachers proclaim 'Benevolence' to all the four winds, and have TRUTH engraved on their watch-seals: unhappily with little or no effect. Were the limbs in right walking order, why so much demonstrating of motion? The barrenest of all mortals is the Sentimentalist. Granting even that he were sincere, and did not wilfully deceive us, or without first deceiving himself, what good is in him? Does he not lie there as a perpetual lesson of despair, and type of bedrid valetudinarian impotence? His is emphatically a Virtue that has become, through every fibre, conscious of itself; it is all sick, and feels as if it were made of glass, and durst not touch or be touched: in the shape of work, it can do nothing; at the utmost, by incessant nursing and caudling, keep itself alive. At the last stage of all, when Virtue, properly so called, has ceased to be practised, and become extinct, and a mere remembrance, we have the era of Sophists, descanting of its existence, proving it, denying it, mechanically 'accounting' for it;—as dissectors and demonstrators cannot operate till once the body be dead.

Thus is true Moral genius, like true Intellectual, which indeed is but a lower phasis thereof, 'ever a secret to itself.' The healthy moral nature loves Goodness, and without wonder wholly lives in it: the unhealthy makes love to it, and would fain get to live in it; or, finding such courtship fruitless, turns round, and not without contempt abandons it. These curious relations of the Voluntary and Conscious to the Involuntary and Unconscious, and the small proportion which, in all departments of our life, the former bears to the latter,—might lead us into deep questions of Psychology and Physiology: such, however, belong not to our present object. Enough, if the fact itself become apparent, that Nature so meant it with us; that in this wise we are made. We may now say, that view man's individual Existence under what aspect we will, under the highest spiritual, as under the merely animal aspect, everywhere the grand vital energy, while in its sound state, is an unseen unconscious one; or, in the words of our old Aphorism, 'the healthy know not of their health, but only the sick.'

To understand man, however, we must look beyond the individual man and his actions or interests, and view him in combination with his fellows. It is in Society that man first feels what he is; first becomes what he can be. In Society an altogether new set of spiritual activities are evolved in him, and the old immeasurably quickened and strengthened. Society is the genial element wherein his nature first lives and grows; the solitary man were but a small portion of himself, and must continue forever folded in, stunted and only half alive. 'Already,' says a deep Thinker, with more meaning than will disclose itself at once, 'my opinion, my conviction, gains *infinitely* in strength and sureness, the moment a second mind has adopted it.' Such, even in its simplest form, is association; so wondrous the communion of soul with soul as directed to the mere act of Knowing! In other higher acts, the wonder is still more manifest; as in that portion of our being which we name the Moral: for properly, indeed, all communion is of a moral sort, whereof such intellectual communion (in the act of knowing) is itself an example. But with regard to Morals strictly so called, it is in Society, we might almost say, that Morality begins; here at least it takes an altogether new form, and on every side, as in living growth, expands itself. The Duties of Man to himself, to what is Highest in himself, make but the First Table of the Law: to the First Table is now superadded a Second, with the Duties of Man to his Neighbour; whereby also the significance of the First now assumes its true importance. Man has joined himself with man; soul acts and reacts on soul; a mystic miraculous unfathomable Union establishes itself; Life, in all its elements, has become intensated, consecrated. The lightning-spark of Thought generated, or say rather, heaven-kindled, in the solitary mind, awakens its express likeness in another mind, in a thousand other minds, and all blaze up together in combined fire; reverberated from mind to mind, fed also with fresh fuel in each, it acquires incalculable new light as Thought, incalculable new heat as converted into Action. By and by, a common store of Thought can accumulate, and be transmitted as an everlasting possession: Literature, whether as preserved in the memory of Bards, in Runes and Hieroglyphs engraved on stone, or in Books of written or printed paper, comes into existence, and begins to play its wondrous part. Polities are formed; the weak submitting to the strong; with a willing loyalty, giving obedience that he may receive guidance: or say rather, in honour of our nature, the ignorant submitting to the wise; for so it is in all even the rudest communities, man never yields himself wholly to brute Force, but always to moral Greatness; thus the universal title of respect, from the Oriental *Sheik*, from the *Sachem* of the Red Indians, down to our English *Sir*, implies only that he whom we mean to honour is our *senior*. Last, as the crown and all-supporting keystone of the fabric, Religion arises. The devout meditation of the isolated man, which flitted through his soul, like a transient tone of Love and Awe from unknown lands, acquires certainty, continuance, when it is shared-in by his brother men. 'Where two or three are gathered together' in the name of the Highest, then first does the Highest, as it is written, 'appear among them to bless them;' then first does an Altar and act of united Worship open a way from Earth to Heaven; whereon, were it but a simple Jacob's-ladder, the heavenly Messengers will travel, with glad tidings and unspeakable gifts for men. Such is SOCIETY, the vital articulation of many individuals into a new collective individual: greatly the most important of man's attainments on this earth; that in which, and by virtue of which, all his other attainments and attempts find their arena, and have their value. Considered well, Society is the standing wonder of our existence; a true region of the Supernatural; as it were, a second all-embracing Life, wherein our first individual Life becomes doubly and trebly alive, and whatever of Infinitude was in us bodies itself forth, and becomes visible and active.

To figure Society as endowed with life is scarcely a metaphor; but rather the statement of a fact by such imperfect methods as language affords. Look at it closely, that mystic Union, Nature's highest work with man, wherein man's volition plays an indispensable yet so subordinate a part, and the small Mechanical grows so mysteriously and indissolubly out of the infinite Dynamical, like Body out of Spirit,—is truly enough vital, what we can call vital, and bears the distinguishing character of life. In the same style also, we can say that Society has its periods of sickness and vigour, of youth, manhood, decrepitude, dissolution and new-birth; in one or other of which stages we may, in all times, and all places where men inhabit, discern it; and do ourselves, in this time and place, whether as coöperating or as contending, as healthy members or as diseased ones, to our joy and sorrow, form part of it. The question, What is the actual condition of Society? has in these days unhappily become important enough. No one of us is unconcerned in that question; but for the majority of thinking men a true answer to it, such is the state of matters, appears almost as the one thing needful. Meanwhile, as the true answer, that is to say, the complete and fundamental answer and settlement, often as it has been demanded, is nowhere forthcoming, and indeed by its nature is impossible, any honest approximation towards such is not without value. The feeblest light, or even so much as a more precise recognition of the darkness, which is the first step to attainment of light, will be welcome.

This once understood, let it not seem idle if we remark that here too our old Aphorism holds; that again in the Body Politic, as in the animal body, the sign of right performance is Unconsciousness. Such indeed is virtually the meaning of that phrase, 'artificial state of society,' as contrasted with the natural state, and indicating something so inferior to it. For, in all vital things, men distinguish an Artificial and a Natural; founding on some dim perception or sentiment of the very truth we here insist on: the artificial is the conscious, mechanical; the natural is the unconscious, dynamical.

Thus, as we have an artificial Poetry, and prize only the natural; so likewise we have an artificial Morality, an artificial Wisdom, an artificial Society. The artificial Society is precisely one that knows its own structure, its own internal functions; not in watching, not in knowing which, but in working outwardly to the fulfilment of its aim, does the well-being of a Society consist. Every Society, every Polity, has a spiritual principle; is the embodiment, tentative and more or less complete, of an Idea: all its tendencies of endeavour, specialties of custom, its laws, politics and whole procedure (as the glance of some Montesquieu, across innumerable superficial entanglements, can partly decipher), are prescribed by an Idea, and flow naturally from it, as movements from the living source of motion. This Idea, be it of devotion to a man or class of men, to a creed, to an institution, or even, as in more ancient times, to a piece of land, is ever a true Loyalty; has in it something of a religious, paramount, quite infinite character; it is properly the Soul of the State, its Life; mysterious as other forms of Life, and like these working secretly, and in a depth beyond that of consciousness.

Accordingly, it is not in the vigorous ages of a Roman Republic that Treatises of the Commonwealth are written: while the Decii are rushing with devoted bodies on the enemies of Rome, what need of preaching Patriotism? The virtue of Patriotism has already sunk from its pristine all-transcendent condition, before it has received a name. So long as the Commonwealth continues rightly athletic, it cares not to dabble in anatomy. Why teach obedience to the Sovereign; why so much as admire it, or separately recognise it, while a divine idea of Obedience perennially inspires all men? Loyalty, like Patriotism, of which it is a form, was not praised till it had begun to decline; the *Preux Chevaliers* first became rightly admirable, when 'dying for their king' had ceased to be a habit with chevaliers. For if the mystic significance of the State, let this be what it may, dwells vitally in every heart, encircles every life as with a second higher life, how should it stand self-questioning? It must rush outward, and express itself by works. Besides, if perfect, it is there as by necessity, and does not excite inquiry: it is also by nature infinite, has no limits; therefore can be circumscribed by no conditions and definitions; cannot be reasoned of; except *musically*, or in the language of Poetry, cannot yet so much as be spoken of.

In those days, Society was what we name healthy, sound at heart. Not indeed without suffering enough; not without perplexities, difficulty on every side: for such is the appointment of man; his highest and sole blessedness is, that he toil, and know what to toil at: not in ease, but in united victorious labour, which is at once evil, and the victory over evil, does his Freedom lie. Nay, often, looking no deeper than such superficial perplexities of the early Time, historians have taught us that it was all one mass of contradiction and disease; and in the antique Republic, or feudal Monarchy, have seen only the confused chaotic quarry, not the robust labourer, or the stately edifice he was building of it. If Society, in such ages, had its difficulty, it had also its strength; if sorrowful masses of rubbish so encumbered it, the tough sinews to hurl them aside, with indomitable heart, were not wanting. Society went along without complaint; did not stop to scrutinise itself, to say, How well I perform, or, Alas, how ill! Men did not yet feel themselves to be 'the envy of surrounding nations;' and were enviable on that very account. Society was what we can call *whole*, in both senses of the word. The individual man was in himself a whole, or complete union; and could combine with his fellows as the living member of a greater whole. For all men, through their life, were animated by one great Idea: thus all efforts pointed one way, everywhere there was *wholeness*. Opinion and Action had not yet become disunited; but the former could still produce the latter, or attempt to produce it; as the stamp does its impression while the wax is not hardened. Thought, and the voice of thought were also a unison; thus, instead of Speculation, we had Poetry; Literature, in its rude utterance, was as yet a heroic Song, perhaps too a devotional Anthem. Religion was everywhere; Philosophy lay hid under it, peacefully included in it. Herein, as in the life-centre of all, lay the true health and oneness. Only at a later era must Religion split itself into Philosophies; and thereby, the vital union of Thought being lost, disunion and mutual collision in all provinces of Speech and Action more and more prevail. For if the Poet or Priest, or by whatever title the inspired thinker may be named, is the sign of vigour and well-being; so likewise is the Logician, or uninspired thinker, the sign of disease, probably of decrepitude and decay. Thus, not to mention other instances, one of them much nearer hand,—so soon as Prophecy among the Hebrews had ceased, then did the reign of Argumentation begin; and the ancient Theocracy, in its Sadduceeisms and Phariseeisms, and vain jangling of sects and doctors, give token that the *soul* of it had fled, and that the *body* itself, by natural dissolution, 'with the old forces still at work, but working in reverse order,' was on the road to final disappearance.

We might pursue this question into innumerable other ramifications; and everywhere, under new shapes, find the same truth, which we here so imperfectly enunciate, disclosed; that throughout the whole world of man, in all manifestations and performances of his nature, outward and inward, personal and social, the Prefect, the Great is a mystery to itself, knows not itself; whatsoever does know itself is already little, and more or less imperfect. Or otherwise we may say, Unconsciousness belongs to pure unmixed life; Consciousness to a diseased mixture and conflict of life and death: Unconsciousness is a sign of creation; Consciousness, at best, that of manufacture. So deep, in this existence of ours, is the significance of Mystery. Well might the Ancients make Silence a god; for it is the element of all godhood, infinitude, or transcendental greatness; at once the source and the ocean wherein all such begins and ends. In the same sense too, have Poets sung 'Hymns to the Night;' as if Night were nobler than Day; as if Day were but a small motley-coloured veil spread transiently over the infinite bosom of Night, and did but deform and hide from us its purely transparent, eternal deeps. So likewise have they spoken and sung as if Silence were the grand epitome and complete sum-total of all Harmony; and Death, what mortals call Death, properly the beginning of Life. Under such figures, since except in figures there is no speaking of the Invisible, have men endeavoured to express a great Truth;—a Truth, in our Times, as nearly as is perhaps possible, forgotten by the most; which nevertheless continues forever true, forever all-important, and will one day, under new figures, be again brought home to the bosoms of all.

But indeed, in a far lower sense, the rudest mind has still some intimation of the greatness there is in Mystery. If Silence was made a god of by the Ancients, he still continues a government-clerk among us Moderns. To all quacks, moreover, of what sort soever, the effect of Mystery is well known: here and there some Cagliostro, even in latter days, turns it to notable account: the blockhead also, who is ambitious, and has no talent, finds sometimes in 'the talent of silence,' a kind of succedaneum. Or again, looking on the opposite side of the matter, do we not see, in the common understanding of mankind, a certain distrust, a certain contempt of what is altogether self-conscious and mechanical? As nothing that is wholly seen through has other than a trivial character; so anything professing to be great, and yet wholly to see through itself, is already known to be false, and a failure. The evil repute your 'theoretical men' stand in, the acknowledged inefficiency of 'paper constitutions,' and all that class of objects, are instances of this. Experience often repeated, and perhaps a certain instinct of something far deeper that lies under such experiences, has taught men so much. They know beforehand, that the loud is generally the insignificant, the empty. Whatsoever can proclaim itself from the house-tops may be fit for the hawker, and for those multitudes that must needs buy of him; but for any deeper use, might as well continue unproclaimed. Observe too, how the converse of the proposition holds; how the insignificant, the empty, is usually the loud; and, after the manner of a drum, is loud even because of its emptiness. The uses of some Patent Dinner Calefactor can be bruited abroad over the whole world in the course of the first winter; those of the Printing Press are not so well seen into for the first three centuries: the passing of the Select-Vestries Bill raises more noise and hopeful expectancy among mankind than did the promulgation of the Christian Religion. Again, and again, we say the great, the creative and enduring is ever a secret to itself; only the small, the barren and transient is otherwise.

If we now, with a practical medical view, examine, by this same test of Unconsciousness, the Condition of our own Era, and of man's Life therein, the diagnosis we arrive at is nowise of a flattering sort. The state of Society in our days is, of all possible states, the least an unconscious one: this is specially the Era when all manner of Inquiries into what was once the unfelt, involuntary sphere of man's existence, find their place, and, as it were, occupy the whole domain of thought. What, for example, is all this that we hear, for the last generation or two, about the Improvement of the Age, the Spirit of the Age, Destruction of Prejudice, Progress of the Species, and the March of Intellect, but an unhealthy state of self-sentience, self-survey; the precursor and prognostic of still worse health? That Intellect do march, if possible at double-quick time, is very desirable; nevertheless, why should she turn round at every stride, and cry: See you what a stride I have taken! Such a marching of Intellect is distinctly of the spavined kind; what the Jockeys call 'all action and no go.' Or at best, if we examine well, it is the marching of that gouty Patient, whom his Doctors had clapt on a metal floor artificially heated to the searing point, so that he was obliged to march, and did march with a vengeance—nowhither. Intellect did not awaken for the first time yesterday; but has been under way from Noah's Flood downwards: greatly her best progress, moreover, was in the old times, when she said nothing about it. In those same 'dark ages,' Intellect (metaphorically as well as literally) could invent *glass*, which now she has enough ado to grind into *spectacles*. Intellect built not only Churches, but a Church, *the* Church, based on this firm Earth, yet reaching up, and leading up, as high as Heaven; and now it is all she can do to keep its doors bolted, that there be no tearing of the Surplices, no robbery of the Alms-box. She built a Senate-house likewise, glorious in its kind; and now it costs her a well-nigh mortal effort to sweep it clear of vermin, and get the roof made rain-tight.

But the truth is, with Intellect, as with most other things, we are now passing from that first or boastful stage of Self-sentience into the second or painful one: out of these often-asseverated declarations that 'our system is in high order,' we come now, by natural sequence, to the melancholy conviction that it is altogether the reverse. Thus, for instance, in the matter of Government, the period of the 'Invaluable Constitution' must be followed by a Reform Bill; to laudatory Delolmes succeed objurgatory Benthams. At any rate, what Treatises on the Social Contract, on the Elective Franchise, the Rights of Man, the Rights of Property, Codifications, Institutions, Constitutions, have we not, for long years, groaned under! Or again, with a wider survey, consider those Essays on Man, Thoughts on Man, Inquiries concerning Man; not to mention Evidences of the Christian Faith, Theories of Poetry, Considerations on the Origin of Evil, which during the last century have accumulated on us to a frightful extent. Never since the beginning of Time was there, that we hear or read of, so intensely self-conscious a Society. Our whole relations to the Universe and to our fellow-man have become an Inquiry, a Doubt; nothing will go on of its own accord, and do its function quietly; but all things must be probed into, the whole working of man's world be anatomically studied. Alas, anatomically studied, that it may be medically aided! Till at length indeed, we have come to such a pass, that except in this same *medicine*, with its artifices and appliances, few can so much as imagine any strength or hope to remain for us. The whole Life of Society must now be carried on by drugs: doctor after doctor appears with his nostrum, of Coöperative Societies, Universal Suffrage, Cottage-and-Cow systems, Repression of Population, Vote by Ballot. To such height has the dyspepsia of Society reached; as indeed the constant grinding internal pain, or from time to time the mad spasmodic throes, of all Society do otherwise too mournfully indicate.

Far be it from us to attribute, as some unwise persons do, the disease itself to this unhappy sensation that there is a disease! The Encyclopedists did not produce the troubles of France; but the troubles of France produced the Encyclopedists, and much else. The Self-consciousness is the symptom merely; nay, it is also the attempt towards cure. We record the fact, without special censure; not wondering that Society should feel itself, and in all ways complain of aches and twinges, for it has suffered enough. Napoleon was but a Job's-comforter, when he told his wounded Staff-officer, twice unhorsed by cannon-balls, and with half his limbs blown to pieces: "*Vous vous écoutez trop!*"

On the outward, as it were, Physical diseases of Society, it were beside our purpose to insist here. These are diseases which he who runs may read; and sorrow over, with or without hope. Wealth has accumulated itself into masses; and Poverty, also in accumulation enough, lies impassably separated from it; opposed, uncommunicating, like forces in positive and negative poles. The gods of this lower world sit aloft on glittering thrones, less happy than Epicurus's gods, but as indolent, as impotent; while the boundless living chaos of Ignorance and Hunger welters terrific, in its dark fury, under their feet. How much among us might be likened to a whited sepulchre; outwardly all pomp and strength; but inwardly full of horror and despair and dead-men's bones! Iron highways, with their wains firewinged, are uniting all ends of the firm Land; quays and moles, with their innumerable stately fleets, tame the Ocean into our pliant bearer of burdens; Labour's thousand arms, of sinew and of metal, all-conquering everywhere, from the tops of the mountain down to the depths of the mine and the caverns of the sea, ply unweariedly for the service of man: yet man remains unserved. He has subdued this Planet, his habitation and inheritance; yet reaps no profit from the victory. Sad to look upon: in the highest stage of civilisation, nine-tenths of mankind must struggle in the lowest battle of savage or even animal man, the battle against Famine. Countries are rich, prosperous in all manner of increase, beyond example: but the Men of those countries are poor, needier than ever of all sustenance outward and inward; of Belief, of Knowledge, of Money, of Food. The rule, *Sic vos non vobis*, never altogether to be got rid of in men's Industry, now presses with such incubus weight, that Industry must shake it off, or utterly be strangled under it; and, alas, can as yet but gasp and rave, and aimlessly struggle, like one in the final deliration. Thus Change, or the inevitable approach of Change, is manifest everywhere. In one Country we have seen lava-torrents of fever-frenzy envelop all things; Government succeed Government, like the phantasms of a dying brain. In another Country, we can even now see, in maddest alternation, the peasant governed by such guidance as this: To labour earnestly one month in raising wheat, and the next month labour earnestly in burning it. So that Society, were it not by nature immortal, and its death ever a new-birth, might appear, as it does in the eyes of some, to be sick to dissolution, and even now writhing in its last agony. Sick enough we must admit it to be, with disease enough, a whole nosology of diseases; wherein he perhaps is happiest that is not called to prescribe as physician;—wherein, however, one small piece of policy, that of summoning the Wisest in the Commonwealth, by the sole method yet known or thought of, to come together and with their whole soul consult for it, might, but for late tedious experiences, have seemed unquestionable enough.

But leaving this, let us rather look within, into the Spiritual condition of Society, and see what aspects and prospects offer themselves there. For after all, it is there properly that the secret and origin of the whole is to be sought: the Physical derangements of Society are but the image and impress of its Spiritual; while the heart continues sound, all other sickness is superficial, and temporary. False Action is the fruit of false Speculation; let the spirit of Society be free and strong, that is to say, let true Principles inspire the members of Society, then neither can disorders accumulate in its Practice; each disorder will be promptly, faithfully inquired into, and remedied as it arises. But alas, with us the Spiritual condition of Society is no less sickly than the Physical. Examine man's internal world, in any of its social relations and performances, here too all seems diseased self-consciousness, collision and mutually-destructive struggle. Nothing acts from within outwards in undivided healthy force; everything lies impotent, lamed, its force turned inwards, and painfully 'listens to itself.'

To begin with our highest Spiritual function, with Religion, we might ask, Whither has Religion now fled? Of Churches and their establishments we here say nothing: nor of the unhappy domains of Unbelief, and how innumerable men, blinded in their minds, must 'live without God in the world;' but, taking the fairest side of the matter, we ask, What is the nature of that same Religion, which still lingers in the hearts of the few who are called, and call themselves, specially the Religious? Is it a healthy religion, vital, unconscious of itself; that shines forth spontaneously in doing of the Work, or even in preaching of the Word? Unhappily, no. Instead of heroic martyr Conduct, and inspired and soul-inspiring Eloquence, whereby Religion itself were brought home to our living bosoms, to live and reign there, we have 'Discourses on the Evidences,' endeavouring, with smallest result, to make it probable that such a thing as Religion exists. The most enthusiastic Evangelicals do not preach a Gospel, but keep describing how it should and might be preached: to awaken the sacred fire of faith, as by a sacred contagion, is not their endeavour; but, at most, to describe how Faith shows and acts, and scientifically distinguish true Faith from false. Religion, like all else, is conscious of itself, listens to itself; it becomes less and less creative, vital; more and more mechanical. Considered as a whole, the Christian Religion, of late ages has been continually dissipating itself into Metaphysics; and threatens now to disappear, as some rivers do, in deserts of barren sand.

Of Literature, and its deep-seated, wide-spread maladies, why speak?

Literature is but a branch of Religion, and always participates in its character: however, in our time, it is the only branch that still shows any greenness; and, as some think, must one day become the main stem. Now, apart from the subterranean and tartarean regions of Literature;—leaving out of view the frightful, scandalous statistics of Puffing, the mystery of Slander, Falsehood, Hatred and other convulsion-work of rabid Imbecility, and all that has rendered Literature on that side a perfect 'Babylon the mother of Abominations,' in very deed making the world 'drunk' with the wine of her iniquity;—forgetting all this, let us look only to the regions of the upper air; to such Literature as can be said to have some attempt towards truth in it, some tone of music, and if it be not poetical, to hold of the poetical. Among other characteristics, is not this manifest enough: that it knows itself? Spontaneous devotedness to the object, being wholly possessed by the object, what we can call Inspiration, has well-nigh ceased to appear in Literature. Which melodious Singer forgets that he is singing melodiously? We have not the love of greatness, but the love of the love of greatness. Hence infinite Affectations, Distractions; in every case inevitable Error. Consider, for one example, this peculiarity of Modern Literature, the sin that has been named View-hunting. In our elder writers, there are no paintings of scenery for its own sake; no euphuistic gallantries with Nature, but a constant heartlove for her, a constant dwelling in communion with her. View-hunting, with so much else that is of kin to it, first came decisively into action through the *Sorrows of Werter;* which wonderful Performance, indeed, may in many senses be regarded as the progenitor of all that has since become popular in Literature; whereof, in so far as concerns spirit and tendency, it still offers the most instructive image; for nowhere, except in its own country, above all in the mind of its illustrious Author, has it yet fallen wholly obsolete. Scarcely ever, till that late epoch, did any worshipper of Nature become entirely aware that he was worshipping, much to his own credit; and think of saying to himself: Come let us make a description! Intolerable enough: when every puny whipster draws out his pencil, and insists on painting you a scene; so that the instant you discern such a thing as 'wavy outline,' 'mirror of the lake,' 'stern headland,' or the like, in any Book, you must timorously hasten on; and scarcely the Author of Waverley himself can tempt you not to skip.

Nay, is not the deceased self-conscious state of Literature disclosed in this one fact, which lies so near us here, the prevalence of Reviewing! Sterne's wish for a reader 'that would give up the reins of his imagination into his author's hands, and be pleased he knew not why, and cared not wherefore,' might lead him a long journey now. Indeed, for our best class of readers, the chief pleasure, a very stinted one, is this same knowing of the Why; which many a Kames and Bossu has been, ineffectually enough, endeavouring to teach us: till at last these also have laid down their trade; and now your Reviewer is a mere *taster;* who tastes, and says, by the evidence of such palate, such tongue, as he has got, It is good, It is bad. Was it thus that the French carried out certain inferior creatures on their Algerine

Expedition, to taste the wells for them, and try whether they were poisoned? Far be it from us to disparage our own craft, whereby we have our living! Only we must note these things: that Reviewing spreads with strange vigour; that such a man as Byron reckons the Reviewer and the Poet equal; that at the last Leipzig Fair, there was advertised a Review of Reviews. By and by it will be found that all Literature has become one boundless self-devouring Review; and as in London routs, we have to *do* nothing, but only to *see* others do nothing.—Thus does Literature also, like a sick thing, superabundantly 'listen to itself.'

No less is this unhealthy symptom manifest, if we cast a glance on our Philosophy, on the character of our speculative Thinking. Nay already, as above hinted, the mere existence and necessity of a Philosophy is an evil. Man is sent hither not to question, but to work; 'the end of man,' it was long ago written, 'is an Action, not a Thought.' In the perfect state, all Thought were but the picture and inspiring symbol of Action; Philosophy, except as Poetry and Religion, would have no being. And yet how, in this imperfect state, can it be avoided, can it be dispensed with? Man stands as in the centre of Nature; his fraction of Time encircled by Eternity, his hand-breadth of Space encircled by Infinitude: how shall he forbear asking himself, What am I; and Whence; and Whither? How too, except in slight partial hints, in kind asseverations and assurances, such as a mother quiets her fretfully inquisitive child with, shall he get answer to such inquiries?

The disease of Metaphysics, accordingly, is a perennial one. In all ages, those questions of Death and Immortality, Origin of Evil, Freedom and Necessity, must, under new forms, anew make their appearance; ever, from time to time, must the attempt to shape for ourselves some Theorem of the Universe be repeated. And ever unsuccessfully: for what Theorem of the Infinite can the Finite render complete? We, the whole species of Mankind, and our whole existence and history, are but a floating speck in the illimitable ocean of the All; yet *in* that ocean; indissoluble portion thereof; partaking of its infinite tendencies: borne this way and that by its deep-swelling tides, and grand ocean currents;—of which what faintest chance is there that we should ever exhaust the significance, ascertain the goings and comings? A region of Doubt, therefore, hovers forever in the background; in Action alone can we have certainty. Nay properly Doubt is the indispensable inexhaustible material whereon Action works, which Action has to fashion into Certainty and Reality; only on a canvas of Darkness, such is man's way of being, could the many-coloured picture of our Life paint itself and shine.

Thus if our eldest system of Metaphysics is as old as the *Book of Genesis*, our latest is that of Mr. Thomas Hope, published only within the current year. It is a chronic malady that of Metaphysics, as we said, and perpetually recurs on us. At the utmost, there is a better and a worse in it; a stage of convalescence, and a stage of relapse with new sickness: these forever succeed each other, as is the nature of all Life-movement here below. The first, or convalescent stage, we might also name that of Dogmatical or Constructive Metaphysics; when the mind constructively endeavours to scheme out, and assert for itself an actual Theorem of the Universe, and therewith for a time rests satisfied. The second or sick stage might be called that of Sceptical or Inquisitory Metaphysics; when the mind having widened its sphere of vision, the existing Theorem of the Universe no longer answers the phenomena, no longer yields contentment; but must be torn in pieces, and certainty anew sought for in the endless realms of denial. All Theologies and sacred Cosmogonies belong, in some measure, to the first class; in all Pyrrhonism, from Pyrrho down to Hume and the innumerable disciples of Hume, we have instances enough of the second. In the former, so far as it affords satisfaction, a temporary anodyne to doubt, an arena for wholesome action, there may be much good; indeed in this case, it holds rather of Poetry than of Metaphysics, might be called Inspiration rather than Speculation. The latter is Metaphysics proper; a pure, unmixed, though from time to time a necessary evil.

For truly, if we look into it, there is no more fruitless endeavour than this same, which the Metaphysician proper toils in: to educe Conviction out of Negation. How, by merely testing and rejecting what is not, shall we ever attain knowledge of what is? Metaphysical Speculation, as it begins in No or Nothingness, so it must needs end in Nothingness; circulates and must circulate in endless vortices; creating, swallowing—itself. Our being is made up of Light and Darkness, the Light resting on the Darkness, and balancing it; everywhere there is Dualism, Equipoise; a perpetual Contradiction dwells in us: "Where shall I place myself to escape from my own shadow?" Consider it well, Metaphysics is the attempt of the mind to rise above the mind; to environ, and shut in, or as we say, *comprehend* the mind. Hopeless struggle, for the wisest, as for the foolishest! What strength of sinew, or athletic skill, will enable the stoutest athlete to fold his own body in his arms, and, by lifting, lift up *himself?* The Irish Saint swam the Channel 'carrying his head in his teeth;' but the feat has never been imitated.

That this is the age of Metaphysics, in the proper, or sceptical Inquisitory sense; that there was a necessity for its being such an age, we regard as our indubitable misfortune. From many causes, the arena of free Activity has long been narrowing, that of sceptical Inquiry becoming more and more universal, more and more perplexing. The Thought conducts not to the Deed; but in boundless chaos, self-devouring, engenders monstrosities, fantasms, fire-breathing chimeras. Profitable Speculation were this: What is to be done; and How is it to be done? But with us not so much as the What can be got sight of. For some generations, all Philosophy has been a painful, captious, hostile question towards everything in the Heaven above, and in the Earth beneath: Why art thou there? Till at length it has come to pass that the worth and authenticity of all things seems dubitable or deniable: our best effort must be unproductively spent not in working, but in ascertaining our mere Whereabout, and so much as whether we are to work at all. Doubt, which, as was said, ever hangs in the background of our world, has now become our middle-ground and foreground; whereon, for the time, no fair Life-picture can be painted, but only the dark air-canvas itself flow round us, bewildering and benighting.

Nevertheless, doubt as we will, man is actually Here; not to ask questions but to do work: in this time, as in all times, it must be the heaviest evil for him, if his faculty of Action lie dormant, and only that of sceptical Inquiry exert itself. Accordingly, whoever looks abroad upon the world, comparing these days is one of the saddest; burdened with miseries which are in a the Past with the Present, may find that the practical condition of man in considerable degree peculiar. In no time was man's life what he calls a happy one; in no time can it be so. A perpetual dream there has been of Paradises, and some luxurious Lubberland, where the brooks should run wine, and the trees bend with ready-baked viands; but it was a dream merely; an impossible dream. Suffering, contradiction, error, have their quite perennial, and even indispensable abode in this Earth. Is not labour the inheritance of man? And what labour for the present is joyous, and not grievous? Labour, effort, is the very interruption of that ease, which man foolishly enough fancies to be his happiness; and yet without labour there were no ease, no rest, so much as conceivable. Thus Evil, what we call Evil, must ever exist while man exists: Evil, in the widest sense we can give it, is precisely the dark, disordered material out of which man's Freewill has to create an edifice of order and Good. Ever must Pain urge us to Labour; and only in free Effort can any blessedness be imagined for us.

But if man has, in all ages, had enough to encounter, there has, in most civilised ages, been an inward force vouchsafed him, whereby the pressure of things outward might be withstood. Obstruction abounded; but Faith also was not wanting. It is by Faith that man removes mountains: while he had Faith, his limbs might be wearied with toiling, his back galled with bearing; but the heart within him was peaceable and resolved. In the thickest gloom there burnt a lamp to guide him. If he struggled and suffered, he felt that it even should be so; knew for what he was suffering and struggling. Faith gave him an inward Willingness; a world of Strength wherewith to front a world of Difficulty. The true wretchedness lies here: that the Difficulty remain and the Strength be lost; that Pain cannot relieve itself in free Effort; that we have the Labour, and want the Willingness. Faith strengthens us, enlightens us, for all endeavours and endurances; with Faith we can do all, and dare all, and life itself has a thousand times been joyfully given away. But the sum of man's misery is even this, that he feel himself crushed under the Juggernaut wheels, and know that Juggernaut is no divinity, but a dead mechanical idol.

Now this is specially the misery which has fallen on man in our Era. Belief, Faith has well-nigh vanished from the world. The youth on awakening in this wondrous Universe, no longer finds a competent theory of its wonders. Time was, when if he asked himself, What is man, What are the duties of man? the answer stood ready written for him. But now the ancient 'ground-plan of the All' belies itself when brought into contact with reality;

Mother Church has, to the most, become a superannuated Step-mother, whose lessons go disregarded; or are spurned at, and scornfully gainsaid. For Young Valour and thirst of Action no ideal Chivalry invites to heroism, prescribes what is heroic: the old ideal of Manhood has grown obsolete, and the new is still invisible to us, and we grope after it in darkness, one clutching this phantom, another that; Werterism, Byronism, even Brummelism, each has its day. For Contemplation and love of Wisdom, no Cloister now opens its religious shades; the Thinker must, in all senses, wander homeless, too often aimless, looking up to a Heaven which is dead for him, round to an Earth which is deaf. Action, in those old days, was easy, was voluntary, for the divine worth of human things lay acknowledged; Speculation was wholesome, for it ranged itself as the handmaid of Action; what could not so range itself died out by its natural death, by neglect. Loyalty still hallowed obedience, and made rule noble; there was still something to be loyal to: the Godlike stood embodied under many a symbol in men's interests and business; the Finite shadowed forth the Infinite; Eternity looked through Time. The Life of man was encompassed and overcanopied by a glory of Heaven, even as his dwelling-place by the azure vault.

How changed in these new days! Truly may it be said, the Divinity has withdrawn from the Earth; or veils himself in that wide-wasting Whirlwind of a departing Era, wherein the fewest can discern his goings. Not Godhead, but an iron, ignoble circle of Necessity embraces all things; binds the youth of these times into a sluggish thrall, or else exasperates him into a rebel. Heroic Action is paralysed; for what worth now remains unquestionable with him? At the fervid period when his whole nature cries aloud for Action, there is nothing sacred under whose banner he can act; the course and kind and conditions of free Action are all but undiscoverable. Doubt storms-in on him through every avenue; inquiries of the deepest, painfullest sort must be engaged with; and the invincible energy of young years waste itself in sceptical, suicidal cavillings; in passionate 'questionings of Destiny, whereto no answer will be returned.'

For men, in whom the old perennial principle of Hunger (be it Hunger of the poor Day-drudge who stills it with eighteenpence a-day, or of the ambitious Placehunter who can nowise still it with so little) suffices to fill up existence, the case is bad; but not the worst. These men have an aim, such as it is; and can steer towards it, with chagrin enough truly; yet, as their hands are kept full, without desperation. Unhappier are they to whom a higher instinct has been given; who struggle to be persons, not machines; to whom the Universe is not a warehouse, or at best a fancy-bazaar, but a mystic temple and hall of doom. For such men there lie properly two courses open. The lower, yet still an estimable class, take up with worn-out Symbols of the Godlike; keep trimming and truckling between these and Hypocrisy, purblindly enough, miserably enough. A numerous intermediate class end in Denial; and form a theory that there is no theory; that nothing is certain in the world, except this fact of Pleasure being pleasant; so they try to realise what trifling modicum of Pleasure they can come at, and to live contented therewith, winking hard. Of these we speak not here; but only of the second nobler class, who also have dared to say No, and cannot yet say Yea; but feel that in the No they dwell as in a Golgotha, where life enters not, where peace is not appointed them. Hard, for most part, is the fate of such men; the harder the nobler they are. In dim forecastings, wrestles within them the 'Divine Idea of the World,' yet will nowhere visibly reveal itself. They have to realise a Worship for themselves, or live unworshipping. The Godlike has vanished from the world; and they, by the strong cry of their soul's agony, like true wonder-workers, must again evoke its presence. This miracle is their appointed task; which they must accomplish, or die wretchedly: this miracle has been accomplished by such; but not in our land; our land yet knows not of it. Behold a Byron, in melodious tones, 'cursing his day:' he mistakes earthborn passionate Desire for Heaven-inspired Freewill: without heavenly loadstar, rushes madly into the dance of Meteoric lights that hover on the mad Mahlstrom; and goes down among its eddies. Hear a Shelley filling the earth with inarticulate wail; like the infinite, inarticulate grief and weeping of forsaken infants. A noble Friedrich Schlegel, stupefied in that fearful loneliness, as of a silenced battlefield, flies back to Catholicism; as a child might to its slain mother's bosom, and cling there. In lower regions, how many a poor Hazlitt must wander on God's verdant earth, like the Unblest on burning deserts; passionately dig wells, and draw up only the dry quicksand; believe that he is seeking Truth, yet only wrestle among endless Sophisms, doing desperate battle as with spectre-hosts; and die and make no sign!

To the better order of such minds any mad joy of Denial has long since ceased: the problem is not now to deny, but to ascertain and perform. Once in destroying the False, there was a certain inspiration; but now the genius of Destruction has done its work, there is now nothing more to destroy. The doom of the Old has long been pronounced, and irrevocable; the Old has passed away: but, alas, the New appears not in its stead; the Time is still in pangs of travail with the New. Man has walked by the light of conflagrations, and amid the sound of falling cities; and now there is darkness, and long watching till it be morning. The voice even of the faithful can but exclaim: 'As yet struggles the twelfth hour of the Night: birds of darkness are on the wing, spectres uproar, the dead walk, the living dream. —Thou, Eternal Providence, wilt cause the day to dawn!'[2]

Such being the condition, temporal and spiritual, of the world at our Epoch, can we wonder that the world 'listens to itself,' and struggles and writhes, everywhere externally and internally, like a thing in pain? Nay, is not even this unhealthy action of the world's Organisation, if the symptom of universal disease, yet also the symptom and sole means of restoration and cure? The effort of Nature, exerting her medicative force to cast out foreign impediments, and once more become One, become whole? In Practice, still more in Opinion, which is the precursor and prototype of Practice,

[2] Jean Paul's *Hesperus*. Vorrede.

there must needs be collision, convulsion; much has to be ground away. Thought must needs be Doubt and Inquiry, before it can again be Affirmation and Sacred Precept. Innumerable 'Philosophies of Man,' contending in boundless hubbub, must annihilate each other, before an inspired Poesy and Faith for Man can fashion itself together.

From this stunning hubbub, a true Babylonish confusion of tongues, we have here selected two Voices; less as objects of praise or condemnation, than as signs how far the confusion has reached, what prospect there is of its abating. Friedrich Schlegel's *Lectures*, delivered at Dresden, and Mr. Hope's *Essay*, published in London, are the latest utterances of European Speculation: far asunder in external place, they stand at a still wider distance in inward purport; are, indeed, so opposite and yet so cognate that they may, in many senses, represent the two Extremes of our whole modern system of Thought; and be said to include between them all the Metaphysical Philosophies, so often alluded to here, which, of late times, from France, Germany, England, have agitated and almost overwhelmed us. Both in regard to matter and to form, the relation of these two Works is significant enough.

Speaking first of their cognate qualities, let us remark, not without emotion, one quite extraneous point of agreement; the fact that the Writers of both have departed from this world; they have now finished their search, and had all doubts resolved: while we listen to the voice, the tongue that uttered it has gone silent forever. But the fundamental, all-pervading similarity lies in this circumstance, well worthy of being noted, that both these Philosophers are of the Dogmatic or Constructive sort: each in its way is a kind of Genesis; an endeavour to bring the Phenomena of man's Universe once more under some theoretic Scheme: in both there is a decided principle of unity; they strive after a result which shall be positive; their aim is not to question, but to establish. This, especially if we consider with what comprehensive concentrated force it is here exhibited, forms a new feature in such works.

Under all other aspects, there is the most irreconcilable opposition; a staring contrariety, such as might provoke contrasts, were there far fewer points of comparison. If Schlegel's Work is the apotheosis of Spiritualism; Hope's again is the apotheosis of Materialism: in the one, all Matter is evaporated into a Phenomenon, and terrestrial Life itself, with its whole doings and showings, held out as a Disturbance (*Zerrüttung*) produced by the *Zeitgeist* (Spirit of Time); in the other, Matter is distilled and sublimated into some semblance of Divinity: the one regards Space and Time as mere forms of man's mind, and without external existence or reality; the other supposes Space and Time to be 'incessantly created,' and rayed in upon us like a sort of 'gravitation.' Such is their difference in respect of purport: no less striking is it in respect of manner, talent, success and all outward characteristics. Thus, if in Schlegel we have to admire the power of Words, in Hope we stand astonished, it might almost be said, at the want of an articulate Language. To Schlegel his Philosophic Speech is obedient, dextrous, exact, like a promptly ministering genius; his names are so clear, so precise and vivid, that they almost (sometimes altogether) become things for him: with Hope there is no Philosophical Speech; but a painful, confused stammering, and struggling after such; or the tongue, as in dotish forgetfulness, maunders, low, long-winded, and speaks not the word intended, but another; so that here the scarcely intelligible, in these endless convolutions, becomes the wholly unreadable; and often we could ask, as that mad pupil did of his tutor in Philosophy, "But whether is Virtue a fluid, then, or a gas?" If the fact, that Schlegel, in the city of Dresden, could find audience for such high discourse, may excite our envy; this other fact, that a person of strong powers, skilled in English Thought and master of its Dialect, could write the *Origin and Prospects of Man*, may painfully remind us of the reproach, that England has now no language for Meditation; that England, the most calculative, is the least meditative, of all civilised countries.

It is not our purpose to offer any criticism of Schlegel's Book; in such limits as were possible here, we should despair of communicating even the faintest image of its significance. To the mass of readers, indeed, both among the Germans themselves, and still more elsewhere, it nowise addresses itself, and may lie forever sealed. We point it out as a remarkable document of the Time and of the Man; can recommend it, moreover, to all earnest Thinkers, as a work deserving their best regard; a work full of deep meditation, wherein the infinite mystery of Life, if not represented, is decisively recognised. Of Schlegel himself, and his character, and spiritual history, we can profess no thorough or final understanding; yet enough to make us view him with admiration and pity, nowise with harsh contemptuous censure; and must say, with clearest persuasion, that the outcry of his being 'a renegade,' and so forth, is but like other such outcries, a judgment where there was neither jury, nor evidence, nor judge. The candid reader, in this Book itself, to say nothing of all the rest, will find traces of a high, far-seeing, earnest spirit, to whom 'Austrian Pensions,' and the Kaiser's crown, and Austria altogether, were but a light matter to the finding and vitally appropriating of Truth. Let us respect the sacred mystery of a Person; rush not irreverently into man's Holy of Holies! Were the lost little one, as we said already, found 'sucking its dead mother, on the field of carnage,' could it be other than a spectacle for tears? A solemn mournful feeling comes over us when we see this last Work of Friedrich Schlegel, the unwearied seeker, end abruptly in the middle; and, as if he *had not* yet found, as if emblematically of much, end with an '*Aber*—,' with a 'But—!' This was the last word that came from the Pen of Friedrich Schlegel: about eleven at night he wrote it down, and there paused sick; at one in the morning, Time for him had merged itself in Eternity; he was, as we say, no more.

Still less can we attempt any criticism of Mr. Hope's new *Book of Genesis*. Indeed, under any circumstances, criticism of it were now impossible. Such an utterance could only be responded to in peals of laughter; and laughter sounds hollow and hideous through the vaults of the dead. Of this monstrous Anomaly, where all sciences are heaped and huddled together, and the principles of all are, with a childlike innocence, plied hither and thither, or wholly abolished in case of need; where the First Cause is figured as a huge Circle, with nothing to do but radiate 'gravitation' towards its centre; and so construct a Universe, wherein all, from the lowest cucumber with its coolness, up to the highest seraph with his love, were but 'gravitation,' direct or reflex, 'in more or less central globes,'—what can we say, except, with sorrow and shame, that it could have originated nowhere save in England? It is a general agglomerate of all facts, notions, whims and observations, as they lie in the brain of an English gentleman; as an English gentleman, of unusual thinking power, is led to fashion them, in his schools and in his world: all these thrown into the crucible, and if not fused, yet soldered or conglutinated with boundless patience; and now tumbled out here, heterogeneous, amorphous, unspeakable, a world's wonder. Most melancholy must we name the whole business; full of long-continued thought, earnestness, loftiness of mind; not without glances into the Deepest, a constant fearless endeavour after truth; and with all this nothing accomplished, but the perhaps absurdest Book written in our century by a thinking man. A shameful Abortion; which, however, need not now be smothered or mangled, for it is already dead; only, in our love and sorrowing reverence for the writer of *Anastasius*, and the heroic seeker of Light, though not bringer thereof, let it be buried and forgotten.

For ourselves, the loud discord which jars in these two Works, in innumerable works of the like import, and generally in all the Thought and Action of this period, does not any longer utterly confuse us. Unhappy who, in such a time, felt not, at all conjunctures, ineradicably in his heart the knowledge that a God made this Universe, and a Demon not! And shall Evil always prosper, then? Out of all Evil comes Good; and no Good that is possible but shall one day be real. Deep and sad as is our feeling that we stand yet in the bodeful Night; equally deep, indestructible is our assurance that the Morning also will not fail. Nay already, as we look round, streaks of a dayspring are in the east; it is dawning; when the time shall be fulfilled, it will be day. The progress of man towards higher and nobler developments of whatever is highest and noblest in him, lies not only prophesied to Faith, but now written to the eye of Observation, so that he who runs may read.

One great step of progress, for example, we should say in actual circumstances, was this same; the clear ascertainment that we are in progress. About the grand Course of Providence, and his final Purposes with us, we can know nothing, or almost nothing: man begins in darkness, ends in darkness; mystery is everywhere around us and in us, under our feet, among our hands. Nevertheless so much has become evident to every one, that this wondrous Mankind is advancing somewhither; that at least all human things are, have been and forever will be, in Movement and Change;—as, indeed, for beings that exist in Time, by virtue of Time, and are made of Time, might have been long since understood. In some provinces, it is true, as in Experimental Science, this discovery is an old one; but in most others it belongs wholly to these latter days. How often, in former ages, by eternal Creeds, eternal Forms of Government and the like, has it been attempted, fiercely enough, and with destructive violence, to chain the Future under the Past; and say to the Providence, whose ways with man are mysterious, and through the great deep: Hitherto shalt thou come, but no farther! A wholly insane attempt; and for man himself, could it prosper, the frightful-lest of all enchantments, a very Life-in-Death. Man's task here below, the destiny of every individual man, is to be in turns Apprentice and Workman; or say rather, Scholar, Teacher, Discoverer: by nature he has a strength for learning, for imitating; but also a strength for acting, for knowing on his own account. Are we not in a world seen to be Infinite; the relations lying closest together modified by those latest discovered and lying farthest asunder? Could you ever spellbind man into a scholar merely, so that he had nothing to discover, to correct; could you ever establish a Theory of the Universe that were entire, unimprovable, and which needed only to be got by heart; man then were spiritually defunct, the Species we now name Man had ceased to exist. But the gods, kinder to us than we are to ourselves, have forbidden such suicidal acts. As Phlogiston is displaced by Oxygen, and the Epicycles of Ptolemy by the Ellipses of Kepler; so does Paganism give place to Catholicism, Tyranny to Monarchy, and Feudalism to Representative Government,—where also the process does not stop. Per-fection of Practice, like completeness of Opinion, is always approaching, never arrived; Truth, in the words of Schiller, *immer wird, nie est;* never *is,* always *is a-being.*

Sad, truly, were our condition did we know but this, that Change is universal and inevitable. Launched into a dark shoreless sea of Pyrrhonism, what would remain for us but to sail aimless, hopeless; or make madly merry, while the devouring Death had not yet engulfed us? As indeed, we have seen many, and still see many do. Nevertheless so stands it not. The venerator of the Past (and to what pure heart is the Past, in that 'moonlight of memory,' other than sad and holy?) sorrows not over its departure, as one utterly bereaved. The true Past departs not, nothing that was worthy in the Past departs; no Truth or Goodness realised by man ever dies, or can die; but is all still here, and, recognised or not, lives and works through endless changes. If all things, to speak in the German dialect, are discerned by us, and exist for us, in an element of Time, and therefore of Mortality and Mutability; yet Time itself reposes on Eternity; the truly Great and Transcendental has its basis and substance in Eternity: stands revealed to us as Eternity in a vesture of Time. Thus in all Poetry, Worship, Art, Society, as one form passes into another, nothing is lost: it is but the super-ficial, as it were the *body* only, that grows obsolete and dies; under the mortal body lies a *soul* which is immortal; which anew incarnates itself in fairer revelation; and the Present is the living sum-total of the whole Past.

In Change, therefore, there is nothing terrible, nothing supernatural: on the contrary, it lies in the very essence of our lot and life in this world. To-day is not yesterday: we ourselves change; how can our Works and Thoughts, if they are always to be the fittest, continue always the same? Change, indeed, is painful; yet ever needful: and if Memory have its force and worth, so also has Hope. Nay, if we look well to it, what is all Derangement, and necessity of great Change, in itself such an evil, but the product simply of *increased resources* which the old *methods* can no longer administer; of new wealth which the old coffers will no longer contain? What is it, for example, that in our own day bursts asunder the bonds of ancient Political Systems, and perplexes all Europe with the fear of Change, but even this: the increase of social resources, which the old social methods will no longer sufficiently administer? The new omnipotence of the Steam-engine is hewing asunder quite other mountains than the physical. Have not our economical distresses, those barnyard Conflagrations themselves, the frightfullest madness of our mad epoch, their rise also in what is a real increase: increase of Men; of human Force; properly, in such a Planet as ours, the most precious of all increases? It is true again, the ancient methods of administration will no longer suffice. Must the indomitable millions, full of old Saxon energy and fire, lie cooped up in this Western Nook, choking one another, as in a Blackhole of Calcutta, while a whole fertile untenanted Earth, desolate for want of the ploughshare, cries: Come and till me, come and reap me? If the ancient Captains can no longer yield guidance, new must be sought after: for the difficulty lies not in nature, but in artifice; the European Calcutta-Blackhole has no walls but air ones and paper ones.—So too, Scepticism itself, with its innumerable mischiefs, what is it but the sour fruit of a most blessed increase, that of Knowledge; a fruit too that will not always continue *sour?*

In fact, much as we have said and mourned about the unproductive prevalence of Metaphysics, it was not without some insight into the use that lies in them. Metaphysical Speculation, if a necessary evil, is the forerunner of much good. The fever of Scepticism must needs burn itself out, and burn out thereby the Impurities that caused it; then again will there be clearness, health. The principle of life, which now struggles painfully, in the outer, thin and barren domain of the Conscious or Mechanical, may then withdraw into its inner sanctuaries, its abysses of mystery and miracle; withdraw deeper than ever into that domain of the unconscious, by nature infinite and inexhaustible; and creatively work there. From that mystic region, and from that alone, all wonders, all Poesies, and Religions, and Social Systems have proceeded: the like wonders, and greater and higher, lie slumbering there; and, brooded on by the spirit of the waters, will evolve themselves, and rise like exhalations from the Deep.

Of our Modern Metaphysics, accordingly, may not this already be said, that if they have produced no Affirmation, they have destroyed much Negation? It is a disease expelling a disease: the fire of Doubt, as above hinted, consuming away the Doubtful; that so the Certain come to light, and again lie visible on the surface. English or French Metaphysics, in reference to this last stage of the speculative process, are not what we allude to here; but only the Metaphysics of the Germans. In France or England, since the days of Diderot and Hume, though all thought has been of a sceptico-metaphysical texture, so far as there was any Thought, we have seen no Metaphysics; but only more or less ineffectual questionings whether such could be. In the Pyrrhonism of Hume and the Materialism of Diderot, Logic had, as it were, overshot itself, overset itself. Now, though the athlete, to use our old figure, cannot, by much lifting, lift up his own body, he may shift it out of a laming posture, and get to stand in a free one. Such a service have German Metaphysics done for man's mind. The second sickness of Speculation has abolished both itself and the first. Friedrich Schlegel complains much of the fruitlessness, the tumult and transiency of German as of all Metaphysics; and with reason. Yet in that wide-spreading, deep-whirling vortex of Kantism, so soon metamorphosed into Fichteism, Schellingism, and then as Hegelism, and Cousinism, perhaps finally evaporated, is not this issue visible enough? That Pyrrhonism and Materialism, themselves necessary phenomena in European culture, have disappeared; and a Faith in Religion has again become possible and inevitable for the scientific mind; and the word *Free*-thinker no longer means the Denier or Caviller, but the Believer, or the Ready to believe? Nay, in the higher Literature of Germany, there already lies, for him that can read it, the beginning of a new revelation of the Godlike; as yet unrecognised by the mass of the world; but waiting there for recognition, and sure to find it when the fit hour comes. This age also is not wholly without its Prophets.

Again, under another aspect, if Utilitarianism, or Radicalism, or the Mechanical Philosophy, or by whatever name it is called, has still its long task to do; nevertheless we can now see through it and beyond it: in the better heads, even among us English, it has become obsolete; as in other countries, it has been, in such heads, for some forty or even fifty years. What sound mind among the French, for example, now fancies that men can be governed by 'Constitutions;' by the never so cunning mechanising of Self-interests, and all conceivable adjustments of checking and balancing; in a word, by the best possible solution of this quite insoluble and impossible problem, *Given a world of Knaves, to produce an Honesty from their united action?* Were not experiments enough of this kind tried before all Europe, and found wanting, when, in that doomsday of France, the infinite gulf of human Passion shivered asunder the thin rinds of Habit; and burst forth all-devouring, as in seas of Nether Fire? Which cunningly-devised 'Constitution,' constitutional, republican, democratic, sansculottic, could bind that raging chasm together? Were they not all burnt up, like paper as they were, in its molten eddies; and still the fire-sea raged fiercer than before? It is not by Mechanism, but by Religion; not by Self-interest, but by Loyalty, that men are governed or governable.

Remarkable it is, truly, how everywhere the eternal fact begins again to be recognised, that there is a Godlike in human affairs; that God not only made us and beholds us, but is in us and around us; that the Age of Miracles, as it ever was, now is. Such recognition we discern on all hands and in all countries: in each country after its own fashion. In France, among the younger nobler minds, strangely enough; where, in their loud contention with the Actual and Conscious, the Ideal or Unconscious is, for the time, without exponent; where Religion means not the parent of Polity, as of all that is highest, but of Polity itself; and this and the other earnest man has not been wanting, who could audibly whisper to himself: "Go to, I will make a religion." In England still more strangely; as in all things, worthy England will have its way: by thy shrieking of hysterical women, casting out of devils, and other 'gifts of the Holy Ghost.' Well might Jean Paul say, in this his twelfth hour of the Night, 'the living dream;' well might he say, 'the dead walk.' Meanwhile let us rejoice rather that so much has been seen into, were it through never so diffracting media, and never so madly distorted; that in all dialects, though but half-articulately, this high Gospel begins to be preached: Man is still Man. The genius of Mechanism, as was once before predicted, will not always sit like a choking incubus on our soul; but at length when by a new magic Word the old spell is broken, become our slave, and as familiar-spirit do all our bidding. 'We are near awakening when we dream that we dream.'

He that has an eye and a heart can even now say: Why should I falter? Light has come into the world; to such as love Light, so as Light must be loved, with a boundless all-doing, all-enduring love. For the rest, let that vain struggle to read the mystery of the Infinite cease to harass us. It is a mystery which, through all ages, we shall only read here a line of, there another line of. Do we not already know that the name of the Infinite is GOOD, is GOD? Here on Earth we are as Soldiers, fighting in a foreign land; that understand not the plan of the campaign, and have no need to understand it; seeing well what is at our hand to be done. Let us do it like Soldiers, with submission, with courage, with a heroic joy. 'Whatsoever thy hand findeth to do, do it with all thy might.' Behind us, behind each one of us, lie Six Thousand Years of human effort, human conquest: before us is the boundless Time, with its as yet uncreated and unconquered Continents and Eldorados, which we, even we, have to conquer, to create; and from the bosom of Eternity there shine for us celestial guiding stars.

> 'My inheritance how wide and fair!
> Time is my fair seed-field, of Time I'm heir.'

PAST AND PRESENT: THE MODERN WORKER

PAST AND PRESENT: THE MODERN WORKER

CHAPTER I.

PHENOMENA.

But, it is said, our religion is gone; we no longer believe in St. Edmund, no longer see the figure of him 'on the rim of the sky,' minatory or confirmatory! God's absolute Laws, sanctioned by an eternal Heaven and an eternal Hell, have become Moral Philosophies, sanctioned by able computations of Profit and Loss, by weak considerations of Pleasures of Virtue and the Moral Sublime.

It is even so. To speak in the ancient dialect, we 'have forgotten God;'— in the most modern dialect and very truth of the matter, we have taken up the Fact of this Universe as it *is not*. We have quietly closed our eyes to the eternal Substance of things, and opened them only to the Shews and Shams of things. We quietly believe this Universe to be intrinsically a great unintelligible PERHAPS; extrinsically, clear enough, it is a great, most extensive Cattlefold and workhouse, with most extensive Kitchen-ranges, Dining-tables,—whereat he is wise who can find a place! All the Truth of this Universe is uncertain; only the profit and loss of it, the pudding and praise of it, are and remain very visible to the practical man.

There is no longer any God for us! God's Laws are become a Greatest-Happiness Principle, a Parliamentary Expediency: the Heavens overarch us only as an Astronomical Time-keeper; a butt for Herschel-telescopes to shoot science at, to shoot sentimentalities at:—in our and old Johnson's dialect, man has lost the *soul* out of him; and now, after the due period,— begins to find the want of it! This is verily the plague-spot; centre of the universal Social Gangrene, threatening all modern things with frightful death. To him that will consider it, here is the stem, with its roots and taproot, with its world-wide upas-boughs and accursed poison exudations, under which the world lies writhing in apathy and agony. You touch the focal-centre of all our diseases, of our frightful nosology of diseases, when you lay your hand on this. There is no religion; there is no God; man has lost his soul, and vainly seeks antiseptic salt. Vainly: in killing Kings, in passing Reform Bills, in French Revolutions, Manchester Insurrections, is found no remedy. The foul elephantine leprosy, alleviated for an hour, reappears in new force and desperateness next hour.

For actually this is *not* the real fact of the world; the world is not made so, but otherwise!—Truly, any Society setting out from this No-God hypothesis will arrive at a result or two. The *Un*veracities, escorted, each *Un*veracity of them by its corresponding Misery and Penalty; the Phantasms, and Fatuities, and ten-years Corn-Law Debatings, that shall walk the

Earth at noonday,—must needs be numerous! The Universe *being* intrinsically a Perhaps, being too probably an 'infinite Humbug,' why should any minor Humbug astonish us? It is all according to the order of Nature; and Phantasms riding with huge clatter along the streets, from end to end of our existence, astonish nobody, Enchanted St. Ives Workhouses and Joe-Manton Aristocracies; giant Working Mammonism near strangled in the partridge-nets of giant-looking Idle Dilettantism,—this, in all its branches, in its thousand thousand modes and figures, is a sight familiar to us.

The Popish Religion, we are told, flourishes extremely in these years; and is the most vivacious-looking religion to be met with at present. "*Elle a trois cents ans dans le ventre,*" counts M. Jouffroy; "*c'est pourquoi je la respecte!*" —The old Pope of Rome, finding it laborious to kneel so long while they cart him through the streets to bless the people on *Corpus-Christi* Day, complains of rheumatism; whereupon his Cardinals consult;—construct him, after some study, a stuffed cloaked figure, of iron and wood, with wool or baked hair; and place it in a kneeling posture. Stuffed figure, or rump of a figure; to this stuffed rump he, sitting at his ease on a lower level, joins, by the aid of cloaks and drapery, his living head and outspread hands; the rump with its cloak kneels, the Pope looks, and holds his hands spread; and so the two in concert bless the Roman population on *Corpus-Christi* Day, as well as they can.

I have considered this amphibious Pope, with the wool-and-iron back, with the flesh head and hands; and endeavoured to calculate his horoscope. I reckon him the remarkablest Pontiff that has darkened God's daylight, or painted himself in the human retina, for these several thousand years. Nay, since Chaos first shivered, and 'sneezed,' as the Arabs say, with the first shaft of sunlight shot through it, what stranger product was there of Nature and Art working together? Here is a Supreme Priest who believes God to be—What, in the name of God, *does* he believe God to be?—and discerns that all worship of God is a scenic phantasmagory of wax-candles, organ-blasts, Gregorian Chants, mass-brayings, purple monsignori, wool-and-iron rumps, artistically spread out,—to save the ignorant from worse.

O reader, I say not who are Belial's elect. This poor amphibious Pope too gives loaves to the Poor; has in him more good latent than he is himself aware of. His poor Jesuits, in the late Italian Cholera, were, with a few German Doctors, the only creatures whom dastard terror had not driven mad: they descended fearless into all gulfs and bedlams; watched over the pillow of the dying, with help, with counsel and hope; shone as luminous fixed stars, when all else had gone out in chaotic night: honour to them! This Poor Pope,—who knows what good is in him? In a Time otherwise too prone to forget, he keeps up the mournfulest ghastly memorial of the Highest, Blessedest, which once was; which, in new fit forms, will again partly have to be. Is he not as a perpetual death's-head and cross-bones, with their *Resurgam*, on the grave of a Universal Heroism,—grave of a Christianity? Such Noblenesses, purchased by the world's best heart's-blood, must not be lost; we cannot afford to lose them, in what confusions soever. To all of us the day will come, to a few of us it has already come, when no mortal, with his heart yearning for a 'Divine Humility,' or other 'Highest form of Valour,' will need to look for it in death's-heads, but will see it round him in here and there a beautiful living head.

Besides, there is in this poor Pope, and his practice of the Scenic Theory of Worship, a frankness which I rather honour. Not half and half, but with undivided heart does *he* set about worshipping by stage machinery; as if there were now, and could again be, in Nature no other. He will ask you, What other? Under this my Gregorian Chant, and beautiful wax-light Phantasmagory, kindly hidden from you is an Abyss, of black Doubt, Scepticism, nay Sansculottic Jacobinism; an Orcus that has no bottom. Think of that. 'Groby Pool *is* thatched with pancakes,'—as Jeannie Deans's Innkeeper defied it to be! The Bottomless of Scepticism, Atheism, Jacobinism, behold, it is thatched over, hidden from your despair, by stage-properties judiciously arranged. This stuffed rump of mine saves not me only from rheumatism, but you also from what other *isms!* In this your Life-pilgrimage No-whither, a fine Squallacci marching-music, and Gregorian Chant, accompanies you, and the hollow Night of Orcus is well hid!

Yes truly, few men that worship by the rotatory Calabash of the Calmucks do it in half so great, frank or effectual a way. Drury-lane, it is said, and that is saying much, might learn from him in the dressing of parts, in the arrangement of lights and shadows. He is the greatest Play-actor that at present draws salary in this world. Poor Pope; and I am told he is fast growing bankrupt too; and will, in a measurable term of years (a great way *within* the 'three hundred') not have a penny to make his pot boil! His old rheumatic back will then get to rest; and himself and his stage-properties sleep well in Chaos for evermore.

Or, alas, why go to Rome for Phantasms walking the streets? Phantasms, ghosts, in this midnight hour, hold jubilee, and screech and jabber; and the question rather were, What high Reality anywhere is yet awake? Aristocracy has become Phantasm-Aristocracy, no longer able to *do* its work, not in the least conscious that it has any work longer to do. Unable, totally careless to *do* its work; careful only to clamour for the *wages* of doing its work,—nay for higher, and *palpably* undue wages, and Corn-Laws and *increase* of rents; the old rate of wages not being adequate now! In hydra-wrestle, giant '*Millo*cracy' so called, a real giant, though as yet a blind one and but half-awake, wrestles and wrings in choking nightmare, 'like to be strangled in the partridge-nets of Phantasm-Aristocracy,' as we said, which fancies itself still to be a giant. Wrestles, as under nightmare, till it do awaken; and gasps and struggles thousand-fold, we may say, in a truly painful manner, through all fibres of our English Existence, in these hours and years! Is our poor English Existence wholly becoming a Nightmare; full of mere Phantasms?—

The Champion of England, cased in iron or tin, rides into Westminster Hall, 'being lifted into his saddle with little assistance,' and there asks, If in the four quarters of the world, under the cope of Heaven, is any man or demon that dare question the right of this King? Under the cope of Heaven no man makes intelligible answer,—as several men ought already to have done. Does not this Champion too know the world; that it is a huge Imposture, and bottomless Inanity, thatched over with bright cloth and other ingenious tissues? Him let us leave there, questioning all men and demons.

Him we have left to his destiny; but whom else have we found? From this the highest apex of things, downwards through all strata and breadths, how many fully awakened Realities have we fallen in with: alas, on the contrary, what troops and populations of Phantasms, not God-Veracities but Devil-Falsities, down to the very lowest stratum,—which now, by such superincumbent weight of Unveracities, lies enchanted in St. Ives' Workhouses, broad enough, helpless enough! You will walk in no public thoroughfare or remotest byway of English Existence but you will meet a man, an interest of men, that has given up hope in the Everlasting, True, and placed its hope in the Temporary, half or wholly False. The Honourable Member complains unmusically that there is 'devil's-dust' in Yorkshire cloth. Yorkshire cloth—why, the very Paper I now write on is made, it seems, partly of plaster-lime well-smoothed, and obstructs my writing! You are lucky if you can find now any good Paper,—any work really *done;* search where you will, from highest Phantasm apex to lowest Enchanted basis.

Consider for example that great Hat seven-feet high, which now perambulates London Streets; which my Friend Sauerteig regarded justly as one of our English notabilities; "the topmost point as yet," said he, "would it were your culminating and returning point, to which English Puffery has been observed to reach!"—the Hatter in the Strand of London, instead of making better felt-hats than another, mounts a huge lath-and-plaster Hat, seven-feet high, upon wheels; sends a man to drive it through the streets; hoping to be saved *thereby.* He has not attempted to *make* better hats, as he was appointed by the Universe to do, and as with this ingenuity of his he could very probably have done; but his whole industry is turned to *persuade* us that he has made such! He too knows that the Quack has become God. Laugh not at him, O Reader; or do not laugh only. He has ceased to be comic; he is fast becoming tragic. To me this all-deafening blast of Puffery, of poor Falsehood grown necessitous, of poor Heart-Atheism fallen now into Enchanted Workhouses, sounds too surely like a Doom's-blast. I have to say to myself in old dialect: "God's blessing is not written on all this; His curse is written on all this!" Unless perhaps the Universe *be* a chimera; —some old totally deranged eightday clock, dead as brass; which the Maker, if there ever was any Maker, has long ceased to meddle with?—To my friend Sauerteig this poor seven-feet Hat-Manufacturer, as the top-stone of English Puffery, was very notable.

Alas, that we natives note him little, that we view him as a thing of course, is the very burden of the misery. We take it for granted, the most rigorous of us, that all men who have made anything are expected and entitled to make the loudest possible proclamation of it, and call on a discerning public to reward them for it. Every man his own trumpeter; that is, to a really alarming extent, the accepted rule. Make loudest possible proclamation of your Hat: true proclamation if that will do; if that will not do, then false proclamation,—to such extent of falsity as will serve your purpose; as will not seem too false to be credible!—I answer, once for all, that the fact is not so. Nature requires no man to make proclamation of his doings and hat-makings; Nature forbids all men to make such. There is not a man or hat-maker born into the world but feels, or has felt, that he is degrading himself if he speak of his excellencies and prowesses, and supremacy in his craft: his inmost heart says to him, "Leave thy friends to speak of these; if possible, thy enemies to speak of these; but at all events, thy friends!" He feels that he is already a poor braggart; fast hastening to be a falsity and speaker of the Untruth.

Nature's Laws, I must repeat, are eternal: her small still voice, speaking from the inmost heart of us, shall not, under terrible penalties, be disregarded. No one man can depart from the truth without damage to himself; no one million of men; no Twenty-seven Millions of men. Shew me a Nation fallen everywhere into this course, so that each expects it, permits it to others and himself, I will shew you a nation travelling with one assent on the broad way. The broad way, however many Banks of England, Cotton-Mills and Duke's Palaces it may have. Not at happy Elysian fields, and everlasting crowns of victory, earned by silent Valour, will this Nation arrive; but at precipices, devouring gulfs, if it pause not. Nature has appointed happy fields, victorious laurel-crowns; but only to the brave and true: *Un*nature, what we call Chaos, holds nothing in it but vacuities, devouring gulfs. What are Twenty-seven Millions, and their unanimity? Believe them not: the Worlds and the Ages, God and Nature and All Men say otherwise.

'Rhetoric all this?' No, my brother, very singular to say, it is Fact all this. Cocker's Arithmetic is not truer. Forgotten in these days, it is old as the foundations of the Universe, and will endure till the Universe cease. It is forgotten now; and the first mention of it puckers thy sweet countenance into a sneer: but it will be brought to mind again,—unless indeed the Law of Gravitation chance to cease, and men find that they *can* walk on vacancy. Unanimity of the Twenty-seven Millions will do nothing; walk not thou with them; fly from them as for thy life. Twenty-seven Millions travelling on such courses, with gold jingling in every pocket, with vivats heaven-high, are incessantly advancing, let me again remind thee, towards the *firm-land's end*,—towards the end and extinction of what Faithfulness, Veracity, real Worth, was in their way of life. Their noble ancestors have fashioned for them a 'life-road;'—in how many thousand senses, this! There is not an old wise Proverb on their tongue, an honest Principle articulated in their hearts into utterance, a wise true method of doing and despatching any work or commerce of men, but helps yet to carry them forward. Life is still possible to them, because all is not yet Puffery, Falsity, Mammon-worship and

Unnature; because somewhat is yet Faithfulness, Veracity and Valour. With a certain very considerable finite quantity of Unveracity and Phantasm, social life is still possible; not with an infinite quantity! Exceed your certain quantity, the seven-feet Hat, and all things upwards to the very Champion cased in tin, begin to reel and flounder,—in Manchester Insurrections, Chartisms, Sliding-scales; the Law of Gravitation not forgetting to act. You advance incessantly towards the land's end; you are, literally enough, 'consuming the way.' Step after step, Twenty-seven Million unconscious men;—till you are *at* the land's end; till there is not faithfulness enough among you any more: and the next step now is lifted *not* over land, but into air, over ocean-deeps and roaring abysses:—unless perhaps the Law of Gravitation have forgotten to act?

Oh, it is frightful when a whole Nation, as our Fathers used to say, has 'forgotten God;' has remembered only Mammon, and what Mammon leads to! When your self-trumpeting Hat-maker is the emblem of almost all makers, and workers, and men, that make anything,—from soul-overseerships, body-overseerships, epic poems, acts of parliament, to hats and shoe-blacking! Not one false man but does unaccountable mischief: how much, in a generation or two, will Twenty-seven Millions, mostly false, manage to accumulate? The sum of it, visible in every street, market-place, senate-house, circulating library, cathedral, cotton-mill, and union-workhouse, fills one *not* with a comic feeling!

CHAPTER II.

GOSPEL OF MAMMONISM.

READER, even Christian Reader as thy title goes, hast thou any notion of Heaven and Hell? I rather apprehend, not. Often as the words are on our tongue, they have got a fabulous or semi-fabulous character for most of us, and pass on like a kind of transient similitude, like a sound signifying little.

Yet it is well worth while for us to know, once and always, that they are not a similitude, nor a fable nor a semi-fable; that they are an everlasting highest fact! "No Lake of Sicilian or other sulphur burns now anywhere in these ages," sayest thou? Well, and if there did not! Believe that there does not; believe it if thou wilt, nay hold by it as a real increase, a rise to higher stages, to wider horizons and empires. All this has vanished, or has not vanished; believe as thou wilt as to all this. But that an Infinite of Practical Importance, speaking with strict arithmetical exactness, an *Infinite*, has vanished or can vanish from the Life of any Man: this thou shalt not believe! O brother, the Infinite of Terror, of Hope, of Pity, did it not at any moment disclose itself to thee, indubitable, unnameable? Came it never, like the gleam of *preter*-natural eternal Oceans, like the voice of old Eternities, far-sounding through thy heart of hearts? Never? Alas, it was not thy Liberalism then; it was thy Animalism! The Infinite is more sure than any other fact. But only men can discern it; mere building beavers, spinning arachnes, much more the predatory vulturous and vulphine species, do not discern it well!—

'The word Hell,' says Sauerteig, 'is still frequently in use among the English People: but I could not without difficulty ascertain what they meant by it. Hell generally signifies the Infinite Terror, the thing a man *is* infinitely afraid of, and shudders and shrinks from, struggling with his whole soul to escape from it. There is a Hell therefore, if you will consider, which accompanies man, in all stages of his history, and religious or other development: but the Hells of men and Peoples differ notably. With Christians it is the infinite terror of being found guilty before the Just Judge. With old Romans, I conjecture, it was the terror not of Pluto, for whom probably they cared little, but of doing unworthily, doing unvirtuously, which was their word for un*man*fully. And now what is it, if you pierce through his Cants, his oft-repeated Hearsays, what he calls his Worships and so forth,— what is it that the modern English soul does, in very truth, dread infinitely, and contemplate with entire despair? What *is* his Hell; after all these reputable, oft-repeated Hearsays, what is it? With hesitation, with astonishment, I pronounce it to be: The terror of "Not succeeding;" of not making money, fame, or some other figure in the world,—chiefly of not making money! Is not that a somewhat singular Hell?'

Yes, O Sauerteig, it is very singular. If we do not 'succeed,' where is the use of us? We had better never have been born. "Tremble intensely," as our friend the Emperor of China says: *there* is the black Bottomless of Terror; what Sauerteig calls the 'Hell of the English!'—But indeed this Hell belongs naturally to the Gospel of Mammonism, which also has its corresponding Heaven. For there *is* one Reality among so many phantasms; about one thing we are entirely in earnest: The making of money. Working Mammonism does divide the world with idle game-preserving Dilettantism:—thank Heaven that there is even a Mammonism, *any*thing we are in earnest about! Idleness is worst, Idleness alone is without hope: work earnestly at anything, you will by degrees learn to work at almost all things. There is endless hope in work, were it even work at making money.

True, it must be owned, we for the present, with our Mammon-Gospel, have come to strange conclusions. We call it a Society; and go about professing openly the totalest separation, isolation. Our life is not a mutual helpfulness; but rather, cloaked under due laws-of-war, named 'fair competition' and so forth, it is a mutual hostility. We have profoundly forgotten everywhere that *Cash-payment* is not the sole relation of human beings; we think, nothing doubting, that *it* absolves and liquidates all engagements of man. "My starving workers?" answers the rich Mill-owner. "Did not I hire them fairly in the market? Did I not pay them, to the last sixpence, the sum covenanted for? What have I to do with them more?"—Verily Mammon-worship is a melancholy creed. When Cain, for his own behoof, had killed Abel, and was questioned, "Where is thy brother?" he too made answer,

"Am I my brother's keeper?" Did I not pay my brother *his* wages, the thing he had merited from me?

O sumptuous Merchant-Prince, illustrious game-preserving Duke, is there no way of 'killing' thy brother but Cain's rude way! 'A good man by the very look of him, by his very presence with us as a fellow wayfarer in this Life-pilgrimage, *promises* so much:' wo to him if he forget all such promises, if he never know that they were given! To a deadened soul, seared with the brute Idolatry of Sense, to whom going to Hell is equivalent to not making money, all 'promises,' and moral duties, that cannot be pleaded for in Courts of Requests, address themselves in vain. Money he can be ordered to pay, but nothing more. I have not heard in all Past History, and expect not to hear in all Future History, of any Society anywhere under God's Heaven supporting itself on such Philosophy. The Universe is not made so; it is made otherwise than so. The man or nation of men that thinks it is made so, marches forward nothing doubting, step after step; but marches— whither we know! In these last two centuries of Atheistic Government (near two centuries now, since the blessed restoration of his Sacred Majesty, and Defender of the Faith, Charles Second), I reckon that we have pretty well exhausted what of 'firm earth' there was for us to march on;—and are now, very ominously, shuddering, reeling, and let us hope trying to recoil, on the cliff's edge!—

For out of this that we call Atheism come so many other *isms* and falsities, each falsity with its misery at its heels!—A soul is not like wind (*spiritus*, or breath) contained within a capsule; the ALMIGHTY MAKER is not like a Clockmaker that once, in old immemorial ages, having *made* his Horologe of a universe, sits ever since and sees it go! Not at all. Hence comes Atheism; come, as we say, many other *isms;* and as the sum of all, comes Valetism, the *reverse* of Heroism; sad root of all woes whatsoever. For indeed, as no man ever saw the above-said wind-element enclosed within its capsule, and finds it at bottom more deniable than conceivable; so too he finds, in spite of Bridgewater Bequests, your Clockmaker Almighty an entirely questionable affair, a deniable affair;—and accordingly denies it, and along with it so much else. Alas, one knows not what and how much else! For the faith in an Invisible, Unnameable, God-like, present everywhere in all that we see and work and suffer, is the essence of all faith whatsoever; and that once denied, or still worse, asserted with lips only, and out of bound prayer-books only, what other thing remains believable? That Cant well-ordered is marketable Cant: that Heroism means gas-lighted Histrionism; that seen with 'clear eyes' (as they call Valet-eyes), no man is a Hero, or ever was a Hero, but all men are Valets and Varlets. The accursed practical quintessence of all sorts of Unbelief! For if there be now no Hero, and the Histrio himself begin to be seen into, what hope is there for the seed of Adam here below? We are the doomed everlasting prey of the Quack; who, now in this guise, now in that, is to filch us, to pluck and eat us, by such modes as are convenient for him. For the modes and guises I care little. The Quack once inevitable, let him come swiftly, let him pluck and eat me;

—swiftly, that I may at least have done with him; for in his Quack-world I can have no wish to linger. Though he slay me, yet will I *not* trust in him. Though he conquer nations, and have all the Flunkeys of the Universe shouting at his heels, yet will I know well that *he* is an Inanity; that for him and his there is no continuance appointed, save only in Gehenna and the Pool. Alas, the Atheist world, from its utmost summits of Heaven and Westminster Hall, downwards through his poor seven-feet Hats and 'Unveracities fallen hungry,' down to the lowest cellars and neglected hunger-dens of it, is very wretched.

One of Dr. Alison's Scotch facts struck us much.[1] A poor Irish Widow, her husband having died in one of the Lanes of Edinburgh, went forth with her three children, bare of all resource, to solicit help from the Charitable Establishments of that City. At this Charitable Establishment and then at that she was refused: referred from one to the other, helped by none;—till she had exhausted them all; till her strength and heart failed her: she sank down in typhus fever; died, and infected her Lane with fever, so that 'seventeen other persons' died of fever there in consequence. The humane Physician asks thereupon, as with a heart too full for speaking, Would it not have been *economy* to help this poor Widow? She took typhus fever, and killed seventeen of you!—Very curious. The forlorn Irish Widow applies to her fellow-creatures, as if saying, "Behold I am sinking, bare of help; ye must help me! I am your sister, bone of your bone; one God made us; ye must help me!" They answer, "No; impossible: thou art no sister of ours." But she proves her sisterhood; her typhus fever kills *them;* they actually were her brothers, though denying it! Had human creature ever to go lower for a proof?

For, as indeed was very natural in such case, all government of the Poor by the Rich has long ago been given over to Supply-and-demand, Laissez-faire and such like, and universally declared to be 'impossible.' "You are no sister of ours; what shadow of proof is there? Here are our parchments, our padlocks, proving indisputably our money-safes to be *ours,* and you to have no business with them. Depart! It is impossible!"—Nay, what wouldst thou thyself have us do? cry indignant readers. Nothing, my friends,—till you have got a soul for yourselves again. Till then all things are 'impossible.' Till then I cannot even bid you buy, as the old Spartans would have done, two-pence worth of powder and lead, and compendiously shoot to death this poor Irish Widow: even that is 'impossible' for you. Nothing is left but that she prove her sisterhood by dying, and infecting you with typhus. Seventeen of you lying dead will not deny such proof that she *was* flesh of your flesh; and perhaps some of the living may lay it to heart.

'Impossible:' of a certain two-legged animal with feathers it is said, if you draw a distinct chalk-circle round him, he sits imprisoned, as if girt with the iron ring of Fate; and will die there, though within sight of victuals, or sit

[1] Observations on the Management of the Poor in Scotland: By William Pulteney Alison, M.D. (Edinburgh, 1840.)

in sick misery there, and be fatted to death. The name of this poor two-legged animal is—Goose; and they make of him, when well fattened, *Pâté de foie gras*, much prized by some!

CHAPTER III.

Gospel of Dilettantism.

But after all, the Gospel of Dilettantism, producing a Governing Class who do not govern, nor understand in the least that they are bound or expected to govern, is still mournfuler than that of Mammonism. Mammonism, as we said, at least work; this goes idle. Mammonism has seized some portion of the message of Nature to man; and seizing that, and following it, will seize and appropriate more and more of Nature's message: but Dilettantism has missed it wholly. 'Make money;' that will mean withal, 'Do work in order to make money.' But, 'Go gracefully idle in Mayfair,' what does or can that mean? An idle, game-preserving and even corn-lawing Aristocracy, in such an England as ours: has the world, if we take thought of it, ever seen such a phenomenon till very lately? Can it long continue to see such?

Accordingly the impotent, insolent Donothingism in Practice, and Say-nothingism in Speech, which we have to witness on that side of our affairs, is altogether amazing. A Corn-Law demonstrating itself openly, for ten years or more, with 'arguments' to make the angels, and some other classes of creatures, weep! For men are not ashamed to rise in Parliament and elsewhere, and speak the things they do *not* think. 'Expediency,' 'Necessities of Party,' &c. &c.! It is not known that the Tongue of Man is a sacred organ; that Man himself is definable in Philosophy as an 'Incarnate *Word;*' the Word not there, you have no Man there either, but a Phantasm instead! In this way it is that Absurdities may live long enough,—still walking, and talking for themselves, years and decades after the brains are quite out! How are 'the knaves and dastards' ever to be got 'arrested' at that rate?—

"No man in this fashionable London of yours," friend Sauerteig would say, "speaks a plain word to me. Every man feels bound to be something more than plain; to be pungent withal, witty, ornamental. His poor fraction of sense has to be perked into some epigrammatic shape, that it may prick into me;—perhaps (this is the commonest) to be topsyturvied, left standing on its head, that I may remember it the better! Such grinning inanity is very sad to the soul of man. Human faces should not grin on one like masks; they should look on one like faces! I love honest laughter, as I do sunlight; but not dishonest: most kinds of dancing too; but the St. Vitus kind not at all! A fashionable wit, *ach Himmel*, if you ask, Which, he or a Death's head, will be the cheerier company for me? pray send *not* him!"

Insincere Speech, truly, is the prime material of insincere Action. Action hangs, as it were, *dissolved* in Speech, in Thought whereof Speech is the shadow; and precipitates itself therefrom. The kind of Speech in a man betokens the kind of Action you will get from him. Our Speech, in these modern days, has become amazing. Johnson complained, "Nobody speaks in earnest, Sir; there is no serious conversation." To us all serious speech of men, as that of Seventeenth-Century Puritans, Twelfth-Century Catholics, German Poets of this Century, has become jargon, more or less insane. Cromwell was mad and a quack; Anselm, Becket, Goethe, *ditto, ditto*.

Perhaps few narratives in History or Mythology are more significant than that Moslem one, of Moses and the Dwellers by the Dead Sea. A tribe of men dwelt on the shores of that same Asphaltic Lake; and having forgotten, as we are all too prone to do, the inner facts of Nature, and taken up with the falsities and outer semblances of it, were fallen into sad conditions, —verging indeed towards a certain far deeper Lake. Whereupon it pleased kind Heaven to send them the Prophet Moses, with an instructive word of warning out of which might have sprung 'remedial measures' not a few. But no: the men of the Dead Sea discovered, as the valet-species always does in heroes or prophets, no comeliness in Moses; listened with real tedium to Moses, with light grinning, or with splenetic sniffs and sneers, affecting even to yawn; and signified, in short, that they found him a humbug, and even a bore. Such was the candid theory these men of the Asphalt Lake formed to themselves of Moses, That probably he was a humbug, and certainly he was a bore.

Moses withdrew; but Nature and her rigorous veracities did not withdraw. The men of the Dead Sea, when we next went to visit them, were all 'changed into Apes;'[1] sitting on the trees there, grinning now in the most *un*affected manner; gibbering and chattering very genuine nonsense; finding the whole Universe now a most indisputable Humbug! The Universe has *become* a Humbug to these Apes who thought it one. There they sit and chatter, to this hour: only, I believe, every Sabbath there returns to them a bewildered half-consciousness, half-reminiscence; and they sit, with their wizzened smoke-dried visages, and such an air of supreme tragicality as Apes may; looking out through those blinking smoke-bleared eyes of theirs, into the wonderfulest universal smoky Twilight and undecipherable disordered Dusk of Things; wholly an Uncertainty, Unintelligibility, they and it; and for commentary thereon, here and there an unmusical chatter or mew:— truest, tragicalest Humbug conceivable by the mind of man or ape! They made no use of their souls; and so have lost them. Their worship on the Sabbath now is to roost there, with unmusical screeches, and half-remember that they had souls.

Didst thou never, O Traveller, fall in with parties of this tribe? Meseems they are grown somewhat numerous in our day.

[1] Sale's Koran (*Introduction*).

CHAPTER IV.

HAPPY.

ALL WORK, even cotton-spinning, is noble; work is alone noble: be that here said and asserted once more. And in like manner, too, all dignity is painful; a life of ease is not for any man, nor for any god. The life of all gods figures itself to us as a Sublime Sadness,—earnestness of Infinite Battle against Infinite Labour. Our highest religion is named the 'Worship of Sorrow.' For the son of man there is no noble crown, well worn, or even ill worn, but is a crown of thorns!—These things, in spoken words, or still better, in felt instincts alive in every heart, were once well known.

Does not the whole wretchedness, the whole *Atheism* as I call it, of man's ways, in these generations, shadow itself for us in that unspeakable Life-philosophy of his: The pretension to be what he calls 'happy?' Every pitifulest whipster that walks within a skin has his head filled with the notion that he is, shall be, or by all human and divine laws ought to be, 'happy.' His wishes, the pitifulest whipster's, are to be fulfilled for him; his days, the pitifulest whipster's, are to flow on in ever-gentle current of enjoyment, impossible even for the gods. The prophets preach to us, Thou shalt be happy; thou shalt love pleasant things, and find them. The people clamour, Why have we not found pleasant things?

We construct our theory of Human Duties, not on any Greatest-Nobleness Principle, never so mistaken; no, but on a Greatest-Happiness Principle. 'The word *Soul* with us, as in some Slavonic dialects, seems to be synonymous with *Stomach*.' We plead and speak, in our Parliaments and elsewhere, not as from the Soul, but from the Stomach;—wherefore, indeed, our pleadings are so slow to profit. We plead not for God's Justice; we are not ashamed to stand clamouring and pleading for our own 'interests,' our own rents and trade-profits; we say, They are the 'interests' of so many; there is such an intense desire in us for them! We demand Free-Trade, with much just vociferation and benevolence, That the poorer classes, who are terribly ill-off at present, may have cheaper New-Orleans bacon. Men ask on Free-trade platforms, How can the indomitable spirit of Englishmen be kept up without plenty of bacon? We shall become a ruined Nation!— Surely, my friends, plenty of bacon is good and indispensable: but I doubt, you will never get even bacon by aiming only at that. You are men, not animals of prey, well-used or ill-used! Your Greatest-Happiness Principle seems to me fast becoming a rather unhappy one.—What if we should cease babbling about 'happiness,' and leave *it* resting on its own basis, as it used to do!

A gifted Byron rises in his wrath; and feeling too surely that he for his part is not 'happy,' declares the same in very violent language, as a piece of news that may be interesting. It evidently has surprised him much. One dislikes to see a man and poet reduced to proclaim on the streets such tidings; but on the whole, as matters go, that is not the most dislikable. Byron speaks the *truth* in this matter. Byron's large audience indicates how true it is felt to be.

'Happy,' my brother? First of all, what difference is it whether thou art happy or not! Today becomes Yesterday so fast, all Tomorrows become Yesterdays; and then there is no question whatever of the 'happiness,' but quite another question. Nay, thou hast such a sacred pity left at least for thyself, thy very pains, once gone over into Yesterday, become joys to thee. Besides, thou knowest not what heavenly blessedness and indispensable sanative virtue was in them; thou shalt only know it after many days, when thou art wiser!—A benevolent old Surgeon sat once in our company, with a Patient fallen sick by gourmandising, whom he had just, too briefly in the Patient's judgment, been examining. The foolish Patient still at intervals continued to break in on our discourse, which rather promised to take a philosophic turn: "But I have lost my appetite," said he, objurgatively, with a tone of irritated pathos; "I have no appetite; I can't eat!"—"My dear fellow," answered the Doctor in mildest tone, "it isn't of the slightest consequence;"—and continued his philosophical discoursings with us!

Or does the reader not know the history of that Scottish iron Misanthrope? The inmates of some town mansion, in those Northern parts, were thrown into the fearfulest alarm by indubitable symptoms of a ghost inhabiting the next house, or perhaps even the partition-wall! Ever at a certain hour, with preternatural gnarring, growling and screeching, which attended as running bass, there began, in a horrid, semi-articulate, unearthly voice, this song: "Once I was hap-hap-happy, but now I'm *mees*-erable! Clack-clack-clack, gnarr-r-r, whuz-z: Once I was hap-hap-happy, but now I'm *mees*-erable!"—Rest, rest, perturbed spirit;—or indeed, as the good old Doctor said: My dear fellow, it isn't of the slightest consequence! But no; the perturbed spirit could not rest; and to the neighbours, fretted, affrighted, or at least insufferably bored by him, it *was* of such consequence that they had to go and examine in his haunted chamber. In his haunted chamber, they find that the perturbed spirit is an unfortunate—Imitator of Byron? No, is an unfortunate rusty Meat-jack, gnarring and creaking with rust and work; and this, in Scottish dialect, is *its* Byronian musical Life-philosophy, sung according to ability!

Truly, I think the man who goes about pothering and uproaring for his 'happiness,'—pothering, and were it ballot-boxing, poem-making, or in what way soever fussing and exerting himself,—he is not the man that will help us to 'get our gnaves and dastards arrested!' No; he rather is on the way to increase the number,—by at least one unit and his tail! Observe, too, that this is all a modern affair; belongs not to the old heroic times, but to these dastard new times. 'Happiness our being's end and aim,' all that very paltry speculation, is at bottom, if we will count well, not yet two centuries old in the world.

The only happiness a brave man ever troubled himself with asking much about was, happiness enough to get his work done. Not "I can't eat!" but "I can't work!" that was the burden of all wise complaining among men. It is, after all, the one unhappiness of a man. That he cannot work; that he cannot get his destiny as a man fulfilled. Behold, the day is passing swiftly over, our life is passing swiftly over; and the night cometh when no man can work. The night once come, our happiness, our unhappiness,—it is all abolished; vanished, clean gone; a thing that has been: 'not of the slightest consequence' whether we were happy as eupeptic Curtis, as the fattest pig of Epicurus, or unhappy as Job with potsherds, as musical Byron with Giaours and sensibilities of the heart; as the unmusical Meat-jack with hard labour and rust! But our work,—behold that is not abolished, that has not vanished: our work, behold it remains, or the want of it remains;—for endless Times and Eternities, remains; and that is now the sole question with us forevermore! Brief brawling Day, with its noisy phantasms, its poor paper-crowns tinsel-gilt, is gone; and divine-everlasting Night with her star-diadems, with her silences and her veracities, is come! What hast thou done, and how? Happiness, unhappiness: all that was but the *wages* thou hadst; thou hast spent all that, in sustaining thyself hitherward; not a coin of it remains with thee, it is all spent, eaten: and now thy work, where is thy work? Swift, out with it, let us see thy work!

Of a truth, if man were not a poor hungry dastard, and even much of a blockhead withal, he would cease criticising his victuals to such extent; and criticise himself rather, what he does with his victuals!

CHAPTER V.

The English.

And yet, with all thy theoretic platitudes, what a depth of practical sense in thee, great England! Depth of sense, of justice, and courage; in which, under all emergencies and world-bewilderments, and under this most complex of emergencies we now live in, there is still hope, there is still assurance! The English are a dumb people. They can do great acts, but not describe them. Like the old Romans and some few others, *their* Epic Poem is written on the earth's surface: England her Mark! It is complained that they have no artists: one Shakspeare indeed; but for Raphael only a Reynolds; for Mozart nothing but a Mr. Bishop; not a picture, not a song. And yet they did produce one Shakspeare: consider how the element of Shakspearean melody does lie imprisoned in their nature; reduced to unfold itself in mere Cotton-mills, Constitutional Governments, and such like;—all the more interesting when it does become visible, as even in such unexpected shapes it succeeds in doing! Goethe spoke of the Horse, how impressive, almost affecting it was that an animal of such qualities should stand obstructed so;

its speech nothing but an inarticulate neighing, its handiness mere *hoof*iness, the fingers all constricted, tied together, the finger-nails coagulated into a mere hoof, shod with iron. The more significant, thinks he, are those eye-flashings of the generous noble quadruped; those prancings, curvings of the neck clothed with thunder.

A Dog of Knowledge has free utterance; but the Warhorse is almost mute, very far from free! It is even so. Truly, your freest utterances are not by any means always the best: they are the worst rather; the feeblest, trivialest; their meaning prompt, but small, ephemeral. Commend me to the silent English, to the silent Romans. Nay, the silent Russians too I believe to be worth something: are they not even now drilling, under much obloquy, an immense semi-barbarous half-world from Finland to Kamchatka, into rule, subordination, civilisation,—really in an old Roman fashion; speaking no word about it; quietly hearing all manner of vituperative Able Editors speak! While your ever-talking, ever-gesticulating French, for example, what are they at this moment drilling?—Nay, of all animals, the freest of utterance, I should judge, is the genus *Simia:* go into the Indian woods, say all Travellers, and look what a brisk, adroit, unresting Ape-population it is!

The spoken Word, the written Poem, is said to be an epitome of the man; how much more the done Work. Whatsoever of morality and of intelligence; what of patience, perseverance, faithfulness, of method, insight, ingenuity, energy; in a word, whatsoever of Strength the man had in him will lie written in the Work he does. To work: why, it is to try himself against Nature, and her everlasting unerring Laws; these will tell a true verdict as to the man. So much of virtue and of faculty did *we* find in him; so much and no more! He had such capacity of harmonising himself with *me* and my unalterable ever-veracious Laws; of coöperating and working as *I* bade him;—and has prospered, and has not prospered, as you see?— Working as great Nature bade him: does not that mean virtue of a kind; nay, of all kinds? Cotton can be spun and sold, Lancashire operatives can be got to spin it, and at length one has the woven webs and sells them, by following Nature's regulations in that matter: by not following Nature's regulations, you have them not. You have them not;—there is no Cotton-web to sell: Nature finds a bill against you; your 'Strength' is not Strength, but Futility! Let faculty be honoured, so far as it is faculty. A man that can succeed in working is to me always a man.

How one loves to see the burly figure of him, this thick-skinned, seemingly opaque, perhaps sulky, almost stupid Man of Practice, pitted against some light adroit Man of Theory, all equipt with clear logic, and able anywhere to give you Why for Wherefore! The adroit Man of Theory, so light of movement, clear of utterance, with his bow full-bent and quiver full of arrow-arguments,—surely he will strike down the game, transfix everywhere the heart of the matter; triumph everywhere, as he proves that he shall and must do? To your astonishment, it turns out oftenest No. The cloudy-browed, thick-soled, opaque Practicality, with no logic-utterance, in silence mainly, with here and there a low grunt or growl, has in him what transcends all logic-utterance: a Congruity with the Unuttered. The Speakable, which lies atop, as a superficial film, or outer skin, is his or is not his: but the Doable, which reaches down to the World's centre, you find him there!

The rugged Brindley has little to say for himself; the rugged Brindley, when difficulties accumulate on him, retires silent, 'generally to his bed;' retires 'sometimes for three days together to his bed, that he may be in perfect privacy there,' and ascertain in his rough head how the difficulties can be overcome. The ineloquent Brindley, behold he *has* chained seas together; his ships do visibly float over valleys, invisibly through the hearts of mountains; the Mersey and the Thames, the Humber and the Severn have shaken hands: Nature most audibly answers, Yes! The Man of Theory twangs his full-bent bow; Nature's Fact ought to fall stricken, but does not: his logic-arrow glances from it as from a scaly dragon, and the obstinate Fact keeps walking its way. How singular! At bottom you will have to grapple closer with the dragon; take it home to you, by real faculty, not by seeming faculty; try whether you are stronger or it is stronger. Close with it, wrestle it: sheer obstinate toughness of muscle; but much more, what we call toughness of heart, which will mean persistence hopeful and even desperate, unsubduable patience, composed candid openness, clearness of mind: all this shall be 'strength' in wrestling your dragon; the whole man's real strength is in this work, we shall get the measure of him here.

Of all the Nations in the world at present the English are the stupidest in speech, the wisest in action. As good as a 'dumb' Nation, I say, who cannot speak, and have never yet spoken,—spite of the Shakspeares and Miltons who shew us what possibilities there are!—O Mr. Bull, I look in that surly face of thine with a mixture of pity and laughter, yet also with wonder and veneration. Thou complainest not, my illustrious friend; and yet I believe the heart of thee is full of sorrow, of unspoken sadness, seriousness,—profound melancholy (as some have said) the basis of thy being. Unconsciously, for thou speakest of nothing, this great Universe is great to thee. Not by levity of floating, but by stubborn force of swimming, shalt thou make thy way. The Fates sing of thee that thou shalt many times be thought an ass and a dull ox, and shalt with a godlike indifference believe it. My friend,—and it is all untrue, nothing ever falser in point of fact! Thou art of those great ones whose greatness the small passer-by does not discern. Thy very stupidity is wiser than their wisdom. A grand *vis inertiæ* is in thee; how many grand qualities unknown to small men! Nature alone knows thee, acknowledges the bulk and strength of thee: thy Epic, unsung in words, is written in huge characters on the face of this Planet,—sea-moles, cotton-trades, railways, fleets and cities, Indian Empires, Americas, New-Hollands; legible throughout the Solar System!

But the dumb Russians too, as I said, they, drilling all wild Asia and wild Europe into military rank and file, a terrible yet hitherto a prospering enterprise, are still dumber. The old Romans also could not *speak*, for many centuries:—not till the world was theirs; and so many speaking Greekdoms, their logic-arrows all spent, had been absorbed and abolished. The logic-arrows, how they glanced futile from obdurate thick-skinned Facts; Facts to be wrestled down only by the real vigour of Roman thews! —As for me, I honour, in these loud-babbling days, all the Silent rather. A grand Silence that of Romans;—nay the grandest of all, is it not that of the gods! Even Triviality, Imbecility, that can sit silent, how respectable is it in comparison! The 'talent of silence' is our fundamental one. Great honour to him whose Epic is a melodious hexameter Iliad; not a jingling Sham-Iliad, nothing true in it but the hexameters and forms merely. But still greater honour, if his Epic be a mighty Empire slowly built together, a mighty Series of Heroic deeds,—a mighty Conquest over Chaos; *which* Epic the 'Eternal Melodies' have, and must have, informed and dwelt in, as *it* sung itself! There is no mistaking that latter Epic. Deeds are greater than Words. Deeds have such a life, mute but undeniable, and grow as living trees and fruit-trees do; they people the vacuity of Time, and make it green and worthy. Why should the oak prove logically that it ought to grow, and will grow? Plant it, try it; what gifts of diligent judicious assimilation and secretion it has, of progress and resistance, of *force* to grow, will then declare themselves. My much-honoured, illustrious, extremely inarticulate Mr. Bull!—

Ask Bull his spoken opinion of any matter,—oftentimes the force of dulness can no farther go. You stand silent, incredulous, as over a platitude that borders on the Infinite. The man's Churchisms, Dissenterisms, Pusey-isms, Benthamisms, College Philosophies, Fashionable Literatures, are unex-ampled in this world. Fate's prophecy is fulfilled; you call the man an ox and an ass. But set him once to work,—respectable man! His spoken sense is next to nothing, nine-tenths of it palpable *non*sense: but his unspoken sense, his inner silent feeling of what is true, what does agree with fact, what is doable and what is not doable,—this seeks its fellow in the world. A terrible worker; irresistible against marshes, mountains, impediments, dis-order, incivilisation; everywhere vanquishing disorder, leaving it behind him as method and order. He 'retires to his bed three days' and considers!

Nay withal, stupid as he is, our dear John,—ever, after infinite tumblings, and spoken platitudes innumerable from barrel-heads and parliament-benches, he does settle down somewhere about the just conclusion; you are certain that his jumblings and tumblings will end, after years or centuries, in the stable equilibrium. Stable equilibrium, I say; centre-of-gravity lowest; —not the unstable, with centre-of-gravity highest, as I have known it done by quicker people! For indeed, do but jumble and tumble sufficiently, you avoid that worst fault, of settling with your centre-of-gravity highest; your centre-of-gravity is certain to come lowest, and to stay there. If slowness, what we in our impatience call 'stupidity,' be the price of stable equilibrium over unstable, shall we grudge a little slowness? Not the least admirable quality of Bull is, after all, that of remaining insensible to logic; holding out for considerable periods, ten years or more, as in this of the Corn-Laws, after all arguments and shadow of arguments have faded away from him, till the very urchins on the street titter at the arguments he brings. Logic,— Λογική, the 'Art of Speech,'—does indeed speak so and so; clear enough: nevertheless Bull still shakes his head; will see whether nothing else *illogical*, not yet 'spoken,' not yet able to be 'spoken,' do not lie in the business, as there so often does!—My firm belief is, that, finding himself now enchanted, hand-shackled, foot-shackled, in Poor-Law Bastilles and elsewhere, he will retire three days to his bed, and *arrive* at a conclusion or two! His three years 'total stagnation of trade,' alas, is not that a painful enough 'lying in bed to consider himself?' Poor Bull!

Bull is a born Conservative; for this too I inexpressibly honour him. All great Peoples are conservatives; slow to believe in novelties; patient of much error in actualties; deeply and forever certain of the greatness that is in Law, in Custom once solemnly established, and now long recognised as just and final.—True, O Radical Reformer, there is no Custom that can, properly speaking, be final; none. And yet thou seest *Customs* which, in all civilised countries, are accounted final; nay, under the Old-Roman name of *Mores*, are accounted *Morality*, Virtue, Laws of God Himself. Such, I assure thee, not a few of them are; such almost all of them once were. And greatly do I respect the solid character,—a block-head, thou wilt say; yes, but a well-conditioned block-head, and the best-conditioned,—who esteems all 'Customs once solemnly acknowledged' to be ultimate, divine, and the rule for a man to walk by, nothing doubting, not inquiring farther. What a time of it had we, were all men's life and trade still, in all parts of it, a problem, a hypothetic seeking, to be settled by painful Logics and Baconian Inductions! The Clerk in Eastcheap cannot spend the day in verifying his Ready-Reckoner; he must take it as verified, true and indisputable; or his Book-keeping by Double Entry will stand still. "Where is your Posted Ledger?" asks the Master at night.—"Sir," answers the other, "I was verifying my Ready-Reckoner, and find some errors. The Ledger is—!"—Fancy such a thing!

True, all turns on your Ready-Reckoner being moderately correct,— being *not* insupportably incorrect! A Ready-Reckoner which has led to distinct entries in your Ledger such as these: '*Creditor* an English People by fifteen hundred years of good Labour; and *Debtor* to lodging in enchanted Poor-Law Bastilles: *Creditor* by conquering the largest Empire the Sun ever saw; and *Debtor* to Donothingism and "Impossible" written on all departments of the government thereof: *Creditor* by mountains of gold ingots earned; and *Debtor* to No Bread purchasable by them:' *such* Ready-Reckoner, methinks, is beginning to be suspect; nay is ceasing, and has ceased, to be suspect! Such Ready-Reckoner is a Solecism in Eastcheap; and must, whatever be the press of business, and will and shall be rectified a little. Business can go on no longer with *it*. The most Conservative English People, thickest-skinned, most patient of Peoples, is driven alike by its Logic and its Unlogic, by things 'spoken,' and by things not yet spoken or very speakable, but only felt and very unendurable, to be wholly a Reforming People. Their Life as it is has ceased to be longer possible for them.

Urge not this noble silent People; rouse not the Berserkirrage that lies in them! Do you know their Cromwells, Hampdens, their Pyms and Bradshaws? Men very peaceable, but men that can be made very terrible! Men who, like their old Teutsch Fathers in Agrippa's days, 'have a soul that despises death;' to whom 'death,' compared with falsehoods and injustices, is light;—'in whom there is a rage unconquerable by the immortal gods!' Before this, the English People have taken very preternatural-looking Spectres by the beard; saying virtually: "And if thou *wert* 'preternatural?' Thou with thy 'divine-rights' grown diabolical wrongs? Thou—not even 'natural;' decapitable; totally extinguishable!"——Yes, just so godlike as this People's patience was, even so godlike will and must its impatience be. Away, ye scandalous Practical Solecisms, children actually of the Prince of Darkness; ye have near broken our hearts; we can and will endure you no longer. Begone, we say; depart while the play is good! By the Most High God, whose sons and born missionaries true men are, ye shall not continue here! You and we have become incompatible; can inhabit one house no longer. Either you must go, or we. Are ye ambitious to try *which* it shall be?

O my Conservative friends, who still specially name and struggle to approve yourselves 'Conservative,' would to Heaven I could persuade you of this world-old fact, than which Fate is not surer, That Truth and Justice alone are *capable* of being 'conserved' and preserved! The thing which is unjust, which is *not* according to God's Law, will you, in a God's Universe, try to conserve that? It is so old, say you? Yes, and the hotter haste ought *you*, of all others, to be in to let it grow no older! If but the faintest whisper in your hearts intimate to you that it is not fair,—hasten, for the sake of Conservatism itself, to probe it rigorously, to cast it forth at once and forever if guilty. How will or can you preserve *it*, the thing that is not fair? 'Impossibility' a thousandfold is marked on that. And ye call yourselves Conservatives, Aristocracies:—ought not honour and nobleness of mind, if they had departed from all the Earth elsewhere, to find their last refuge with you? Ye unfortunate!

The bough that is dead shall be cut away, for the sake of the tree itself. Old? Yes, it is too old. Many a weary winter has it swung and creaked there, and gnawed and fretted, with its dead wood, the organic substance and still living fibre of this good tree; many a long summer has its ugly naked brown defaced the fair green umbrage; every day it has done mischief, and that only: off with it, for the tree's sake, if for nothing more: let the Conservatism that would preserve cut *it* away. Did no wood-forester apprise you that a dead bough with its dead root left sticking there is extraneous, poisonous; is as a dead iron spike, some horrid rusty plough-share driven into the living substance;—nay is far worse; for in every wind-storm ('commercial crisis' or the like), it frets and creaks, jolts itself to and fro, and cannot lie quiet as your dead iron spike would!

If I were the Conservative Party of England (which is another bold figure of speech), I would not for a hundred thousand pounds an hour allow those Corn-Laws to continue. Potosi and Golconda put together would not purchase my assent to them. Do you count what treasuries of bitter indignation they are laying up for you in every just English heart? Do you know what questions, not as to Corn-prices and Sliding-scales alone, they are *forcing* every reflective Englishman to ask himself? Questions insoluble, or hitherto unsolved; deeper than any of our Logic plummets hitherto will sound: questions deep enough,—which it were better that we did not name even in thought! You are forcing us to think of them, to begin uttering them. The utterance of them is begun; and where will it be ended, think you? When two millions of one's brother-men sit in Work-houses, and five millions, as is insolently said, 'rejoice in potatoes,' there are various things that must be begun, let them end where they can.

CHAPTER VI.

Two Centuries.

THE SETTLEMENT effected by our 'Healing Parliament' in the Year of Grace 1660, though accomplished under universal acclamations from the four corners of the British Dominions, turns out to have been one of the mourn-fulest that ever took place in this land of ours. It called and thought itself a Settlement of the brightest hope and fulfilment, bright as the blaze of universal tar-barrels and bonfires could make it: and we find it now, on looking back on it with the insight which trial has yielded, a Settlement as of despair. Considered well, it was a settlement to govern henceforth without God, with only some decent Pretence of God.

Governing by the Christian Law of God had been found a thing of battle, convulsion, confusion, an infinitely difficult thing: wherefore let us now abandon it, and govern only by so much of God's Christian Law as—as may prove quiet and convenient for us. What is the end of Government? To guide men in the way wherein they should go; towards their true good in this life, the portal of infinite good in a life to come? To guide men in such way, and ourselves in such way, as the Maker of men, whose eye is upon us, will sanction at the Great Day?—Or alas, perhaps at bottom *is* there no Great Day, no sure outlook of any life to come; but only this poor life, and what of taxes, felicities, Nell-Gwyns and entertainments we can manage to muster here? In that case, the end of Government will be, To suppress all noise and disturbance, whether of Puritan preaching, Camer-onian psalm-singing, thieves'-riot, murder, arson, or what noise soever, and —be careful that supplies do not fail! A very notable conclusion, if we will think of it; and not without an abundance of fruits for us. Oliver Crom-well's body hung on the Tyburn-gallows, as the type of Puritanism found futile, inexecutable, execrable,—yes, that gallows-tree has been a fingerpost into very strange country indeed. Let earnest Puritanism die; let decent

Formalism, whatsoever cant it be or grow to, live! We have had a pleasant journey in that direction; and are—arriving at our inn?

To support the Four Pleas of the Crown, and keep Taxes coming in: in very sad seriousness, has not this been, ever since, even in the best times, almost the one admitted end and aim of Government? Religion, Christian Church, Moral Duty; the fact that man had a soul at all; that in man's life there was any eternal truth or justice at all,—has been as good as left quietly out of sight. Church indeed,—alas, the endless talk and struggle we have had of High-Church, Low-Church, Church-Extension, Church-in-Danger: we invite the Christian reader to think whether it has not been a too miserable screech-owl phantasm of talk and struggle, as for a 'Church,' which one had rather not define at present!

But now in these godless two centuries, looking at England and her efforts and doings, if we ask, What of England's doings the Law of Nature had accepted, Nature's King had actually furthered and pronounced to have truth in them,—where is our answer? Neither the 'Church' of Hurd and Warburton, nor the Anti-church of Hume and Paine; not in any shape the Spiritualism of England: all this is already seen, or beginning to be seen, for what it is; a thing that Nature does *not* own. On the one side is dreary Cant, with a *reminiscence* of things noble and divine; on the other is but acrid Candour, with a *prophecy* of things brutal, infernal. Hurd and War- burton are sunk into the sere and yellow leaf; no considerable body of true- seeing men looks thitherward for healing: the Paine-and-Hume Atheistic theory of 'things well let alone,' with Liberty, Equality and the like, is also in these days declaring itself naught, unable to keep the world from taking fire.

The theories and speculations of both these parties, and we may say, of all intermediate parties and persons, prove to be things which the Eternal Veracity did not accept; things superficial, ephemeral, which already a near Posterity, finding them already dead and brown-leafed, is about to suppress and forget. The Spiritualism of England, for those godless years, is, as it were, all forgettable. Much has been written: but the perennial Scriptures of Mankind have had small accession: from all English Books, in rhyme or prose, in leather binding or in paper wrappage, how many verses have been added to these? Our most melodious Singers have sung as from the throat outwards: from the inner Heart of Man, from the great Heart of Nature, through no Pope or Philips, has there come any tone. The Oracles have been dumb. In brief, the Spoken Word of England has not been true. The Spoken Word of England turns out to have been trivial; of short endurance; not valuable, not available as a Word, except for the passing day. It has been accordant with transitory Semblance; discordant with eternal Fact. It has been unfortunately not a Word, but a Cant; a helpless involuntary Cant, nay too often a cunning voluntary one: either way, a very mournful Cant; the Voice not of Nature and Fact, but of something other than these.

With all its miserable shortcomings, with its wars, controversies, with its trades-unions, famine-insurrections,—it is her Practical Material Work alone that England has to shew for herself. This, and hitherto almost nothing more; yet actually this. The grim inarticulate veracity of the English People, unable to speak its meaning in words, has turned itself silently on things; and the dark powers of Material Nature have answered, "Yes, this at least is true, this is not false!" So answers Nature. "Waste desert-shrubs of the Tropical swamps have become Cotton-trees; and here, under my furtherance, are verily woven shirts,—hanging unsold, undistributed, but capable to be distributed, capable to cover the bare backs of my children of men. Mountains, old as the Creation, I have permitted to be bored through: bituminous fuel-stores, the wreck of forests that were green a million years ago,—I have opened them from my secret rock-chambers, and they are yours, ye English. Your huge fleets, steamships, do sail the sea: huge Indias do obey you; from huge *New* Englands and Antipodal Australias, comes profit and traffic to this Old England of mine!" So answers Nature. The Practical Labour of England is *not* a chimerical Triviality: it is a Fact, acknowledged by all the Worlds; which no man and no demon will contradict. It is, very audibly, though very inarticulately as yet, the one God's Voice we have heard in these two atheistic centuries.

And now to observe with what bewildering obscurations and impediments all this as yet stands entangled, and is yet intelligible to no man! How, with our gross Atheism, we hear it not to be the Voice of God to us, but regard it merely as a Voice of earthly Profit-and-Loss. And have a Hell in England,—the Hell of not making money. And coldly see the all-conquering valiant Sons of Toil sit enchanted, by the million, in their Poor-Law Bastille, as if this were Nature's Law;—mumbling to ourselves some vague janglement of Laissez-faire, Supply-and-demand, Cash-payment the one nexus of man to man: Free-trade, Competition, and Devil take the hindmost, our latest Gospel yet preached!

As if, in truth, there were no God of Labour; as if godlike Labour and brutal Mammonism were convertible terms. A serious, most earnest Mammonism grown Midas-eared; an unserious Dilettantism, earnest about nothing, grinning with inarticulate incredulous incredible jargon about all things, as the *enchanted* Dilettanti do by the Dead Sea! It is mournful enough, for the present hour; were there not an endless hope in it withal. Giant LABOUR, truest emblem there is of God the World-Worker, Demiurgus, and Eternal Maker; noble LABOUR, which is yet to be the King of this Earth, and sit on the highest throne,—staggering hitherto like a blind irrational giant, hardly allowed to have his common place on the street-pavements; idle Dilettantism, Dead-Sea Apism, crying out, "Down with him, he is dangerous!"

Labour must become a seeing rational giant, with a *soul* in the body of him, and take his place on the throne of things,—leaving his Mammonism, and several other adjuncts, on the lower steps of said throne.

CHAPTER VII.

Over-production.

But what will reflective readers say of a Governing Class, such as ours, addressing its Workers with an indictment of 'Over-production!' Over-production: runs it not so? "Ye miscellaneous, ignoble manufacturing individuals, ye have produced too much! We accuse you of making above two-hundred thousand shirts for the bare backs of mankind. Your trousers, too, which you have made, of fustian, of cassimere, of Scotch-plaid, of jane, nankeen and woollen broad-cloth, are they not manifold? Of hats for the human head, of shoes for the human foot, of stools to sit on, spoons to eat with—Nay, what say we hats or shoes? You produce gold watches, jewelleries, silver forks and epergnes, commodes, chiffoniers, stuffed sofas—Heavens, the Commercial Bazaar and multitudinous Howel-and-Jameses cannot contain you. You have produced, produced;—he that seeks your indictment let him look around. Millions of shirts, and empty pairs of breeches, hang there in judgment against you. We accuse you of over-producing: you are criminally guilty of producing shirts, breeches, hats, shoes and commodities, in a frightful over-abundance. And now there is a glut, and your operatives cannot be fed!"

Never, surely, against an earnest Working Mammonism was there brought, by Game-preserving aristocratic Dilettantism, a stranger accusation, since this world began. My lords and gentleman,—why, it was *you* that were appointed, by the fact and by the theory of your position on the Earth, to 'make and administer Laws,' that is to say, in a world such as ours, to guard against 'gluts;' against honest operatives, who had done their work, remaining unfed! I say, *you* were appointed to preside over the Distribution and Apportionment of the Wages of Work done; and to see well that there went no labourer without his hire, were it of money-coins, were it of hemp gallows-ropes: that function was yours, and from immemorial time has been; yours, and as yet no other's. These poor shirt-spinners have forgotten much, which by the virtual unwritten law of their position they should have remembered: but by any written recognised law of their position, what have they forgotten? They were set to make shirts. The Community with all its voices commanded them, saying, "Make shirts;"—and there the shirts are! Too many shirts? Well, that is a novelty, in this intemperate Earth, with its nine-hundred millions of bare backs! But the Community commanded you, saying, "See that the shirts are well apportioned, that our Human Laws be emblem of God's Laws;"—and where is the apportionment? Two million shirtless or ill-shirted workers sit enchanted in Workhouse Bastilles, five million more (according to some) in Ugolino Hunger-cellars; and for remedy, you say,—what say you?—Raise *our* rents!" I have not in my time heard any stranger speech, not even on the Shores of the Dead Sea. You continue addressing these poor shirt-spinners and over-producers, in really a *too* triumphant a manner:

"Will you bandy accusations, will you accuse *us* of over-production? We take the Heavens and the Earth to witness that we have produced nothing at all. Not from us proceeds this frightful overplus of shirts. In the wide domains of created Nature, circulates no shirt or thing of our producing. Certain fox-brushes nailed upon our stable-door, the fruit of fair audacity at Melton Mowbray; these we have produced, and they are openly nailed up there. He that accuses us of producing, let him shew himself, let him name what and when. We are innocent of producing;—ye ungrateful, what mountains of things have we not, on the contrary, had to 'consume,' and make away with! Mountains of those your heaped manufacturers, wheresoever edible or wearable, have they not disappeared before us, as if we had the talent of ostriches, of cormorants, and a kind of divine faculty to eat? Ye ungrateful!—and did you not grow under the shadow of our wings? Are not your filthy mills built on these fields of ours; on this soil of England, which belongs to—whom think you? And we shall not offer you our own wheat at the price that pleases us, but that partly pleases you? A precious notion! What would become of you, if we chose, at any time, to decide on growing no wheat more?"

Yes, truly, *here* is the ultimate rock-basis of all Corn-Laws; whereon, at the bottom of much arguing, they rest, as securely as they can: What would become of you, if we decided, some day, on growing no more wheat at all? If we chose to grow only partridges henceforth, and a modicum of wheat for our own uses? Cannot we do what we like with our own?—Yes, indeed! For my share, if I could melt Gneiss Rock, and create Law of Gravitation; if I could stride out to the Doggerbank, some morning, and striking down my trident there into the mud-waves, say, "Be land, be fields, meadows, mountains, and fresh-rolling streams!" by Heaven, I should incline to have the letting of *that* land in perpetuity, and sell the wheat of it, or burn the wheat of it, according to my own good judgment! My Corn-Lawing friends, you affright me.

To the 'Millo-cracy' so-called, to the Working Aristocracy, steeped too deep in mere ignoble Mammonism, and as yet all unconscious of its noble destinies, as yet but an irrational or semi-rational giant, struggling to awake some soul in itself,—the world will have much to say, reproachfully, re-provingly, admonishingly. But to the Idle Aristocracy, what will the world have to say? Things painful and not pleasant!

To the man who *works*, who attempts, in never so ungracious barbarous a way, to get forward with some work, you will hasten out with further-ances, with encouragements, corrections; you will say to him: "Welcome; thou art ours; our care shall be of thee." To the Idler, again, never so gracefully going idle, coming forward with never so many parchments, you will not hasten out; you will sit still, and be disinclined to rise. You will say to him: "Not welcome, O complex Anomaly; would thou hadst stayed out of doors: for who of mortals knows what to do with thee? Thy parchments: yes, they are old, of venerable yellowness; and we too honour parchment, old-established settlements, and venerable use and wont. Old parchments in very truth:—yet on the whole, if thou wilt remark, they are young to the Granite Rocks, to the Groundplan of God's Universe! We advise thee to put up thy parchments; to go home to thy place, and make no needless noise whatever. Our heart's wish is to save thee: yet there as thou art, hapless Anomaly, with nothing but thy yellow parchments, noisy futilities, and shotbelts and fox-brushes, who of gods or men can avert dark Fate? Be counselled, ascertain if no work exist for thee on God's Earth; if thou find no commanded-duty there but that of going gracefully idle? Ask, inquire earnestly, with a half-frantic earnestness; for the answer means Existence or Annihilation to thee. We apprise thee of the world-old fact, becoming sternly disclosed again in these days, That he who cannot work in this Universe cannot get existed in it: had he parchments to thatch the face of the world, these, combustible fallible sheepskin, cannot avail him. Home, thou unfortunate; and let us have at least no noise from thee!"

Suppose the unfortunate Idle Aristocracy, as the unfortunate Working one has done, were to 'retire three days to *its* bed,' and consider itself there, what o'clock it had become?—

How have we to regret not only that men have 'no religion,' but that they have next to no reflection; and go about with heads full of mere extraneous noises, with eyes wide-open but visionless,—for most part, in the somnambulist state!

CHAPTER VIII.

Unworking Aristocracy.

It is well said, 'Land is the right basis of an Aristocracy;' whoever possesses the Land, he, more emphatically than any other, is the Governor, Viceking of the people on the Land. It is in these days as it was in those of Henry Plantagenet and Abbot Samson; as it will in all days be. The Land is *Mother* of us all; nourishes, shelters, gladdens, lovingly enriches us all; in how many ways, from our first wakening to our last sleep on her blessed mother-bosom, does she, as with blessed mother-arms, enfold us all!

The Hill I first saw the Sun rise over, when the Sun and I and all things were yet in their auroral hour, who can divorce me from it? Mystic, deep as the world's centre, are the roots I have struck into my Native Soil; no *tree* that grows is rooted so. From noblest Patriotism to humblest industrial Mechanism; from highest dying for your country, to lowest quarrying and coal-boring for it, a Nation's Life depends upon its Land. Again and again we have to say, there can be no true Aristocracy but must possess the Land.

Men talk of 'selling' Land. Land, it is true, like Epic Poems and even higher things, in such a trading world, has to be presented in the market for what it will bring, and as we say be 'sold:' but the notion of 'selling,' for certain bits of metal, the *Iliad* of Homer, how much more the *Land* of the World-Creator, is a ridiculous impossibility! We buy what is saleable of it; nothing more was ever buyable. Who can, or could, sell it to us? Properly speaking, the Land belongs to these two: To the Almighty God; and to all His Children of Men that have ever worked well on it, or that shall ever work well on it. No generation of men can or could, with never such solemnity and effort, sell Land on any other principle: it is not the property of any generation, we say, but that of all the past generations that have worked on it, and of all the future ones that shall work on it.

Again, we hear it said, The soil of England, or of any country, is properly worth nothing, except 'the labour bestowed on it.' This, speaking even in the language of Eastcheap, is not correct. The rudest space of country equal in extent to England, could a whole English Nation, with all their habitudes, arrangements, skills, with whatsoever they do carry within the skins of them, and cannot be stript of, suddenly take wing, and alight on it,—would be worth a very considerable thing! Swiftly, within year and day, this English Nation, with its multiplex talents of ploughing, spinning, hammering, mining, road-making and trafficking, would bring a handsome value out of such a space of country. On the other hand, fancy what an English Nation, once 'on the wing,' could have done with itself, had there been simply no soil, not even an inarable one, to alight on? Vain all its talents for ploughing, hammering, and whatever else; there is no Earth-room for this Nation with its talents: this Nation will have to *keep* hovering on the wing, dolefully shrieking to and fro; and perish piecemeal; burying itself, down to the last soul of it, in the waste unfirmamented seas. Ah yes, soil, with or without ploughing, is the gift of God. The soil of all countries belongs evermore, in a very considerable degree, to the Almighty Maker! The last stroke of labour bestowed on it is not the making of its value, but only the increasing thereof.

It is very strange, the degree to which these truisms are forgotten in our days; how, in the ever-whirling chaos of Formulas, we have quietly lost sight of Fact,—which it is so perilous not to keep for ever in sight. Fact, if we do not see it, will make us *feel* it by and by!—From much loud controversy and Corn-Law debating there rises, loud though inarticulate, once more in these years, this very question among others, Who made the Land of England? Who made it, this respectable English Land, wheat-growing, metalliferous, carboniferous, which will let readily hand over head for seventy millions or upwards, as it here lies: who did make it?—"We!" answer the much-*consuming* Aristocracy; "We!" as they ride in, moist with the sweat of Melton Mowbray: "It is we that made it; or are the heirs, assigns and representatives of those who did!"—My brothers, You? Everlasting honor to you, then; and Corn-Laws as many as you will, till your own deep stomachs cry Enough, or some voice of human pity for our famine bids you Hold! Ye are as gods, that can create soil. Soil-creating gods there is no withstanding. They have the might to sell wheat at what price they list; and the right, to all lengths, and famine-lengths,—if they be pitiless infernal gods! Celestial gods, I think, would stop short of the famine-price; but no infernal nor any kind of god can be bidden stop!——Infatuated mortals, into what questions are you driving every thinking man in England!

I say, you did *not* make the Land of England; and, by the possession of it, you *are* bound to furnish guidance and governance to England! That is the law of your position on this God's-Earth; an everlasting act of Heaven's Parliament, not repealable in St. Stephen's or elsewhere! True government and guidance; not no-government and Laissez-faire; how much less, *mis*-government and Corn-Law! There is not an imprisoned Worker looking out from these Bastilles but appeals, very audibly in Heaven's High Courts, against you, and me, and every one who is not imprisoned, "Why am I here?" His appeal is audible in Heaven; and will become audible enough on Earth too, if it remain unheeded here. His appeal is against you, foremost of all; you stand in the front rank of the accused; you, by the very place you hold, have first of all to answer him and Heaven!

What looks maddest, miserablest in these mad and miserable Corn-Laws is independent altogether of their 'effect on wages,' their effect on 'increase of trade,' or any other such effect: it is the continual maddening proof they protrude into the faces of all men, that our Governing Class, called by God and Nature and the inflexible law of Fact, either to do something towards governing, or to die and be abolished,—have not yet learned even to sit still, and do no mischief! For no Anti-Corn-Law League yet asks more of them than this;—Nature and Fact, very imperatively, asking so much more of them. Anti-Corn-Law League asks not, Do something; but, Cease your destructive misdoing, Do ye nothing!

Nature's message will have itself obeyed: messages of mere Free-Trade, Anti-Corn-Law League and Laissez-faire, will then need small obeying!— Ye fools, in the name of Heaven, work, work, at the Ark of Deliverance for yourselves and us, while hours are still granted you! No: instead of working at the Ark, they say, "We cannot get our hands kept rightly warm;" and *sit obstinately burning the planks.* No madder spectacle at present exhibits itself under this Sun.

The Working Aristocracy; Mill-owners, Manufacturers, Commanders of Working Men: alas, against them also much shall be brought in accusation; much,—and the freest Trade in Corn, total abolition of Tariffs, and utter-most 'Increase of Manufactures' and 'Prosperity of Commerce,' will perma-nently mend no jot of it. The Working Aristocracy must strike into a new path; must understand that money alone is *not* the representative either of man's success in the world, or of man's duties to man; and reform their own selves from top to bottom, if they wish England reformed. England will not be habitable long unreformed.

The Working Aristocracy—Yes, but on the threshold of all this, it is again and again to be asked, What of the Idle Aristocracy? Again and again, What shall we say of the Idle Aristocracy, the Owners of the Soil of England; whose recognised function is that of handsomely consuming the rents of England, shooting the partridges of England, and as an agreeable amusement (if the purchase-money and other conveniences serve), dilettante-ing in Parliament and Quarter-Sessions for England? We will say mournfully, in the presence of Heaven and Earth,—that we stand speechless, stupent, and know not what to say! That a class of men entitled to live sumptuously on the marrow of the earth; permitted simply, nay entreated, and as yet entreated in vain, to do nothing at all in return, was never heretofore seen on the face of this Planet. That such a class is transitory, exceptional, and, unless Nature's Laws fall dead, cannot continue. That it has continued now a moderate while; has, for the last fifty years, been rapidly attaining its state of perfection. That it will have to find its duties and do them; or else that it must and will cease to be seen on the face of this Planet, which is a Working one, not an Idle one.

Alas, alas, the Working Aristocracy, admonished by Trades-unions, Chartist conflagrations, above all by their own shrewd sense kept in perpetual communion with the fact of things, will assuredly reform themselves, and a working world will still be possible:—but the fate of the Idle Aristocracy, as one reads its horoscope hitherto in Corn-Laws and such like, is an abyss that fills one with despair. Yes, my rosy fox-hunting brothers, a terrible *Hippocratic look* reveals itself (God knows, not to my joy) through those fresh buxom countenances of yours. Through your Corn-Law Majorities, Sliding-Scales, Protecting-Duties, Bribery-Elections and triumphant Kentish-fire, a thinking eye discerns ghastly images of ruin, too ghastly for words; a handwriting as of MENE, MENE. Men and brothers, on your Sliding-scale you seem sliding, and to have slid,—you little know whither! Good God! did not a French Donothing Aristocracy, hardly above half a century ago, declare in like manner, and in its featherhead believe in like manner, "We cannot exist, and continue to dress and parade ourselves, on the just rent of the soil of France; but we must have farther payment than rent of the soil, we must be exempted from taxes too,"—we must have a Corn-Law to extend our rent? This was in 1789: in four years more—Did you look into the Tanneries of Meudon, and the long-naked making for themselves breeches of human skins! May the merciful Heavens avert the omen; may we be wiser, that so we be less wretched.

A High Class without duties to do is like a tree planted on precipices; from the roots of which all the earth has been crumbling. Nature owns no man who is not a Martyr withal. Is there a man who pretends to live luxuriously housed up; screened from all work, from want, danger, hardships, the victory over which is what we name work;—he himself to sit serene, amid down-bolsters and appliances, and have all his work and battling done by other men? And such man calls himself a *noble*-man? His fathers worked for him, he says; or successfully gambled for him: here *he* sits; professes, not in sorrow but in pride, that he and his have done no work, time out of mind. It is the law of the land, and is thought to be the law of the Universe, that he, alone of recorded men, shall have no task laid on him, except that of eating his cooked victuals, and not flinging himself out of window. Once more I will say, there was no stranger spectacle ever shewn under this Sun. A veritable fact in our England of the Nineteenth Century. His victuals he does eat: but as for keeping in the inside of the window,—have not his friends, like me, enough to do? Truly, looking at his Corn-Laws, Game-Laws, Chandos-Clauses, Bribery-Elections and much else, you do shudder over the tumbling and plunging he makes, held back by the lappelles and coatskirts; only a thin fence of window-glass before him,—and in the street mere horrid iron spikes! My sick brother, as in hospital-maladies men do, thou dreamest of Paradises and Eldorados, which are far from thee. 'Cannot I do what I like with my own?' Gracious Heaven, my brother, this that thou seest with those sick eyes is no firm Eldorado, and Corn-Law Paradise of Donothings, but a dream of thy own fevered brain. It is a glass-window, I tell thee, so many stories from the street; where are iron spikes and the law of gravitation!

What is the meaning of nobleness, if this be 'noble?' In a valiant suffering for others, not in a slothful making others suffer for us, did nobleness ever lie. The chief of men is he who stands in the van of men; fronting the peril which frightens back all others; which, if it be not vanquished, will devour the others. Every noble crown is, and on Earth will forever be, a crown of thorns. The Pagan Hercules, why was he accounted a hero? Because he had slain Nemean Lions, cleansed Augean Stables, undergone Twelve Labours only not too heavy for a god. In modern, as in ancient and all societies, the Aristocracy, they that assume the functions of an Aristocracy, doing them or not, have taken the post of honour; which is the post of difficulty, the post of danger,—of death, if the difficulty be not overcome. *Il faut payer de sa vie.* Why was our life given us, if not that we should manfully give it? Descend, O Donothing Pomp: quit thy down-cushions; expose thyself to learn what wretches feel, and how to cure it! The Czar of Russia became a dusty toiling shipwright; worked with his axe in the Docks of Saardam; and his aim was small to thine. Descend thou: undertake this horrid 'living chaos of Ignorance and Hunger' weltering round thy feet; say, "I will heal it, or behold I will die foremost in it." Such is verily the law. Everywhere and everywhen a man has to '*pay* with his life;' to do his work, as a soldier does, at the expense of life. In no Piepowder earthly Court can you sue an Aristocracy to do its work, at this moment: but in the Higher Court, which even *it* calls 'Court of Honour,' and which is the Court of Necessity withal, and the eternal Court of the Universe, in which all Facts come to plead, and every Human Soul is an apparitor,—the Aristocracy is answerable, and even now answering, *there*.

Parchments? Parchments are venerable: but they ought at all times to represent, as near as they by possibility can, the writing of the Adamant

Tablets; otherwise they are not so venerable! Benedict the Jew in vain pleaded parchments; his usuries were too many. The King said, "Go to, for all thy parchments, thou shalt pay just debt; down with thy dust, or observe this tooth-forceps!" Nature, a far juster Sovereign, has far terribler forceps! Aristocracies, actual and imaginary, reach a time when parchment pleading does not avail them. "Go to, for all thy parchments, thou shalt pay due debt!" shouts the Universe to them, in an emphatic manner. They refuse to pay, confidently pleading parchment: their best grinder-tooth, with horrible agony, goes out of their jaw. Wilt thou pay now? A second grinder, again in horrible agony, goes: a second, and a third, and if need be, all the teeth and grinders, and the life itself with them;—and *then* there is free payment, and an anatomist subject into the bargain!

Reform Bills, Corn-Law Abrogation Bills, and then Land-Tax Bill, Property-Tax Bill, and still dimmer list of *etceteras;* grinder after grinder:— my lords and gentlemen, it were better for you to arise, and begin doing your work, than sit there and plead parchments!

We write no chapter on the Corn-Laws, in this place; the Corn-Laws are too mad to have a Chapter. There is a certain immorality, when there is not a necessity, in speaking about things finished; in chopping into small pieces the already slashed and slain. When the brains are out, why does not a Solecism die! It is at its own peril if it refuse to die; it ought to make all conceivable haste to die, and get itself buried! The trade of Anti-Corn-Law Lecturer in these days, still an indispensable, is a highly tragic one.

The Corn-Laws will go, and even soon go: would we were all as sure of the Millennium as they are of going! They go swiftly in these present months; with an increase of velocity, an ever-deepening, ever-widening sweep of momentum, truly notable. It is at the Aristocracy's own damage and peril, still more than at any other's whatsoever, that the Aristocracy maintains them;—at a damage, say only, as above computed, of a 'hundred thousand pounds an hour!' The Corn-Laws keep all the air hot-fostered by their fever-warmth, much that is evil, but much also, how much that is good and indispensable, is rapidly coming to life among us!

CHAPTER IX.

WORKING ARISTOCRACY.

A POOR Working Mammonism getting itself 'strangled in the partridge-nets of an Unworking Dilettantism,' and bellowing dreadfully, and already black in the face, is surely a disastrous spectacle! But of a Midas-eared Mammonism, which indeed at bottom all pure Mammonisms are, what better can you expect? No better;—if not this, then something other equally disastrous, if not still more disastrous. Mammonisms, grown asinine, have to become human again, and rational; they have, on the whole, to cease to be Mammonisms, were it even on compulsion, and pressure of the hemp round their neck!—My friends of the Working Aristocracy, there are now a great many things which you also, in your extreme need, will have to consider.

The Continental people, it would seem, are 'exporting our machinery, beginning to spin cotton and manufacture for themselves, to cut us out of this market and then out of that!' Sad news indeed; but irremediable;—by no means the saddest news. The saddest news is, that we should find our National Existence, as I sometimes hear it said, depend on selling manufactured cotton at a farthing an ell cheaper than any other People. A most narrow stand for a great Nation to base itself on! A stand which, with all the Corn-Law Abrogations conceivable, I do not think will be capable of enduring.

My friends, suppose we quitted that stand; suppose we came honestly down from it, and said: "This is our minimum of cotton-prices. We care not, for the present, to make cotton any cheaper. Do you, if it seem so blessed to you, make cotton cheaper. Fill your lungs with cotton-fuz, your hearts with copperas-fumes, with rage and mutiny; become ye the general gnomes of Europe, slaves of the lamp!"—I admire a Nation which fancies it will die if it do not undersell all other Nations, to the end of the world. Brothers, we will cease to *under*sell them; we will be content to *equal*-sell them; to be happy selling equally with them! I do not see the use of underselling them. Cotton-cloth is already two-pence a yard or lower; and yet bare backs were never more numerous among us. Let inventive men cease to spend their existence incessantly contriving how cotton can be made cheaper; and try to invent, a little, how cotton at its present cheapness could be somewhat justlier divided among us. Let inventive men consider, Whether the Secret of this Universe, and of Man's Life there, does, after all, as we rashly fancy it, consist in making money? There is One God, just, supreme, almighty: but is Mammon the name of him?—With a Hell which means 'Failing to make money,' I do not think there is any Heaven possible that would suit one well; nor so much as an Earth that can be habitable long! In brief, all this Mammon-Gospel, of Supply-and-demand, Competition, Laissez-faire, and Devil take the hindmost, begins to be one of the shabbiest Gospels ever preached; or altogether the shabbiest. Even with Dilettante partridge-nets, and at a horrible expenditure of pain, who shall regret to see the entirely transient, and at best somewhat despicable life strangled out of it? At the best, as we say, a somewhat despicable, unvenerable thing, this same 'Laissez-faire;' and now, at the *worst*, fast growing an altogether detestable one!

"But what is to be done with our manufacturing population, with our agricultural, with our ever-increasing population?" cry many.—Aye, what? Many things can be done with them, a hundred things, and a thousand things,—had we once got a soul and begun to try. This one thing, of doing for them by 'underselling all people,' and filling our own bursten pockets and appetites by the road; and turning over all care for any 'population,' or human or divine consideration except cash only, to the winds, with a

"Laissez-faire" and the rest of it: this is evidently not the thing. Farthing cheaper per yard? No great Nation can stand on the apex of such a pyramid; screwing itself higher and higher; balancing itself on its great-toe! Can England not subsist without being *above* all people in working? England never deliberately purposed such a thing. If England work better than all people, it shall be well. England, like an honest worker, will work as well as she can; and hope the gods may allow her to live on that basis. Laissez-faire and much else being once well dead, how many 'impossibles' will become possible! They are impossible, as cotton-cloth at two-pence an ell was—till men set about making it. The inventive genius of great England will not forever sit patient with mere wheels and pinions, bobbins, straps and billy-rollers whirring in the head of it. The inventive genius of England is not a Beaver's, or a Spinner's or Spider's genius: it is a *Man's* genius, I hope, with a God over him!

Laissez-faire, Supply-and-demand,—one begins to be weary of all that. Leave all to egoism, to ravenous greed of money, of pleasure, of applause;—it is the Gospel of Despair! Man *is* a Patent-Digester, then: only give him Free Trade, Free digesting room; and each of us digest what he can come at, leaving the rest to Fate! My unhappy brethren of the Working Mammonism, my unhappy brethren of the Idle Dilettantism, no world was ever held together in that way for long. A world of mere Patent-Digesters will soon have nothing to digest; such world ends, and by Law of Nature must end, in 'over-population;' in howling universal famine, 'impossibility,' and suicidal madness, as of endless dog-kennels run rabid. Supply-and-demand shall do its full part, and Free Trade shall be free as air; thou of the shot-belts, see thou forbid it not, with those paltry, *worse* than Mammonish swindleries and Sliding-scales of thine, which are seen to be swindleries for all thy canting, which in times like ours are very scandalous to see! And trade never so well freed, and all Tariffs settled or abolished, and Supply-and-demand in full operation,—let us all know that we have yet done nothing; that we have merely cleared the ground for doing.

Yes, were the Corn-Laws ended tomorrow, there is nothing yet ended; there is only room made for all manner of things beginning. The Corn-Laws gone, and Trade made free, it is as good as certain this paralysis of industry will pass away. We shall have another period of commercial enterprise, of victory and prosperity; during which, it is likely, much money will again be made, and all the people may, by the extant methods, still for a space of years, be kept alive and physically fed. The strangling band of Famine will be loosened from our necks; we shall have room again to breathe; time to bethink ourselves, to repent and consider! A precious and thrice-precious space of years; wherein to struggle as for life in reforming our foul ways; in alleviating, instructing, regulating our people; seeking as for life, that something like spiritual food be imparted them, some real governance and guidance be provided them! It will be a priceless time. For our new period or paroxysm of commercial prosperity will and can, on the old methods of 'Competition and Devil take the hindmost,' prove but a paroxysm: a new paroxysm,—likely enough, if we do not use it better, to be our *last*. In this, of itself, is no salvation. If our Trade in twenty years' 'flourishing' as never Trade flourished, could double itself; yet then also, by the old Laissez-faire method, our Population is doubled: we shall then be as we are, only twice as many of us, twice and ten times as unmanageable!

All this dire misery, therefore; all this of our poor Workhouse Workmen, of our Chartisms, Trades-strikes, Corn-Laws, Toryisms, and the general downbreak of Laissez-faire in these days,—may we not regard it as a voice from the dumb bosom of Nature, saying to us: "Behold! Supply-and-demand is not the one Law of Nature; Cash-payment is not the sole nexus of man with man,—how far from it! Deep, far deeper than Supply-and-demand, are Laws, Obligations sacred as Man's Life itself: these also, if you will continue to do work, you shall now learn and obey. He that will learn them, behold Nature is on his side, he shall yet work and prosper with noble rewards. He that will not learn them, Nature is against him, he shall not be able to do work in Nature's empire,—not in hers. Perpetual mutiny, contention, hatred, isolation, execration shall wait on his footsteps, till all men discern that the thing which he attains, however golden it look or be, is not success, but the want of success."

Supply-and-demand,—alas! For what noble work was there ever yet any audible 'demand' in that poor sense? The man of Macedonia, speaking in vision to an Apostle Paul, "Come over and help us," did not specify what rate of wages he would give! Or was the Christian Religion itself accomplished by Prize-Essays, Bridgewater Bequests, and a 'minimum of Four thousand five hundred a year?' No demand that I heard of was made then, audible in any Labour-market, Manchester Chamber of Commerce, or other the like emporium and hiring establishment; silent were all these from any whisper of such demand;—powerless were all these to 'supply' it, had the demand been in thunder and earthquake, with gold Eldorados and Mahometan Paradises for the reward. Ah me, into what waste latitudes, in this Time-Voyage, have we wandered; like adventurous Sindbads;—where the men go about as if by galvanism, with meaningless glaring eyes, and have no soul, but only a beaver-faculty and stomach! The haggard despair of Cotton-factory, Coal-mine operatives, Chandos Farm-labourers, in these days, is painful to behold; but not so painful, hideous to the inner sense, as that brutish godforgetting Profit-and-Loss Philosophy, and Life-theory, which we hear jangled on all hands of us, in senate-houses, spouting-clubs, leading-articles, pulpits and platforms, everywhere, as the Ultimate Gospel and candid Plain-English of Man's Life, from the throats and pens and thoughts of all but all men!—

Enlightened Philosophies, like Molière Doctors, will tell you: "Enthusiasms, Self-sacrifice, Heaven, Hell and such like: yes, all that was true enough for old stupid times; all that used to be true: but we have changed all that, *nous avons changé tout cela!*" Well; if the heart be got round now into the right side, and the liver to the left; if man have no heroism in him deeper than a wish to eat, and in his soul there dwell now no Infinite of Hope and Awe, and no divine Silence can become imperative because it is not Sinai Thunder, and no tie will bind if it be not that of Tyburn gallows-ropes,—then verily you have changed all that; and for it, and for you, and for me, behold the Abyss and nameless Annihilation is ready. So scandalous a beggarly Universe deserves indeed nothing else; I cannot say I would save it from annihilation. Vacuum, and the serene Blue, will be much handsomer; easier too for all of us. I, for one, decline living as a Patent-Digester. Patent-Digester, Spinning-Mule, Mayfair Clothes-Horse: many thanks, but your Chaosships will have the goodness to excuse me!

CHAPTER X.

PLUGSON OF UNDERSHOT.

ONE THING I do know: Never, on this Earth was the relation of man to man long carried on by Cash-payment alone. If, at any time, a philosophy of Laissez-faire, Competition and Supply-and-demand, start up as the exponent of human relations, expect that it will soon end.

Such philosophies will arise: for man's philosophies are usually the 'supplement of his practice;' some ornamental Logic-varnish, some outer skin of Articulate Intelligence, with which he strives to render his dumb Instinctive doings presentable when they are done. Such philosophies will arise; be preached as Mammon-Gospels, the ultimate Evangel of the World; be believed, with what is called belief, with much superficial bluster, and a kind of shallow satisfaction real in its way:—but they are ominous gospels! They are the sure, and even swift forerunner of great changes. Expect that the old System of Society is done, is dying and falling into dotage, when it begins to rave in that fashion. Most Systems that I have watched the death of, for the last three thousand years, have gone just so. The Ideal, the True and Noble that was in them having faded out, and nothing now remaining but naked Egoism, vulturous Greediness, they cannot live; they are bound and inexorably ordained by the oldest Destinies, Mothers of the Universe, to die. Curious enough; they thereupon, as I have pretty generally noticed, devise some light comfortable kind of 'wine-and-walnuts philosophy' for themselves, this of Supply-and-demand or another; and keep saying, during hours of mastication and rumination, which they call hours of meditation: "Soul, take thy ease, it is all *well* that thou art a vulture-soul;"—and pangs of dissolution come upon them, oftenest before they are aware!

Cash-payment never was, or could except for a few years be, the union-bond of man to man. Cash never yet paid one man fully his deserts to another; nor could it, nor can it, now or henceforth to the end of the world. I invite his Grace of Castle Rack-rent to reflect on this,—does he think that a Land Aristocracy when it becomes a Land Auctioneership can have long to live? Or that Sliding-scales will increase the vital stamina of it?

—The indomitable Plugson too, of the respected Firm of Plugson, Hunks and Company, in St. Dolly Undershot, is invited to reflect on this; for to him also it will be new, perhaps even newer. Bookkeeping by double entry is admirable, and records several things in an exact manner. But the Mother-Destinies also keep their Tablets; in Heaven's Chancery also there goes on a recording; and things, as my Moslem friends say, are 'written on the iron-leaf.'

Your Grace and Plugson, it is like, go to Church occasionally: did you never in vacant moments, with perhaps a dull parson droning to you, glance into your New Testament, and the cash-account stated four times over, by a kind of quadruple entry,—in the Four Gospels there? I consider that a cash-account, and balance-statement of work done and wages paid, worth attending to. Precisely *such*, though on a smaller scale, go on at all moments under this Sun; and the statement and balance of them in the Plugson Ledgers and on the Tablets of Heaven's Chancery are discrepant exceedingly;—which ought really to teach, and to have long since taught, an indomitable common-sense Plugson of Undershot, much more an unattackable *un*common-sense Grace of Rack-rent, a thing or two!—In brief, we shall have to dismiss the Cash-Gospel rigorously into its own place: we shall have to know, on the threshold, that either there is some infinitely deeper Gospel, subsidiary, explanatory and daily and hourly corrective, to the Cash one; or else that the Cash one itself and all others are fast travelling!

For all human things do require to have an Ideal in them; to have some Soul in them, as we said, were it only to keep the Body unputrefied. And wonderful it is to see how the Ideal or Soul, place it in what ugliest Body you may, will irradiate said Body with its own nobleness; will gradually, incessantly, mould, modify new-form or reform said ugliest Body, and make it at last beautiful, and to a certain degree divine! O, if you could dethrone that Brute-god Mammon, and put a Spirit-god in his place! One way or other, he must and will have to be dethroned.

Fighting, for example, as I often say to myself, Fighting with steel murder-tools is surely a much uglier operation than Working, take it how you will. Yet even of Fighting, in religious Abbot Samson's days, see what a Feudalism there had grown,—a 'glorious Chivalry,' much besung down to the present day. Was not that one of the 'impossiblest' things? Under the sky is no uglier spectacle than two men with clenched teeth, and hellfire eyes, hacking one another's flesh; converting precious living bodies, and priceless living souls, into nameless masses of putrescence, useful only for turnip-manure. How did a Chivalry ever come out of that; how anything that was not hideous, scandalous, infernal? It will be a question worth considering by and by.

I remark, for the present, only two things: first, that the Fighting itself was not, as we rashly suppose it, a Fighting without cause, but more or less with cause. Man is created to fight; he is perhaps best of all definable as a born-soldier; his life 'a battle and a march,' under the right General. It is forever indispensable for a man to fight: now with Necessity, with Barrenness, Scarcity, with Puddles, Bogs, tangled Forests, unkempt Cotton;—now also with the hallucinations of his poor fellow Men. Hallucinatory visions rise in the head of my poor fellow man; make him claim over me rights which are not his. All Fighting, as we noticed long ago, is the dusty conflict of strengths, each thinking itself the strongest, or, in other words, the justest;—of Mights which do in the long-run, and forever will in this just Universe in the long-run, mean Rights. In conflict the perishable part of them, beaten sufficiently, flies off into dust: this process ended, appears the imperishable, the true and exact.

And now let us remark a second thing: how, in these baleful operations, a noble devout-hearted Chevalier will comfort himself, and an ignoble godless Bucanier and Chactaw Indian. Victory is the aim of each. But deep in the heart of the noble man it lies forever legible, that, as an Invisible Just God made him, so will and must God's Justice and this only, were it never so invisible, ultimately prosper in all controversies and enterprises and battles whatsoever. What an Influence; ever-present,—like a Soul in the rudest Caliban of a body; like a ray of Heaven, and illuminative creative Fiat-Lux, in the wastest terrestrial Chaos! Blessed divine Influence, traceable even in the horror of Battlefields and garments rolled in blood: how it ennobles even the Battlefield; and, in place of a Chactaw Massacre, makes it a Field of Honour! A Battlefield too is great. Considered well, it is a kind of Quintessence of Labour; Labour distilled into its utmost concentration; the significance of years of it compressed into an hour. Here too thou shalt be strong, and not in muscle only, if thou wouldst prevail. Here too thou shalt be strong of heart, noble of soul; thou shalt dread no pain or death, thou shalt not love ease or life; in rage, thou shalt remember mercy, justice; —thou shalt be a Knight and not a Chactaw, if thou wouldst prevail! It is the rule of all battles, against hallucinating fellow Men, against unkempt Cotton, or whatsoever battles they may be, which a man in this world has to fight.

Howel Davies dyes the West Indian Seas with blood, piles his decks with plunder; approves himself the expertest Seaman, the daringest Seafighter: but he gains no lasting victory, lasting victory is not possible for him. Not, had he fleets larger than the combined British Navy all united with him in bucaniering. He, once for all, cannot prosper in his duel. He strikes down his man: yes; but his man, or his man's representative, has no notion to lie struck down: neither, though slain ten times, will he keep so lying;—nor has the Universe any notion to keep him so lying! On the contrary, the Universe and he have, at all moments, all manner of motives to start up again, and desperately fight again. Your Napoleon is flung out, at last to St. Helena; the latter end of him sternly compensating the beginning. The Bucanier strikes down a man, a hundred or a million men: but what profits it? He has one enemy never to be struck down; nay two enemies: Mankind and the Maker of Men. On the great scale or on the small, in fighting of men or fighting of difficulties, I will not embark my venture with Howel

Davies: it is not the Bucanier, it is the Hero only that can gain victory, that can do more than *seem* to succeed. These things will deserve meditating; for they apply to all battle and soldiership, all struggle and effort whatsoever in this Fight of Life. It is a poor Gospel, Cash-Gospel or whatever name it have, that does not, with clear tone, uncontradictable, carrying conviction to all hearts, forever keep men in mind of these things.

Unhappily, my indomitable friend Plugson of Undershot has, in a great degree, forgotten them;—as, alas, all the world has; as, alas, our very Dukes and Soul-Overseers have, whose special trade it was to remember them:[1] Hence these tears.—Plugson, who has indomitably spun Cotton merely to gain thousands of pounds, I have to call as yet a Bucanier and Chactaw; till there come something better, still more indomitable from him. His hundred Thousand-pound Notes, if there be nothing other, are to me but as the hundred Scalps in a Chactaw wigwam. The blind Plugson; he was a Captain of Industry, born member of the Ultimate genuine Aristocracy of this Universe, could he have known it! These thousand men that span and toiled round him, they were a regiment whom he had enlisted, man by man; to make war on a very genuine enemy: Bareness of back, and disobedient Cotton-fibre, which will not, unless forced to it, consent to cover bare backs. Here is a most genuine enemy; over whom all creatures will wish him victory; He enlisted his thousand men; said to them, "Come, brothers, let us have a dash at Cotton!" They follow with cheerful shout; they gain such a victory over Cotton as the Earth has to admire and clap hands at: but, alas, it is yet only of the Bucanier or Chactaw sort,—as good as no victory! Foolish Plugson of St. Dolly Undershot: does he hope to become illustrious by hanging up the scalps in his wigwam, the hundred thousands at his banker's, and saying, Behold my scalps? Why Plugson, even thy own host is all in mutiny: Cotton is conquered; but the 'bare backs'—are worse covered than ever! Indomitable Plugson, thou must cease to be a Chactaw; thou and others; thou thyself, if no other!

Did William the Norman Bastard, or any of his Taillefers, *Ironcutters,* manage so? Ironcutter, at the end of the campaign, did not turn off his thousand fighters, but said to them: "Noble fighters, this is the land we have gained; be I Lord in it,—what we will call *Law-ward,* maintainer and *keeper* of Heaven's *Laws:* be I *Law-ward,* or in brief orthoepy *Lord* in it, and be ye Loyal Men around me in it; and we will stand by one another, as soldiers round a captain, for again we shall have need of one another!" Plugson, bucanier-like, says to them: "Noble spinners, this is the Hundred Thousand we have gained, wherein I mean to dwell and plant vineyards; the hundred thousand is mine, the three and sixpence daily was yours: adieu, noble spinners; drink my health with this groat each, which I give you over and above!" The entirely unjust Captain of Industry, say I; not Chevalier, but Bucanier! 'Commercial Law' does indeed acquit him; asks, with wide eyes, What else? So too Howel Davies asks, Was it not according to the strictest Bucanier Custom? Did I depart in any jot or tittle from the Laws of the Bucaniers?

After all, money, as they say, is miraculous. Plugson wanted victory; as Chevaliers and Bucaniers, and all men alike do. He found money recognised by the whole world with one assent, as the true symbol, exact equivalent and synonym of victory;—and here we have him, a grimbrowed indomitable Bucanier, coming home to us with a 'victory,' which the whole world is *ceasing* to clap hands at! The whole world, taught somewhat impressively, is beginning to recognise that such victory is but half a victory; and that now, if it please the Powers, we must—have the other half!

Money is miraculous. What miraculous facilities has it yielded, will it yield us; but also what never-imagined confusions, obscurations has it brought in; down almost to total extinction of the moral-sense in large masses of mankind! 'Protection of property,' of what is '*mine*,' means with most men protection of money,—the thing which, had I a thousand padlocks over it, is least of all *mine;* is, in a manner, scarcely worth calling mine! The symbol shall be held sacred, defended everywhere with tipstaves, ropes and gibbets; the thing signified shall be composedly cast to the dogs. A human being who has worked with human beings clears all scores with them, cuts himself with triumphant completeness forever loose from them, by paying down certain shillings and pounds. Was it not the wages I promised you? There they are, to the last sixpence,—according to the Laws of the Bucaniers!—Yes, indeed;—and, at such times, it becomes imperatively necessary to ask all persons, Bucaniers and others, Whether these same respectable Laws of the Bucaniers are written on God's eternal Heavens at all, on the inner Heart of Man at all; or on the respectable Bucaniers Logbook merely, for the convenience of bucaniering merely? What a question;—whereat Westminster Hall shudders to its driest parchment; and on the dead wigs each particular horse-hair stands on end!

The Laws of Laissez-faire, O Westminster, the laws of industrial Captain and industrial Soldier, how much more of idle Captain and industrial Soldier, will need to be remodelled, and modified, and rectified in a hundred and a hundred ways,—and *not* in the Sliding-scale direction, but in the totally opposite one! With two million industrial Soldiers already sitting in Bastilles, and five millions pining on potatoes, methinks Westminster cannot begin too soon!—A man has other obligations laid on him in God's Universe, than the payment of cash: these also Westminster, if it will continue to exist and have board-wages, must contrive to take some charge of:—by Westminster or by another, they must and will be taken charge of; be, with whatever difficulty, got articulated, got enforced, and to a certain approximate extent, put in practice. And, as I say, it cannot be too soon! For Mammonism, left to itself, has become Midas-eared; and with all its gold mountains, sits starving for want of bread: and Dilettantism with its partridge-nets, in this extremely earnest Universe of ours, is playing somewhat too high a game. 'A man by the very look of him promises so much:' yes; and by the rent-roll of him does he promise nothing?—

Alas, what a business will this be, which our Continental friends, groping this long while somewhat absurdly about it and about it, call 'Organisation of Labour;'—which must be taken out of the hands of absurd windy persons, and put into the hands of wise, laborious, modest and valiant men, to begin with it straightway: to proceed with it, and succeed in it more and more, if Europe, at any rate if England, is to continue habitable much longer. Looking at the kind of most noble Corn-Law Dukes or Practical *Duces* we have, and also of right reverend Soul-Overseers, Christian Spiritual *Duces* 'on a minimum of four thousand five hundred,' one's hopes are a little chilled. Courage, nevertheless; there are many brave men in England! My indomitable Plugson,—nay is there not even in thee some hope? Thou art hitherto a Bucanier, as it was written and prescribed for thee by an evil world: but in that grim brow, in that indomitable heart which *can* conquer Cotton, do there not perhaps lie other ten-times nobler conquests?

CHAPTER XI.

Labour.

For there is a perennial nobleness, and even sacredness, in Work. Were he never so benighted, forgetful of his high calling, there is always hope in a man that actually and earnestly works: in Idleness alone is there perpetual despair. Work, never so Mammonish, mean, *is* in communication with Nature; the real desire to get Work done will itself lead one more and more to truth, to Nature's appointments and regulations, which are truth.

The latest Gospel in this world is, Know thy work and do it 'Know thyself:' long enough has that poor 'self' of thine tormented thee; thou wilt never get to 'know' it, I believe! Think it not thy business, this of knowing thyself; thou art an unknowable individual: know what thou canst work at; and work at it, like a Hercules! That will be thy better plan.

It has been written, 'an endless significance lies in Work;' a man perfects himself by working. Foul jungles are cleared away, fair seedfields rise instead, and stately cities; and withal the man himself first ceases to be jungle and foul unwholesome desert thereby. Consider how, even in the meanest sorts of Labour, the whole soul of a man is composed into a kind of real harmony, the instant he sets himself to work! Doubt, Desire, Sorrow, Remorse, Indignation, Despair itself, all these like hell-dogs lie beleaguering the soul of the poor dayworker, as of every man: but he bends himself with free valour against his task, and all these are stilled, all these shrink murmuring far off into their caves. The man is now a man. The blessed glow of Labour in him, is it not as purifying fire, wherein all poison is burnt up, and of sour smoke itself there is made bright blessed flame!

Destiny, on the whole, has no other way of cultivating us. A formless Chaos once set it *revolving*, grows round and even rounder; ranges itself, by mere force of gravity, into strata, spherical courses; is no longer a Chaos, but a round compacted World. What would become of the Earth, did she cease to revolve? In the poor old Earth, so long as she revolves, all inequalities, irregularities disperse themselves; all irregularities are incessantly becoming regular. Hast thou looked on the Potter's wheel,—one of the venerablest objects; old as the Prophet Ezechiel and far older? Rude lumps of clay, how they spin themselves up, by mere quick whirling, into beautiful circular dishes. And fancy the most assiduous Potter, but without his wheel; reduced to make dishes, or rather amorphous botches, by mere kneading and baking! Even such a Potter were Destiny, with a human soul that would rest and lie at ease, that would not work and spin! Of an idle unrevolving man the kindest Destiny, like the most assiduous Potter without wheel, can bake and knead nothing other than a botch; let her spend on him what expensive colouring, what gilding and enamelling she will, he is but a botch. Not a dish; no, a bulging, kneaded, crooked, shambling, squint-cornered, amorphous botch,—a mere enamelled vessel of dishonour! Let the idle think of this.

Blessed is he who has found his work; let him ask no other blessedness. He has a work, a life-purpose; he has found it, and will follow it! How, as a free-flowing channel, dug and torn by noble force through the sour mud-swamp of one's existence, like an ever-deepening river there, it runs and flows;—draining off the sour festering water, gradually from the root of the remotest grass-blade; making, instead of pestilential swamp, a green fruitful meadow with its clear-flowing stream. How blessed for the meadow itself, let the stream and *its* value be great or small! Labour is Life: from the inmost heart of the Worker rises his god-given Force, the sacred celestial Life-essence breathed into him by Almighty God; from his inmost heart awakens him to all nobleness,—to all knowledge, 'self-knowledge' and much else, so soon as Work fitly begins. Knowledge? The knowledge that will hold good in working, cleave thou to that; for Nature herself accredits that, says Yea to that. Properly thou hast no other knowledge but what thou hast got by working: the rest is yet all a hypothesis of knowledge; a thing to be argued of in schools, a thing floating in the clouds, in endless logic-vortices, till we try it and fix it. 'Doubt, of whatever kind, can be ended by Action alone.'

And again, hast thou valued Patience, Courage, Perseverance, Openness to light; readiness to own thyself mistaken, to do better next time? All these, all virtues, in wrestling with the dim brute Powers of Fact, in ordering of thy fellows in such wrestle, there and elsewhere not at all, thou wilt continually learn. Set down a brave Sir Christopher in the middle of black ruined Stoneheaps, of foolish unarchitectural Bishops, redtape Officials, idle Nell-Gwyn Defenders of the Faith; and see whether he will ever raise a Paul's Cathedral out of all that, yea or no! Rough, rude, contradictory are all things and persons, from the mutinous masons and Irish hodmen, up to the idle Nell-Gwyn Defenders, to blustering redtape Officials, foolish unarchitectural Bishops. All these things and persons are there not for Christopher's sake and his Cathedral's; they are there for their own sake mainly! Christopher will have to conquer and constrain all these,—if he be able. All these are against him. Equitable Nature herself, who carries her mathematics and architectonics not on the face of her, but deep in the hidden heart of her,—Nature herself is but partially for him; will be wholly against him, if he constrain her not! His very money, where is it to come from? The pious munificence of England lies far-scattered, distant, unable to speak, and say, "I am here;"—must be spoken to before it can speak. Pious munificence, and all help, is so silent, invisible like the gods; impediment, contradictions manifold are so loud and near! O brave Sir Christopher, trust thou in those, notwithstanding, and front all these; understand all these; by valiant patience, noble effort, insight, by man's-strength, vanquish and compel all these,—and, on the whole, strike down victoriously the last topstone of that Paul's Edifice; thy monument for certain centuries, the stamp 'Great Man' impressed very legibly on Portland-stone there!—

Yes, all manner of help, and pious response from Men of Nature, is always what we call silent; cannot speak or come to light, till it be seen, till it be spoken to. Every noble work is at first 'impossible.' In very truth, for every noble work the possibilities will lie diffused through Immensity; inarticulate, undiscoverable except to faith. Like Gideon thou shalt spread out thy fleece at the door of thy tent; see whether under the wide arch of Heaven there be any bounteous moisture, or none. Thy heart and life-purpose shall be as a miraculous Gideon's fleece, spread out in silent appeal to Heaven; and from the kind Immensities, what from the poor unkind Localities and town and country Parishes there never could, blessed dew-moisture to suffice thee shall have fallen!

Work is of a religious nature:—work is of a *brave* nature; which it is the aim of all religion to be. All work of man is as the swimmer's; a waste ocean threatens to devour him; if he front it not bravely, it will keep its word. By incessant wise defiance of it, lusty rebuke and buffet of it, behold how it loyally supports him, bears him as its conqueror along. 'It is so,' says Goethe, 'with all things that man undertakes in this world.'

Brave Sea-captain, Norse Sea-king,—Columbus, my hero, royalest Sea-king of all! it is no friendly environment this of thine, in the waste deep waters; around thee mutinous discouraged souls, behind thee disgrace and ruin, before thee the unpenetrated veil of Night. Brother, these wild water-mountains, bounding from their deep basin (ten miles deep, I am told), are not entirely there on thy behalf! Meseems *they* have other work than floating thee forward:—and the huge Winds, that sweep from Ursa Major to the Tropics and Equators, dancing their giant-waltz through the kingdoms of Chaos and Immensity, they care little about filling rightly or filling wrongly the small shoulder-of-mutton sails in this cockle-skiff of thine! Thou art not among articulate-speaking friends, my brother; thou art among immeasurable dumb monsters, tumbling, howling wide as the world here. Secret, far off, invisible to all hearts but thine, there lies a help in them: see how thou wilt get at that. Patiently thou wilt wait till the mad

South-wester spend itself, saving thyself by dexterous science of defence, the while: valiantly, with swift decision, wilt thou strike in, when the favouring East, the Possible, springs up. Mutiny of men thou wilt sternly repress; weakness, despondency, thou wilt cheerily encourage: thou wilt swallow down complaint, unreason, weariness, weakness of others and thyself;—how much wilt thou swallow down! There shall be a depth of Silence in thee, deeper than this Sea, which is but ten miles deep: a Silence unsoundable; known to God only. Thou shalt be a great Man. Yes, my World-Soldier, thou of the World Marine-service,—thou wilt have to be *greater* than this tumultuous unmeasured World here round thee is; thou, in thy strong soul, as with wrestler's arms, shalt embrace it, harness it down; and make it bear thee on,—to new Americas, or whither God wills!

CHAPTER XII.

Reward.

'RELIGION,' I said; for, properly speaking, all true Work is Religion: and whatsoever Religion is not Work may go and dwell among the Brahmins, Antinomians, Spinning Dervishes, or where it will; with me it shall have no harbour. Admirable was that of the old Monks, '*Laborare est Orare*, Work is Worship.'

Older than all preached Gospels was this unpreached, inarticulate but ineradicable, forever-enduring Gospel: Work, and therein have well being. Man, son of Earth and of Heaven, lies there not, in the innermost heart of thee, a Spirit of active Method, a Force for work;—and burns like a painfully smouldering fire, giving thee no rest till thou unfold it, till thou write it down in beneficent Facts around thee! What is immethodic, waste, thou shalt make methodic, regulated, arable; obedient and productive to thee. Wheresoever thou findest Disorder, there is thy eternal enemy; attack him swiftly, subdue him; make Order of him, the subject not of Chaos, but of Intelligence, Divinity and Thee! The thistle that grows in thy path, dig it out, that a blade of useful grass, a drop of nourishing milk, may grow there instead. The waste cotton-shrub, gather its waste white down, spin it, weave it; that, in place of idle litter, there may be folded webs, and the naked skin of man be covered.

But above all, where thou findest Ignorance, Stupidity, Brute-mindedness, —yes, there, with or without Church-tithes and Shovel-hat, with or without Talfourd-Mahon Copyrights, or were it with mere dungeons and gibbets and crosses, attack it, I say; smite it wisely, unweariedly, and rest not while thou livest and it lives; but smite, smite, in the name of God! The Highest God, as I understand it, does audibly so command thee; still audibly, if thou have ears to hear. He, even He, with his *un*spoken voice, awfuler than any Sinai thunders or syllabled speech of Whirlwinds; for the SILENCE of deep Eternities, of Worlds from beyond the morning-stars, does it not speak to thee? The unborn Ages; the old Graves, with their long-mouldering dust, the very tears that wetted it now all dry,—do not these speak to thee, what ear hath not heard? The deep Death-kingdoms, the Stars in their never-resting courses, all Space and all Time, proclaim it to thee in continual silent admonition. Thou too, if ever man should, shalt work while it is called To-day. For the Night cometh, wherein no man can work.

All true Work is sacred; in all true Work, were it but true hand-labour, there is something of divineness. Labour, wide as the Earth, has its summit in Heaven. Sweat of the brow; and up from that to sweat of the brain, sweat of the heart; which includes all Kepler calculations, Newton meditations, all Sciences, all spoken Epics, all acted Heroisms, Martyrdoms,—up to that 'Agony of bloody sweat,' which all men have called divine! O brother, if this is not 'worship,' then I say, the more pity for worship; for this is the noblest thing yet discovered under God's sky. Who art thou that complainest of thy life of toil? Complain not. Look up, my wearied brother: see thy fellow Workmen there, in God's Eternity; surviving there, they alone surviving: sacred Band of the Immortals, celestial Bodyguard of the Empire of Mankind. Even in the weak Human Memory they survive so long, as saints, as heroes, as gods; they alone surviving; peopling, they alone, the unmeasured solitudes of Time! To Thee Heaven, though severe, is *not* unkind; Heaven is kind,—as a noble Mother; as that Spartan Mother, saying while she gave her son his shield, "With it, my son, or upon it!" Thou too, shalt return *home* in honour; to thy far-distant Home, in honour; doubt it not,—if in the battle thou keep thy shield! Thou, in the Eternities and deepest Death-kingdoms, art not an alien; thou everywhere art a denizen! Complain not; the very Spartans did not *complain*.

And who art thou that braggest of thy life of Idleness; complacently shewest thy bright gilt equipages; sumptuous cushions; appliances for folding of the hands to mere sleep? Looking up, looking down, around, behind or before, discernest thou, if it be not in Mayfair alone, any *idle* hero, saint, god, or even devil? Not a vestige of one. In the Heavens, in the Earth, in the Waters under the Earth, is none like unto thee. Thou art an original figure in this Creation; a denizen in Mayfair alone, in this extraordinary Century or Half-Century alone! One monster there is in the world: the idle man. What is his 'Religion?' That Nature is a Phantasm, where cunning beggary or thievery may sometimes find good victual. That God is a lie; and that Man and his Life are a lie.—Alas, alas, who of us *is* there that can say, I have worked? The faithfulest of us are unprofitable servants; the faithfulest of us know that best. The faithfulest of us may say, with sad and true old Samuel, "Much of my life has been trifled away!" But he that has, and except 'on public occasions' professes to have, no function but that of going idle in a graceful or graceless manner; and of begetting sons to go idle; and to address Chief Spinners and Diggers, who at least *are* spinning and digging, "Ye scandalous persons who produce too much"—My Corn-Law Friends, on what imaginary still richer Eldorados, and true iron-spikes with law of gravitation, are ye rushing!

As to the Wages of Work there might innumerable things be said; there will and must yet innumerable things be said and spoken, in St. Stephen's and out of St. Stephen's; and gradually not a few things be ascertained and written, on Law-parchment, concerning this very matter:—'Fair day's-wages for a fair day's-work' is the most unrefusable demand! Money-wages 'to the extent of keeping your worker alive that he may work more;' these, unless you mean to dismiss him straightway out of this world, are indispensable alike to the noblest Worker and to the least noble!

One thing only I will say here, in special reference to the former class, the noble and noblest; but throwing light on all the other classes and their arrangements of this difficult matter: The 'wages' of every noble Work do yet lie in Heaven or else Nowhere. Not in Bank-of-England bills, in Owen's Labour-bank, or any the most improved establishment of banking and money-changing, needest thou, heroic soul, present thy account of earnings. Human banks and labour-banks know thee not; or know thee after generations and centuries have passed away, and thou art clean gone from 'rewarding,'—all manner of bank-drafts, shop-tills, and Downing-street Exchequers lying very invisible, so far from thee! Nay, at bottom, dost thou need any reward? Was it thy aim and life-purpose to be filled with good things for thy heroism; to have a life of pomp and ease, and be what men call 'happy,' in this world, or in any other world? I answer for thee deliberately, No. The whole spiritual secret of the new epoch lies in this, that thou canst answer for thyself, with thy whole clearness of head and heart, deliberately, No!

My brother, the brave man has to give his Life away. Give it, I advise thee;—thou dost not expect to *sell* thy Life in an adequate manner? What price, for example, would content thee? The just price of thy LIFE to thee,—why, God's entire Creation to thyself, the whole Universe of Space, the whole Eternity of Time, and what they hold: that is the price which would content thee; that, and if thou wilt be candid, nothing short of that! It is thy all; and for it thou wouldst have all. Thou art an unreasonable mortal;—or rather thou art a poor *infinite* mortal, who, in thy narrow clay-prison here, *seemest* so unreasonable! Thou wilt never sell thy Life, or any part of thy Life, in a satisfactory manner. Give it, like a royal heart; let the price be Nothing: thou *hast* then, in a certain sense, got All for it! The heroic man,—and is not every man, God be thanked, a potential hero?—has to do so, in all times and circumstances. In the most heroic age, as in the most unheroic, he will have to say, as Burns said proudly and humbly of his little Scottish Songs, little dewdrops of Celestial Melody in an age when so much was unmelodious: "By Heaven, they shall either be invaluable or of no value; I do not need your guineas for them!" It is an element which should, and must, enter deeply into all settlements of wages here below. They never will be 'satisfactory' otherwise; they cannot, O Mammon Gospel, they never can! Money for my little piece of work 'to the extent that will allow me to keep working;' yes, this,—unless you mean that I shall go my ways *before* the work is all taken out of me: but as to 'wages'—!—

On the whole, we do entirely agree with those old Monks, *Laborare est Orare*. In a thousand senses, from one end of it to the other, true Work *is* Worship. He that works, whatsoever be his work, he bodies forth the form of Things Unseen; a small Poet every Worker is. The idea, were it but of his poor Delf Platter, how much more of his Epic Poem, is as yet 'seen,' half-seen, only by himself; to all others it is a thing unseen, impossible; to Nature herself it is a thing unseen, a thing which never hitherto was;— very 'impossible,' for it is as yet a No-thing! The Unseen Powers had need to watch over such a man; he works in and for the Unseen. Alas, if he look to the Seen Powers only, he may as well quit the business; his No-thing will never rightly issue as a Thing, but as a Deceptivity, a Sham-thing, —which it had better not do!

Thy No-thing of an Intended Poem, O Poet who hast looked merely to reviewers, copyrights, booksellers, popularities, behold it has not yet become a Thing; for the truth is not in it! Though printed, hotpressed, reviewed, celebrated, sold to the twentieth edition: what is all that? The Thing, in philosophical uncommercial language, is still a No-thing, mostly semblance, and deception of the sight;—benign Oblivion incessantly gnawing at it, impatient till Chaos to which it belongs do reabsorb it!—

He who takes not counsel of the Unseen and Silent, from him will never come real visibility and speech. Thou must descend to the *Mothers*, to the *Manes*, and Hercules-like long suffer and labour there, wouldst thou emerge with victory into the sunlight. As in battle and the shock of war,—for is not this a battle?—thou too shalt fear no pain or death, shalt love no ease or life; the voice of festive Lubberlands, the noise of greedy Acheron shall alike lie silent under thy victorious feet. Thy work, like Dante's, shall 'make thee lean for many years.' The world and its wages, its criticisms, counsels, helps, impediments, shall be as a waste ocean-flood; the chaos through which thou art to swim and sail. Not the waste waves and their weedy gulf-streams, shalt thou take for guidance: thy star alone,—'*Se tu segui tua stella!*' Thy star alone, now clear-beaming over Chaos, nay now by fits gone out, disastrously eclipsed: this only shalt thou strive to follow. O, it is a business, as I fancy, that of weltering your way through Chaos and the murk of Hell! Green-eyed dragons watching you, three-headed Cerberuses, —not without sympathy of *their* sort! "*Eccovi l' uom ch' è stato all' Inferno.*" For in fine, as Poet Dryden says, you do walk hand in hand with sheer Madness, all the way,—who is by no means pleasant company! You look fixedly into Madness, and *her* undiscovered, boundless, bottomless Night-empire; that you may extort new Wisdom out of it, as an Eurydice from Tartarus. The higher the Wisdom, the closer was its neighbourhood and kindred with mere Insanity; literally so:—and thou wilt, with a speechless feeling, observe how highest Wisdom, struggling up into this world, has oftentimes carried such tinctures and adhesions of Insanity still cleaving to it hither!

All Works, each in their degree, are a making of Madness sane;—truly enough a religious operation; which cannot be carried on without religion.

You have not work otherwise; you have eye-service, greedy grasping of wages, swift and ever swifter manufacture of semblances to get hold of wages. Instead of better felt-hats to cover your head, you have bigger lath-and-plaster hats set travelling the streets on wheels. Instead of heavenly and earthly Guidance for the souls of men, you have 'Black or White Surplice' Controversies, stuffed hair-and-leather Popes;—terrestrial *Law-wards*, Lords and Law-bringers, 'organizing Labour' in these years, by passing Corn-Laws. With all which, alas, this distracted Earth is now full, nigh to bursting. Semblances most smooth to the touch and eye; most accursed nevertheless to body and soul. Semblances, be they of Sham-woven Cloth or of Dilettante Legislation, which are *not* real wool or substance, but Devil's-dust, accursed of God and man! No man has worked, or can work, except religiously; not even the poor day-labourer, the weaver of your coat, the sewer of your shoes. All men, if they work not as in a Great Taskmaster's eye, will work wrong, work unhappily for themselves and you.

Industrial work, still under bondage to Mammon, the rational soul of it not yet awakened, is a tragic spectacle. Men in the rapidest motion and self-motion; restless, with convulsive energy, as if driven by Galvanism, as if possessed by a Devil; tearing asunder mountains,—to no purpose, for Mammonism is always Midas-eared! This is sad, on the face of it. Yet courage: the beneficent Destinies, kind in their sternness, are apprising us that this cannot continue. Labour is not a devil, even while encased in Mammonism; Labour is ever an imprisoned god, writhing unconsciously or consciously to escape out of Mammonism! Plugson of Undershot, like Taillefer of Normandy, wants victory; how much happier will even Plugson be to have a Chivalrous victory than a Chactaw one. The unredeemed ugliness is that of a slothful People. Shew me a People energetically busy; heaving, struggling, all shoulders at the wheel; their heart pulsing, every muscle swelling, with man's energy and will;—I shew you a People of whom great good is already predicable; to whom all manner of good is yet certain, if their energy endure. By very working, they will learn; they have, Antæus-like, their foot on Mother Fact: how can they but learn?

The vulgarest Plugson of a Master-Worker, who can command Workers, and get work out of them, is already a considerable man. Blessed and thrice-blessed symptoms I discern of Master-Workers who are not vulgar men; who are Nobles, and begin to feel that they must act as such: all speed to these, they are England's hope at present! But in this Plugson himself, conscious of almost no nobleness whatever, how much is there! Not without man's faculty, insight, courage, hard energy, is this rugged figure. His words none of the wisest; but his actings cannot be altogether foolish. Think, how were it, stoodest thou suddenly in his shoes! He has to command a thousand men. And not imaginary commanding; no, it is real, incessantly practical. The evil passions of so many men (with the Devil in them, as in all of us) he has to vanquish; by manifold force of speech and of silence, to repress or evade. What a force of silence, to say nothing of the others, is in Plugson! For these his thousand men he has to provide raw-material, machinery, arrangement, house-room; and ever at the week's end, wages by due sale. No Civil-List, or Goulburn-Baring Budget has he to fall back upon, for paying of his regiment; he has to pick his supplies from the confused face of the whole Earth and Contemporaneous History, by his dexterity alone. There will be dry eyes if he fail to do it!—He exclaims, at present, 'black in the face,' near strangled with Dilettante Legislation: "Let me have elbow-room, throat-room, and I will not fail! No, I will spin yet, and conquer like a giant; what 'sinews of war' lie in me, untold resources towards the Conquest of this Planet, if instead of hanging me, you husband them, and help me!"—My indomitable friend, it is *true*; and thou shalt and must be helped.

This is not a man I would kill and strangle by Corn-Laws, even if I could! No, I would fling my Corn-Laws and Shot-belts to the Devil; and try to help this man. I would teach him, by noble precept and law-precept, by noble example most of all, that Mammonism was not the essence of his or of my station in God's Universe; but the adscititious excrescence of it; the gross, terrene, godless embodiment of it; which would have to become, more or less, a godlike one. By noble *real* legislation, by true *noble's*-work, by unwearied, valiant, and were it wageless effort, in my Parliament and in my Parish, I would aid, constrain, encourage him to effect more or less this blessed change. I should know that it would have to be effected; that unless it were in some measure effected, he and I and all of us, I first and soonest of all, were doomed to perdition!—Effected it will be; unless it were a Demon that made this Universe; which I, for my own part, do at no moment, under no form, in the least believe.

May it please your Serene Highnesses, your Majesties, Lordships and Law-wardships, the proper Epic of this world is not now 'Arms and the Man;' how much less, 'Shirt-frills and the Man:' no, it is now 'Tools and the Man:' that, henceforth to all time is now our Epic; and you, first of all others, I think, were wise to take note of that!

CHAPTER XIII.

DEMOCRACY.

IF THE Serene Highnesses and Majesties do not take note of that, then, as I perceive, *that* will take note of itself! The time for levity, insincerity, and idle babble and play-acting, in all kinds, is gone by; it is a serious, grave time. Old long-vexed questions, not yet solved in logical words or parliamentary laws, are fast solving themselves in facts, somewhat unblessed to behold! This largest of questions, this question of Work and Wages, which ought, had we heeded Heaven's voice to have begun two generations ago or more, cannot be delayed longer without hearing Earth's voice. 'Labour' will verily need to be somewhat 'organised,' as they say,—God knows with what difficulty. Man will actually need to have his debts and earnings a little better paid by man; which, let Parliaments speak of them or be silent of them, are eternally his due from man, and cannot, without penalty and at length not without death-penalty, be withheld. How much ought to cease among us straightway; how much ought to begin straightway, while the hours yet are!

Truly they are strange results to which this of leaving all to 'Cash;' of quietly shutting up the God's Temple, and gradually opening wide-open the Mammon's Temple, with 'Laissez-faire, and Every man for himself,'—have led us in these days! We have Upper, speaking Classes, who indeed do 'speak' as never man spake before; the withered flimsiness, the godless baseness and barrenness of whose Speech might of itself indicate what kind of Doing and practical Governing went on under it! For Speech is the gaseous element out of which most kinds of Practice and Performance, especially all kinds of moral Performance, condense themselves, and take shape; as the one is, so will the other be. Descending, accordingly, into the Dumb Class in its Stockport Cellars and Poor-Law Bastilles, have we not to announce that they also are hitherto unexampled in the History of Adam's Posterity?

Life was never a May-game for men: in all times the lot of the dumb millions born to toil was defaced with manifold sufferings, injustices, heavy burdens, avoidable and unavoidable; not play at all, but hard work that made the sinews sore, and the heart sore. As bond-slaves, *villani, bordarii, sochemanni,* nay indeed as dukes, earls and kings, men were oftentimes made weary of their life; and had to say, in the sweat of their brow and of their soul, Behold it is not sport, it is grim earnest, and our back can bear no more! Who knows not what massacrings and harryings there have been; grinding, long-continuing, unbearable injustices,—till the heart had to rise in madness, and some "*Eu Sachsen, nimith euer sachses,* You Saxons, out with your gully-knives then!" You Saxons, some 'arrestment,' partial 'arrestment of the Knaves and Dastards' has become indispensable!—The page of Dryasdust is heavy with such details.

And yet I will venture to believe that in no time, since the beginnings of Society, was the lot of those same dumb millions of toilers so entirely unbearable as it is even in the days now passing over us. It is not to die, or even to die of hunger, that makes a man wretched; many men have died; all men must die,—the last exit of us all is in a Fire-Chariot of Pain. But it is to live miserable we know not why; to work sore and yet gain nothing; to be heart-worn, weary, yet isolated, unrelated, girt in with a cold universal Laissez-faire: it is to die slowly all our life long, imprisoned in a deaf, dead, Infinite Injustice, as in the accursed iron belly of a Phalaris' Bull! This is and remains forever intolerable to all men whom God has made. Do we wonder at French Revolutions, Chartisms, Revolts of Three Days? The times, if we will consider them, are really unexampled.

Never before did I hear of an Irish Widow reduced to 'prove her sisterhood by dying of typhus fever and infecting seventeen persons,'—saying in such undeniable way, "You *see,* I was your sister!" Sisterhood, brotherhood was often forgotten: but not till the rise of these ultimate Mammon and Shotbelt Gospels, did I ever see it so expressly denied. If no pious Lord or *Law-ward* would remember it, always some pious Lady ('*Hlaf-dig,*' Benefactress, '*Loaf-giveress,*' they say she is,—blessings on her beautiful heart!) was there, with mild mother-voice and hand, to remember it; some pious thoughtful *Elder,* what we now call 'Prester,' *Presbyter* or 'Priest,' was there to put all men in mind of it, in the name of the God who had made all.

Not even in Black Dahomey was it ever, I think, forgotten to the typhus-fever length. Mungo Park, resourceless, had sunk down to die under the Negro Village-Tree, a horrible White object in the eyes of all. But in the poor Black Woman, and her daughter who stood aghast at him, whose earthly wealth and funded capital consisted of one small calabash of rice, there lived a heart richer than '*Laissez-faire:*' they, with a royal munificence, boiled their rice for him; they sang all night to him, spinning assiduous on their cotton distaffs, as he lay to sleep: "Let us pity the poor white man; no mother has he to fetch him milk, no sister to grind him corn!" Thou poor black Noble One,—thou *Lady* too: did not a God make thee too; was there not in thee too something of a God!—

Gurth born thrall of Cedric the Saxon has been greatly pitied by Dryas-dust and others. Gurth with the brass collar round his neck, tending Cedric's pigs in the glades of the·wood, is not what I call an exemplar of human felicity: but·Gurth, with the sky above him, with the free air and tinted boscage and umbrage round him, and in him at least the certainty of supper and social lodging when he came home; Gurth to me seems happy, in comparison with many a Lancashire and Buckinghamshire man, of these days, not born thrall of anybody! Gurth's brass collar did not gall him: Cedric *deserved* to be his Master. The pigs were Cedric's, but Gurth too would get his parings of them. Gurth had the inexpressible satisfaction of feeling himself related indissolubly, though in a rude brass-collar way, to his fellow-mortals in this Earth. He had superiors, inferiors, equals.— Gurth is now 'emancipated' long since; has what we call 'Liberty.' Liberty, I am told, is a Divine thing. Liberty when it becomes the 'Liberty to die by starvation' is not so divine!

Liberty? The true liberty of a man you would say, consisted in his finding out, or being forced to find out the right path, and to walk thereon. To learn or to be taught, what work he actually was able for; and then by permission, persuasion, and even compulsion, to set about doing of the same! That is his true blessedness, honour, 'liberty' and maximum of well being: if liberty be not that, I for one have small care about liberty. You do not allow a palpable madman to leap over precipices; you violate his liberty, you that are wise; and keep him, were it in straight-waistcoats, away from the precipices! Every stupid, every cowardly and foolish man is but a less palpable madman: his true liberty were that a wiser man, that any and every wiser man, could, by brass collars, or in whatever milder or sharper way, lay hold of him when he was going wrong, and order and compel him to go a little righter. O if thou really art my *Senior*, Seigneur, my *Elder*, Presbyter or Priest,—if thou art in very deed my *Wiser*, may a beneficent instinct lead and impel thee to 'conquer' me, to command me! If thou do know better than I what is good and right, I conjure you in the name of God, force me to do it; were it by never such brass collars, whips and handcuffs, leave me not to walk over precipices! That I have been called, by all the Newspapers, a 'free man' will avail me little, if my pilgrimage have ended in death and wreck. O that the Newspapers had called me slave, coward, fool, or what it pleased their sweet voices to name me, and I had attained not death, but life!—Liberty requires new definitions.

A conscious abhorrence and intolerance of Folly, of Baseness, Stupidity, Poltroonery and all that brood of things, dwells deep in some men: still deeper in others and *un*conscious abhorrence and intolerance, clothed moreover by the beneficent Supreme Powers in what stout appetites, energies, egoisms so-called, are suitable to it;—these latter are your Conquerors, Romans, Normans, Russians, Indo-English; Founders of what we call Aristocracies. Which indeed have they not the most 'divine right' to found;—being themselves very truly Ἄριστοι, BRAVEST, BEST; and conquering generally a confused rabble of WORST, or at lowest, clearly enough, of WORSE? I think their divine right, tried with affirmatory verdict, in the greatest Law-Court known to me, was good! A class of men who are dreadfully exclaimed against by Dryasdust; of whom nevertheless beneficent Nature has oftentimes had need; and may, alas, again have need.

When, across the hundredfold poor scepticisms, trivialisms, and constitutional cobwebberies of Dryasdust, you catch any glimpse of a William the Conqueror, a Tancred of Hauteville or such like,—do you not discern veritably some rude outline of a true God-made King; whom not the Champion of England cased in tin, but all Nature and the Universe were calling to the throne? It is absolutely necessary that he get thither. Nature does not mean her poor Saxon children to perish, of obesity, stupor or other malady, as yet: a stern Ruler and Line of Rulers therefore is called in,—a stern but most beneficent *Perpetual House-Surgeon* is by Nature herself called in, and even the appropriate *fees* are provided for him! Dryasdust talks lamentably about Hereward and the Fen Counties; fate of Earl Waltheof; Yorkshire and the North reduced to ashes; all which is undoubtedly lamentable. But even Dryasdust apprises me of one fact: 'A child, in this William's reign, might have carried a purse of gold from end to end of England.' My erudite friend, it is a fact which outweighs a thousand! Sweep away thy constitutional, sentimental and other cobwebberies; look eye to eye, if thou still have any eye, in the face of this big burly William Bastard: thou wilt see a fellow of most flashing discernment, of most strong lion-heart;—in whom, as it were, within a frame of oak and iron, the gods have planted the soul of 'a man of genius!' Dost thou call that nothing? I call it an immense thing!—Rage enough was in this Willelmus Conquestor, rage enough for his occasions;—and yet the essential element of him, as of all such men, is not scorching *fire*, but shining illuminative *light*. Fire and light are strangely interchangeable; nay, at bottom, I have found them different forms of the same most godlike 'elementary substance' in our world; a thing worth stating in these days. The essential element of this Conquestor is, first of all, the most sun-eyed perception of what *is* really what on this God's-Earth;—which, thou wilt find, does mean at bottom 'Justice,' and 'Virtues' not a few: *Conformity* to what the Maker has been good to make; that, I suppose, will mean Justice and a Virtue or two?—

Dost thou think Willelmus Conquestor would have tolerated ten years' jargon, on the propriety of killing Cotton-manufactures by partridge Corn-Laws? I fancy, this was not the man to knock out of his night's-rest with nothing but a noisy bedlamism in your mouth! "Assist us still better to bush the partridges; strangle Plugson who spins the shirts?"—*"Par la Splendeur de Dieu!"*—Dost thou think Willelmus Conquestor, in this new time, with Steamengine Captains of Industry on one hand of him, and Joe-Manton Captains of Idleness on the other, would have doubted which *was* really the BEST; which did deserve strangling, and which not?

I have a certain indestructible regard for Willelmus Conquestor. A resident House-Surgeon, provided by Nature for her beloved English People, and even furnished with the requisite fees as I said; for he by no means felt himself doing Nature's work, this Willelmus, but his own work exclusively! And his own work withal it was; informed *'par la Splendeur de Dieu.'*—I say, it is necessary to get the work out of such a man, however harsh that be! When a world, not yet doomed for death, is rushing down to ever-deeper Baseness and Confusion, it is a dire necessity of Nature's to bring in her ARISTOCRACIES, her BEST, even by forcible methods. When their descendants or representatives cease entirely to *be* the Best, Nature's poor world will very soon rush down again to Baseness; and it becomes a dire necessity of Nature's to cast them out. Hence French Revolutions, Five-point Charters, Democracies, and a mournful list of *Etceteras*, in these our afflicted times.

To what extent Democracy has now reached, how it advances irresistible with ominous, ever-increasing speed, he that will open his eyes on any province of human affairs may discern. Democracy is everywhere the inexorable demand of these ages, swiftly fulfilling itself. From the thunder of Napoleon battles, to the jabbering of Open-vestry in St. Mary Axe, all things announce Democracy. A distinguished man, whom some of my readers will hear again with pleasure, thus writes to me what in these days he notes from the Wahngasse of Weissnichtwo, where our London fashions seem to be in full vogue. Let us hear the Herr Teufelsdröckh again, were it but the smallest word!

'Democracy, which means despair of finding any Heroes to govern you, and contented putting up with the want of them,—alas, thou too, *mein Lieber*, seest well how close it is of kin to *Atheism*, and other sad *Isms*: he who discovers no God whatever, how shall he discover Heroes, the visible Temples of God?—Strange enough meanwhile it is, to observe with what thoughtlessness, here in our rigidly Conservative Country, men rush into Democracy with full cry. Beyond doubt, his Excellenz the Titular Herr Ritter Kauderwälsch von Pferdefuss-Quacksalber, be our distinguished Conservative Premier himself, and all but the thicker-headed of his Party, discern Democracy to be inevitable as death, and are even desperate of delaying it much!

'You cannot walk the streets without beholding Democracy announce itself: the very Tailor has become, if not properly Sansculottic, which to him would be ruinous, yet a Tailor unconsciously symbolising, and prophesying with his scissors, the reign of Equality. What now is our fashionable coat? A thing of superfinest texture, of deeply meditated cut; with Malineslace cuffs; quilted with gold; so that a man can carry without difficulty an estate of land on his back? *Keineswegs*, By no manner of means! The Sumptuary Laws have fallen into such a state of desuetude as was never before seen. Our fashionable coat is an amphibium between barnsack and drayman's doublet. The cloth of it is studiously coarse; the colour a speckled soot-black or rust-brown grey;—the nearest approach to a Peasant's. And for shape, thou shouldst see it! The last consummation of the year now passing over us is definable as Three Bags: a big bag for the body, two small bags for the arms, and by way of collar a hem! The first Antique Cheruscan who, of felt-cloth or bear's-hide, with bone or metal needle, set about making himself a coat, before Tailors had yet awakened out of Nothing,—did not he make it even so? A loose wide poke for body, with two holes to let out the arms; this was his original coat: to which holes it was soon visible that two small loose pokes, or sleeves, easily appended, would be an improvement.

'Thus has the Tailor art, so to speak, overset itself, like most other things; changed its centre-of-gravity; whirled suddenly over from zenith to nadir. Your Stulz, with huge somerset, vaults from his high shopboard down to the depths of primal savagery,—carrying much along with him! For I will invite thee to reflect that the Tailor, as topmost ultimate froth of Human Society, is indeed swift-passing, evanescent, slippery to decipher; yet significant of much, nay of all. Topmost evanescent froth, he is churned up from the very lees, and from all intermediate regions of the liquor. The general outcome he, visible to the eye, of what men aimed to do, and were obliged and enabled to do, in this one public department of symbolising themselves to each other by covering of their skins. A smack of all Human Life lies in the Tailor: its wild struggles towards beauty, dignity, freedom, victory; and how, hemmed in by Sedan and Huddersfield, by Nescience, Dulness, Prurience, and other sad necessities and laws of Nature, it has attained just to this: Grey savagery of Three Sacks with a hem!

'When the very Tailor verges toward Sansculottism, is it not ominous? The last Divinity of poor mankind dethroning himself; sinking *his* taper too, flame downmost, like the Genius of Sleep or of Death; admonitory that Tailor-time shall be no more!—For, little as one could advise Sumptuary Laws at the present epoch, yet nothing is clearer than that where ranks do actually exist, strict division of costumes will also be enforced; that if we ever have a new Hierarchy and Aristocracy, acknowledged veritably as such, for which I daily pray Heaven, the Tailor will reawaken; and be, by volunteering and appointment, consciously and unconsciously, a safeguard of that same.'—Certain further observations, from the same invaluable pen, on our never-ending changes of mode, our 'perpetual nomadic and even ape-like appetite for change and mere change' in all the equipments of our existence, and the 'fatal revolutionary character' thereby manifested, we suppress for the present. It may be admitted that Democracy, in all meanings of the word, is in full career; irresistible by any Ritter Kauderwälsch or other Son of Adam, as times go. 'Liberty' is a thing men are determined to have.

But truly, as I have to remark in the meanwhile, 'the liberty of not being oppressed by your fellow man' is an indispensable, yet one of the most insignificant fractional parts of Human Liberty. No man oppresses thee, can bid thee fetch or carry, come or go, without reason shown. True; from all men thou art emancipated: but from Thyself and from the Devil—? No man, wiser, unwiser, can make thee come or go: but thy own futilities, bewilderments, thy false appetites for Money, Windsor Georges and such like? No man oppresses thee, O free and independent Franchiser: but does not this stupid Porter-pot oppress thee? No Son of Adam can bid thee come or go; but this absurd Pot of Heavy-wet, this can and does! Thou art the thrall not of Cedric the Saxon, but of thy own brutal appetites, and this scoured dish of liquor. And thou pratest of thy 'liberty?' Thou entire blockhead!

Heavy-wet and gin: alas, these are not the only kinds of thraldom. Thou who walkest in a vain shew, looking out with ornamental dilettante sniff, and serene supremacy, at all Life and all Death; and amblest jauntily; perking up thy poor talk into crochets, thy poor conduct into fatuous somnambulisms;—and *art* as an 'enchanted Ape' under God's sky, where thou mightest have been a man, had proper Schoolmasters and Conquerors, and Constables with cat-o'-nine tails, been vouchsafed thee; dost thou call that 'liberty?' Or your unreposing Mammon-worshipper, again, driven, as if by Galvanisms, by Devils and Fixed-Ideas, who rises early and sits late, chasing the impossible; straining every faculty to 'fill himself with the east wind,'—how merciful were it, could you, by mild persuasion or by the severest tyranny so-called, check him in his mad path, and turn him into a wiser one! All painful tyranny, in that case again, were but mild 'surgery;' the pain of it cheap, as health and life, instead of galvanism and fixed-idea, are cheap at any price.

Sure enough, of all paths a man could strike into, there *is*, at any given moment, a *best path* for every man; a thing which, here and now, it were of all things *wisest* for him to do;—which could he be but led or driven to do, he were then doing 'like a man,' as we phrase it; all men and gods agreeing with him, the whole Universe virtually exclaiming Well-done to him! His success, in such case, were complete; his felicity a maximum. This path, to find this path and walk in it, is the one thing needful for him. Whatsoever forwards him in that, let it come to him even in the shape of blows and spurnings, is liberty: whatsoever hinders him, were it wardmotes, open-vestries, pollbooths, tremendous cheers, rivers of heavy-wet, is slavery.

The notion that a man's liberty consists in giving his vote at election-hustings, and saying, "Behold now I too have my twenty-thousandth part of a Talker in our National Palaver; will not all the gods be good to me?" —is one of the pleasantest! Nature nevertheless is kind at present; and puts it into the heads of many, almost of all. The liberty especially which has to purchase itself by social isolation, and each man standing separate from the other, having 'no business with him' but a cash-account: this is such a liberty as the Earth seldom saw;—as the Earth will not long put up with, recommend it how you may. This liberty turns out, before it have long continued in action, with all men flinging up their caps round it, to be, for the Working Millions a liberty to die by want of food; for the Idle Thousands and Units, alas, a still more fatal liberty to live in want of work; to have no earnest duty to do in this God's-World any more. What becomes of a man in such predicament? Earth's Laws are silent; and Heaven's speak in a voice which is not heard. No work, and the ineradicable need of work, give rise to new very wondrous life-philosophies, new very wondrous life-practices! Dilettantism, Pococurantism, Beau-Brummelism, with perhaps an occasional, half-mad, protesting burst of Byronism, establish themselves: at the end of a certain period, if you go back to 'the Dead Sea,' there is, say our Moslem friends, a very strange 'Sabbath-day' transacting itself there!— Brethren, we know but imperfectly yet, after ages of Constitutional Government, what Liberty and Slavery are.

Democracy, the chase of Liberty in that direction, shall go its full course; unrestrainable by him of Pferdefuss-Quacksalber, or any of *his* household. The Toiling Millions of Mankind, in most vital need and passionate instinctive desire of Guidance, shall cast away False-Guidance; and hope, for an hour, that No-Guidance will suffice them: but it can be for an hour only. The smallest item of human Slavery is the oppression of man by his Mock-Superiors; the palpablest, but I say at bottom the smallest. Let him shake off such oppression, trample it indignantly under his feet; I blame him not, I pity and commend him. But oppression by your Mock-Superiors well shaken off, the grand problem yet remains to solve: That of finding government by your Real-Superiors! Alas, how shall we ever learn the solution of that, benighted, bewildered, sniffing, sneering, godforgetting unfortunates as we are? It is a work for centuries; to be taught us by tribulations, confusions, insurrections, obstructions; who knows if not by conflagration and despair! It is a lesson inclusive of all other lessons; the hardest of all lessons to learn.

One thing I do know: Those Apes, chattering on the branches by the Dead Sea, never got it learned; but chatter there to this day. To them no Moses need come a second time; a thousand Moseses would be but so many painted Phantasms, interesting Fellow-Apes of new strange aspect,—whom they would 'invite to dinner,' be glad to meet with in lion-soirées. To them the voice of Prophecy, of heavenly monition, is quite ended. They chatter there, all Heaven shut to them, to the end of the world. The unfortunates! O, what is dying of hunger, with honest tools in your hand, with a manful purpose in your heart, and much real labour lying round you done in comparison? You honestly quit your tools; quit a most muddy, confused coil of sore work, short rations, of sorrows, dispiritments and contradictions, having now honestly done with it all;—and await, not entirely in a distracted manner, what the Supreme Powers, and the Silences and the Eternities may have to say to you.

A second thing I know: This lesson will have to be learned,—under penalties! England will either learn it, or England also will cease to exist among Nations. England will either learn to reverence its Heroes, and discriminate them from its Sham-Heroes and Valets and gaslighted Histrios; and to prize them as the audible God's-voice, amid all inane jargons and temporary market-cries, and say to them with heart-loyalty, "Be ye King and Priest, and Gospel and Guidance for us:" or else England will continue to worship new and ever-new forms of Quackhood,—and so, with what resiliences and reboundings matters little, go down to the Father of Quacks! Can I dread such things of England? Wretched, thick-eyed, gross-hearted mortals, why will ye worship lies, and 'Stuffed Clothes-suits, created by the ninth-parts of men!' It is not your purses that suffer; your farm-rents, your commerces, your mill-revenues, loud as ye lament over these; no, it is not these alone, but a far deeper than these: it is your souls that lie dead, crushed down under despicable Nightmares, Atheisms, Brain-fumes; and are not souls at all, but mere succedanea for *salt* to keep your bodies and their appetites from putrefying! Your cotton-spinning and thrice-miraculous mechanism, what is this too, by itself, but a larger kind of Animalism? Spiders can spin, Beavers can build and shew contrivance; the Ant lays up accumulation of capital, and has, for aught I know, a Bank of Antland. If there is no soul in man higher than all that, did it reach to sailing on the cloud-rack and spinning sea-sand; then I say, man is but an animal, a more cunning kind of brute: he has no soul, but only a succedaneum for salt. Whereupon, seeing himself to be truly of the beasts that perish, he ought to admit it, I think;—and also straightway universally to kill himself; and so, in a manlike manner, at least, *end*, and wave these brute-worlds *his* dignified farewell!—

CHAPTER XIV.

Sir Jabesh Windbag.

OLIVER CROMWELL, whose body they hung on their Tyburn Gallows because he had found the Christian Religion inexecutable in this country, remains to me by far the remarkablest Governor we have had here for the last five centuries or so. For the last five centuries, there has been no Governor among us with anything like similar talent; and for the last two centuries, no Governor, we may say, with the possibility of similar talent, —with an idea in the heart of him capable of inspiring similar talent, capable of coexisting therewith. When you consider that Oliver believed in a God, the difference between Oliver's position and that of any subsequent Governor of this Country becomes, the more you reflect on it, the more immeasurable!

Oliver, no volunteer in Public Life, but plainly a ballotted soldier strictly ordered thither, enters upon Public Life; comports himself there like a man who carried his own life in his hand; like a man whose Great Commander's eye was always on him. Not without results. Oliver, well advanced in years, finds now, by Destiny and his own Deservings, or as he himself better phrased it, by wondrous successive 'Births of Providence,' the Government of England put into his hands. In senate-house and battlefield, in counsel and in action, in private and in public, this man has proved himself a man: England and the voice of God, through waste awful whirlwinds and environments, speaking to his great heart, summon him to assert formally, in the way of solemn Public Fact and as a new piece of English Law, what informally and by Nature's eternal Law needed no asserting, That he, Oliver, was the Ablest-Man of England, the King of England; that he, Oliver, would undertake governing England. His way of making the same 'assertion,' the one way he had of making it, has given rise to immense criticism: but the assertion itself in what way soever 'made,' is it not somewhat of a solemn one, somewhat of a tremendous one!

And now do but contrast this Oliver with my right honourable friend Sir Jabesh Windbag, Mr. Facing-both-ways, Viscount Mealymouth, Earl of Windlestraw, or what other Cagliostro, Cagliostrino, Cagliostraccio, the course of Fortune and Parliamentary Majorities has constitutionally guided to that dignity, any time during these last sorrowful hundred-and-fifty years! Windbag, weak in the faith of a God, which he believes only at Church on Sundays, if even then; strong only in the faith that Paragraphs and Plausibilities bring votes; that force of Public Opinion as he calls it, is the primal Necessity of Things, and highest God we have:—Windbag, if we will consider him, has a problem set before him which may be ranged in the impossible class. He is a Columbus minded to sail to the indistinct country of NOWHERE, to the indistinct country of WHITHERWARD, by the *friendship* of those same waste-tumbling Water-Alps and howling waltz of All the Winds; not by conquest of them and in spite of them, but by friendship of them, when once *they* have made up their mind! He is the most original Columbus I ever saw. Nay, his problem is not an impossible one: he will infallibly *arrive* at that same country of NOWHERE; his indistinct Whitherward will be a *Thither*-ward! In the Ocean Abysses and Locker of Davy Jones, there certainly enough do he and *his* ship's company, and all their cargo and navigatings, at last find lodgement.

Oliver knew that his America lay THERE, Westward Ho:—and it was not entirely by *friendship* of the Water-Alps, and yeasty insane Froth-Oceans, that he meant to get thither! He sailed accordingly; had compass-card, and Rules of Navigation,—older and greater than these Froth-Oceans, old as the Eternal God! Or again, do but think of this. Windbag in these his probable five years of office has to prosper and get Paragraphs: the Paragraphs of these five years must be his salvation, or he is a lost man; redemption nowhere in the Worlds or in the Times discoverable for him. Oliver too would like his Paragraphs; successes, popularities in these five years are not undesirable to him: but mark, I say, this enormous circumstance: *after* these five years are gone and done, comes an Eternity for Oliver! Oliver has to appear before the Most High Judge: the utmost flow of Paragraphs, the utmost ebb of them, is now, in strictest arithmetic, verily no matter at all; its exact value *zero;* an account altogether erased! Enormous;—which a man, in these days, hardly fancies with an effort! Oliver's Paragraphs are all done, his battles, division-lists, successes all summed: and now in that awful unerring Court of Review, the real question first rises, Whether he has succeeded at all; whether he has not been defeated miserably forevermore? Let him come with world-wide *Io-Pæans*, these avail him not. Let him come covered over with the world's execrations, gashed with ignominious death-wounds, the gallows-rope about his neck: what avails that? The word is, Come thou brave and faithful; the word is, Depart thou quack and accursed!

O Windbag, my right honourable friend, in very truth I pity thee. I say, these Paragraphs, and low or loud votings of thy poor fellow-blockheads of mankind, will never guide thee in any enterprise at all. Govern a country on such guidance? Thou canst not make a pair of shoes, sell a penny-worth of tape, on such. No, thy shoes are vamped up falsely to meet the market; behold, the leather only *seemed* to be tanned; thy shoes melt under me to rubbishy pulp, and are not veritable mud-defying shoes, but plausible vendible similitudes of shoes,—thou unfortunate, and I! O my right honourable friend, when the Paragraphs flowed in, who was like Sir Jabesh? On the swelling tide he mounted; higher, higher, triumphant, heaven-high. But the Paragraphs again ebbed out, as unwise Paragraphs needs must: Sir Jabesh lies stranded, sunk and forever sinking in ignominious ooze; the Mud-nymphs, and ever-deepening bottomless Oblivion, his portion to eternal time. 'Posterity?' Thou appealest to Posterity, thou? My right honourable friend, what will Posterity do for thee! The voting of Posterity, were it continued through centuries in thy favour, will be quite inaudible, extra-forensic, without any effect whatever. Posterity can do simply nothing for a man; nor even seem to do much, if the man be not brainsick. Besides, to tell thee truth, the bets are a thousand to one, Posterity will not hear of thee, my right honourable friend! Posterity, I have found, has generally his own Windbags sufficiently trumpeted in all market-places, and no leisure to attend to ours. Posterity which has made of Norse Odin a similitude, and of Norman William a brute monster, what will or can it make of English Jabesh? O Heavens, 'Posterity!'—

"These poor persecuted Scotch Covenanters," said I to my inquiring Frenchman, in such stinted French as stood at command, *"ils s'en appelaient à"*—*"A la Postérité,"* interrupted he, helping me out.—*"Ah, Monsieur, non, mille fois non!* They appealed to the Eternal God; not to Posterity at all! *C'était différent."*

CHAPTER XV.

MORRISON AGAIN.

NEVERTHELESS, O advanced Liberal, one cannot promise thee any 'New Religion,' for some time; to say truth, I do not think we have the smallest chance of any! Will the candid reader, by way of closing this Book Third, listen to a few transient remarks on that subject?

Candid readers have not lately met with any man who had less notion to interfere with their Thirty-Nine, or other Church-Articles; wherewith, very helplessly, as is like, they may have struggled to form for themselves some not inconceivable hypothesis about this Universe, and their own Existence there. Superstition, my friend, is far from me; Fanaticism, for any *Fanum* likely to arise soon on this Earth, is far. A man's Church-Articles are surely articles of price to him; and in these times one has to be tolerant of many strange 'Articles,' and of many still stranger 'No-articles,' which go about placarding themselves in a very distracted manner,—the numerous long placard poles, and questionable infirm paste-pots, interfering with one's peaceable thoroughfare sometimes!

Fancy a man, moreover, recommending his fellow-men to believe in God, that so Chartism might abate, and the Manchester Operatives be got to spin peaceably! The idea is more distracted than any placard-pole seen hitherto in a public thoroughfare of men! My friend, if thou ever do come to believe in God, thou wilt find all Chartism, Manchester riot, Parliamentary incompetence, Ministries of Windbag, and the wildest Social Dissolutions, and the burning up of this entire Planet, a most small matter in comparison. Brother, this Planet, I find, is but an inconsiderable sand-grain in the continents of Being: this Planet's poor temporary interests, thy interests and my interests there, when I looked fixedly into that eternal Light-Sea and Flame-Sea with *its* eternal interests, dwindle literally into Nothing; my speech of it is—silence for the while. I will as soon think of making Galaxies and Star-Systems to guide little herring-vessels by, as of preaching Religion that the Constable may continue possible. O my Advanced-Liberal friend, this new second progress, of proceeding 'to invent God,' is a very strange one! Jacobinism unfolded into Saint-Simonism bodes innumerable blessed things; but the thing itself might draw tears from a Stoic!—As for me, some twelve or thirteen New Religions, heavy Packets, most of them unfranked, having arrived here from various parts of the world, in a space of six calendar months, I have instructed my invaluable friend the Stamped Postman to introduce no more of them, if the charge exceed one penny.

Henry of Essex, duelling in that Thames Island, 'near to Reading Abbey,' had a religion. But was it in virtue of his seeing armed Phantasms of St. Edmund 'on the rim of the horizon,' looking minatory on him? Had that, intrinsically, anything to do with his religion at all? Henry of Essex's religion was the Inner Light or Moral Conscience of his own soul; such as is vouchsafed still to all souls of men;—which Inner Light shone here 'through such intellectual and other media' as there were; producing 'Phantasms,' Kircherean Visual-Spectra, according to circumstances! It is so with all men. The clearer my Inner Light may shine, through the *less* turbid media; the *fewer* Phantasms it may produce,—the gladder surely shall I be, and not the sorrier! Hast thou reflected, O serious reader, Advanced-Liberal or other, that the one end, essence, use of all religion past, present and to come, was this only: To keep that same Moral Conscience or Inner Light of ours alive and shining;—which certainly the 'Phantasms' and the 'turbid media' were not essential for! All religion was here to remind us, better or worse, of what we already know better or worse, of the quite *infinite* difference there is between a Good man and a Bad; to bid us love infinitely the one, abhor and avoid infinitely the other,—strive infinitely to *be* the one, and not to be the other. 'All religion issues in due Practical Hero-worship.' He that has a soul unasphyxied will never want a religion; he that has a soul asphyxied, reduced to a succedaneum for salt, will never find any religion, though you rose from the dead to preach him one.

But indeed, when men and reformers ask for 'a religion,' it is analogous to their asking, 'What would you have us to do?' and such like. They fancy that their religion too shall be a kind of Morrison's Pill, which they have only to swallow once, and all will be well. Resolutely once gulp down your Religion, your Morrison's Pill, you have it all plain sailing now: you can follow your affairs, your no-affairs, go along money-hunting, pleasure-hunting, dilettanting, dangling, and miming and chattering like a Dead-Sea Ape: your Morrison will do your business for you. Men's notions are very strange!—Brother, I say there is not, was not, nor will ever be, in the wide circle of Nature, any Pill or Religion of that character. Man cannot afford thee such; for the very gods it is impossible. I advise thee to renounce Morrison; once for all, quit hope of the Universal Pill. For body, for soul, for individual or society, there has not any such article been made. *Non extat.* In Created Nature it is not, was not, will not be. In the void imbroglios of Chaos only, and realms of Bedlam, does some shadow of it hover, to bewilder and bemock the poor inhabitants *there*.

Rituals, Liturgies, Creeds, Hierarchies: all this is not religion; all this, were it dead as Odinism, as Fetishism, does not kill religion at all! It is Stupidity alone, with never so many rituals, that kills religion. Is not this still a world? Spinning Cotton under Arkwright and Adam Smith; founding Cities by the Fountain of Juturna, on the Janiculum Mount; tilling

Canaan under Prophet Samuel and Psalmist David, man is ever man; the missionary of Unseen Powers; and great and victorious, while he continues true to his mission; mean, miserable, foiled, and at last annihilated and trodden out of sight and memory, when he proves untrue. Brother, thou art a Man, I think; thou are not a mere building Beaver, or two-legged Cotton-Spider; thou hast verily a Soul in thee, asphyxied or otherwise! Sooty Manchester,—it too is built on the infinite Abysses; overspanned by the skyey Firmaments; and there is birth in it, and death in it;—and it is every whit as wonderful, as fearful, unimaginable, as the oldest Salem or Prophetic City. Go or stand, in what time, in what place we will, are there not Immensities, Eternities over us, around us, in us:

> 'Solemn before us,
> Veiled, the dark Portal,
> Goal of all mortal;—
> Stars silent rest o'er us,
> Graves under us silent!'

Between *these* two great Silences, the hum of all our spinning cylinders, Trades-Unions, Anti-Corn-Law Leagues and Carlton Clubs goes on. Stupidity itself ought to pause a little, and consider that. I tell thee, through all thy Ledgers, Supply-and-demand Philosophies, and daily most modern melancholy Business and Cant, there does shine the presence of a Primeval Unspeakable; and thou wert wise to recognise, not with lips only, that same!

The Maker's Laws, whether they are promulgated in Sinai Thunder, to the ear or imagination, or quite otherwise promulgated, are the Laws of God; transcendent, everlasting, imperatively demanding obedience from all men. This, without any thunder, or with never so much thunder, thou, if there be any soul left in thee, canst know of a truth. The Universe, I say, is made by Law; the great Soul of the World is just and not unjust. Look thou, if thou have eyes or soul left, into this great shoreless Incomprehensible; in the heart of its tumultuous Appearances, Embroilments, and mad Time-vortexes, is there not, silent, eternal, an All-just, an All-beautiful; sole Reality and ultimate controlling Power of the whole? This is not a figure of speech; this is a fact. The fact of Gravitation known to all animals, is not surer than this inner Fact, which may be known to all men. He who knows this, it will sink, silent, awful, unspeakable, into his heart. He will say with Faust: "Who *dare* name HIM?" Most rituals or 'namings' he will fall in with at present, are like to be 'namings'—which shall be nameless! In silence, in the Eternal Temple, let him worship, if there be no fit word. Such knowledge, the crown of his whole spiritual being, the life of his life, let him keep and sacredly walk by. He has a religion. Hourly and daily, for himself and for the whole world, a faithful, unspoken, but not ineffectual prayer rises, "Thy will be done." His whole work on Earth is an emblematic spoken or acted prayer, Be the will of God done on Earth,—not the Devil's will, or any of the Devil's servants' wills! He has a religion, this man; an everlasting Loadstar that beams the brighter in the Heavens, the darker here on Earth grows the night around him. Thou, if thou know not this, what are all rituals, liturgies, mythologies, mass-chantings, turnings of the rotatory calabash? They are as nothing; in a good many respects they are as *less*. Divorced from this, getting half-divorced from this, they are a thing to fill one with a kind of horror; with a sacred inexpressible pity and fear. The most tragical thing a human eye can look on. It was said to the Prophet, "Behold, I will shew thee worse things than these: women weeping to Thammuz." That was the acme of the Prophet's vision—then as now.

Rituals, Liturgies, Credos, Sinai Thunder: I know more or less the history of these; the rise, progress, decline and fall of these. Can thunder from all the thirty-two azimuths, repeated daily for centuries of years, make God's Laws more godlike to me? Brother, No. Perhaps I am grown to be a man now; and do not need the thunder and the terror any longer! Perhaps I am above being frightened; perhaps it is not Fear, but Reverence alone, that shall now lead me!—Revelations, Inspirations? Yes: and thy own god-created Soul; dost thou not call that a 'revelation?' Who made THEE? Where didst Thou come from? The Voice of Eternity, if thou be not a blasphemer and poor asphyxied mute, speaks with that tongue of thine! *Thou* art the latest Birth of Nature; it is 'the Inspiration of the Almighty' that giveth *thee* understanding! My brother, my brother!—

Under baleful Atheisms, Mammonisms, Joe-Manton Dilettantisms, with their appropriate Cants and Idolisms, and whatsoever scandalous rubbish obscures and all but extinguishes the soul of man,—religion now is; its Laws, written if not on stone tables, yet on the Azure of Infinitude, in the inner heart of God's Creation, certain as Life, certain as Death! I say the Laws are there, and thou shalt not disobey them. It were better for thee not. Better a hundred deaths than yes. Terrible 'penalties' withal, if thou still need 'penalties,' are there for disobeying. Dost thou observe, O redtape Politician, that fiery infernal Phenomenon, which men name FRENCH REVO-LUTION, sailing unlooked-for, unbidden; through thy inane Protocol Domin-ion:—far-seen, with splendour not of Heaven? Ten centuries will see it. There were Tanneries at Meudon for human skins. And Hell, very truly Hell, had power over God's upper Earth for a season. The cruelest Portent that has risen into created Space these ten centuries: let us hail it, with awestruck repentant hearts, as the voice once more of a God, though of one in wrath. Blessed be the God's voice; for *it* is true, and Falsehoods have to cease before it! But for that same preternatural quasi-infernal Portent, one could not know what to make of this wretched world, in these days, at all. The deplorablest quack-ridden, and now hunger-ridden, down-trodden Despicability and *Flebile Ludibrium,* of redtape Protocols, rotatory Calabashes, Poor-Law Bastilles: who is there that could think of *its* being fated to continue?—

Penalties enough, my brother! This penalty inclusive of all: Eternal Death to thy own hapless Self, if thou heed no other. Eternal Death, I say,—with many meanings old and new, of which let this single one suffice us here: The eternal impossibility for thee to be aught but a Chimera, and swift-vanishing deceptive Phantasm, in God's Creation;—swift-vanishing, never to reappear: why should it reappear! Thou hadst one chance, thou wilt never have another. Everlasting ages will roll on, and no other be given thee. The foolishest articulate-speaking soul now extant, may not he say to himself: "A whole Eternity I waited to be born; and now I have a whole Eternity waiting to see what I will do when born!" This is not Theology, this is Arithmetic. And thou but half-discernest this; thou but half believest it? Alas, on the shores of the Dead Sea on Sabbath there goes on a Tragedy!—

But we will leave this of 'Religion;' of which, to say truth, it is chiefly profitable in these unspeakable days to keep silence. Thou needest no 'New Religion;' nor art thou like to get any. Thou hast already more 'religion' than thou makest use of. This day, thou knowest ten commanded duties, seest in thy mind ten things which should be done, for one that thou doest! Do one of them; this of itself will shew thee ten others which can and shall be done. "But my future fate?" Yes, thy future fate, indeed? Thy future fate, while thou makest it the chief question, seems to me—extremely questionable! I do not think it can be good. Norse Odin, immemorial centuries ago, did not he, though a poor Heathen, in the dawn of Time, teach us that for the Dastard there was, and could be, no good fate; no harbour anywhere, save down with Hela, in the pool of Night! Dastards, Knaves, are they that lust for Pleasure, that tremble at Pain. For this world and for the next, Dastards are a class of creatures made to be 'arrested:' they are good for nothing else, can look for nothing else. A greater than Odin has been here. A greater than Odin has taught us—not a greater Dastardism, I hope! My brother, thou must pray for a soul; struggle, as with life-and-death energy, to get back thy soul! Know that 'religion' is no Morrison's Pill from without, but a reawakening of thy own Self from within:—and, above all, leave me alone of thy 'religions' and 'new religions' here and elsewhere! I am weary of this sick croaking for a Morrison's-Pill religion; for any and for every such. I want none such; and discern all such to be impossible. The resuscitation of old liturgies fallen dead; much more, the manufacture of new liturgies that will never be alive: how hopeless! Stylitisms, eremite fanaticisms and fakeerisms; spasmodic agonistic posture-makings, and narrow, cramped, morbid, if forever noble wrestlings: all this is not a thing desirable to me. It is a thing the world has done once,—when its beard was not grown as now!

And yet there is, at worst, one Liturgy which does remain forever unexceptionable: that of Praying (as the old Monks did withal) by Working. And indeed the Prayer which accomplished itself in special chapels at stated hours, and went not with a man, rising up from all his Work and Action, at all moments sanctifying the same,—what was it ever good for? 'Work is Worship:' yes, in a highly considerable sense,—which, in the present state of all 'worship,' who is there that can unfold! He that understands it well, understands the Prophecy of the whole Future; the last Evangel, which has included all others. *Its* cathedral the Dome of Immensity,—hast thou seen it? coped with the star-galaxies; paved with the green mosaic of land and ocean; and for altar, verily, the Star-throne of the Eternal! Its litany and psalmody the noble acts, the heroic work and suffering, and true heart-utterance of all the Valiant of the Sons of Men. Its choir-music the ancient Winds and Oceans, and deep-toned, inarticulate, but most speaking voices of Destiny and History,—supernal ever as of old. Between two great silences:

> '*Stars silent rest o'er us,*
> *Graves under us silent.*'

Between which two great Silences, do not, as we said, all human Noises, in the naturalist times, most *preter*naturally march and roll?—

I will insert this also, in a lower strain, from Sauerteig's *Æsthetische Springwürzel*. 'Worship?' says he: 'Before that inane tumult of Hearsay filled men's heads, while the world lay yet silent, and the heart true and open, many things were Worship! To the primeval man whatsoever good came, descended on him (as, in mere fact, it ever does) direct from God; whatsoever duty lay visible for him, this a Supreme God had prescribed. To the present hour I ask thee, Who else? For the primeval man, in whom dwelt Thought, this Universe was all a Temple; Life everywhere a Worship.

'What Worship, for example, is there not in mere Washing! Perhaps one of the most moral things a man, in common cases, has it in his power to do. Strip thyself, go into the bath, or were it into the limpid pool and running brook, and there wash and be clean; thou wilt step out again a purer and a better man. This consciousness of perfect outer pureness, that to thy skin there now adheres no foreign speck of imperfection, how it radiates in on thee, with cunning symbolic influences, to thy very soul! Thou hast an increase of tendency towards all good things whatsoever. The oldest Eastern Sages, with joy and holy gratitude, had felt it so,—and that it was the Maker's gift and will. Whose else *is* it? It remains a religious duty, from oldest times, in the East.—Nor could Herr Professor Strauss, when I put the question, deny that for us at present it is still such here in the West! To that dingy fuliginous Operative, emerging from his soot-mill, what is the first duty I will prescribe, and offer help towards? That he clean the skin of him. *Can* he pray, by any ascertained method? One knows not entirely:—but with soap and a sufficiency of water, he can wash. Even the dull English feel something of this; they have a saying, "Cleanliness is near of kin to Godliness:"—yet never, in any country, saw I operative men worse washed, and, in a climate drenched with the softest cloud-water, such a scarcity of baths!'—Alas, Sauerteig, our 'operative men' are at present short even of potatoes: what 'duty' can you prescribe to them!

Or let us give a glance at China. Our new friend, the Emperor there, is Pontiff of three hundred million men; who do all live and work, these many centuries now; authentically patronised by Heaven so far; and therefore must have some 'religion' of a kind. This Emperor-Pontiff has, in fact, a religious belief of certain Laws of Heaven; observes, with a religious rigour, his 'three thousand punctualities,' given out by men of insight, some sixty generations since, as a legible transcript of the same,—the Heavens do seem to say, not totally an incorrect one. He has not much of a ritual, this Pontiff-Emperor; believes, it is likest, with the old Monks, that 'Labour is Worship.' His most public Act of Worship, it appears, is the drawing solemnly at a certain day, on the green bosom of our Mother Earth, when the Heavens, after dead black winter, have again with their vernal radiances awakened her, a distinct red Furrow with the Plough,—signal that all the Ploughs of China are to begin ploughing and worshipping! It is notable enough. He, in sight of the Seen and Unseen Powers, draws his distinct red Furrow there; saying, and praying, in mute symbolism, so many most eloquent things!

If you ask this Pontiff, "Who made him? What is to become of him and us?" he maintains a dignified reserve; waves his hand and pontiff-eyes over the unfathomable deep of Heaven, the 'Tsien,' the azure kingdoms of Infinitude; as if asking, "Is it doubtful that we are right *well* made? Can aught that is *wrong* become of us?"—He and his three hundred millions (it is their chief 'punctuality') visit yearly the Tombs of their Fathers; each man the Tomb of his Father and his Mother; alone there, in silence, with what of 'worship' or of other thought there may be, pauses solemnly each man; the divine Skies all silent over him; the divine Graves, and this divinest Grave, all silent under him; the pulsing of his own soul, if he have any soul, alone audible. Truly it may be a kind of worship! Truly, if a man cannot get some glimpse into the Eternities, looking through this portal,—through what other need he try it?

Our friend the Pontiff-Emperor permits cheerfully, though with contempt, all manner of Buddhists, Bonzes, Talapoins and such like, to build brick Temples, on the voluntary principle; to worship with what of chantings, paper-lanterns and tumultuous brayings, pleases them; and make night hideous, since they find some comfort in so doing. Cheerfully, though with contempt. He is a wiser Pontiff than many persons think! He is as yet the one Chief Potentate or Priest in this Earth who has made a distinct systematic attempt at what we call the ultimate result of all religion, 'Practical Hero-worship:' he does incessantly, with true anxiety, in such way as he can, search and sift (it would appear) his whole enormous population for the Wisest born among them; by which Wisest, as by born Kings, these three hundred million men are governed. The Heavens, to a certain extent, do appear to countenance him. These three hundred millions actually make porcelain, souchong tea, with innumerable other things; and fight, under Heaven's flag, against Necessity;—and have fewer Seven-Years Wars, Thirty-Years Wars, French Revolution Wars, and infernal fightings with each other, than certain millions elsewhere have!

Nay, in our poor distracted Europe itself, in these newest times, have there not religious voices risen,—with a religion new and yet the oldest;

entirely indisputable to all hearts of men? Some I do know, who did not call or think themselves 'Prophets,' far enough from that; but who were, in very truth, melodious Voices from the eternal Heart of Nature once again; souls forever venerable to all that have a soul. A French Revolution is one phenomenon; as complement and spiritual exponent thereof, a Poet Goethe and German Literature is to me another. The old Secular or Practical World, so to speak, having gone up in fire, is not here the prophecy and dawn of a new Spiritual World, parent of far nobler, wider, new Practical Worlds? A life of Antique devoutness, Antique veracity and heroism, has again become possible, is again *seen* actual there, for the most modern man. A phenomenon, as quiet as it is, comparable for greatness to no other! 'The great event for the world is, now as always, the arrival in it of a new Wise Man.' Touches there are, be the Heavens ever thanked, of new Sphere-melody; audible once more, in the infinite jargoning discords and poor scrannel-pipings of the thing called Literature:—priceless there, as the voice of new Heavenly Psalms! Literature, like the old Prayer-Collections of the first centuries, were it 'well selected from and burnt,' contains precious things. For Literature, with all its printing presses, puffing-engines and shoreless deafening triviality, *is* yet 'the Thought of Thinking Souls.' A sacred 'religion,' if you like the name, does live in the heart of that strange froth-ocean, not wholly froth, which we call Literature; and will more and more disclose itself therefrom;—not now as scorching Fire: the red smoky scorching Fire has purified itself into white sunny Light. Is not Light grander than Fire? It is the same element in a state of purity.

My ingenuous readers, we will march out of this Third Book with a rhythmic word of Goethe's on our lips; a word which perhaps has already sung itself, in dark hours and in bright, through many a heart. To me, finding it devout yet wholly credible and veritable, full of piety yet free of cant; to me joyfully finding much in it, and joyfully missing so much in it, this little snatch of music, by the greatest German Man, sounds like a stanza in the grand *Road-Song* and *Marching-Song* of our great Teutonic Kindred, wending, wending, valiant and victorious, through the undiscovered Deeps of Time! He calls it *Mason-Lodge,*—not Psalm or Hymn:

> 'The Mason's ways are
> A type of Existence,
> And his persistence
> Is as the days are
> Of men in this world.
>
> The Future hides in it
> Gladness and sorrow;
> We press still thorow,
> Nought that abides in it
> Daunting us,—onward.

And solemn before us,
Veiled, the dark Portal,
Goal of all mortal;—
Stars silent rest o'er us,
Graves under us silent.

While earnest thou gazest,
Comes boding of terror,
Comes phantasm and error,
Perplexes the bravest
With doubt and misgiving.

But heard are the Voices,—
Heard are the Sages,
The Worlds and the Ages:
"Choose well, your choice is
Brief and yet endless:

Here eyes do regard you,
In Eternity's stillness;
Here is all fulness,
Ye brave, to reward you:
Work, and despair not."'

HOROSCOPE

HOROSCOPE

CHAPTER I.

ARISTOCRACIES.

To PREDICT the Future, to manage the Present, would not be so impossible, had not the Past been so sacrilegiously mishandled; effaced, and what is worse, defaced! The Past cannot be seen; the Past, looked at through the medium of 'Philosophical History' in these times, cannot even be *not* seen: it is misseen; affirmed to have existed,—and to have been a godless Impossibility. Your Norman Conquerors, true royal souls, crowned kings as such, were vulturous irrational tyrants: your Becket was a noisy egoist and hypocrite; getting his brains spilt on the floor of Canterbury Cathedral, to secure the main chance,—somewhat uncertain how! 'Policy, Fanaticism;' or say 'Enthusiasm,' even 'honest Enthusiasm,'—ah, yes, of course:

> *'The Dog, to gain his private ends,*
> Went *mad, and bit the Man!'*

For in truth, the eye sees in all things 'what it brought with it the means of seeing.' A godless century, looking back on centuries that were godly, produces portraitures more miraculous than any other. All was inane discord in the Past; brute Force bore rule everywhere; Stupidity, savage Unreason, fitter for Bedlam than for a human World! Whereby indeed it become sufficiently natural that the like qualities, in new sleeker habiliments, should continue in our time to rule. Millions enchanted in Bastille Workhouses; Irish Widows proving their relationship by typhus-fever: what would you have? It was ever so, or worse. Man's History, was it not always even this: The cookery and eating up of imbecile Dupedom by successful Quackhood; the battle, with various weapons, of vulturous Quack and Tyrant against vulturous Tyrant and Quack? No God was in the Past Time; nothing but Mechanisms and Chaotic Brute-gods:—how shall the poor 'Philosophic Historian,' to whom his own century is all godless, see any God in other centuries?

Men believe in Bibles, and disbelieve in them: but of all Bibles the frightfulest to disbelieve in is this 'Bible of Universal History.' This is the Eternal Bible and God's-Book, 'which every born man,' till once the soul and eyesight are extinguished in him, 'can and must, with his own eyes, see the God's-Finger writing!' To discredit this, is an *infidelity* like no other. Such infidelity you would punish, if not by fire and faggot, which are difficult to manage in our times, yet by the most peremptory order, To hold its peace till it got something wiser to say. Why should the blessed Silence be broken into noises, to communicate only the like of this? If the Past have no God's-Reason in it, nothing but Devil's-Unreason, let the Past be eternally forgotten: mention *it* no more;—we whose ancestors were all hanged, why should we talk of ropes!

It is, in brief, not true that men ever lived by Delirium, Hypocrisy, Injustice, or any form of Unreason, since they came to inhabit this Planet. It is not true that they ever did, or ever will, live except by the reverse of these. Men will again be taught this. Their acted History will then again be a Heroism; their written History, what it once was, an Epic. Nay, forever it is either such; or else it virtually is—Nothing. Were it written in a thousand volumes, the Unheroic of such volumes hastens incessantly to be forgotten; the net content of an Alexandrian Library of Unheroics is, and will ultimately shew itself to be, *zero*. What man is interested to remember *it*; have not all men, at all times, the liveliest interest to forget it?—'Revelations,' if not celestial, then infernal, will teach us that God is; we shall then, if needful, discern without difficulty that He has always been! The Dryasdust Philosophisms and enlightened Scepticisms of the Eighteenth Century, historical and other, will have to survive for a while with the Physiologists, as a memorable *Nightmare-Dream*. All this haggard epoch, with its ghastly Doctrines and death's-head Philosophies 'teaching by example' or otherwise, will one day have become, what to our Moslem friends their godless ages are, 'the Period of Ignorance.'

If the convulsive struggles of the last Half-Century have taught poor struggling convulsed Europe any truth, it may perhaps be this as the essence of innumerable others: That Europe requires a real Aristocracy, a real Priesthood, or it cannot continue to exist. Huge French Revolutions, Napoleonisms, then Bourbonisms with their corollary of Three Days, finishing in very unfinal Louis-Philippisms: all this ought to be didactic! All this may have taught us, That False Aristocracies, are insupportable; that No-Aristocracies, Liberty-and-Equalities are impossible; that True Aristocracies are at once indispensable and not easily attained.

Aristocracy and Priesthood, a Governing Class and a Teaching Class: these two, sometimes separate, and endeavouring to harmonise themselves, sometimes conjoined as one, and the King a Pontiff-King:—there did no Society exist without these two vital elements, there will none exist. It lies in the very nature of man: you will visit no remotest village in the most republican country of the world, where virtually or actually you do not find these two powers at work. Man, little as he may suppose it, is necessitated to obey superiors. He is a social being in virtue of this necessity; nay he could not be gregarious otherwise. He obeys those whom he esteems better than himself, wiser, braver; and will forever obey such; and even be ready and delighted to do it.

The Wiser, Braver: these, a Virtual Aristocracy everywhere and everywhen, do in all Societies that reach any articulate shape, develop themselves into a ruling class, an Actual Aristocracy, with settled modes of operating, what are called laws and even *private-laws* or privileges, and so forth; very notable to look upon in this world.—Aristocracy and Priesthood, we say, are sometimes united. For indeed the Wiser and the Braver are properly but one class: no wise man but needed first of all to be a brave man, or he never had been wise. The noble Priest was always a noble *Aristos* to begin with, and something more to end with. Your Luther, your Knox, your Anselm, Becket, Abbot Samson, Samuel Johnson, if they had not been brave enough, by what possibility could they ever have been wise?—If, from accident or forethought, this your Actual Aristocracy have got discriminated into Two Classes, there can be no doubt but the Priest Class is the more dignified; supreme over the other, as governing head is over active hand. And yet in practice again, it is likeliest the reverse will be found arranged; a sign that the arrangement is already vitiated; that a split is introduced into it, which will widen and widen till the whole be rent asunder.

In England, and in Europe generally, we may say that these two Virtualities have unfolded themselves into Actualities, in by far the noblest and richest manner any region of the world ever saw. A Spiritual Guideship, a practical Governorship, fruit of the grand conscious endeavours, say rather of the immeasurable unconscious instincts and necessities of men, have established themselves; very strange to behold. Everywhere, while so much has been forgotten, you find the King's Palace, and the Viceking's Castle, Mansion, Manorhouse; till there is not an inch of ground from sea to sea but has both its King and Viceking, long due series of Vicekings, its Squire, Earl, Duke or whatever the title of him—to whom you have given the land that he may govern you in it.

More touching still, there is not a hamlet where poor peasants congregate, but by one means and another a Church-Apparatus has been got together, —roofed edifice, with revenues and belfries; pulpit, reading-desk, with Books and Methods; possibility, in short, and strict prescription, That a man stand there and speak of spiritual things to men. It is beautiful;—even in its great obscuration and decadence, it is among the beautifulest, most touching objects one sees on the Earth. This Speaking Man has indeed, in these times, wandered terribly from the point; has, alas, as it were, totally lost sight of the point: yet, at bottom, whom have we to compare with him? Of all public functionaries boarded and lodged on the Industry of Modern Europe, is there one worthier of the board he has? A man even professing, and never so languidly making still some endeavour, to save the souls of men: contrast him with a man professing to do little but shoot the partridges of men! I wish he could find the point again, this Speaking One; and stick to it with tenacity, with deadly energy; for there is need of him yet! The Speaking Function, this of Truth coming to us with a living voice, nay in a living shape, and as a concrete practical exemplar: this, with all our Writing and Printing Functions, has a perennial place. Could he but find the point again,— take the old spectacles off his nose, and looking up discover, almost in contact with him, what the *real* Satanas, and soul-devouring, world-devouring *Devil*, now is! Original Sin and such like are bad enough, I doubt not: but distilled Gin, dark Ignorance, Stupidity, dark Corn-Law, Bastille and Company, what are they! *Will* he discover our new real Satan, whom he has to fight; or go on droning through his old nose-spectacles about old extinct Satans; and never see the real one, till he *feel* him at his own throat and ours? That is a question, for the world! Let us not intermeddle with it here.

Sorrowful, phantasmal as this same Double Aristocracy of Teachers and Governors now looks, it is worth all men's while to know that the purport of it is and remains noble and most real. Dryasdust, looking merely at the surface, is greatly in error as to those ancient Kings. William Conqueror, William Rufus or Redbeard, Stephen Curthose himself, much more Henry Beauclerc and our brave Plantagenet Henry: the life of these men was not a vulturous Fighting; it was a valorous Governing,—to which occasionally Fighting did, and alas must yet, though far seldomer now, superadd itself as an accident a distressing impedimental adjunct. The fighting too was indispensable, for ascertaining who had the might over whom, the right over whom. By much hard fighting, as we once said, 'the unrealities, beaten into dust, flew gradually off;' and left the plain reality and fact, "Thou stronger than I; thou wiser than I; thou king, and subject I," in a somewhat clearer condition.

Truly we cannot enough admire, in those Abbot-Samson and William-Conqueror times, the arrangement they had made of their Governing Classes. Highly interesting to observe how the sincere insight, on their part, into what did, of primary necessity, behove to be accomplished, had led them to the way of accomplishing it, and in the course of time to get it accomplished! No imaginary Aristocracy would serve their turn; and accordingly they attained a real one. The Bravest men, who, it is ever to be repeated and remembered, are also on the whole the Wisest, Strongest, everyway Best, had here, with a respectable degree of accuracy, been got selected; seated each on his piece of territory, which was lent him, then gradually given him, that he might govern it. These Vicekings, each on his portion of the common soil of England, with a Head King over all, were a 'Virtuality perfected into an Actuality' really to an astonishing extent.

For those were rugged stalwart ages; full of earnestness, of a rude God's-truth:—nay, at any rate, their *quilting* was so unspeakably *thinner* than ours; Fact came swiftly on them, if at any time they had yielded to Phantasm! 'The Knaves and Dastards' had to be 'arrested' in some measure; or the world, almost within year and day, found that it could not live. The Knaves and Dastards accordingly were got arrested. Dastards upon the very throne had to be got arrested, and taken off the throne,—by such methods as there were; by the roughest method, if there chanced to be no smoother one! Doubtless there was much harshness of operation, much severity; as indeed government and surgery are often somewhat severe. Gurth born thrall of Cedric, it is like, got cuffs as often as pork-parings, if he misdemeaned himself: but Gurth did belong to Cedric: no human creature then went about connected with nobody; left to go his ways into Bastilles or worse, under *Laissez-faire;* reduced to prove his relationship by dying of typhus-fever! —Days come when there is no King in Israel, but every man is his own king, doing that which is right in his own eyes;—and tarbarrels are burnt to

'Liberty,' 'Tenpound Franchise' and the like, with considerable effect in various ways!—

That Feudal Aristocracy, I say, was no imaginary one. To a respectable degree, its *Jarls*, what we now call Earls, were *Strong-Ones* in fact as well as etymology; its Dukes *Leaders;* its Lords *Law-wards*. They did all the Soldiering and Police of the country, all the Judging, Law-making, even the Church-Extension; whatsoever in the way of Governing, of Guiding and Protecting could be done. It was a Land Aristocracy; it managed the Governing of this English People, and had the reaping of the Soil of England in return. It is, in many senses, the Law of Nature, this same Law of Feudalism;—no right Aristocracy but a Land one! The curious are invited to meditate upon it in these days. Soldiering, Police and Judging, Church-Extension, nay real Government and Guidance, all this was actually *done* by the Holders of the Land in return for their Land. How much of it is now done by them; done by anybody? Good Heavens, "Laissez-faire, Do ye nothing, eat your wages and sleep," is everywhere the passionate half-wise cry of this time; and they will not so much as do nothing, but must do mere Corn-Laws! We raise Fifty-two millions, from the general mass of us, to get our Governing done,—or, alas, to get ourselves persuaded that it is done: and the 'peculiar burden of the Land' is to pay, not all this, but to pay, as I learn, one twenty-fourth part of all this. Our first Chartist Parliament, or Oliver *Redivivus,* you would say, will know where to lay the new taxes of England!—Or, alas, taxes? If we made the Holders of the land pay every shilling still of the expense of Governing the Land, what were all that? The Land, by mere hired Governors, cannot be got governed. You cannot hire men to govern the Land: it is by a mission not contracted for in the Stock-Exchange, but felt in their own hearts as coming out of Heaven, that men can govern a Land. The mission of a Land Aristocracy is a *sacred* one, in both the senses of that old word. The footing it stands on, at present, might give rise to thoughts other than of Corn-Laws!—

But truly a 'Splendour of God,' as in William Conqueror's rough oath, did dwell in those old rude veracious ages; did inform, more and more, with a heavenly nobleness, all departments of their work and life. Phantasms could not yet walk abroad in mere Cloth Tailorage; they were at least Phantasms 'on the rim of the horizon,' pencilled there by an eternal Light-beam from within. A most 'practical' Hero-worship went on, unconsciously or half-consciously, everywhere. A Monk Samson, with a maximum of two shillings in his pocket, could, without ballot-box, be made a Viceking of, being seen to be worthy. The difference between a good man and a bad man was as yet felt to be, what it forever is, an immeasurable one. Who *durst* have elected a Pandarus Dog-draught, in those days, to any office, Carlton Club, Senatorship, or place whatsoever? It was felt that the arch Satanas and no other had a clear right of property in Pandarus; that it were better for you to have no hand in Pandarus, to keep out of Pandarus his neighbour-hood! Which is, to this hour, the mere fact; though for the present, alas, the forgotten fact. I think they were comparatively blessed times those, in their way! 'Violence,' 'war,' 'disorder:' well, what is war, and death itself, to such a perpetual life-in-death, and 'peace, peace where there is no peace!' Unless some Hero-worship, in its new appropriate form, can return, this world does not promise to be very habitable long.

Old Anselm, exiled Archbishop of Canterbury, one of the purest-minded 'men of genius,' was travelling to make his appeal to Rome against King Rufus—a man of rough ways, in whom the 'inner Light-beam' shone very fitfully. It is beautiful to read, in Monk Eadmer, how the Continental populations welcomed and venerated this Anselm, as no French population now venerates Jean-Jacques or giant-killing Voltaire; as not even an American population now venerates a Schnüspel the distinguished Novelist! They had, by phantasy and true insight, the intensest conviction that a God's blessing dwelt in this Anselm,—as is my conviction too. They crowded round, with bent knees and enkindled hearts, to receive his blessing, to hear his voice, to see the light of his face. My blessings on them and on him!—But the notablest was a certain necessitous or covetous Duke of Burgundy, in straitened circumstances we shall hope,—who reflected that in all likelihood this English Archbishop, going towards Rome to appeal, must have taken store of cash with him to bribe the Cardinals. Wherefore he of Burgundy, for his part, decided to lie in wait and rob him. 'In an open space of a wood,' some 'wood' then green and growing, eight centuries ago, in Burgundian Land,—this fierce Duke, with fierce steel followers, shaggy, savage, as the Russian bear, dashes out on the weak old Anselm; who is riding along there, on his small quiet-going pony; escorted only by Eadmer and another poor Monk on ponies; and, except small modicum of roadmoney, not a gold coin in his possession. The steelclad Russian bear emerges, glaring: the old white-bearded man starts not,—paces on unmoved, looking into him with those clear old earnest eyes, with that venerable sorrowful time-worn face; of whom no man or thing need be afraid, and who also is afraid of no created man or thing. The fire-eyes of his Burgundian Grace meet these clear eye-glances, convey them swift to his heart: he bethinks him that probably this feeble, fearless, hoary Figure has in it something of the Most High God; that probably he shall be damned if he meddle with it,—that, on the whole, he had better not. He plunges, the rough savage, from his war-horse, down to his knees; embraces the feet of old Anselm: he too begs his blessing; orders men to escort him, guard him from being robbed, and under dread penalties see him safe on his way. *Per os Dei*, as his Majesty was wont to ejaculate!

Neither is this quarrel of Rufus and Anselm, of Henry and Becket, uninstructive to us. It was, at bottom, a great quarrel. For, admitting that Anselm was full of divine blessing, he by no means included in him all forms of divine blessing:—there were far other forms withal, which he little dreamed of; and William Redbeard was unconsciously the representative and spokesman of these. In truth, could your divine Anselm, your divine Pope Gregory have had their way, the results had been very notable. Our Western World had all become a European Thibet, with one Grand Lama sitting at Rome; our one honourable business that of singing mass, all day and all night. Which would not in the least have suited us! The Supreme Powers willed it not so.

It was as if King Redbeard unconsciously, addressing Anselm, Becket and the others, had said: "Right Reverend, your Theory of the Universe is indisputable by man or devil. To the core of our heart we feel that this divine thing, which you call Mother Church, does fill the whole world hitherto known, and is and shall be all our salvation and all our desire. And yet—and yet—Behold though it is an unspoken secret, the world is *wider* than any of us think, Right Reverend! Behold, there are yet other immeasurable Sacrednesses in this that you call Heathenism, Secularity! On the whole I, in an obscure but most rooted manner feel that I cannot comply with you. Western Thibet and perpetual mass-chanting.—No. I am, so to speak, in the family-way; with child, of I know not what,—certainly of something far different from this! I have—*Per os Dei,* I have Manchester Cotton-trades, Bromwicham Iron-trades, American Commonwealths, Indian Empires, Steam Mechanisms and Shakspeare Dramas, in my belly; and cannot do it, Right Reverend!"—So accordingly it was decided: and Saxon Becket spilt his life in Canterbury Cathedral, as Scottish Wallace did on Tower-Hill, and as generally a noble man and martyr has to do,—not for nothing; no, but for a divine something, other than *he* had altogether calculated. We will now quit this of the hard, organic, but limited Feudal Ages; and glance timidly into the immense Industrial Ages, as yet all inorganic, and in a quite pulpy condition, requiring desperately to harden themselves into some organism!

Our Epic having now become *Tools and the Man,* it is more than usually impossible to prophesy the Future. The boundless Future does lie there, predestined, nay already extant though unseen; hiding, in its Continents of Darkness, 'gladness and sorrow:' but the supremest intelligence of man cannot prefigure much of it:—the united intelligence and effort of All Men in all coming generations, this alone will gradually prefigure it, and figure and form it into a seen fact! Straining our eyes hitherto, the utmost effort of intelligence sheds but some most glimmering dawn, a little way into its dark enormous Deeps: only huge outlines loom uncertain on the sight; and the ray of prophecy, at a short distance, expires. But may we not say, here as always, Sufficient for the day is the evil thereof! To shape the whole Future is not our problem; but only to shape faithfully a small part of it, according to rules already known. It is perhaps possible for each of us, who will with due earnestness inquire, to ascertain clearly what he, for his own part, ought to do: this let him, with true heart do, and continue doing. The general issue will, as it has always done, rest well with a Higher Intelligence than ours.

One grand 'outline,' or even two, many earnest readers may perhaps, at this stage of the business, be able to prefigure for themselves,—and draw some guidance from. One prediction, or even two, are already possible. For the Life-tree Igdrasil, in all its new developments, is the self-same world-old Life-tree: having found an element or elements there, running from the very roots of it in Hela's Realms, in the Well of Mimer and of the Three Nornas or TIMES, up to this present hour of it in our own hearts, we conclude that such will have to continue. A man has in his own soul, an Eternal; can read something of the Eternal there, if he will look! He already knows what will continue; what cannot, by any means or appliance whatsoever, be made to continue!

One wide and widest 'outline' ought really, in all ways, to be becoming clear to us; this namely: That a 'Splendour of God,' in one form or other, will have to unfold itself from the heart of these our Industrial Ages too; or they will never get themselves 'organised;' but continue chaotic, distressed, distracted evermore, and have to perish in frantic suicidal dissolution. A second 'outline' or prophecy, narrower, but also wide enough, seems not less certain: That there will again *be* a King in Israel; a system of Order and Government; and every man shall, in some measure, see himself constrained to do that which is right in the King's eyes. This too we may call a sure element of the Future; for this too is of the Eternal;—this too is of the Present, though hidden from most; and without it no fibre of the Past ever was. An actual new Sovereignty, Industrial Aristocracy, real not imaginary Aristocracy, is indispensable and indubitable for us.

But what an Aristocracy; on what new, far more complex and cunningly devised conditions than that old Feudal fighting one! For we are to bethink us that the Epic verily is not *Arms and the Man*, but *Tools and the Man*, —an infinitely wider kind of Epic. And again we are to bethink us that men cannot now be bound to men by *brass-collars*,—not at all: that this brass-collar method, in all figures of it, has vanished out of Europe forevermore! Huge Democracy, walking the streets everywhere in its Sack Coat, has asserted so much; irrevocably, brooking no reply! True enough, man *is* forever the 'born thrall' of certain men, born master of certain other men, born equal of certain others, let him acknowledge the fact or not. It is unblessed for him when he cannot acknowledge this fact; he is in the chaotic state, ready to perish, till he do get the fact acknowledged. But no man is, or can henceforth be, the brass-collar thrall of any man; you will have to bind him by other, far nobler and cunninger methods. Once for all, he is to be loose of the brass-collar, to have a scope *as* wide as his faculties now are:—will he not be all the usefuler to you, in that new state? Let him go abroad as a trusted one, as a free one; and return home to you with rich earnings at night! Gurth could only tend pigs; this one will build cities, conquer waste worlds.—How, in conjunction with inevitable Democracy, indispensable Sovereignty is to exist: certainly it is the hugest question ever heretofore propounded to Mankind! The solution of which is work for long years and centuries. Years and centuries, of one knows not what complexion;—blessed or unblessed, according as they shall, with earnest valiant effort, make progress therein, or, in slothful unveracity and dilettantism, only talk of making progress. For either progress therein, or swift and ever swifter progress towards dissolution, is henceforth a necessity.

It is of importance that this grand reformation were begun; that Corn-Law Debatings and other jargon, little less than delirious in such a time, had fled far away, and left us room to begin! For the evil has grown practical, extremely conspicuous; if it be not seen and provided for, the blindest fool will have to feel it ere long. There is much that can wait; but there is something also that cannot wait. With millions of eager Working Men imprisoned in 'Impossibility' and Poor-Law Bastilles, it is time that some means of dealing with them were trying to become 'possible!' Of the Government of England, of all articulate-speaking functionaries, real and imaginary Aristocracies, of me and of thee, it is imperatively demanded, "How do you mean to manage these men? Where are they to find a supportable existence? What is to become of them,—and of you?"

CHAPTER II.

Bribery Committee.

In the case of the late Bribery Committee, it seemed to be the conclusion of the soundest practical minds that Bribery could not be put down; that Pure Election was a thing we had seen the last of, and must now go on without, as we best could. A conclusion not a little startling; to which it requires a practical mind of some seasoning to reconcile yourself at once! It seems, then, we are henceforth to get ourselves constituted Legislators not according to what merit we may have, or even what merit we may seem to have, but according to the length of our purse, and our frankness, impudence and dexterity in laying out the contents of the same. Our theory, written down in all books and law-books, spouted forth from all barrel-heads, is perfect purity of Tenpound Franchise,—absolute sincerity of question put and answer given;—and our practice is irremediable bribery; irremediable, unpunishable, which you will do more harm than good by attempting to punish! Once more, a very startling conclusion indeed; which, whatever the soundest practical minds in Parliament may think of it, invites all British men to meditations of various kinds.

A Parliament, one would say, which proclaims itself elected and eligible by bribery, tells the Nation that is governed by it a piece of singular news. Bribery: have we reflected what bribery is? Bribery means not only length of purse, which is neither qualification nor the contrary for legislating well; but it means dishonesty, and even impudent dishonesty;—brazen insensibility to lying and to making others lie; total oblivion, and flinging overboard, for the nonce, of any real thing you can call veracity, morality; with dextrous putting on the cast-clothes of that real thing, and strutting about in them!

What Legislating can you get out of a man in that fatal situation? None that will profit much, one would think! A Legislator who has left his veracity lying on the door-threshold, he, why verily *he*—ought to be sent out to seek it again!

Heavens, what an improvement, were there once fairly in Downing-street, an Election-Office opened, with a Tariff of Boroughs! Such and such a population, amount of property-tax, ground-rental, extent of trade; returns two Members, returns one Member, for so much money down: Ipswich so many thousands, Nottingham so many,—as they happened, one by one, to fall into this new Downing-street Schedule A! An incalculable improvement, in comparison: for now at least you have it fairly by length of purse, and leave the dishonesty, the impudence, the unveracity all handsomely aside. Length of purse, and desire to be a Legislator ought to get a man into Parliament, not *with*, but if possible *without* the unveracity, the impudence and the dishonesty! Length of purse and desire, these are, as intrinsic qualifications, correctly equal to zero; but they are not yet *less* than zero,—as the smallest addition of that latter sort will make them!

And is it come to this? And does our venerable Parliament announce itself elected and eligible in this manner? Surely such a Parliament promulgates strange horoscopes of itself. What is to become of a Parliament elected or eligible in this manner? Unless Belial and Beelzebub have got possession of the throne of this Universe, such Parliament is preparing itself for new Reform-bills. We shall have to try it by Chartism, or any conceivable *ism*, rather than put up with this! There is already in England 'religion' enough to get six hundred and fifty-eight Consulting Men brought together who do *not* begin work with a lie in their mouth. Our poor old Parliament, thousands of years old, is still good for something, for several things;—though many are beginning to ask, with ominous anxiety, in these days: For what thing? But for whatever thing and things Parliament be good, indisputably it must start with other than a lie in its mouth! On the whole, a Parliament working with a lie in its mouth, will have to take itself away. To no Parliament or thing, that one has heard of, did this Universe ever long yield harbour on that footing. At all hours of the day and night, some Chartism is advancing, some armed Cromwell is advancing, to apprise such Parliament: "Ye are no Parliament. In the name of God,—go!"

In sad truth, once more, how is our whole existence, in these present days, built on Cant, Speciosity, Falsehood, Dilettantism; with this one serious Veracity in it: Mammonism! Dig down where you will, through the Parliament-floor or elsewhere, how infallibly do you, at spade's depth below the surface, come upon this universal *Liars*-rock sub-stratum! Much else is ornamental; true on barrel-heads, in pulpits, hustings, Parliamentary benches; but this is forever true and truest: "Money does bring money's worth; Put money in your purse." Here, if nowhere else, is the human soul still in thorough earnest; sincere with a prophet's sincerity: and 'the Hell of the English,' as Sauerteig said, 'is the infinite terror of Not getting on, especially of Not making money.' With results!

To many persons the horoscope of Parliament is more interesting than to me: but surely all men with souls must admit that sending members to Parliament by bribery is an infamous solecism; an act entirely immoral, which no man can have to do with, more or less, but he will soil his fingers more or less. No Carlton Clubs, Reform Clubs, nor any sort of clubs or creatures, or of accredited opinions or practices, can make a Lie Truth, can make Bribery a Propriety. The Parliament should really either punish and put away Bribery, or legalise it by some Office in Downing-street. As I read the Apocalypses, a Parliament that can do neither of these things is not in a good way.—And yet, alas, what of Parliaments and their Elections? Parliamentary Elections are but the topmost ultimate outcome of an electioneering which goes on at all hours, in all places, in every meeting of two or more men. It is *we* that vote wrong, and teach the poor ragged Freemen of Boroughs to vote wrong. We pay respect to those worthy of no respect.

Is not Pandarus Dogdraught a member of select clubs, and admitted into the drawingrooms of men? Visibly to all persons he is of the offal of Creation; but he carries money in his purse, due lacker on his dog-visage, and it is believed will not steal spoons. The human species does not with one voice, like the Hebrew Psalmist, 'shun to sit' with Dogdraught, refuse totally to dine with Dogdraught; men called of honour are willing enough to dine with him, his talk being lively, and his champagne excellent. We say to ourselves, "The man is in good society,"—others have already voted for him; why should not I? We *forget* the indefeasible right of property that Satan has in Dogdraught,—we are not afraid to be near Dogdraught! It is we that vote wrong; blindly, nay with falsity prepense! It is we that no longer know the difference between Human Worth and Human Unworth; or feel that the one is admirable and alone admirable, the other detestable, damnable! How shall *we* find out a Hero and Viceking Samson with a maximum of two shillings in his pocket? We have no chance to do such a thing. We have got out of the Ages of Heroism, deep into the Ages of Flunkeyism—and must return or die. What a noble set of mortals are we, who, because there is no Saint Edmund threatening us at the rim of the horizon, are not afraid to be whatever, for the day and hour, is smoothest for us!

And now, in good sooth, why should an indigent discerning Freeman give his vote without bribes? Let us rather honour the poor man that he does discern clearly wherein lies, for him, the true kernel of the matter. What is it to the ragged grimy Freeman of a Tenpound-Franchise Borough, whether Aristides Rigmarole Esq. of the Destructive, or the Hon. Alcides Dolittle of the Conservative Party be sent to Parliament;—much more, whether the two-thousandth part of them be sent, for that is the amount of his faculty in it? Destructive or Conservative, what will either of them destroy or conserve of vital moment to this Freeman? Has he found either of them care, at bottom, a sixpence for him or his interests, or those of his class or of his cause, or of any class or cause that is of much value to God or to man? Rigmarole and Dolittle have alike cared for themselves hitherto: and for their own clique, and self-conceited crotchets,—their greasy dishonest interests of pudding, or windy dishonest interests of praise; and not very perceptibly for any other interest whatever. Neither Rigmarole nor Dolittle will accomplish any good or any evil for this grimy Freeman, like giving him a five-pound note, or refusing to give it him. It will be smoothest to vote according to value received. That is the veritable fact; and he indigent, like others that are not indigent, acts comformably thereto.

Why, reader, truly, if they asked thee or me, Which way we meant to vote?—were it not our likeliest answer: Neither way! I, as a Tenpound Franchiser, will receive no bribe: but also I will not vote for either of these men. Neither Rigmarole nor Dolittle shall, by furtherance of mine, go and make laws for this country. I will have no hand in such a mission. How dare I! If other men cannot be got in England, a totally other sort of men, different as light is from dark, as star-fire is from street-mud, what is the use of votings, or of Parliaments in England? England ought to resign herself; there is no hope or possibility for England. If England cannot get her Knaves and Dastards, 'arrested,' in some degree, but only get them 'elected,' what is to become of England?

I conclude, with all confidence, that England will verily have to put an end to briberies on her Election Hustings and elsewhere, at what cost soever;—and likewise that we, Electors and Eligibles, one and all of us, for our own behoof and hers, cannot too soon begin, at what cost soever, to put an end to *bribeabilities* in ourselves. The death-leprosy, attacked in this manner, by purifying lotions from without and by rallying of the vital energies and purities from within, will probably abate somewhat! It has otherwise no chance to abate.

CHAPTER III.

The One Institution.

What our Government can do in this grand Problem of the Working Classes of England? Yes, supposing the insane Corn-Laws totally abolished, all speech of them ended, and 'from ten to twenty years of new possibility to live and find wages' conceded us in consequence: What the English Government might be expected to accomplish or attempt towards rendering the existence of our Labouring Millions somewhat less anomalous, somewhat less impossible, in the years that are to follow those 'ten or twenty,' if either 'ten' or 'twenty' there be?

It is the most momentous question. For all this of the Corn-Law Abrogation, and what can follow therefrom, is but as the shadow on King Hezekiah's Dial: the shadow has gone back twenty years; but will again, in spite of Free-Trades and Abrogations, travel forward its old fated way. With our present system of individual Mammonism, and Government by Laissezfaire, this Nation cannot live. And if, in the priceless interim, some new life and healing be not found, there is no second respite to be counted on. The shadow on the Dial advances thenceforth without pausing. What Government can do? This that they call 'Organising of Labour' is, if well understood, the Problem of the whole Future, for all who will in future pretend to govern men. But our first preliminary stage of it, How to deal with the Actual Labouring Millions of England? this is the imperatively pressing Problem of the Present, pressing with a truly fearful intensity and imminence in these very years and days. No Government can longer neglect it: once more, what can our Government do in it?

Governments are of very various degrees of activity: some, altogether Lazy Governments, in 'free countries' as they are called, seem in these times almost to profess to do, if not nothing, one knows not at first what. To debate in Parliament, and gain majorities; and ascertain who shall be, with a toil hardly second to Ixion's, the Prime Speaker and Spoke-holder, and keep the Ixion's-Wheel going, if not forward, yet round? Not altogether so:— much, to the experienced eye, is not what it seems! Chancery and certain other Law-Courts seem nothing; yet in fact they are, the worst of them, something: chimneys for the devilry and contention of men to escape by;— a very considerable something! Parliament too has its tasks, if thou wilt look; fit to wear out the lives of toughest men. The celebrated Kilkenny Cats, through their tumultuous congress, cleaving the ear of Night, could they be said to do nothing? Hadst thou been of them, thou hadst seen! The feline heart laboured, as with steam up—to the bursting point; and death-doing energy nerved every muscle: they had a work there; and did it! On the morrow, two tails were found left, and peaceable annihilation; a neighbourhood *delivered* from despair.

Again, are not Spinning-Dervishes an eloquent emblem, significant of much? Hast thou noticed him, that solemn-visaged Turk, the eyes shut; dingy wool mantle circularly hiding his figure;—bell-shaped; like a dingy bell set spinning on the *tongue* of it? By centrifugal force the dingy wool mantle heaves itself; spreads more and more, like upturned cup widening into upturned saucer: thus spins he, to the praise of Allah and advantage of mankind, fast and faster, till collapse ensue, and sometimes death!—

A Government such as ours, consisting of from seven to eight hundred Parliamentary Talkers, with their escort of Able Editors and Public Opinion; and for head, certain Lords and Servants of the Treasury, and Chief Secretaries and others, who find themselves at once Chiefs and No-Chiefs, and often commanded rather than commanding,—is doubtless a most complicate entity, and none of the alertest for getting on with business! Clearly enough, if the Chiefs be not self-motive and what we call men, but mere patient lay-figures without self-motive principle, the Government will not move anywhither; it will tumble disastrously, and jumble, round its own axis, as for many years past we have seen it do.—And yet a self-motive man who is not a lay-figure, place him in the heart of what entity you may, will make it move more or less! The absurdest in Nature he will make a little *less* absurd, he. The unwieldiest he will make to move;—that is the use of his existing there. He will at least have the manfulness to depart out of it, if not; to say: "I cannot move in thee, and be a man; like a wretched drift-log dressed in man's clothes and minister's clothes, doomed to a lot baser than belongs to man, I will not continue with thee, tumbling aimless on the Mother of Dead Dogs here:—Adieu!"

For, on the whole, it is the lot of Chiefs everywhere, this same. No Chief in the most despotic country, but was a Servant withal; at once an absolute commanding General, and a poor Orderly-Sergeant, ordered by the very men in the ranks,—obliged to collect the vote of the ranks too, in some articulate or inarticulate shape, and weigh well the same. The proper name of all Kings is minister, Servant. In no conceivable Government can a lay-figure get forward! *This* Worker, surely he above all others has to 'spread out his Gideon's Fleece,' and collect the monitions of Immensity; the poor Localities, as we said, and Parishes of Palace-yard or elsewhere, having no due monition in them. A Prime Minister, even here in England, who shall dare believe the heavenly omens, and address himself like a man and hero to the great dumb-struggling heart of England; and speak out for it, and act out for it, the God's-Justice it is writhing to get uttered and perishing for want of,—yes, he too, will see awaken round him, in passionate burning all-defiant loyalty, the heart of England, and such a 'support' as no Division-List or Parliamentary Majority was ever yet known to yield a man! Here as there, now as then, he who can and dare trust the heavenly Immensities, all earthly Localities are subject to him. We will pray for such a Man and First-Lord; —yes, and far better, we will strive and incessantly make ready, each of us, to be worthy to serve and second such a First-Lord! We shall then be as good as sure of his arriving; sure of many things, let him arrive or not.

Who can despair of Governments that passes a Soldiers' Guardhouse, or meets a redcoated man on the streets! That a body of men could be got together to kill other men when you bade them: this, *a priori*, does it not seem one of the impossiblest things? Yet look, behold it: in the stolidest of Donothing Governments, that impossibility is a thing done. See it there with buff-belts, red coats on its back; walking sentry at guard-houses, brushing white breeches in barracks; an indisputable palpable fact. Out of grey Antiquity, amid all finance-difficulties, *scaccarium*-tallies, ship-moneys, coat-and-conduct moneys, and vicissitudes of Chance and Time, there, down to the present blessed hour, it is.

Often, in these painfully decadent and painfully nascent Times, with their distresses, inarticulate gaspings and 'impossibilities;' meeting a tall Life-guardsman in his snow-white trousers, or seeing those two statuesque Life-guardsmen in their frowning bearskins, pipe-clayed buckskins, on their coal-black sleek fiery quadrupeds, riding sentry at the Horse-Guards,—it strikes one with a kind of mournful interest, how, in such universal down-rushing and wrecked impotence of almost all old institutions, this oldest Fighting Institution is still so young! Fresh-complexioned, firm-limbed, six feet by the standard, this fighting-man has verily been got up, and can fight.

While so much has not yet got into being; while so much has gone gradually out of it, and become an empty Semblance of Clothes-suit; and highest king's-cloaks, mere chimeras parading under them so long, are getting unsightly to the earnest eye, unsightly, almost offensive, like a costlier kind of scarecrow's-blanket,—here still is a reality!

The man in horsehair wig advances, promising that he will get me 'justice:' he takes me into Chancery Law-Courts, into decades, half-centuries of hubbub, of distracted jargon; and does *get* me—disappointment, almost desperation; and one refuge: that of dismissing him and his 'justice' altogether out of my head. For I have work to do; I cannot spend my decades in mere arguing with other men about the exact wages of my work: I will work cheerfully with no wages, sooner than with a ten-years gangrene or Chancery Lawsuit in my heart! He of the horsehair wig is a sort of failure; no substance, but a fond imagination of the mind. He of the shovel-hat, again, who comes forward professing that he will save my soul— O ye Eternities, of him in this place be absolute silence!—But he of the red coat, I say, is a success and no failure! He will veritably, if he get orders, draw out a long sword and kill me. No mistake there. He is a fact and not a shadow. Alive in this Year Forty-three, able and willing to do *his* work. In dim old centuries, with William Rufus, William of Ipres, or far earlier, he began; and has come down safe so far. Catapult has given place to cannon, pike has given place to musket, iron mail-shirt to coat of red cloth, saltpetre ropematch to percussion cap; equipments, circumstances have all changed, and again changed: but the human battle-engine, in the inside of any or of each of these, ready still to do battle, stands there, six feet in standard size. There are Pay-Offices, Woolwich Arsenals, there is a Horse-Guards, War-Office, Captain-General: persuasive Sergeants, with tap of drum, recruit in market-towns and villages;—and, on the whole, I say, here is your actual drilled fighting-man; here are your actual Ninety-thousand of such, ready to go into any quarter of the world and fight!

Strange, interesting, and yet most mournful to reflect on. Was this, then, of all the things mankind had some talent for, the one thing important to learn well, and bring to perfection; this of successfully killing one another? Truly you have learned it well, and carried the business to a high perfection. It is incalculable what, by arranging, commanding and regimenting, you can make of men. These thousand straight-standing firmset individuals, who shoulder arms, who march, wheel, advance, retreat; and are, for your behoof, a magazine charged with fiery death, in the most perfect condition of potential activity: few months ago, till the persuasive sergeant came, what were they? Multiform ragged losels, runaway apprentices, starved weavers, thievish valets; an entirely broken population, fast tending towards the treadmill. But the persuasive sergeant came; by tap of drum enlisted, or formed lists of them, took heartily to drilling them;—and he and you have made them this! Most potent, effectual for all work whatsoever, is wise planning, firm combining and commanding among men. Let no man despair of Governments who look on these two sentries at the Horse-Guards, and our United-Service Clubs! I could conceive an Emigration Service, a Teaching Service, considerable varieties of United and Separate Services, of the due thousands strong, all effective as this Fighting Service is; all doing *their* work, like it;—which work, much more than fighting, is henceforth the necessity of these New Ages we are got into! Much lies among us, convulsively, nigh desperately *struggling to be born.*

But mean Governments, as mean-limited individuals do, have stood by the physically indispensable; have realised that and nothing more. The Soldier is perhaps one of the most difficult things to realise; but Governments, had they not realised him, could not have existed: accordingly he is here. O Heavens if we saw an army ninety-thousand strong, maintained and fully equipt, in continual real action and battle against Human Starvation, against Chaos, Necessity, Stupidity, and our real 'natural enemies,' what a business were it! Fighting and molesting not 'the French,' who, poor men, have a hard enough battle of their own in the like kind, and need no additional molesting from us; but fighting and incessantly spearing down and destroying Falsehood, Nescience, Delusion, Disorder, and the Devil and his Angels! Thou thyself, cultivated reader, hast done something in that alone true warfare; but, alas, under what circumstances was it? Thee no beneficent drill-sergeant, with any effectiveness, would rank in line beside thy fellows; train, like a true didactic artist, by the wit of all past experience, to do thy soldiering; encourage thee when right, punish thee when wrong, and everywhere with wise word-of-command say, Forward on this hand, Forward on that! Ah, no: thou hadst to learn thy small-sword and platoon exercise where and how thou couldst; to all mortals but thyself it was indifferent whether thou shouldst ever learn it. And the rations, and shilling a day, were they provided thee,—reduced as I have known brave Jean-Pauls, learning their exercise, to live on 'water *without* the bread?' The rations; or any furtherance of promotion to corporalship, lance-corporalship, or due cat-o'-nine tails, with the slightest reference to thy deserts were not provided. Forethought, even as of a pipe-clayed drill-sergeant, did not preside over thee. To corporalship, lance-corporalship, thou didst attain; alas, also to the halberts and cat; but thy rewarder and punisher seemed blind as the Deluge; neither lance-corporalship, nor even drummer's cat, because both appeared delirious, brought thee due profit.

It was well, all this, we know;—and yet it was not well! Forty soldiers, I am told, will disperse the largest Spitalfields mob: forty to ten-thousand, that is the proportion between drilled and undrilled. Much there is which cannot yet be organised in this world; but somewhat also which can, somewhat also which must. When one thinks, for example, what Books are become and becoming for us, what Operative Lancashires are become; what a Fourth Estate, and innumerable Virtualities not yet got to be Actualities are become and becoming,—one sees Organisms enough in the dim huge Future; and 'United Services' quite other than the redcoat one; and much, even in these years, struggling to be born!

Of Time-Bill, Factory-Bill and other such Bills the present Editor has no authority to speak. He knows not, it is for others than him to know, in what specific ways it may be feasible to interfere, with Legislation, between the Workers and the Master-Workers;—knows only and sees, what all men are beginning to see, that Legislative interference, and interferences not a few are indispensable; that as a lawless anarchy of supply-and-demand, on market-wages alone, this province of things cannot longer be left. Nay interference has begun: there are already Factory Inspectors,—who seem to have no *lack* of work. Perhaps there might be Mine-Inspectors too:— might there not be Furrowfield Inspectors withal, and ascertain for us how on seven and sixpence a week a human family does live! Interference has begun; it must continue, must extensively enlarge itself, deepen and sharpen itself. Such things cannot longer be idly lapped in darkness, and suffered to go on unseen: the Heavens do see them; the curse, not the blessing of the Heavens is on an Earth that refuses to see them.

Again, are not Sanitary Regulations possible for a Legislature? The old Romans had their Ædiles; who would, I think, in direct contravention to supply-and-demand, have rigorously seen rammed up into total abolition many a foul cellar in our Southwarks, Saint-Gileses, and dark poison-lanes; saying sternly, "Shall a Roman man dwell there?" The Legislature, at whatever cost of consequences, would have had to answer, "God forbid!"—The Legislature, even as it now is, could order all dingy Manufacturing Towns to cease from their soot and darkness; to let in the blessed sunlight, the blue of Heaven, and become clear and clean; to burn their coal-smoke, namely, and make flame of it. Baths, free air, a wholesome temperature, ceilings twenty feet high, might be ordained, by Act of Parliament, in all establishments licensed as Mills. There are such Mills already extant;—honour to the builders of them! The Legislature can say to others: Go ye and do likewise; better if you can.

Every toiling Manchester, its smoke and soot all burnt, ought it not, among so many world-wide conquests, to have a hundred acres or so of free greenfield, with trees on it, conquered, for its little children to disport in; for its all conquering workers to take a breath of twilight air in? You would say so! A willing Legislature could say so with effect. A willing Legislature could say very many things! And to whatsoever 'vested interest,' or such like, stood up, gainsaying merely, "I shall lose profits,"—the willing Legislature would answer, "Yes, but my sons and daughters will gain health, and life, and a soul."—"What is to become of our Cotton-trade?" cried certain Spinners, when the Factory-Bill was proposed; "What is to become of our invaluable Cotton-trade?" The Humanity of England answered stedfastly: "Deliver me these rickety perishing souls of infants, and let your Cotton-trade take its chance. God Himself commands the one thing; not God especially the other thing. We cannot have prosperous Cotton-trades at the expense of keeping the Devil a partner in them!"—

Bills enough, were the Corn-Law Abrogation Bill once passed, and a Legislature willing! Nay this one Bill, which lies yet unenacted, a right

Education Bill, is not this of itself the sure parent of innumerable wise Bills,—wise regulations, practical methods and proposals, gradually ripening towards the state of Bills? To irradiate with intelligence, that is to say, with order, arrangement and all blessedness, the Chaotic, Unintelligent: how, except by educating, *can* you accomplish this? That thought, reflection, articulate utterance and understanding be awakened in these individual million heads, which are the atoms of your Chaos: there is no other way of illuminating any Chaos! The sum-total of intelligence that is found in it, determines the extent of order that is possible for your Chaos,—the feasibility and rationality of what your Chaos will dimly demand from you, and will gladly obey when proposed by you! It is an exact equation; the one accurately measures the other.—If the whole English People, during these 'twenty years of respite,' be not educated, with at least schoolmaster's educating, a tremendous responsibility, before God and men, will rest somewhere! How dare any man, especially a man calling himself minister of God, stand up in any Parliament or place, under any pretext or delusion, and for a day or an hour forbid God's Light to come into the world, and bid the Devil's Darkness continue in it one hour more! For all light and science, under all shapes, in all degrees of perfection, is of God; all darkness, nescience, is of the Enemy of God. 'The schoolmaster's creed is somewhat awry?' Yes, I have found few creeds entirely correct; few light-beams shining *white*, pure of admixture: but of all creeds and religions now or ever before known, was not that of thoughtless thriftless Animalism, of Distilled Gin, and Stupor and Despair, unspeakably the least orthodox? We will exchange *it* even with Paganism, with Fetishism; and, on the whole, must exchange it with something.

An effective 'Teaching Service' I do consider that there must be; some Education Secretary, Captain-General of Teachers, who will actually contrive to get us *taught*. Then again, why should there not be an 'Emigration Service,' and Secretary, with adjuncts, with funds, forces, idle Navy-ships, and ever-increasing apparatus; in fine an *effective system* of Emigration; so that, at length, before our twenty years of respite ended, every honest willing Workman who found England too strait, and the 'Organisation of Labour' not yet sufficiently advanced, might find likewise a bridge built to carry him into new Western Lands, there to 'organise' with more elbow-room some labour for himself? There to be a real blessing, raising new corn for us, purchasing new webs and hatchets from us; leaving us at least in peace;—instead of staying here to be a Physical-Force Chartist, unblessed and no blessing! Is it not scandalous to consider that a Prime Minister could raise within the year, as I have seen it done, a Hundred and Twenty Millions sterling to shoot the French; and we are stopt short for want of the hundredth part of that to keep the English living? The bodies of the English living; and the souls of English living:—these two 'Services,' an Education Service and an Emigration Service, these with others will actually have to be organised!

A free bridge for Emigrants: why, we should then be on a par with

America itself, the most favoured of all lands that have no government; and we should have, besides, so many traditions and mementos of priceless things which America has cast away. We could proceed deliberately to 'organise Labour,' not doomed to perish unless we effected it within year and day;—every willing Worker that proved superfluous, finding a bridge ready for him. This verily will have to be done; the Time is big with this. Our little Isle is grown too narrow for us; but the world is wide enough yet for another Six Thousand Years. England's sure markets will be among new Colonies of Englishmen in all quarters of the Globe. All men trade with all men, when mutually convenient; and are even bound to do it by the Maker of men. Our friends of China, who guiltily refused to trade, in these circumstances,—had we not to argue with them, in cannon-shot at last, and convince them that they ought to trade! 'Hostile Tariffs' will arise, to shut us out; and then again will fall, to let us in: but the Sons of England, speakers of the English language were it nothing more, will in all times have the ineradicable predisposition to trade with England. Mycale was the *Pan-Ionion*, rendezvous of all the Tribes of Ion, for old Greece: why should not London long continue the *All-Saxon-home*, rendezvous of all the 'Children of the Harz-Rock,' arriving, in select samples, from the Antipodes and elsewhere, by steam and otherwise, to the 'season' here!—What a Future; wide as the world, if we have the heart and heroism for it,—which, by Heaven's blessing we shall:

> '*Keep not standing fixed and rooted,*
> *Briskly venture, briskly roam;*
> *Head and hand, where'er thou foot it,*
> *And stout heart are still at home.*
>
> *In what land the sun does visit,*
> *Brisk are we, whate'er betide:*
> *To give space for wandering is it*
> *That the world was made so wide.*'[1]

Fourteen hundred years ago, it was by a considerable 'Emigration Service,' never doubt it, by much enlistment, discussion and apparatus, that we ourselves arrived in this remarkable Island,—and got into our present difficulties among others!

It is true the English Legislature, like the English People, is of slow temper; essentially conservative. In our wildest periods of reform, in the Long Parliament itself, you notice always the invincible instinct to hold fast by the Old; to admit the *minimum* of New; to expand, if it be possible, some old habit or method, already found fruitful, into new growth for the new need. It is an instinct worthy of all honour; akin to all strength and all wisdom. The Future hereby is not dissevered from the Past, but based continuously on it; grows with all the vitalities of the Past, and is rooted

[1] Goethe, *Wilhelm Meister.*

down deep into the beginnings of us. The English Legislature is entirely repugnant to believe in 'new epochs.' The English Legislature does not occupy itself with epochs; has, indeed, other business to do than looking at the Time-Horologe and hearing it tick! Nevertheless new epochs do actually come; and with them new imperious peremptory necessities; so that even an English Legislature has to look up, and admit, though with reluctance, that the hour has struck. The hour having struck, let us not say 'impossible;'—it will have to be possible! 'Contrary to the habits of Parliament, the habits of Government?' Yes: but did any Parliament or Government ever sit in a Year Forty-three before? One of the most original, unexampled years and epochs; in several important respects, totally unlike any other! For Time, all-edacious and all-feracious, does run on: and the Seven Sleepers, awakening hungry after a hundred years, find that it is not their old nurses who can now give them suck!

For the rest, let not any Parliament, Aristocracy, Millocracy, or Member of the Governing Class, condemn with much triumph this small specimen of 'remedial measures;' or ask again, with the least anger, of this Editor, What is to be done, How that alarming problem of the Working Classes is to be managed? Editors are not here, foremost of all, to say How. A certain Editor thanks the gods that nobody pays him three hundred thousand pounds a year, two hundred thousand, twenty thousand, or any similar sum of cash for saying How:—that his wages are very different, his work somewhat fitter for him. An Editor's stipulated work is to apprise *thee* that it must be done. The 'way to do it,'—is to try it, knowing that thou shalt die if it be not done. There is the bare back, there is the web of cloth; thou shalt cut me a coat to cover the bare back, thou whose trade it is. 'Impossible?' Hapless Fraction, dost thou discern Fate there, half unveiling herself in the gloom of the future, with her gibbet-cords, her steel-whips, and very authentic Tailor's Hell; waiting to see whether it is 'possible?' Out with thy scissors, and cut that cloth or thy own windpipe!

CHAPTER IV.

CAPTAINS OF INDUSTRY.

IF I BELIEVED that Mammonism with its adjuncts was to continue henceforth the one serious principle of our existence, I should reckon it idle to solicit remedial measures from any Government, the disease being insusceptible of remedy. Government can do much, but it can in no wise do all. Government, as the most conspicuous object in Society, is called upon to give signal of what shall be done; and, in many ways, to preside over, further, and command the doing of it. But the Government cannot do, by all its signalling and commanding, what the Society is radically indisposed to do. In the long-run every Government is the exact symbol of its People, with their wisdom and unwisdom; we have to say, Like People like Government.—

The main substance of this immense Problem of Organising Labour, and first of all of Managing the Working Classes, will, it is very clear, have to be solved by those who stand practically in the middle of it; by those who themselves work and preside over work. Of all that can be enacted by any Parliament in regard to it, the germs must already lie potentially extant in those two Classes, who are to obey such enactment. A human Chaos *in* which there is no light, you vainly attempt to irradiate by light shed *on* it; order never can arise there.

But it is my firm conviction that the 'Hell of England' will *cease* to be that of 'not making money;' that we shall get a nobler Hell and a nobler Heaven! I anticipate light *in* the Human Chaos, glimmering, shining more and more; under manifold true signals from without That light shall shine. Our deity no longer being Mammon,—O Heavens, each man will then say to himself: "Why such deadly haste to make money? I shall not go to Hell, even if I do not make money! There is another Hell, I am told!" Competition, at railway-speed, in all branches of commerce and work will then abate:—good felt-hats for the head, in every sense, instead of seven-feet lath-and-plaster hats on wheels, will then be discoverable! Bubble-periods, with their panics and commercial crises, will again become infrequent; steady modest industry will take the place of gambling speculation. To be a noble Master, among noble Workers, will again be the first ambition with some few; to be a rich Master only the second. How the Inventive Genius of England, with the whirr of its bobbins and billy-rollers shoved somewhat into the backgrounds of the brain, will contrive and devise, not cheaper produce exclusively, but fairer distribution of the produce at its present cheapness! By degrees, we shall again have a Society with something of Heroism in it, something of Heaven's Blessing on it; we shall again have, as my German friend asserts, 'instead of Mammon-Feudalism with unsold cotton-shirts and Preservation of the Game, noble just Industrialism and Government by the Wisest!'

It is with the hope of awakening here and there a British man to know himself for a man and divine soul, that a few words of parting admonition, to all persons to whom the Heavenly Powers have lent power of any kind in this land, may now be addressed. And first to those same Master-Workers, Leaders of Industry; who stand nearest, and in fact powerfulest, though not most prominent, being as yet in too many senses a Virtuality rather than an Actuality.

The Leaders of Industry, if Industry is ever to be led, are virtually the Captains of the World; if there be no nobleness in them, there will never be an Aristocracy more. But let the Captains of Industry consider: once again, are they born of other clay than the old Captains of Slaughter; doomed forever to be no Chivalry, but a mere gold-plated *Doggery*,—what the French well name *Canaille*, 'Doggery' with more or less gold carrion at its disposal? Captains of Industry are the true Fighters, henceforth recognisable, as the only true ones: Fighters against Chaos, Necessity and the Devils and Jötuns; and lead on Mankind in that great, and alone true, and universal warfare; the stars in their courses fighting for them, and all Heaven and all Earth saying audibly, Well-done! Let the Captains of Industry retire into their own hearts, and ask solemnly, If there is nothing but vulturous hunger, for fine wines, valet reputation and gilt carriages, discoverable there? Of hearts made by the Almighty God I will not believe such a thing. Deep-hidden under wretchedest godforgetting Cants, Epicurisms, Dead-Sea Apisms; forgotten as under foulest fat Lethe mud and weeds, there is yet, in all hearts born into this God's-World, a spark of the God-like slumbering. Awake, O nightmare sleepers; awake, arise, or be forever fallen! This is not playhouse poetry; it is sober fact. Our England, our world cannot live as it is. It will connect itself with a God again, or go down with nameless throes and fire-consummation to the Devils. Thou who feelest aught of such a God-like stirring in thee, any faintest intimation of it, as through heavy-laden dreams, follow *it*, I conjure thee. Arise, save thyself, be one of those that save thy country.

Bucaniers, Chactaw Indians, whose supreme aim in fighting is that they may get the scalps, the money, that they may amass scalps and money: out of such came no Chivalry, and never will! Out of such came only gore and wreck, infernal rage and misery; desperation quenched in annihilation. Behold it, I bid thee, behold there, and consider! What is it that thou have a hundred thousand-pound bills laid up in thy strong-rooms, a hundred scalps hung up in thy wigwam? I value not them or thee. Thy scalps and thy thousand-pound bills are as yet nothing, if no nobleness from within irradiate them; if no Chivalry, in action, or in embryo ever struggling towards birth and action, be there.

Love of men cannot be bought by cash-payment; and without love, men cannot endure to be together. You cannot lead a Fighting World without having it regimented, chivalried: the thing in a day becomes impossible; all men in it, the highest at first, the very lowest at last, discern consciously, or by a noble instinct, this necessity. And can you any more continue to lead a Working World unregimented, anarchic? I answer, and the Heavens and Earth are now answering, No! The thing becomes not 'in a day' impossible; but in some two generations it does. Yes, when fathers and mothers, in Stockport hunger-cellars, begin to eat their children, and Irish widows have to prove their relationship by dying of typhus-fever; and amid Governing 'Corporations of the Best and Bravest,' busy to preserve their game by 'bushing,' dark millions of God's human creatures start up in mad Chartisms, impracticable Sacred-Months, and Manchester Insurrections; and there is a virtual Industrial Aristocracy as yet only half-alive, spell-bound amid money-bags and ledgers; and an actual Idle Aristocracy seemingly near dead in somnolent delusions, in trespasses and double-barrels; 'sliding,' as on inclined planes, which every new year they *soap* with new Hansard's-jargon under God's sky, and so are 'sliding' ever faster, towards a 'scale' and balance-scale whereon is written *Thou art found Wanting:*—in such days, after a generation or two, I say, it does become, even to the low and simple, very palpably impossible! No Working World, any more than a Fighting World, can be led on without a noble Chivalry of Work, and laws and fixed rules which follow out of that,—far nobler than any Chivalry of Fighting was. As an anarchic multitude on mere Supply-and-demand, it is becoming inevitable that we dwindle in horrid suicidal convulsion, and self-abrasion, frightful to the imagination, into *Chactaw* Workers. With wigwams and scalps,—with palaces and thousand-pound bills; with savagery, depopulation, chaotic desolation! Good Heavens, will not one French Revolution and Reign of Terror suffice us, but must there be two? There will be two if needed; there will be twenty if needed; there will be precisely as many as are needed. The Laws of Nature will have themselves fulfilled. That is a thing certain to me.

Your gallant battle-hosts, and work-hosts, as the others did, will need to be made loyally yours; they must and will be regulated, methodically secured in their just share of conquest under you;—joined with you in veritable brotherhood, sonhood, by quite other and deeper ties than those of temporary day's wages! How would mere red-coated regiments, to say nothing of chivalries, fight for you, if you could discharge them on the evening of the battle, on payment of the stipulated shillings,—and they discharge you on the morning of it! Chelsea Hospitals, pensions, promotions, rigorous lasting covenant on the one side and on the other, are indispensable even for a hired fighter. The Feudal Baron, much more,—how could he subsist with mere temporary mercenaries round him, at sixpence a day; ready to go over to the other side, if sevenpence were offered? He could not have subsisted;—and his noble instinct saved him from the necessity of even trying! The Feudal Baron had a Man's Soul in him! to which anarchy, mutiny, and the other fruits of temporary mercenaries, were intolerable: he had never been a Baron otherwise, but had continued a Chactaw and Bucanier. He felt it precious, and at last it became habitual, and his fruitful enlarged existence included it as a necessity, to have men round him who in heart loved him; whose life he watched over with rigour yet with love; who were prepared to give their life for him, if need came. It was beautiful; it was human! Man lives not otherwise, nor can live contented, anywhere or anywhen. Isolation is the sum-total of wretchedness to man. To be cut off, to be left solitary: to have a world alien, not your world; all a hostile camp for you; not a home at all, of hearts and faces who are yours, whose you are! It is the frightfulest enchantment; too truly a work of the Evil One. To have neither superior, nor inferior, nor equal, united manlike to you. Without father, without child, without brother. Man knows no sadder destiny. 'How is each of us,' exclaims Jean Paul, 'so lonely, in the wide bosom of the All!' Encased each as in his transparent 'ice-palace;' our brother visible in his, making signals and gesticulations to us;—visible, but forever unattainable: on his bosom we shall never rest, nor he on ours. It was not a God that did this; no!

Awake, ye noble Workers, warriors in the one true war: all this must be remedied. It is you who are already half-alive, whom I will welcome into life; whom I will conjure in God's name to shake off your enchanted sleep, and live wholly! Cease to count scalps, gold-purses; not in these lies your or our salvation. Even these, if you count only these, will not long be left. Let bucaniering be put far from you; alter, speedily abrogate all laws of the bucaniers, if you would gain any victory that shall endure. Let God's justice, let pity, nobleness and manly valour, with more gold-purses or with fewer, testify themselves in this your brief Life-transit to all the Eternities, the Gods and Silences. It is to you I call; for ye are not dead, ye are already half-alive: there is in you a sleepless dauntless energy, the prime-matter of all nobleness in man. Honour to you in your kind. It is to you I call: ye know at least this, That the mandate of God to His creature man is: Work! The future Epic of the World rests not with those that are near dead, but with those that are alive, and those that are coming into life.

Look around you. Your world-hosts are all in mutiny, in confusion, destitution; on the eve of fiery wreck and madness! They will not march farther for you, on the sixpence a day and supply-and-demand principle: they will not; nor ought they, nor can they. Ye shall reduce them to order, begin reducing them. To order, to just subordination; noble loyalty in return for noble guidance. Their souls are driven nigh mad; let yours be sane and ever saner. Not as a bewildered bewildering mob; but as a firm regimented mass, with real captains over them, will these men march any more. All human interests, combined human endeavours, and social growths in this world, have, at a certain stage of their development, required organising: and Work, the grandest of human interests, does now require it.

God knows, the task will be hard: but no noble task was ever easy. This task will wear away your lives, and the lives of your sons and grandsons: but for what purpose, if not for tasks like this, were lives given to men? Ye shall cease to count your thousand-pound scalps, the noble of you shall cease! Nay the very scalps, as I say, will not long be left if you count only these. Ye shall cease wholly to be barbarous vulturous Chactaws, and become noble European Nineteenth-Century Men. Ye shall know that Mammon, in never such gigs and flunkey 'respectabilities,' is not the alone God; that of himself he is but a Devil, and even a Brute-god.

Difficult? Yes, it will be difficult. The short-fibre Cotton; that too was difficult. The waste cotton-shrub, long useless, disobedient, as the thistle by the wayside,—have ye not conquered it; made it into beautiful bandana webs; white woven shirts for men; bright-tinted air-garments wherein flit goddesses? Ye have shivered mountains asunder, made the hard iron pliant to you as soft putty: the Forest-giants, Marsh-jötuns bear sheaves of golden grain; Ægir the Sea-demon himself stretches his back for a sleek highway to you, and on Firehorses and Windhorses ye career. Ye are most strong. Thor red-bearded, with his blue sun-eyes, with his cheery heart and strong thunder-hammer, he and you have prevailed. Ye are most strong, ye Sons of the icy North, of the far East,—far marching from your rugged Eastern Wildernesses, hitherward from the grey Dawn of Time! Ye are Sons of the Jötun-land; the land of Difficulties Conquered. Difficult? You must try this thing. Once try it with the understanding that it will and shall have to be done. Try it as ye try the paltrier thing, making of money! I will bet on you once more, against all Jötuns, Tailor-gods, Double-barrelled Law-wards, and Denizens of Chaos whatsoever!

CHAPTER V.

PERMANENCE.

STANDING on the threshold, nay as yet outside the threshold, of a 'Chivalry of Labour,' and an immeasurable Future which it is to fill with fruitfulness and verdant shade; where so much has not yet come even to the rudimental state, and all speech of positive enactments were hazardous in those who know this business only by the eye,—let us here hint at simply one widest universal principle, as the basis from which all organisation hitherto has grown up among men, and all henceforth will have to grow: The principle of Permanent Contract instead of Temporary.

Permanent not Temporary:—you do not hire the mere redcoated fighter by the day, but by the score of years! Permanence, persistence is the first condition of all fruitfulness in the ways of men. The 'tendency to persevere,' to persist in spite of hindrances, discouragements and 'impossibilities:' it is this that in all things distinguishes the strong soul from the weak; the civilised burgher from the nomadic savage,—the Species Man from the Genus Ape! The Nomad has his very house set on wheels; the Nomad, and in a still higher degree the Ape, are all for 'liberty;' the privilege to flit continually is indispensable for them. Alas, in how many ways, does our humour, in this swift-rolling self-abrading Time, shew itself nomadic, apelike; mournful enough to him that looks on it with eyes! This humour will have to abate; it is the first element of all fertility in human things, that such 'liberty' of apes and nomads do by freewill or constraint abridge itself, give place to a better. The civilised man lives not in wheeled houses. He builds stone castles, plants lands, makes lifelong marriage-contracts;—has long-dated hundred-fold possessions, not to be valued in the money-market; has pedigrees, libraries, law-codes; has memories and hopes, even for this Earth, that reach over thousands of years. Life-long marriage-contracts: how much preferable were year-long or month-long—to the nomad or ape!

Month-long contracts please me little, in any province where there can by possibility be found virtue enough for more. Month-long contracts do not answer well even with your house-servants; the liberty on both sides to change every month is growing very apelike, nomadic;—and I hear philosophers predict that it will alter, or that strange results will follow: that wise men, pestered with nomads, with unattached ever-shifting spies and enemies rather than friends and servants, will gradually, weighing substance against semblance, with indignation, dismiss such, down almost to the very shoe-black, and say, "Begone; I will serve myself rather, and have peace!" Gurth was hired for life to Cedric, and Cedric to Gurth. O Anti-Slavery Convention, loud-sounding long-eared Exeter-Hall—But in thee too is a kind of instinct towards justice, and I will complain of nothing. Only, black Quashee over the seas being once sufficiently attended to, wilt thou not perhaps open thy dull sodden eyes to the 'sixty-thousand valets in London itself who are yearly dismissed to the streets, to be what they can, when the season ends;'—or to the hungerstricken, pallid, *yellow*-coloured 'Free Labourers' in Lancashire, Yorkshire, Buckinghamshire, and all other shires! These Yellow-coloured, for the present, absorb all my sympathies: if I had a Twenty Millions, with Model-Farms and Niger Expeditions, it is to these that I would give it! Quashee has already victuals, clothing; Quashee is not dying of such despair as the yellow-coloured pale man's. Quashee, it must be owned, is hitherto a kind of blockhead. The Haiti Duke of Marmalade, educated now for almost half a century, seems to have next to no sense in him. Why, in one of those Lancashire Weavers, dying of hunger, there is more thought and heart, a greater arithmetical amount of misery and desperation, than in whole gangs of Quashees. It must be owned, thy eyes are of the sodden sort; and with thy emancipations, and thy twenty-millionings and long-eared clamourings, thou, like Robespierre and his pasteboard *Etre Suprême*, threatenest to become a bore to us: *Avec ton Etre Suprême tu commences m'embêter!*—

In a Printed Sheet of the assiduous, much-abused, and truly useful Mr. Chadwick's, containing queries and responses from far and near, as to this great question, 'What is the effect of Education on workingmen, in respect of their value as mere workers?' the present Editor, reading with satisfaction a decisive unanimous verdict as to Education, reads with inexpressible interest this special remark, put in by way of marginal incidental note, from a practical manufacturing Quaker, whom, as he is anonymous, we will call Friend Prudence. Prudence keeps a thousand workmen; has striven in all ways to attach them to him; has provided conversational soirées; play-grounds, bands of music for the young ones; went even 'the length of buying them a drum:' all which has turned out to be an excellent invest-ment. For a certain person, marked here by a black stroke, whom we shall name Blank, living over the way,—he also keeps somewhere about a thousand men; but has done none of these things for them, nor any other thing, except due payment of the wages by supply-and-demand. Blank's workers are perpetually getting into mutiny, into broils and coils: every six months, we suppose, Blank has a strike; every one month, every day and every hour, they are fretting and obstructing the short-sighted Blank; pilfering from him, wasting and idling for him, omitting and committing for him. "I would not," says Friend Prudence, "exchange my workers for his *with seven thousand pounds to boot.*"[1]

Right, O honourable Prudence; thou art wholly in the right: Seven

[1] Report on the Training of Pauper Children (1841), p. 18.

thousand pounds even as a matter of profit for this world, nay for the mere cash-market of this world! And as a matter of profit not for this world only, but for the other world and all worlds, it outweighs the Bank of England!—Can the sagacious reader descry here, as it were the outmost inconsiderable rockledge of a universal rock-foundation, deep once more as the Centre of the World, emerging so, in the experience of this good Quaker, through the Stygian mud-vortexes and general Mother of Dead Dogs, whereon, for the present, all swags and insecurely hovers, as if ready to be swallowed?

Some Permanence of Contract is already almost possible; the principle of Permanence, year by year, better seen into and elaborated, may enlarge itself, expand gradually on every side into a system. This once secured, the basis of all good results were laid. Once permanent, you do not quarrel with the first difficulty on your path, and quit it in weak disgust; you reflect that it cannot be quitted, that it must be conquered, a wise arrangement fallen on with regard to it. Ye foolish Wedded Two, who have quarrelled, between whom the Evil Spirit has stirred up transient strife and bitterness, so that 'incompatibility' seems almost nigh, ye are nevertheless the Two who, by long habit, were it by nothing more, do best of all others suit each other: it is expedient for your own two foolish selves, to say nothing of the infants, pedigrees and public in general, that ye agree again; that ye put away the Evil Spirit, and wisely on both hands struggle for the guidance of a Good Spirit!

The very horse that is permanent, how much kindlier do his rider and he work, than the temporary one, hired on any hack principle yet known! I am for permanence in all things, at the earliest possible moment, and to the latest possible. Blessed is he that continueth where he is. Here let us rest, and lay out seedfields; here let us learn to dwell. Here, even here, the orchards that we plant will yield us fruit; the acorns will be wood and pleasant umbrage, if we wait. How much grows everywhere, if we do but wait! Through the swamps we will shape causeways, force purifying drains; we will learn to thread the rocky inaccessibilities; and beaten tracks, worn smooth by mere travelling of human feet, will form themselves. Not a difficulty but can transfigure itself into a triumph; not even a deformity but, if our own soul have imprinted worth on it, will grow dear to us. The sunny plains and deep indigo transparent skies of Italy are all indifferent to the great sick heart of a Sir Walter Scott: on the back of the Apennines, in wild spring weather, the sight of bleak Scotch firs, and snow-spotted heath and desolation, brings tears into his eyes.[2]

O unwise mortals that forever change and shift, and say, Yonder, not Here! Wealth richer than both the Indies lies everywhere for man, if he will endure. Not his oaks only and his fruit-trees, his very heart roots itself wherever he will abide;—roots itself, draws nourishment from the deep fountains of Universal Being!—Vagrant Sam-Slicks, who rove over

[2]Lockhart's *Life of Scott.*

the Earth doing 'strokes of trade,' what wealth have they? Horseloads, ship-loads of white or yellow metal: in very sooth, what *are* these? Slick rests nowhere, he is homeless. He can build stone or marble houses; but to con-tinue in them is denied him. The wealth of a man is the number of things which he loves and blesses, which he is loved and blessed by! The herdsman in his poor clay shealing, where his very cow and dog are friends to him, and not a cataract but carries memories for him, and not a mountain-top but nods old recognition: his life, all encircled as in blessed mother's-arms, is it poorer than Slick's with the ass-loads of yellow metal on his back? Unhappy Slick! Alas, there has so much grown nomadic, apelike, with us: so much will have, with whatever pain, repugnance and 'impossibility,' to alter itself, to fix itself again,—in some wise way, in any not delirious way!

A question arises here: Whether, in some ulterior, perhaps some not far-distant stage of this 'Chivalry of Labour,' your Master-Worker may not find it possible, and needful, to grant his Workers permanent *interest* in his enterprise and theirs? So that it become, in practical result, what in essential fact and justice it ever is, a joint enterprise; all men, from the Chief Master down to the lowest Overseer and Operative, economically as well as loyally concerned for it?—Which question I do not answer. The answer, near or else far, is perhaps, Yes;—and yet one knows the difficulties. Despotism is essential in most enterprises; I am told, they do not tolerate 'freedom of debate' on board a Seventy-four! Republican senate and *plebiscita* would not answer well in Cotton-Mills. And yet observe there too: Freedom, not nomad's or ape's Freedom, but man's Freedom; this is indispensable. We must have it, and will have it! To reconcile Despotism with Freedom:—well, is that such a mystery? Do you not already know the way? It is to make your Despotism *just*. Rigorous as Destiny; but just too, as Destiny and its Laws. The Laws of God: all men obey these, and have no 'Freedom' at all but in obeying them. The way is already known, part of the way;—and courage and some qualities are needed for walking on it!

CHAPTER VI.

The Landed.

A MAN with fifty, with five hundred, with a thousand pounds a day, given him freely, without condition at all,—on condition, as it now runs, that he will sit with his hands in his pockets and do no mischief, pass no Corn-Laws or the like,—he too, you would say, is or might be a rather strong Worker! He is a Worker with such tools as no man in this world ever before had. But in practice, very astonishing, very ominous to look at, he proves not a strong Worker;—you are too happy if he will prove but a No-worker, do nothing, and not be a Wrong-worker.

You ask him, at the year's end: "Where is your three-hundred thousand pound; what have you realised to us with that?" He answers, in indignant surprise: "Done with it? Who are you that ask? I have eaten it; I and my flunkeys, and parasites, and slaves two-footed and four-footed, in an ornamental manner; and I am here alive by it; *I* am realised by it to you!"—It is, as we have often said, such an answer as was never before given under this Sun. An answer that fills me with boding apprehension, with foreshadows of despair. O stolid Use-and-wont of an atheistic Half-century, O Ignavia, Tailor-godhood, soul-killing Cant, to what passes art thou bringing us!—Out of the loud-piping whirlwind, audibly to him that has ears, the Highest God is again announcing in these days: "Idleness shall not be." God has said it, man cannot gainsay.

Ah, how happy were it, if he this Aristocrat Worker would, in like manner, see *his* work and do it! It is frightful seeking another to do it for him. Guillotines, Meudon Tanneries, and half-a-million men shot dead, have already been expended in that business; and it is yet far from done. This man too is something; nay he is a great thing. Look on him there: a man of manful aspect; something of the 'cheerfulness of pride' still lingering in him. A free air of graceful stoicism, of easy silent dignity sits well on him; in his heart, could we reach it, lie elements of generosity, self-sacrificing justice, true human valour. Why should he, with such appliances, stand an incumbrance in the Present; perish disastrously out of the Future! From no section of the Future would we lose these noble courtesies, impalpable yet all-controlling; these dignified reticences, these kingly simplicities;—lose aught of what the fruitful Past still gives us token of, memento of, in this man. Can we not save him:—can he not help us to save him! A brave man he too; had not undivine Ignavia, Hearsay, Speech without meaning,—had not Cant, thousand-fold Cant within him and around him, enveloping him like choke-damp, like thick Egyptian darkness, thrown his soul into asphyxia, as it were extinguished his soul; so that he sees not, hears not, and Moses and all the Prophets address him in vain.

Will he awaken, be alive again, and have a soul; or is this death-fit very death? It is a question of questions, for himself and for us all! Alas, is there no noble work for this man too? Has he not thick-headed ignorant boors; lazy, enslaved farmers; weedy lands? Lands! Has he not weary heavy-laden ploughers of land; immortals souls of men, ploughing, ditching, day-drudging; bare of back, empty of stomach, nigh desperate of heart; and none peaceably to help them but he, under Heaven? Does he find, with his three hundred thousand pounds, no noble thing trodden down in the thoroughfares which it were godlike to help up? Can he do nothing for his Burns but make a Gauger of him; lionise him, bedinner him, for a foolish while; then whistle him down the wind, to desperation and bitter death?—His work too is difficult, in these modern, far-dislocated ages. But it may be done; it may be tried;—it must be done.

A modern Duke of Weimar, not a god he either, but a human duke, levied, as I reckon, in rents and taxes and all incomings whatsoever, less than several of our English Dukes do in rent alone. The Duke of Weimar, with these incomings, had to govern, judge, defend, every way administer *his* Dukedom. He does all this as few others did: and he improves lands besides all this, makes river-embankments, maintains not soldiers only, but Universities and Institutions:—and in his Court were these four men: Wieland, Herder, Schiller, Goethe. Not as parasites, which was impossible; not as table-wits and poetic Katerfeltoes; but as noble Spiritual Men working under a noble Practical Man. Shielded by him from many miseries; perhaps from many shortcomings, destructive aberrations. Heaven had sent, once more, heavenly Light into the world; and this man's honour was that he gave it welcome. A new noble kind of Clergy, under an old but still noble kind of King! I reckon that this one Duke of Weimar did more for the Culture of his Nation than all the English Dukes and *Duces* now extant, or that were extant since Henry the Eighth gave them the Church Lands to eat, have done for theirs!—I am ashamed, I am alarmed for my English Dukes: what word have I to say?

If our Actual Aristocracy, appointed 'Best-and-Bravest,' will be wise, how inexpressibly happy for us! If not,—the voice of God from the whirlwind is very audible to me. Nay, I will thank the Great God, that He has said, in whatever fearful ways, and just wrath against us, "Idleness shall be no more!" Idleness? The awakened soul of man, all but the asphyxied soul of man, turns from it as from worse than death. It is the life-in-death of Poet Coleridge. That fable of the Dead-Sea Apes ceases to be a fable. The poor Worker starved to death is not the saddest of sights. He lies there, dead on his shield; fallen down into the bosom of his old Mother; with haggard pale face, sorrow-worn, but stilled now into divine peace, silently appeals to the Eternal God and all the Universe—the most silent, the most eloquent of men.

Exceptions,—ah yes, thank Heaven, we know there are exceptions. Our case were too hard, were there not exceptions, and partial exceptions not a few, whom we know, and whom we do not know. Honour to the name of Ashley,—honour to this and the other valiant Abdiel, found faithful still; who would fain by work and by word, admonish their Order not to rush upon destruction! These are they who will, if not save their Order, postpone the wreck of it;—by whom, under blessing of the Upper Powers, 'a quiet euthanasia spread over generations, instead of a swift torture-death concentred into years,' may be brought about for many things. All honour and success to these. The noble man can still strive nobly to save and serve his Order;—at lowest, he can remember the precept of the Prophet: "Come out of her, my people; come out of her!"

To sit idle aloft, like living statues, like absurd Epicurus'-gods, in pampered isolation, in exclusion from the glorious fateful battlefield of this God's-World: it is a poor life for a man, when all Upholsterers and French-Cooks have done their utmost for it!—Nay, what a shallow delusion is this we have all got into, That any man should or can keep himself apart from men, have 'no business' with them, except a cash-account 'business'! It is the silliest tale a distressed generation of men ever took to telling one another. Men cannot live isolated: we *are* all bound together, for mutual good or else for mutual misery, as living nerves in the same body. No highest man can disunite himself from any lowest. Consider it. Your poor 'Werter blowing out his distracted existence because Charlotte will not have the keeping thereof:' this is no peculiar phasis; it is simply the highest expression of a phasis traceable wherever one human creature meets another! Let the meanest crookbacked Thersites teach the supremest Agamemnon that he actually does not reverence him, the supremest Agamemnon's eyes flash fire responsive; a real pain, and partial insanity has seized Agamemnon. Strange enough: a many-counselled Ulysses is set in motion by a scoundrel-block-head; plays tunes, like a barrel-organ, at the scoundrel-blockhead's touch,— has to snatch, namely, his sceptre cudgel, and weal the crooked back with bumps and thumps! Let a chief of men, reflect well on it. Not in having 'no business' with men, but in having no unjust business with them, and in *having* all manner of true and just business, can either his or their blessed-ness be found possible, and this waste world become, for both parties, a home and peopled garden.

Men do reverence men. Men do worship in that 'one, temple of the world,' as Novalis calls it, the Presence of a Man! Hero-worship, true and blessed, or else mistaken, false and accursed, goes on everywhere and every-when. In this world there is one godlike thing, the essence of all that was or ever will be of godlike in this world: the veneration done to Human Worth by the hearts of men. Hero-worship, in the souls of the heroic, of the clear and wise,—it is the perpetual presence of Heaven in our poor Earth: when it is not there, Heaven is veiled from us; and all is under Heaven's ban and interdict, and there is no worship, or worthship, or worth or blessedness in the Earth any more!—

Independence, 'lord of the lion-heart and eagle-eye,'—alas, yes, he is one we have got acquainted with in these late times: a very indispensable one, for spurning off with due energy innumerable sham-superiors, Tailor-made: honour to him, entire success to him! Entire success is sure to him. But he must not stop there, at that small success, with his eagle-eye. He has now a second far greater success to gain: to seek out his real superiors, whom not the Tailor but the Almighty God has made superior to him, and see a little what he will do with these! Rebel against these also? Pass by with minatory eagle-glance, with calm-sniffing mockery, or even without any mockery or sniff, when these present themselves? The lion-hearted will never dream of such a thing. Forever far be it from him! His minatory eagle-glance will veil itself in softness of the dove: his lion-heart will become a lamb's; all its just indignation changed into just reverence, dis-solved in blessed floods of noble humble love, how much heavenlier than any pride, nay, if you will, how much prouder! I know him, this lion-hearted, eagle-eyed one; have met him, rushing on, 'with bosom bare,' in a very distracted dishevelled manner, the times being hard;—and can say, and guarantee on my life, That in him is no rebellion; that in him is the reverse of rebellion, the needful preparation for obedience. For if you do mean to obey God-made superiors, your first step is to sweep out the Tailor-made ones; order them, under penalties, to vanish, to make ready for vanishing!

Nay, what is best of all, he cannot rebel, if he would. Superiors whom God has made for us we cannot order to withdraw! Not in the least. No Grand-Turk himself, thickest-quilted tailor-made Brother of the Sun and Moon can do it: but an Arab Man, in cloak of his own clouting; with black beaming eyes, with flaming sovereign-heart direct from the centre of the Universe; and also, I am told, with terrible 'horse-shoe vein' of swelling wrath in his brow, and lightning (if you will not have it as light) tingling through every vein of him,—he rises; says authoritatively: "Thickest-quilted Grand-Turk, tailor-made Brother of the Sun and Moon, No:—*I* withdraw not; thou shalt obey me or withdraw!" And so accordingly it is: thickest-quilted Grand-Turks and all their progeny, to this hour, obey that man in the remarkablest manner; preferring *not* to withdraw.

O brother, it is an endless consolation to me, in this disorganic, as yet so quack-ridden, what you may well call hag-ridden and hell-ridden world, to find that disobedience to the Heavens, when they send any messenger whatever, is and remains impossible. It cannot be done; no Turk grand or small can do it. 'Shew the dullest clod-pole,' says my invaluable German friend, 'shew the haughtiest featherhead, that a soul higher than himself is here; were his knees stiffened into brass, he must down and worship.'

CHAPTER VII.

The Gifted.

Yes, in what tumultuous huge anarchy soever a Noble human Principle may dwell and strive, such tumult is in the way of being calmed into a fruitful sovereignty. It is inevitable. No Chaos can continue chaotic with a soul in it. Besouled with earnest human Nobleness, did not slaughter, violence and fire-eyed fury, grow into a Chivalry; into a blessed Loyalty of Governor and Governed? And in Work, which is of itself noble, and the only true fighting, there shall be no such possibility? Believe it not; it is incredible; the whole Universe contradicts it. Here too the Chactaw Principle will be subordinated; the Man Principle will, by degrees, become superior, become supreme.

I know Mammon, too; Banks-of-England, Credit-Systems, world-wide possibilities of work and traffic; and applaud and admire them. Mammon is like Fire; the usefulest of all servants, if the frightfulest of all masters! The Cliffords, Fitzadelms and Chivalry Fighters 'wished to gain victory,' never doubt it: but victory, unless gained in a certain spirit, was no victory; defeat, sustained in a certain spirit, was itself victory. I say again and again, had they counted the scalps alone, they had continued Chactaws, and no Chivalry or lasting victory had been. And in Industrial Fighters and Captains is there no nobleness discoverable? To them, alone of men, there shall forever be no blessedness but in swollen coffers? To see beauty, order, gratitude, loyal human hearts around them, shall be of no moment; to see fuliginous deformity, mutiny, hatred and despair, with the addition of half a million guineas, shall be better? Heaven's blessedness not there; Hell's cursedness, and your half million bits of metal, a substitute for that! Is there no profit in diffusing Heaven's blessedness, but only in gaining gold?—If so, I apprise the Mill-owner and Millionaire, that he too must prepare for vanishing; that neither is *he* born to be of the sovereigns of this world; that he will have to be trampled and chained down in whatever terrible ways, and brass-collared safe, among the born thralls of this world! We cannot have *Canailles* and Doggeries that will not make some Chivalry of themselves: our noble Planet is impatient of such; in the end totally intolerant of such!

For the Heavens, unwearying in their bounty, do send other souls into this world, to whom yet, as to their forerunners, in Old Roman, in Old Hebrew and all noble times, the omnipotent guinea is, on the whole, an impotent guinea. Has your half-dead avaricious Corn-Law Lord, your half-alive avaricious Cotton-Law Lord, never seen one such? Such are, not one, but several; are, and will be, unless the gods have doomed this world to swift dire ruin. These are they, the elect of the world; the born champions, strong men, and liberatory Samsons of this poor world: whom the poor Delilah-world will not always shear of their strength and eyesight, and set to grind in darkness at *its* poor gin-wheel! Such souls are, in these days, getting somewhat out of humour with the world. Your very Byron, in these days, is at least driven mad; flatly refuses fealty to the world. The world with its injustices, its golden brutalities, and dull yellow guineas, is a disgust to such souls: the ray of Heaven that is in them does at least predoom them to be very miserable here. Yes:—and yet all misery is faculty misdirected, strength that has not yet found its way. The black whirlwind is mother of the lightning. No *smoke*, in any sense, but can become flame and radiance! Such soul, once graduated in Heaven's stern University, steps out superior to your guinea.

Dost thou know, O sumptuous Corn-Lord, Cotton-Lord, O mutinous Trades-Unionist, gin-vanquished, undeliverable; O much enslaved World, —this man is not a slave with thee! None of thy promotions is necessary for him. His place is with the stars of Heaven: to thee it may be momentous, to thee it may be life or death, to him it is indifferent, whether thou place him in the lowest hut, or forty feet higher at the top of thy stupendous high tower, while here on Earth. The joys of Earth that are precious, they depend not on thee and thy promotions. Food and raiment and, round a social hearth, souls who love him, whom he loves: these are already his. He wants none of thy rewards; behold also, he fears none of thy penalties. Thou canst not answer even by killing him: the case of Anaxarchus thou canst kill; but the self of Anaxarchus, the word or act of Anaxarchus, in no wise whatever. To this man death is not a bugbear; to this man life is already as earnest and awful, and beautiful and terrible as death.

Not a May-game is this man's life; but a battle and a march, a warfare with principalities and powers. No idle promenade through fragrant-orange-groves and green flowery spaces, waited on by the choral Muses and the rosy Hours; it is a stern pilgrimage through burning sandy solitudes, through regions of thick-ribbed ice. He walks among men; loves men, with inexpressible soft pity,—as they *cannot* love him; but his soul dwells in solitude, in the uttermost parts of Creation. In green oases by the palm-tree wells, he rests a space; but anon he has to journey forward, escorted by the Terrors and the Splendours, the Archdemons and Archangels. All Heaven, all Pandemonium are his escort. The stars keen-glancing, from the Immensities, send tidings to him; the graves, silent with their dead, from the Eternities. Deep calls for him unto Deep.

Thou, O World, how wilt thou secure thyself against this man? Thou canst not hire him by thy guineas; nor by thy gibbets and law-penalties restrain him. He eludes thee like a Spirit. Thou canst not forward him, thou canst not hinder him. Thy penalties, thy poverties, neglects, contumelies: behold, all these are good for him. Come to him as an enemy; turn from him as an unfriend; only do not this one thing,—infect him not with thy own delusion: the benign Genius, were it by very death, shall guard him against this!—What wilt thou do with him? He is above thee, like a god. Thou, in thy stupendous three-inch pattens, art under him. He is thy born king, thy conqueror and supreme law-giver: not all the guineas and cannons, and leather and prunella, under the sky can save thee from him. Hardest thickskinned Mammon-world, ruggedest Caliban shall obey him, or become not Caliban but a cramp. Oh, if in this man, whose eyes can flash Heaven's lightning, and make all Calibans into a cramp, there dwelt not, as the essence of his very being, a God's Justice, human Nobleness, Veracity and Mercy,—I should tremble for the world. But his strength, let us rejoice to understand, is even this: The quantity of Justice, of Valour and Pity that is in him. To hypocrites and tailored quacks in high places, his eyes are lightning; but they melt in dewy pity softer than a mother's to the downpressed, maltreated; in his heart, in his great thought, is a sanctuary for all the wretched. This world's improvement is forever sure.

'Man of Genius?' Thou hast small notion, meseems, O Mecænas Twiddledee, of what a Man of Genius is. Read in thy New Testament and elsewhere,—if, with floods of mealy-mouthed inanity, with miserable froth-vortices of Cant now several centuries old, thy New Testament is not all bedimmed for thee. *Canst* thou read in thy New Testament at all? The highest Man of Genius, knowest thou him; Godlike and a God to this hour? His crown a Crown of Thorns? Thou fool, with *thy* empty Godhoods, Apotheoses *edgegilt;* the Crown of Thorns made into a poor jewel-room crown, fit for the head of blockheads; the bearing of the Cross changed to a riding in the Long-Acre Gig! Pause in thy mass-chantings, in thy litanyings, and Calmuck prayings by machinery; and pray, if noisily, at least in a more human manner. How with thy rubrics and dalmatics, and clothwebs and cobwebs, and with thy stupidities and grovelling base-heartedness, hast thou hidden the Holiest into all but invisibility!—

'Man of Genius:' O Mecænas Twiddledee, hast thou any notion what a Man of Genius is? Genius is 'the inspired gift of God.' It is the clearer presence of God Most High in a man. Dim, potential in all men; in this man it has become clear, actual. So says John Milton, who ought to be a judge; so answer him the Voices of all Ages and all Worlds. Wouldst thou commune with such a one? *Be* his real peer then: does that lie in thee? Know thyself and thy real and thy apparent place, and know him and his real and his apparent place, and act in some noble conformity with all that. What! The star-fire of the Empyrean shall eclipse itself, and illuminate magic-lanterns to amuse grown children? He, the god-inspired, is to twang harps for thee, and blow through scrannel-pipes, to soothe thy sated soul with visions of new, still wider Eldorados, Houri Paradises, richer Lands of Cockaigne? Brother, this is not he; this is a counterfeit, this twangling, jangling, vain, acrid, scrannel-piping man. Thou dost well to say with sick Saul, "It is naught, such harping!"—and in sudden rage, to grasp thy spear, and try if thou canst pin such a one to the wall. King Saul was mistaken in his man, but thou art right in thine. It is the due of such a one: nail him to the wall, and leave him there. So ought copper shillings to be nailed on counters; copper geniuses on walls, and left there for a sign!—

I conclude that the Men of Letters too may become a 'Chivalry,' an actual instead of a virtual Priesthood, with result immeasurable,—so soon as there is nobleness in themselves for that. And, to a certainty, not sooner! Of intrinsic Valetisms you cannot, with whole Parliaments to help you, make a Heroism. Doggeries never so gold-plated, Doggeries never so escutcheoned, Doggeries never so diplomaed, bepuffed, gas-lighted, continue Doggeries, and must take the fate of such.

CHAPTER VIII.

THE DIDACTIC.

CERTAINLY it were a fond imagination to expect that any preaching of mine could abate Mammonism; that Bobus of Houndsditch will love his guineas less, or his poor soul more, for any preaching of mine! But there is one Preacher who does preach with effect, and gradually persuade all persons: his name is Destiny, is Divine Providence, and his Sermon the inflexible Course of Things. Experience does take dreadfully high school-wages; but he teaches like no other!

I revert to Friend Prudence the good Quaker's refusal of 'seven thousand pounds to boot.' Friend Prudence's practical conclusion will, by degrees, become that of all rational practical men whatsoever. On the present scheme and principle, Work cannot continue. Trades' Strikes, Trades' Unions, Chartisms; mutiny, squalor, rage and desperate revolt, growing ever more desperate, will go on their way. As dark misery settles down on us, and our refuges of lies fall in pieces one after one, the hearts of men, now at last serious, will turn to refuges of truth. The eternal stars shine out again, so soon as it is dark *enough*.

Begirt with desperate Trades' Unionism and Anarchic Mutiny, many an Industrial *Law-ward*, by and by, who has neglected to make laws and keep them, will be heard saying to himself: "Why have I realised five hundred thousand pounds? I rose early and sat late, I toiled and moiled, and in the sweat of my brow and of my soul I strove to gain this money, that I might become conspicuous, and have some honour among my fellow-creatures. I wanted them to honour me, to love me. The money is here, earned with my best lifeblood: but the honour? I am encircled with squalor, with hunger, rage, and sooty desperation. Not honoured, hardly even envied; only fools and the flunkey-species so much as envy me. I am conspicuous,—as a mark for curses and brickbats. What good is it? My five hundred scalps hang here in my wigwam: would to Heaven I had sought something else than the scalps; would to Heaven I had been a Christian Fighter, not a Chactaw one! To have ruled and fought not in a Mammonish but in a Godlike spirit; to have had the hearts of the people bless me as a true ruler and captain of my people; to have felt my own heart bless me, and that God above instead of Mammon below was blessing me,—this had been something. Out of my sight, ye beggarly five hundred scalps of banker's-thousands: I will try for something other, or account my life a tragical futility!"

Friend Prudence's 'rock-ledge,' as we called it, will gradually disclose itself to many a man; to all men. Gradually, assaulted from beneath and from above, the Stygian mud-deluge of Laissez-faire, Supply-and-demand, Cash-payment the one Duty, will abate on all hands; and the everlasting mountain-tops, and secure rock-foundations that reach to the centre of the world, and rest on Nature's self, will again emerge, to found on, and to build on. When Mammon-worshippers here and there begin to be God-worshippers, and bipeds-of-prey become men, and there is a Soul felt once more in the huge-pulsing elephantine mechanic Animalism of this Earth, it will be again a blessed Earth.

"Men cease to regard money?" cries Bobus of Houndsditch: "What else do all men strive for? The very Bishop informs me that Christianity cannot get on without a minimum of Four thousand five hundred in its pocket. Cease to regard money? That will be at Doomsday in the afternoon!" —O Bobus, my opinion is somewhat different. My opinion is, that the Upper Powers have not yet determined on destroying this Lower World. A respectable, ever-increasing minority, who do strive for something higher than money, I with confidence anticipate; ever-increasing, till there be a sprinkling of them found in all quarters, as salt of the Earth once more. The Christianity that cannot get on without a minimum of Four thousand five hundred, will give place to something better that can. Thou wilt not join our small minority, thou? Not till Doomsday in the afternoon? Well; *then*, at least, thou wilt join it, thou and the majority in mass!

But truly it is beautiful to see the brutish empire of Mammon cracking everywhere; giving sure promise of dying, or of being changed. A strange, chill, almost ghastly dayspring strikes up in Yankeeland itself: my Transcendental friends announce there in a distinct, though somewhat lank-haired, ungainly manner, that the Demiurgus Dollar is dethroned; that new unheard of Demiurgusships, Priesthoods, Aristocracies, Growths and Destructions, are already visible in the grey of coming Time. Chronos is dethroned by Jove; Odin by St. Olaf: the Dollar cannot rule in Heaven forever. No, I reckon, not. Socinian Preachers quit their pulpits in Yankeeland, saying, "Friends, this is all gone to coloured cobweb, we regret to say!"—and retire into the fields to cultivate onion-beds, and live frugally on vegetables. It is very notable. Old godlike Calvinism declares that its old body is now fallen to tatters, and done; and its mournful ghost, disembodied, seeking new embodiment, pipes again in the winds;—a ghost and spirit as yet, but heralding new Spirit-worlds, and better Dynasties than the Dollar one.

Yes, here as there, light is coming into the world; men love not darkness, they do love light. A deep feeling of the eternal nature of Justice looks out among us everywhere,—even through the dull eyes of Exeter Hall; an unspeakable religiousness struggles, in the most helpless manner, to speak itself, in Puseyisms and the like. Of our Cant, all condemnable, how much is not condemnable without pity; we had almost said, without respect! The *in*-articulate worth and truth that is in England goes down yet to the Foundations.

Some 'Chivalry of Labour,' some noble Humanity and practical Divineness of Labour, will yet be realised on this Earth. Or why *will*; why do we pray to Heaven, without setting our own shoulder to the wheel? The Present, if it will have the Future accomplish, shall itself commence. Thou who prophesiest, who believest, begin thou to fulfil. Here or nowhere, now equally as at any time! That outcast help-needing thing or person, trampled down under vulgar feet or hoofs, no help 'possible' for it, no prize offered for the saving of it,—canst not thou save it then, without prize? Put forth thy hand, in God's name; know that 'impossible,' where Truth and Mercy and the everlasting Voice of Nature order, has no place in the brave man's dictionary. That when all men have said "Impossible" and tumbled noisily elsewhither, and thou alone art left, then first thy time and possibility have come. It is for thee now: do thou that, and ask no man's counsel, but thy own only and God's. Brother, thou hast possibility in thee for much: the possibility of writing on the eternal skies the record of a heroic life. That noble downfallen or yet unborn 'Impossibility,' thou canst lift it up, thou canst, by thy soul's travail, bring it into clear being. That loud inane Actuality, with millions in its pocket, too 'possible' that, which rolls along there, with quilted trumpeters blaring round it, and all the world escorting it as mute or vocal flunkey,—escort it not thou; say to it, either nothing, or else deeply in thy heart: "Loud-blaring Nonentity, no force of trumpets, cash, Long-Acre art, or universal flunkeyhood of men, makes thee an Entity; thou art a *Non*entity, and deceptive Simulacrum, more accursed than thou seemest. Pass on in the Devil's name, unworshipped by at least one man, and leave the thoroughfare clear!"

Not on Ilion's or Latium's plains; on far other plains and places henceforth can noble deeds be now done. Not on Ilion's plains; how much less in Mayfair's drawingrooms! Not in victory over poor brother French or Phrygians; but in victory over Frost-jötuns, Marsh-giants, over Demons of Discord, Idleness, Injustice, Unreason, and Chaos come again. None of the old Epics is longer possible. The Epic of French and Phrygians was comparatively a small Epic: but that of Flirts and Fribbles, what is that? A thing that vanishes at cock-crowing,—that already begins to scent the morning air! Game-preserving Aristocracies, let them 'bush' never so effectually, cannot escape the Subtle Fowler. Game seasons will be excellent, and again will be indifferent, and by and by they will not be at all. The Last Partridge of England, of an England where millions of men can get no corn to eat, will be shot and ended. Aristocracies with beards on their chins will find other work to do than amuse themselves with trundling-hoops.

But it is to you, ye Workers, who do already work, and are as grown men, noble and honourable in a sort, that the whole world calls for new work and nobleness. Subdue mutiny, discord, wide-spread despair, by manfulness, justice, mercy and wisdom. Chaos is dark, deep as Hell; let light be, and there is instead a green flowery World. O, it is great, and there is no other greatness. To make some nook of God's Creation a little fruitfuler, better, more worthy of God; to make some human hearts a little wiser, manfuler, happier,—more blessed, less accursed! It is work for a God. Sooty Hell of mutiny and savagery and despair can, by man's energy, be made a kind of Heaven; cleared of its soot, of its mutiny, of its need to mutiny; the everlasting arch of Heaven's azure overspanning *it* too, and its cunning mechanisms and tall chimney-steeples, as a birth of Heaven; God and all men looking on it well pleased.

Unstained by wasteful deformities, by wasted tears or heart's-blood of men, or any defacement of the Pit, noble fruitful Labour, growing ever nobler, will come forth,—the grand sole miracle of Man; whereby Man has risen from the low places of this Earth, very literally, into divine Heavens. Ploughers, Spinners, Builders; Prophets, Poets, Kings; Brindleys and Goethes, Odins and Arkwrights; all martyrs, and noble men, and gods are of one grand Host: immeasurable; marching ever forward since the Beginnings of the World. The enormous, all-conquering, flame-crowned Host, noble every soldier in it; sacred and alone noble. Let him who is not of it hide himself; let him tremble for himself. Stars at every button cannot make him noble; sheaves of Bath-garters, nor bushels of Georges; nor any other contrivance but manfully enlisting in it, valiantly taking place and step in it. O Heavens, will he not bethink himself; he too is so needed in the Host! It were so blessed, thrice-blessed, for himself and for us all! In hope of the Last Partridge, and some Duke of Weimar among our English Dukes, we will be patient yet a while.

'*The Future hides in it*
Gladness and sorrow;
We press still thorow,
Nought that abides in it
Daunting us,—onward.'